PAPERS ON BACTERIAL VIRUSES

PAPERS ON

BACTERIAL VIRUSES

Selected by

GUNTHER S. STENT

University of California, Berkeley

Boston **Toronto**

LITTLE, BROWN AND COMPANY

LIBRARY OF CONGRESS CATALOG CARD NO. 60-53146

Published simultaneously in Canada
by Little, Brown & Company (Canada) Limited

PRINTED IN THE UNITED STATES OF AMERICA

FOREWORD

IN 1951, the collection *Papers in Microbial Genetics; Bacteria and Bacterial Viruses* appeared under the editorship of Joshua Lederberg. That collection has been an indispensable aid to us and many others in the teaching of microbial genetics. It has enabled every student to read a cross-section of the original literature and thus become directly acquainted with the basic experimental data that often outlive the conclusions based upon them.

The Lederberg collection, however, appeared just at the eve of great discoveries which, since that time, have enormously advanced our understanding of the structure and function of the hereditary substance of bacteria and their viruses. The transduction of bacterial genes by bacteriophages, the polarity of bacterial conjugation, the role of DNA as the germinal substance of bacterial viruses, the structure of DNA itself — all of these were discovered within the two-year period following the publication of Lederberg's collection. New techniques have also greatly changed the course and nature of research in microbial genetics; in particular, the use of isotopic tracers in bacterial virus research and the development of recombination tests of high resolving power for the analysis of genetic fine structure have brought microbial genetics to the molecular level.

Hence it seemed urgent that a new, more up to date, collection should now be made available; we have decided to assume this task, and hope that the present book and its companion volume, *Papers on Bacterial Genetics,* will answer the needs of at least the immediate future. The extent of the changes that have taken place is indicated by the fact that of the more than fifty papers we have selected for the present two volumes, only five have been retained from the twenty papers of Lederberg's collection.

In addition to the reprinted papers, each volume contains an introductory text with its own bibliography, in order to compensate for the necessarily incomplete and arbitrary nature of the selections. The selections themselves were made for the sole purpose of providing students with a cross-section of the literature, at a reasonable cost; in the words of Professor Lederberg "no apologies need be offered for a selection which must be largely arbitrary."

In conclusion, we would like to express our deep appreciation to the copyright owners and the authors who permitted us to reprint these papers, as well as to those who have supplied us with rare reprints from which some of the copy has been made.

GUNTHER S. STENT
EDWARD A. ADELBERG
Berkeley, California, 1960

CONTENTS

Pagination of the papers in this collection is indicated by the boldface number centered at the bottom of the page. Other page numbers appearing on certain papers refer to original publication.

INTRODUCTION

Bacterial viruses were discovered in 1915, when F. W. Twort (149) isolated a filtrable virus which produces a "glassy transformation" of micrococcal colonies during their growth on an agar surface. Twort's paper remained relatively unnoticed, until two years later F. d'Hérelle (64) published his own observations on a filtrable agent, the "bacteriophage," capable of serially transmissible lysis of growing cultures of enteric bacilli. D'Hérelle's announcement caused an immediate sensation among medical bacteriologists, since the bactericidal properties of the bacteriophage offered promise of a generalized prophylaxis and therapy of bacterial diseases. Within two or three years of the publication of his first paper, d'Hérelle had carried out many incisive experiments which allowed him to recognize the essential aspects of these bacterial viruses.

Twort and d'Hérelle did not remain the only bacteriophage workers for very long, and the study of bacterial viruses rapidly became so popular that most of the leading bacteriologists of the decade following the first World War tried their hand at it. This soon led to a number of violent controversies concerning the nature and mode of action of bacteriophages. Some of these controversies were aired at a discussion on the bacteriophage organized by the British Medical Association at its Glasgow meeting of 1922. The presentations which d'Hérelle, Twort, Bordet, and Gratia prepared for this meeting form the first paper of this collection. In his discussion, d'Hérelle demonstrates the self-reproducing, or viral, character of the bacteriophage, a view for which, as is evident from the remarks of Bordet and of Gratia, he had been under attack. Gratia's discussion, however, rectifies two errors of d'Hérelle: the claim that the phenomena discovered by Twort and by d'Hérelle are fundamentally different and the assertion that all bacteriophages represent the same antigen. In 1926, d'Hérelle (65) thus summarized his earlier findings on the multiplication of bacterial viruses: "The first act of bacteriophagy consists in the approach of the bacteriophage corpuscle toward the bacteria, then in the fixation of the corpuscle to the latter . . . The bacteriophage corpuscle penetrates into the interior of the bacterial cell. When, as a result of its faculty of multiplication, the bacteriophage corpuscle which has penetrated into the bacterium forms a colony of a number of elements, the bacterium ruptures suddenly, liberating into the medium young corpuscles which are then ready to continue the action."

The first workers to study in some detail the initial step in bacterial virus growth, i.e. the fixation, or *adsorption,* of the bacteriophage to its bacterial host cell, were Krueger (91) and Schlesinger (129, 130). In his paper (130), the second of this collection, Schlesinger demonstrates that phage adsorption usually is an irreversible process which follows the kinetics expected from a two-body collision model involving freely diffusing virus particles and bacterial cells. Schlesinger's work, which probably represents the first rigorous application of physicochemical principles to the study of bacterial viruses, was extended by Delbrück (39), who showed that the physiological state of the bacteria affects the rate of adsorption, and by Garen and Puck (59), who demonstrated clearly that, under certain conditions, a *reversible* union between phage and bacterium can take place. Contrary to the predictions of the simple two-body collision model of Schlesinger, however, it turned out that the rate of phage adsorption reaches a maximum at high bacterial concentrations and is strongly temperature-dependent. Hence, it appears that the irreversible fixation of the bacteriophage is a two-step process, involving at least one further, temperature-sensitive, step in addition to the collision of virus and host cell (146). Subsequent electron-optical observations by T. F. Anderson revealed that the organ of adsorption is the phage *tail* (5), in particular, that it is the thin *tail fibers* (155) which are the structures undergoing the stereospecific fixation reaction with the phage receptors on the bacterial surface. (Reviews: 58, 148, 73, 125, 154.)

Convincing support for d'Hérelle's conception that the infecting phage particle multiplies within the bacterium and that its progeny are liberated upon lysis of the host cell was adduced in 1929 by Burnet (31), who showed that 20 to 100 viruses suddenly appear some 20 minutes after a bacterial suspension is infected with a single phage particle. The final demonstration, however, that a burst of progeny of the parent virus is liberated by each infected bacterial cell after a *latent* period was only provided in 1939 in the *one step growth* experiment of Ellis and Delbrück (52), whose paper is presented in this collection. In their publication, Ellis and Delbrück also describe for the first time the *single burst experiment,* which made possible the study of phage growth in individual infected bacteria, rather than in mass culture. The appearance of this paper marks the beginning of modern phage research.

The interpretation of the phage-induced lysis of infected bacterial cultures was one of the violent controversies during the first 20 years of phage research. While d'Hérelle (65) correctly thought that intracellular phage growth leads to lysis of the host cell and liberation of the virus progeny, Bordet and Ciuca (20, 22) maintained that the phage-induced dissolution of bacterial cultures is merely the consequence of a stimulation of lytic enzymes endogenous to the bacteria. Other workers, such as Bronfenbrenner (30), or Krueger and Northrop (92), thought that lysis of the bacteria is only a secondary phenomenon, which may or may not follow the growth of phage, and imagined that the bacteriophage can pass freely in and out of bacterial cells. Delbrück (40) finally showed, in his second paper of this collection, that these arguments were bedevilled by the circumstance that there exist not one but two completely different processes by which bacteriophages can lyse susceptible bacterial cells. One of these, *lysis-from-without,* represents an immediate dissolution of bacteria, often encountered when the multiplicity of infection is much greater than one phage per bacterium (9, 123, 92, 124). *Loss* of the input phages, rather than their multiplication, ensues from this form of lysis. Only the second of the lytic processes, *lysis-from-within,* is really the form of lysis properly connected with intracellular phage multiplication, and its onset signals the end of the latent period.

The one-step growth experiment demonstrated clearly the nature and kinetics of the process by which bacterial viruses multiply within cultures of susceptible bacteria. It thus brought into focus the question of fundamental biologic interest: what is taking place *inside* the infected cell during the latent period while the parental phage particle replicates itself several hundredfold? In order to study the kinetics of *intracellular* phage multiplication, Doermann (47) broke open phage-infected bacteria at various times during the latent period and assayed the infectivity of the material released by premature lysis. The result of this experiment, published in the paper included in this collection, was that the infectivity associated with the original parental virus is lost at the outset of the reproductive process, since no infective particles whatsoever can be found in any of the bacteria lysed within ten minutes after their infection. After more than ten minutes have elapsed, however, ever-increasing numbers of infective progeny viruses make their intracellular appearance, until the final crop of progeny has been attained which would have been released by spontaneous lysis-from-within at the end of the normal latent period. The stage of intracellular bacterial virus growth during which the infected host cell contains no material capable of infecting another bacterium is the eclipse (107). Subsequent studies showed that the actual multiplication of the infecting virus takes place during the eclipse, i.e. that the phage multiplies in a non-infectious form, the *vegetative phage* (48).

Schlesinger was also the first to purify a bacterial virus, a feat which he accomplished by high-speed centrifugation of phage lysates (131). Chemical analysis of the purified virus revealed that it consists of approximately equal proportions of protein and deoxyribonucleic acid (DNA) (132). Later studies by Anderson (3, 4) and by Herriott (66) showed that the viral DNA resides within a proteinaceous head membrane, from which it can be released by osmotic shock. Hershey and Chase (75) then demonstrated that the two viral moieties, protein and DNA, have independent functions in the infection process. For, as can be seen in their first paper included in this collection, Hershey and Chase found that practically all of the viral protein remains at the surface of the infected cell, and that it is mainly the viral DNA which enters the bacterium at the outset of intracellular phage growth. The bulk of the phage protein appears to be relieved of any further function in the intracellular reproductive process after the proteinaceous tail has attached the virus particle to the bacterial surface and the DNA has safely entered the interior of the host cell. This historic discovery showed that it must be the viral DNA that is the carrier of the hereditary continuity, i.e. the germinal substance of the extracellular, resting phage. The release of the DNA from its protein envelope at the very moment of infection also accounts for the existence of the eclipse period at the early stages of intracellular virus development. For having been divested of its attachment and injection organs, the DNA of the infecting phage naturally is unable to gain entrance into any further bacterial cells to which it may be presented in the infectivity test.

What happens to the viral DNA after its injection into the host cell? In 1950 Putnam and Kozloff (126) devised an experiment directed toward the question of whether any of the atoms of the parental DNA ultimately reappear among the progeny viruses. In this "transfer experiment," bacteria are infected with phage particles whose DNA is isotopically labeled, and the phage yield issuing from such infected cells assayed for its content of parental isotope. The outcome of Putnam and Kozloff's transfer experiment was that about half of the atoms of the parental DNA were found to be transferred to the progeny. This work was confirmed and extended with improved experimental techniques by Watson and Maaløe (120, 152), one of whose publications is included in this collection. In view of the inference that it is the DNA of the virus which carries the genetic continuity into the host cell, it seemed likely that an understanding of the mechanism of transfer of DNA atoms from parent to offspring might afford valuable insight into the nature of the reproductive process. Further investigations have revealed that the parental DNA complement of a single parental virus is not transferred intact to a single progeny virus, but that the molecular patrimony is dispersed over several offspring phages (76, 143, 101, 145).

Some theories of the nature of phage multiplication envisaged that there are present, within the normal host bacterium, bacteriophage precursors whose metamorphosis into mature bacteriophages is merely triggered by the infecting phage particle (93). This view was finally dispelled in 1948 by an experiment of Cohen (37), designed to determine the origin of the substance of the progeny phages. This work, reported in a paper of this collection, represents the first use of radioisotopes in the study of bacterial viruses. By exposing bacterial cultures to P^{32}, either only prior to or only subsequent to their infection with phage, and analyzing the virus progeny for their relative content of radioisotope, Cohen could show that most of the phage DNA is synthesized from materials still in the growth medium at the moment of infection; hence, the phage particles cannot have been derived from pre-existing bacterial precursors. The complete kinetics of assimilation of phage DNA phosphorus were studied subsequently by modifications of Cohen's original method, by either adding to or withdrawing from the growth medium of bacterial cultures P^{32} at various times before or after their infection. The results of this work led to the idea that, prior to its incorporation into intact, infective progeny particles, the phage DNA exists in an intrabacterial *phage precursor pool* (144, 71).

Further insight into the process of phage multiplication was gained by the discovery of a variety of "incomplete" phage structures which possess one or another of the properties of the virus without being endowed with the power of self-reproduction, the most complex of all its attributes. Thus, premature lysis of infected bacteria at late stages of the eclipse period liberates newly synthesized proteinaceous material already possessing some of the antigenic properties of the intact bacteriophage (119). The total amount of phage antigen finally liberated upon spontaneous lysis of the cells, furthermore, generally exceeds that incorporated into infective progeny (119, 32, 46). Electron-optical observations of such lysates, furthermore, reveal the presence of structures whose morphology bears some resemblance to the characteristic shape of mature bacterial virus particles (161, 63). Prominent among these structures are the "doughnuts" which Levinthal and Fisher (103) found to appear during the eclipse and then to increase in number at about the same rate as the complete phage particles. Later studies have shown that the doughnuts are, in fact, *empty phage heads,* and that the "maturation" of infective progeny at the end of the eclipse seems to represent the stable union of phage precursor DNA with phage precursor protein into structurally intact virus particles (88, 89).

Phage precursor protein and phage precursor DNA are not the only materials whose synthesis within the host cell is induced, or presided over, by the DNA of the infecting parental virus. For, at the outset of intracellular phage growth, the formation of some non-precursor proteins must proceed before replication of the viral DNA can begin. One of these "early" proteins was identified by Flaks and Cohen (53, 54) as the enzyme deoxycytidylate hydroxymethylase, essential for the synthesis of the specific components of the viral DNA, 5-hydroxymethylcytosine (160). Studies by Kornberg, Zimmerman, Kornberg, and Josse (90), presented in a paper of this collection, revealed the phage-induced formation of four further enzymes, all of which are demonstrably involved in the synthesis and replication of the viral DNA. It is important to realize, therefore, that the phenotypic expression of the genetic substance of the phage is not confined solely to the construction of materials that find incorporation into the mature, infective progeny virus.

In common with other organisms, bacterial viruses sport occasional hereditary variants, or *mutants,* in the course of their growth (34, 68, 133). These mutants can differ from their parents in a variety of characteristics, such as the type of plaque formed on agar seeded with sensitive indicator bacteria (67), the strains of bacteria which the phage can infect (105), or the physical or chemical properties of the virus particle (2, 43, 26). The mutation of the vegetative phage during its intracellular growth was used by Luria (108) to probe the nature of the self-duplication of the hereditary material of the infecting particle, as shown in a paper of this collection. In his experiment,

Luria examined the individual phage yield of many thousands of phage-infected bacterial cells and scored the single bursts for the presence of progeny viruses possessing a certain plaque-type mutant character. On the basis of the observed clonal frequency distribution of these mutants, Luria was able to infer that the replication of the hereditary material of the phage is geometric, i.e. that it proceeds by a number of successive cycles of self-duplication, since other conceivable reproductive models, e.g. successive replications of the initial parental element or chain replication of the last element produced, would have led to mutant distributions quite different from that actually found.

In 1946, a most important discovery was made independently by Delbrück and Bailey (44) and by Hershey (67), who examined the genetic character of the phage yield issuing from bacterial cells infected with two related parent viruses differing from each other in two mutant factors. It was found that among the progeny of such mixed infection there appear virus offspring carrying one of the mutant factors of one and one of the mutant factors of the other of the two parents, demonstrating that bacterial viruses can undergo *genetic recombination*. The first detailed study of genetic recombination in phage was undertaken by Hershey and Rotman (77), their paper being included in our collection. This work showed that, on the basis of the frequency with which recombinant progeny for various mutated characters appear in such "crosses," it is possible to construct a *genetic map* of the phage on which the mutant loci can be arranged in a linear order. Hershey and Rotman also examined the frequency of complementary recombinant types in the yields of individual mixed infected bacteria and found that the formation of complementary types does not seem to occur in a single event [Bresch (28) was able to establish this conclusion even more convincingly in a later study]. This fact led Hershey and Rotman to entertain the notion that recombination in phage might not be the consequence of a reciprocal exchange of preformed genetic structures, such as chromosomal recombination in higher forms, but that it might be an act incidental to the replication of the genetic material itself. This hypothesis, which came to be called "partial replicas" (69), or "copy choice" (97), now forms one of the basic concepts in the understanding of the molecular basis of self-duplication and genetic recombination. As more data concerning the process of genetic exchange in phage accumulated, it became evident that the theoretical analysis of a phage "cross" is a problem in population genetics. It was seen that within each mixedly infected bacterial cell, growth and recombination of the numerous vegetative phage replicas proceed concurrently. In 1953, Visconti and Delbrück (150) developed, therefore, a theory which succeeded in explaining quantitatively the recombinant frequency observed in different phage crosses under various conditions. This theory assumes that replication and recombination of vegetative phages proceeds in an intrabacterial *pool*, in which phages repeatedly mate pairwise and at random until lysis of the host cell, and from which pool the vegetative phages are withdrawn irreversibly for maturation into infective progeny phages. A concise statement of this theory can be found in Adams' book (1), and a more generalized formulation is presented in two later analyses of this problem (137, 29).

An important clue to the nature of the elementary recombinational event in phage was uncovered by Hershey and Chase (74), described in their second paper of this collection. They noted that among the progeny of mixed infections about 2% of the particles are *heterozygous,* in that these individuals carry homologous loci, or alleles, from both parents of the cross. The heterozygosity is only partial, however, in that in any one heterozygote virus only a very limited segment of the genome is actually of biparental provenance, most of its loci being homozygous, or derived from only one or the other of the parents. The structure and behavior of these heterozygotes suggested to Hershey and Chase that the formation of heterozygotes and the formation of recombinants might be related processes. The nature of heterozygotes was considered further by Levinthal (100), who demonstrated that such viruses are *recombinant* for genetic loci on opposite sides of the limited region of heterozygosity. Levinthal then inferred that recombinant phages, in fact, arise through the formation of heterozygotes in the course of phage reproduction by the partial replica, or copy-choice, recombination mechanism. This inference found further support from Levinthal's calculation that the observed frequency of heterozygotes is great enough to explain the observed frequency of recombinational events.

Once the viral DNA had been identified as the germinal substance, it became possible to consider in actual chemical terms how the hereditary information is stored in the resting phage and how it is replicated in the vegetative phage. After deoxyribonucleic acid was discovered by Miescher in 1871, some 60 years of chemical study of this substance revealed that its building block is the *nucleotide,* composed of one molecule each of phosphoric acid, deoxyribose, and either adenine, guanine, thymine, or cytosine. More recently, it was established that DNA molecules are, in fact, polymers of very high molecular weight, each molecule containing more than 10^4 nucleotide units joined through phosphate diester bonds linking successive deoxyribose molecules (cf. 36). The actual molecular architecture of DNA was worked out finally by Watson and Crick (151), whose paper is presented here. Watson and Crick showed that the DNA molecule consists of two helically intertwined polynucleotide chains laterally held together by a pair of hydrogen bonds between a complementary pair of purine and pyrimidine residues on opposite chains. The nature of the DNA molecule suggests that the only specific aspect which could distinguish one DNA macromolecule from another is the precise sequence of the four possible purine-pyrimidine base pairs along the complementary nucleotide chains, i.e. that the hereditary information is a message written into the DNA macromolecule in an alphabet containing four letters. This structure also suggested to Watson and Crick a mechanism by which the DNA molecule could replicate itself; for if the two complementary polynucleotide chains separate and each parental chain acts as the template for the *de novo* synthesis of a complementary daughter chain, a *pair* of DNA molecules would be generated, each half-old, half-new, whose specific purine-pyrimidine base pair sequence is identical to that of the parent molecule. A genetic mutation, from this point of view, would then be a rare copy error in the replication process by which a nucleotide carrying an incorrect base is introduced into the replica nucleotide chain, thus producing a change in the genetic information. Even though a number of modifications of this replication scheme of Watson and Crick were subsequently proposed (45), later experiments have shown that in the replication of bacterial DNA the distribution of the atoms of the parental molecules appears to proceed by the *semi-conservative* route (122), a central feature inherent in the Watson-Crick scheme.

One of the first successful attempts to bridge the gap between chemistry and genetics was made by Benzer (12) in his first paper of this collection. Benzer discovered a method for scoring very rare recombinant viruses appearing in phage crosses between parents bearing extremely closely linked mutant loci. This allowed him to construct a *fine structure map* of a large collection of mutants situated in a very restricted region of the phage genome. In consequence of this work, the concept of the gene, traditionally regarded as the unit of recombination, mutation and function, became clarified. For Benzer showed that these three aspects of the genetic material are operationally separable and hence cannot share a common unit. Translated into molecular terms, the unit of recombination appears to represent one, or a few, nucleotide pairs along the DNA molecule, whereas the unit of mutation can be of variable length, ranging from the alteration of a single nucleotide pair, in case of a *point* mutation, to long-span alterations of the phage genome, covering hundreds or thousands of nucleotide pairs. Finally, the unit of function, or *cistron,* assumed to determine the specific chemical structure of an enzyme protein, or more precisely, of a polypeptide chain, is of the order of 1000 nucleotides in length (13).

After Benzer had arranged his set of closely linked spontaneous phage mutants into a linear linkage map, it became obvious that there exists a great variability in mutability of different genetic sites within a single functional group, or cistron, since at some loci, or "hot spots," spontaneous mutations recur with much greater frequency than at other, nearby loci. This differential mutability of individual genetic sites very probably reflects the chemical structure of the hereditary molecule corresponding to each locus; e.g. the chance of making a spontaneous copy error at a given site in the course of viral DNA replication might depend on which particular sequence of purine and pyrimidine residues obtains there and which particular base substitution will produce the mutant genotype in question (13). Benzer and Freese (14), therefore, examined also distribution, or *mutational spectrum,* of mutants induced by the action of chemical mutagens, in particular by replacement of thymine by its analog 5-bromouracil in the viral DNA, which replacement, as

Litman and Pardee had found (104), is highly mutagenic in bacterial viruses. Benzer and Freese's investigation, presented in this collection, showed that the set of mutants induced by the action of 5-bromouracil is completely different from the set of spontaneous mutants in the same general region of the viral genome, demonstrating that "the mutagen does not merely enhance the over-all mutation rate, but acts at specific locations in the hereditary structure." Mutational spectra of other chemical mutagens were subsequently established, and it turned out that each of these substances raises the probability of mutation at a restricted number and individually characteristic set of sites (27, 57). Further insight into the chemical nature of the induced mutations was provided by studies that determined the connection between the induction of a mutation at a specific site by a given mutagen and the ability of the same, or of another mutagen, to revert this mutation to the original state. On the basis of these results, Freese proposed that there exist two basic types of point mutation in the viral genetic material: *transversions*, corresponding to the substitution of a purine by a pyrimidine residue, or vice versa, and *transitions*, corresponding to the replacement of one type of pyrimidine by the other or of one type of purine by the other (56).

Not long after the discovery of the bacteriophage it was found that ultraviolet light (UV) kills the virus particle (65), and since then, UV has been the inactivation agent whose effects have been most extensively studied (136, 95, 110, 139). This work has shown that in addition to simply destroying the reproductive power, UV also produces a number of important physiological and genetic effects. The inactivated phages, furthermore, are by no means inert, being still capable of adsorbing to and killing bacteria, and of interfering with the growth of other, unirradiated phages in the same host cell (111). Some of the lethal effects of UV, finally, are reversible under appropriate conditions. An important example of such reversibility is the existence of *photoreactivation*, discovered by Dulbecco (49) in the work presented herein. Dulbecco found that viability is restored to UV-inactivated phages if bacteria infected with such "dead" particles are illuminated with visible light. Dulbecco's quantitative analysis of photoreactivation showed that a fraction of the UV lesions, the photoreactivable sector, is restored by a light-activated enzyme system of the bacterial host cell. Later work by Bowen (23, 24) revealed that photoreactivation consists of two steps: the first step is a dark reaction requiring no light, which generates the substances adsorbing and "activated" by the quanta of visible light for the second, actually reactivating step. Experiments by Lennox, Luria, and Benzer (99) suggested that photoreactivation constitutes a direct reversal rather than a bypass mechanism of the primary ultraviolet damage, a conclusion that now seems certain since Goodgal, Rupert, and Herriot demonstrated the *in vitro* photoreactivation of UV-inactivated transforming DNA by illuminated bacterial extracts (61).

Viability can also be restored to UV-inactivated phages if two or more "dead" particles, each unable to reproduce itself *in solo*, happen to infect the same bacterial cell. This is the phenomenon of *multiplicity reactivation*, discovered by Luria in 1947 (106) and investigated in some detail by Luria and Dulbecco (112), whose paper is included in this collection. The quantitative results presented here seemed to bear out Luria's proposal that each inactivating UV lesion represents a lethal mutation in one of a certain number of genetic subunits of the phage and that multiplicity reactivation ensues from the genetic exchange of still undamaged units between the two irradiated parent viruses. In order to explain the very high frequency of reactivation, furthermore, it was assumed that phage growth occurs by the independent reproduction of each subunit, followed by reassembly of the units into complete phages. When Dulbecco (50) subsequently continued his multiplicity reactivation studies, he found that the results observed at very high UV doses are no longer compatible with the notion of independently multiplying subunits. In any case, studies on genetic recombination in phage had in the meantime indicated that the genetic material of the phage does not multiply in the form of independent subunits (150). More recently, however, modifications of the original hypothesis of multiplicity reactivation have been proposel by Baricelli (10) and by Harm (62), which still retain that most essential element of Luria's hypothesis that reactivation proceeds by a mechanism of genetic exchange of undamaged parts and which lead to quantitative formulations in satisfactory agreement with the observed data.

Another radiobiological method of inactivation bacterial viruses was discovered by Hershey, Kamen, Kennedy, and Gest (76), who showed that highly P^{32}-labeled bacteriophages lose their infectivity upon decay of radiophosphorus atoms. From the kinetics and efficiency of this inactivation process, it could be inferred that the cause of death is the transmutation of phosphorus into sulfur atoms in the polynucleotide chains of the viral DNA, or the highly energetic nuclear recoil associated with this event. These studies were extended by Stent and Fuerst (141), whose paper appears in this collection. They found that, although the efficiency of killing of one lethal hit per ten P^{32} disintegrations first observed by Hershey and his co-workers also obtains in a variety of different bacteriophage strains, the fraction of disintegrations that are lethal depends on the temperature at which decay is allowed to proceed. A mechanism for the decay inactivation process of the virus was suggested on the basis of these findings. It was proposed that the high proportion of *nonlethal* decays reflects the possibility that the physiological function of the double-stranded DNA molecule is preserved even after radioactive decay has interrupted only *one* of its polynucleotide strands. The *lethal* decays, in contrast, are thought to be those that result by chance in a complete cut of *both* strands of the DNA double helix. The decay of incorporated P^{32} atoms has proven a very useful tool for the study of the structure, physiology, and genetics of bacterial viruses and bacteria. (Review: 142.)

In the hope of measuring the extent to which the infecting parental virus has multiplied within the host cell during the eclipse period before the appearance of any mature progeny, Luria and Latarjet (113) irradiated phage-infected bacteria with UV at various stages of intracellular phage growth. They reasoned that if the UV sensitivity of the vegetative phage is equal to that of the free, extracellular virus, then the result of this irradiation experiment ought to be a family of multiple-hit survival curves from which the instantaneous number of vegetative phages present at the time of irradiation could be inferred. The outcome of Luria and Latarjet's experiment was contrary to their expectation, however; instead of the anticipated multiple-hit survival curves, a family of straight lines of ever decreasing slope was observed, indicative of the fact that the intrinsic UV sensitivity of the vegetative phage is much less than that of the free virus. This is also evident from Benzer's (11) improved experimental design of the Luria-Latarjet technique, presented here as Benzer's third paper. The meaning of the great reduction in UV sensitivity of the vegetative phage has not yet found an entirely satisfactory explanation. On the one hand, as is evident from Benzer's report, some phages do not manifest this effect, so that UV irradiation of bacteria infected with such phages actually gives rise to the family of multiple-hit curves anticipated by Luria and Latarjet. On the other hand, the vegetative phage is also much more resistant to inactivation by decay of incorporated P^{32} atoms than the extracellular P^{32}-labeled virus (138). It seems likely, however, that the reduction in radiosensitivity of the vegetative phage reflects some important aspect of the function and replication of the viral DNA, and some of the possible interpretations have been discussed in several reviews (94, 136, 139, 142). In any case, the method of Luria and Latarjet has found a number of valuable applications in the study of intracellular virus growth, not only with bacteriophages but also with plant and animal viruses (134, 135, 51, 128).

Within a few years of the discovery of the bacteriophage, *lysogenic* bacterial strains were found which appear to "carry" bacteriophages, in the sense that phage particles are always present in the culture fluid of such strains (21, 60). It was soon realized that this association of phage and bacteria cannot be of a casual nature, since it is impossible to permanently free lysogenic strains from the phage they carry by methods which ought to kill or remove the virus particles, such as heating, anti-phage serum neutralization, or single-colony purification (8, 18, 121). The nature and significance of lysogeny then remained a subject of intense controversy for about 30 years, some workers denying the existence of "true" lysogeny and others claiming that lysogeny disproves the whole notion that bacteriophagy involves an infection of bacteria by virus particles. Nevertheless, a few bacteriologists, such as Burnet and McKie (35), and the elder Wollman (156), already envisaged that lysogeny represents an *innate* capacity of bacterial cells for phage production. In order to establish firmly some of the basic but controversial facts of lysogeny, Lwoff began a study of this phenomenon after the Second World War and in 1950 published the paper (116) presented here. In this work Lwoff and Gutmann demonstrate unequivocally that each bacterium of a lysogenic strain harbors and maintains a noninfective structure, the probacteriophage or prophage, which endows the cell with the ability to give rise to infective phage without further intervention of exogenous virus particles. The actual synthesis of infective phage, however, proceeds in only a small fraction of the cells of a growing culture of lysogenic bacteria, whose intracellular content of virus particles is liberated by lysis of the phage-producing individual. Lwoff also inferred from these experiments that the *induction* of phage development in a lysogenic cell is under control of external factors, and his subsequent investigations in collaboration with Siminovitch and Kjelgaard (118) showed that treatment with various agents, in particular irradiation with UV light, will indeed induce phage production and ultimately lysis of almost every cell of a culture of lysogenic bacteria. The first preliminary report of this finding (117) is included in this collection. After the publication of Lwoff's papers and reviews (114), the study of lysogeny not only flowered into a distinct branch of bacterial virus research but also became the bridge leading from the genetics of virus to that of host cell. In fact, the recognition of the existence and nature of the *provirus* state engendered entirely new ideas concerning the origin, evolution, and biological function of viruses (79). (Reviews: 114, 17, 85.)

What is the relationship of the prophage to the remainder of the lysogenic cell? The great stability of the lysogenic character implies that the prophage is transmitted to daughter cells at each bacterial division. This could happen in one of two ways: either the prophage represents numerous *autonomous* structures, replicating in the bacterial cytoplasm in synchrony with the rest of the bacterium and being partitioned at random at each division over the daughter cytoplasms, or the prophage is *integrated* into the nuclear apparatus of the host cell and participates in the specific replication and segregation process which assures, *nolens volens,* that each daughter cell obtains one complete set of parental hereditary factors. The first of these alternatives soon appeared unlikely, when indirect estimates of the number of prophages revealed that each cell seems to carry only one or two prophages per bacterial nucleus (16, 81), and that a given type of prophage appears to saturate a limited number of sites on some bacterial structure (15). Positive indications that the prophage is integrated into the bacterial nucleus became available from experiments in bacterial conjugation, in which non-lysogenic bacteria were crossed with lysogenic bacteria, and a linkage of the lysogeny character with other known genetic factors of the cell inferred from the segregation pattern of the recombinants (96, 158, 7, 55). After the discovery of high-frequency-recombination (Hfr) bacterial strains and of the *oriented* transfer of the bacterial chromosome from donor to recipient cell, Wollman and Jacob (159) could show very clearly in their first paper of this collection that at least one particular prophage has its specific location on the bacterial chromosome; their later work, furthermore, revealed that different prophages have different specific chromosomal sites (83, 84). At the same time, Jacob and Wollman

(82) also discovered the existence of *zygotic induction*, described here in their second paper. For if a chromosome fragment of a donor bacterium bearing a prophage enters a non-lysogenic recipient cell, then the prophage becomes induced, enters the vegetative state, leading to the production of infective progeny and lysis and loss of the bacterial zygote. This phenomenon accounted for the discrepancies that had been observed in earlier attempts to determine the chromosomal location of the prophage by bacterial conjugation experiments, from which different linkage relations could be inferred, depending upon which of the two parents of the cross carried the prophage (160).

A completely independent confirmation of the specific location of the prophage on the bacterial chromosome was provided through transduction experiments by Jacob (78), whose paper is presented here. Transducing virus particles carry a small genetic segment of closely linked loci of a donor bacterium, i.e. the last host cell, into a recipient bacterium, i.e. the next host cell. In this way, recombinant bacteria can arise which have derived a very limited part of their genome from the donor cell (164, 163, 147, 98). Jacob thus showed that a transducing virus can carry the prophage of an entirely unrelated virus strain from a lysogenic donor into a non-lysogenic recipient bacterium, usually in association with the contiguous region of the donor chromosome. The chromosomal region, moreover, turned out to be the same in which the prophage had been already placed by bacterial conjugation studies.

The presence of the prophage not only endows the bacterium with the capacity to produce phage but also confers upon the cell an *immunity* to infection by a homologous phage (8, 18, 121, 157). Such virus particles are usually adsorbed to immune lysogenic bacteria, but the particles neither multiply to give rise to infective progeny nor affect growth and division of the immune cells in any way (16, 15, 81). The immune character is highly specific, in that a bacterium lysogenic for, and hence immune to, infection by one type of phage is not immune to infection by other viruses whose prophage the cell does not happen to carry. It became possible to study the genetic basis of immunity when Wollman and Jacob (84) discovered a number of related phage strains that undergo genetic recombination with one another but that differ in their immune specificity as well as in the locations of their prophages on the host linkage map. The final paper of our collection presents the work of Kaiser and Jacob (87) which established by means of crosses of these related phage strains that there is a definite segment of the viral genome, the C region, which determines the immune specificity of the phage. This same segment also controls the ability of the virus to establish itself as prophage and the locus at which the prophage is situated on the bacterial chromosome. Later experiments by Jacob and Campbell (80) have shown that immunity derives from the presence of a *repressor substance* in the cytoplasm of the lysogenic cell. The specificity of both formation and action of this repressor appears to be determined by the C region of the phage genome.

Before closing this introduction, we must once more call attention to the necessarily very limited and quite arbitrarily restricted scope of this collection. Not only do the twenty-five papers presented make up a very small fraction of the important contributions to the study of bacterial viruses, but even the references listed on the following pages are by no means an adequate, or even representative, coverage of the relevant literature. Some impression of the extent of that literature can be gained from the astounding bacteriophage bibliography prepared by Raettig (127), which lists no fewer than 5655 papers published between 1917 and 1956! The reader who wishes to acquire a more profound knowledge of this subject without working his way through these 5655 papers may do so by studying some of the books and reviews on bacterial viruses which have appeared over the years. This study might begin with Adams' book *Bacteriophages* (1), the most authoritative and comprehensive treatment available at present, and with the more specialized chapters in Burnet and Stanley's treatise *The Viruses* (115, 58, 140, 102, 85, 136). More easily digestible works are Weidel's little book *Virus* (153), a sprightly introduction to bacterial viruses, and Afinsen's *The Molecular Basis of Evolution* (6) which contains an account of the role of bacterial viruses in *avant-garde* molecular biology. A first-hand acquaintance with the evolution of bacterial virus research can be obtained by perusal of the reviews of Bronfenbrenner of 1928 (30), Bordet of 1931 (19), Burnet of 1934 (33), Delbrück of 1942 and 1946 (41, 42), Cohen of 1949 (38), Luria of 1950 (107) and Hershey of 1952, 1953, 1956, and 1957 (69, 70, 72, 73). Finally, some other important reviews that treat special aspects of bacterial viruses are those of Luria (109), Brenner (25), and Jacob and Wollman (86, 79).

BIBLIOGRAPHY

1. Adams, M. H. "Bacteriophages," Interscience, New York, 1959.
2. Adams, M. H., and Lark, G. Mutation to heat resistance in coliphage T5. *J. Immunol.*, *64*, 335 (1950).
3. Anderson, T. F. The reactions of bacterial viruses with their host cells. *Botan. Rev.*, *15*, 464 (1949).
4. Anderson, T. F. Destruction of bacterial viruses by osmotic shock. *J. Appl. Phys.*, *21*, 70 (1950).
5. Anderson, T. F. The morphology and osmotic properties of bacteriophage systems. *Cold Spring Harbor Symp. Quant. Biol.*, *18*, 197 (1953).
6. Anfinsen, C. B. "The Molecular Basis of Evolution." John Wiley and Sons, New York, 1959.
7. Appleyard, R. Segregation of lambda lysogenicity during bacterial recombination in *Escherichia coli* K12. *Genetics*, *39*, 429 (1954).
8. Bail, O. Der Colistamm 88 von Gildemeister und Herzberg. *Med. Klin.* (Munich), *21*, 1271 (1925).

9. Bail, O., and Matusmoto, T. Die Anhäufungsmoglichkeit von Bakteriophagen und Bakterien, *Med. Klin.* (Munich), 19, 1579 (1923).

10. Baricelli, N. A. A "chromosomic" recombination theory for multiplicity reactivation in phages. *Acta biotheoretica (Leiden)*, *11*, 107 (1956).

11. Benzer, S. Resistance to ultraviolet light as an index to the reproduction of bacteriophage. *J. Bacteriol.*, *63*, 59 (1952).

12. Benzer, S. Fine structure of a genetic region in bacteriophage. *Proc. Natl. Acad. Sci. U.S.*, *41*, 344 (1955).

13. Benzer, S. The elementary units of heredity, in "The Chemical Basis of Heredity," W. D. McElroy and B. Glass, eds., p. 70. The Johns Hopkins Press, Baltimore, 1957.

14. Benzer, S., and Freese, E. Induction of specific mutations with 5-bromouracil. *Proc. Natl. Acad. Sci. U.S.*, *44*, 112 (1958).

15. Bertani, G. Lysogenic versus lytic cycle of phage multiplication. *Cold Spring Harbor Symp. Quant. Biol.*, *18*, 65 (1953).

16. Bertani, G. Infections bactériophagiques secondaires des bacteries lysogènes. *Ann. Inst. Pasteur*, *84*, 273 (1953).

17. Bertani, G. Lysogeny. *Advances in Virus Research*, *5*, 151 (1958).

18. Bordet, J. Le problème de l'autolyse microbienne transmissible ou du bactériophage. *Ann. Inst. Pasteur*, *39*, 711 (1925).

19. Bordet, J. The theories of the bacteriophage. *Proc. Roy. Soc. London*, *B83*, 398 (1931).

20. Bordet, J., and Ciuca, M. Exudats leucocytaires et autolyse microbienne transmissible. *Compt. rend. Soc. Biol.*, *83*, 1293 (1920).

21. Bordet, J., and Ciuca, M. Déterminisme de l'autolyse microbienne transmissible. *Compt. rend. Soc. Biol.*, *84*, 276 (1921).

22. Bordet, J., and Ciuca, M. Le bactériophage de d'Hérelle, sa production, et son interpretation. *Compt. rend. Soc. Biol.*, *83*, 1296 (1920).

23. Bowen, G. H. Studies of ultraviolet irradiation phenomena — An approach to the problems of bacteriophage reproduction. *Cold Spring Harbor Symp. Quant. Biol.*, *18*, 245 (1953).

24. Bowen, G. H. Kinetic studies on the mechanism of photoreactivation of bacteriophage T2 inactivated by ultraviolet light. *Ann. Inst. Pasteur*, *84*, 218 (1953).

25. Brenner, S. Physiological aspects of bacteriophage genetics. *Advances in Virus Research*, *6*, 137 (1959).

26. Brenner, S., and Barnett, L. Genetic and chemical studies on the head protein of bacteriophages T2 and T4, in "Structure and Function of Genetic Elements." *Brookhaven Symposia in Biology*, No. 12, p. 86 (1959).

27. Brenner, S., Benzer, S., and Barnett, L. Distribution of proflavin-induced mutations in the genetic fine structure. *Nature*, *182*, 983 (1958).

28. Bresch, C. Zum Paarungsmechanismus von Bakteriophagen. *Z. Naturforsch.*, *10b*, 545 (1955).

29 Bresch, C., and Starlinger, P. Zum Problem der genetischen Rekombination von Bakteriophagen. *Z. Vererbungsl.*, *89*, 459 (1958).

30. Bronfenbrenner, J. J. In "Filtrable Viruses" (T. Rivers, ed.), p. 373. Williams and Wilkins, Baltimore, 1928.

31. Burnet, F. M. A method for the study of bacteriophage multiplication in broth. *Brit. J. Expt. Path.*, *10,* 109 (1929).

32. Burnet, F. M. A specific soluble substance from bacteriophages. *Brit. J. Exptl. Pathol.*, *14,* 100 (1933).

33. Burnet, F. M. The bacteriophages. *Biol. Revs. Biol. Proc. Cambridge Phil. Soc.*, *9,* 332 (1934).

34. Burnet, F. M., and Lush, D. Induced lysogenicity and mutation of bacteriophage within lysogenic bacteria. *Australian J. Exptl. Biol. Med. Sci.*, *14,* 27 (1936).

35. Burnet, F. M., and McKie, M. Observations on a permanently lysogenic strain of B. *enteridis gaertner*. *Austral. J. Exptl. Biol. Med. Sci.*, *6,* 277 (1929).

36. Chargaff, E., and Davidson, J. N. "The Nucleic Acids," Academic Press, New York, 1955.

37. Cohen, S. S. Synthesis of bacterial viruses; origin of phosphorus found in desoxyribonucleic acids of T2 and T4 bacteriophages. *J. Biol. Chem.*, *174,* 295 (1948).

38. Cohen, S. S. Growth requirements of bacterial viruses. *Bacteriol. Rev.*, *13,* 1 (1949).

39. Delbrück, M. Adsorption of bacteriophages under various physiological conditions of the host. *J. Gen. Physiol.*, *23,* 631 (1940).

40. Delbrück, M. The growth of bacteriophage and lysis of the host. *J. Gen. Physiol.*, *23,* 643 (1940).

41. Delbrück, M. Bacterial viruses. *Advances in Enzymol.*, *2,* 1 (1942).

42. Delbrück, M. Bacterial viruses or bacteriophages. *Biol. Rev.*, *21,* 30 (1946).

43. Delbrück, M. Biochemical mutants of bacterial viruses. *J. Bacteriol.*, *56,* 1 (1948).

44. Delbrück, M., and Bailey, W. T. Induced mutations in bacterial viruses. *Cold Spring Harbor Symp. Quant. Biol.*, *11,* 33 (1946).

45. Delbrück, M., and Stent, G. S. On the mechanism of DNA replication, in "The Chemical Basis of Heredity," W. D. McElroy and B. Glass, eds., p. 699. The Johns Hopkins Press, Baltimore, (1957).

46. DeMars, R. I. The production of phage-related material when bacteriophage development is interrupted by proflavine. *Virology*, *1,* 83 (1955).

47. Doermann, A. H. The intracellular growth of bacteriophages. I. Liberation of intracellular bacteriophage T4 by premature lysis with another phage or with cyanide. *J. Gen. Physiol.*, *35,* 645 (1952).

48. Doermann, A. H. The vegetative state in the life cycle of bacteriophage: Evidence for its occurrence and its genetic characterization. *Cold Spring Harbor Symp. Quant. Biol.*, *18,* 3 (1953).

49. Dulbecco, R. Experiments on photoreactivation of bacteriophages inactivated with ultraviolet radiation. *J. Bacteriol.*, *59,* 329 (1950).

50. Dulbecco, R. A critical test for the recombination theory of multiplicity reactivation. *J. Bacteriol.* *63,* 199 (1952).

51. Dulbecco, R., and Vogt, M. Biological properties of poliomyelitis virus as studied by the plaque technique. *Annals New York Acad. Sci.*, *61,* 790 (1955).

52. Ellis, E. L., and Delbrück, M. The growth of bacteriophage. *J. Gen. Physiol.*, *22,* 365 (1939).

53. Flaks, J. G., and Cohen, S. S., Virus-induced acquisition of metabolic function. I. Enzymatic formation of 5-hydroxymethyldeoxycytidylate. *J. Biol. Chem.*, *234,* 1501 (1959).

54. Flaks, J. G., Lichtenstein, J., and Cohen, S. S., Virus-induced acquisition of metabolic function. II. Studies on the origin of the deoxycytidylate hydroxymethylase of bacteriophage-infected *E. coli*. *J. Biol. Chem.*, *234*, 1507 (1959).

55. Fredericq, P. Localisation du prophage sur le chromosome. Son intervention dans le taux de ségrégation apparent des recombinants *d'Escherichia coli* K12. *Compt. rend. Soc. Biol.*, *148*, 1501 (1954).

56. Freese, E. On the molecular explanation of spontaneous and induced mutations, in "Structure and Function of Genetic Elements." *Brookhaven Symposia in Biology.* No. 12, p. 63 (1959).

57. Freese, E. The difference between spontaneous and base-analogue induced mutations of phage T4. *Proc. Natl. Acad. Sci.*, *45*, 622 (1959).

58. Garen, A., and Kozloff, L. M. The initiation of bacteriophage infection, in "The Viruses," F. M. Burnet and W. M. Stanley, eds., Vol. II, p. 204. Academic Press, New York, 1959.

59. Garen, A., and Puck, T. T. The first two steps of the invasion of host cells by bacterial viruses. *J. Exptl. Med. 94*, 177 (1951).

60. Gildemeister, E. Ueber das d'Herellesche Phanomen. *Berlin. klin. Wochschr. 58*, 1355 (1921).

61. Goodgal, S. H., Rupert, C. S., and Herriott, R. M. Photoreactivation of *Hemophilus Influenzae* transforming factor for streptomycin resistance by an extract of *Escherichia coli* B. in "The Chemical Basis of Heredity," W. D. McElroy and B. Glass, eds. p. 341. The Johns Hopkins Press, Baltimore, 1957.

62. Harm, W. On the mechanism of multiplicity reactivation in bacteriophage. *Virology*, *2*, 559 (1956).

63. Hercik, F. Some observations about the morphology of bacteriophage. *Experientia*, *6*, 64 (1950).

64. d'Hérelle, F. Sur un microbe invisible antagoniste des bacilles dysentériques. *Compt. rend. Acad. Sci.*, *165*, 373, (1917).

65. d'Hérelle, F. "The Bacteriophage and its Behaviour." Williams and Wilkins, Baltimore, 1926, p. 135.

66. Herriott, R. M. Nucleic acid-free T2 virus "ghosts" with specific biological action. *J. Bacteriol.*, *61*, 752 (1951).

67. Hershey, A. D. Mutation of bacteriophage with respect to type of plaque. *Genetics*, *31*, 620 (1946).

68. Hershey, A. D. Spontaneous mutations in bacterial viruses. *Cold Spring Harbor Symp. Quant. Biol.*, *11*, 67 (1946).

69. Hershey, A. D. Reproduction of bacteriophage. *Intern. Rev. Cytol.*, Vol I. (1952), p. 119.

70. Hershey, A. D. Inheritance in bacteriophage. *Advances in Genet.*, *5*, 89 (1953).

71. Hershey, A. D. Nucleic acid economy in bacteria infected with bacteriophage T2. II. Phage precursor nucleic acid. *J. Gen. Physiol.*, *37*, 1 (1953).

72. Hershey, A. D. Chemistry and viral growth, in "Currents in Biochemical Research," D. E. Green, ed. p. 1, Interscience, New York, 1956.

73. Hershey, A. D. Bacteriophages as genetic and biochemical systems. *Advances in Virus Research*, *4*, 25 (1957).

74. Hershey, A. D., and Chase, M. Genetic recombination and heterozygosis in bacteriophage. *Cold Spring Harbor Symp. Quant. Biol.*, *16*, 471 (1951).

75. Hershey, A. D., and Chase, M. Independent functions of viral protein and nucleic acid in growth of bacteriophage. *J. Gen. Physiol.*, *36*, 39 (1952).

76. Hershey, A. D., Kamen, M. D., Kennedy, J. W., and Gest, H. The mortality of bacteriophage containing assimilated radioactive phosphorus. *J. Gen. Physiol.* *34*, 305 (1951).

77. Hershey, A. D., and Rotman, R. Genetic recombination between host range and plaque-type mutants of bacteriophage in single bacterial cells. *Genetics*, *34*, 44 (1949).

78. Jacob, F. Transduction of lysogeny in *Escherichia coli*. *Virology*, *1*, 207 (1955).

79. Jacob, F. Genetic control of viral functions, in "The Harvey Lectures," Vol. 54, p. 1, Academic Press, New York, 1960.

80. Jacob, F., and Campbell, A. Sur le système de répression assurant l'immunité chez les bacteries lysogènes. *Compt. rend. Acad. Sci.*, *248*, 3219 (1959).

81. Jacob, F., and Wollman, E. L. Induction of phage development in lysogenic bacteria. *Cold Spring Harbor Symp. Quant. Biol.*, *18*, 101, (1953).

82. Jacob, F., and Wollman, E. L. Induction spontanée du development du bactériophage au cours de la recombinaison génétique, chez *Escherichia coli* K12. *Compt. rend.*, *239*, 317 (1954).

83. Jacob, F., and Wollman, E. L. Genetic aspects of lysogeny, in "The Chemical Basis of Heredity," W. D. McElroy and B. Glass, eds., p. 468. The Johns Hopkins Press, Baltimore, 1957.

84. Jacob, F., and Wollman, E. L. Sur les processus de conjugaison et de récombinaison génétique chez *Escherichia coli*. IV. Prophages inductibles et mesure des segments génétiques transférés au cours de la conjugaison. *Annales Inst. Pasteur*, *95*, 497 (1958).

85. Jacob, F., and Wollman, E. L. Lysogeny, in "The Viruses," F. M. Burnet and W. M. Stanley, eds. Vol. II, p. 319, Academic Press, New York, 1959.

86. Jacob, F., and Wollman, E. L. The relationship between the prophage and the bacterial chromosome in lysogenic bacteria, in "Recent Progress in Microbiology," G. Tuneval, ed. Almquist and Wiksell, Stockholm, 1959.

87. Kaiser, A. D., and Jacob, F. Recombination between related temperate bacteriophages and the genetic control of immunity and prophage localization. *Virology*, *4*, 509 (1957).

88. Kellenberger, E., and Séchaud, J., Electron microscopical studies of phage multiplication. II. Production of phage-related structures during multiplication of phages T2 and T4. *Virology*, *3*, 256 (1957).

89. Kellenberger, E., and Séchaud, J., Electron microscopical studies of phage multiplication. IV. The establishment of the DNA pool of vegetative phages and the maturation of phage particles. *Virology*, *8*, 478 (1959).

90. Kornberg, A., Zimmerman, S. B., Kornberg, S. R., and Josse, J. Enzymatic synthesis of deoxyribonucleic acid. VI. Influence of bacteriophage T2 on the synthetic pathway in host cells. *Proc. Natl. Acad. Sci. U.S.*, *45*, 772 (1959).

91. Krueger, A. P. The sorption of bacteriophage by living and dead susceptible bacteria. *J. Gen. Physiol.* *14*, 493 (1931).

92. Krueger, A. P., and Northrop, J. H. The kinetics of the bacterium-bacteriophage reaction. *J. Gen. Physiol.*, *14*, 223 (1931).

93. Krueger, A. P., and Scribner, E. J. Nature of intracellular phage precursor. *J. Gen. Physiol.*, *22*, 699 (1939).

94. Latarjet, R. Multiplication of bacterial viruses studies by radiobiological methods, in "The Nature of Virus Multiplication," P. Fildes and W. E. van Heyningen, eds. (2nd Symp. Soc. Gen. Microbiol), p. 175. Cambridge University Press, Cambridge (1953).

95. Lea, D. E. "Actions of Radiations on Living Cells." Cambridge University Press, Cambridge, (1947).

96. Lederberg, E. M., and Lederberg, J. Genetic studies of lysogenicity in *Escherichia coli*. *Genetics*, *38*, 51 (1953).

97. Lederberg, J. Recombination mechanisms in bacteria. *J. Cell. Comp. Physiol.*, *45*, Supp. 2, 75 (1955).

98. Lennox, E. S. Transduction of linked genetic characters of the host by bacteriophage P1. *Virology*, *1*, 190 (1955).

99. Lennox, E. S., Luria, S. E., and Benzer, S. On the mechanism of photoreactivation of ultraviolet inactivated bacteriophage. *Biochim. et Biophys. Acta*, *15*, 471 (1954).

100. Levinthal, C. Recombination in phage T2; its relation to heterozygosis and growth. *Genetics*, *39*, 169 (1954).

101. Levinthal, C. The mechanism of DNA replication and genetic recombination in phage. *Proc. Natl. Acad. Sci. U.S.*, *42*, 394 (1956).

102. Levinthal, C. Bacteriophage genetics, in "The Viruses," F. M. Burnet and W. M. Stanley, eds. Vol II., p. 281. Academic Press, New York, 1959.

103. Levinthal, C., and Fisher, H. The structural development of a bacterial virus. *Biochim. et Biophys. Acta*, *9*, 419 (1952).

104. Litman, R. M., and Pardee, A. B. Production of bacteriophage mutants by a disturbance of dexoyribosenucleic acid metabolism. *Nature*, *178*, 529 (1956).

105. Luria, S. E. Mutations of bacterial viruses affecting their host range. *Genetics*, *30*, 84 (1945).

106. Luria, S. E. Reactivation of irradiated bacteriophage by transfer of self-reproducing units. *Proc. Natl. Acad. Sci. U.S.*, *33*, 253 (1947).

107. Luria, S. E. Bacteriophage: An essay on virus reproduction. *Science*, *111*, 507 (1950).

108. Luria, S. E. The frequency distribution of spontaneous bacteriophage mutants as evidence for the exponential rate of phage reproduction. *Cold Spring Harbor Symp. Quant. Biol.*, *16*, 463 (1951).

109. Luria, S. E. Host-induced modifications of bacterial viruses. *Cold Spring Harbor Symp. Quant. Biol.*, *18*, 237 (1953).

110. Luria, S. E. Radiation and viruses, in "Radiation Biology," A. Hollaender, ed. Vol. 11, p. 333. McGraw Hill Book Co., New York, 1955.

111. Luria, S. E., and Delbrück, M. Interference between bacterial viruses: II. Interference between inactivated bacterial virus and active virus of the same strain and of a different strain. *Arch. Biochm.*, *1*, 207 (1942).

112. Luria, S. E., and Dulbecco, R. Genetic recombinations leading to production of active bacteriophage from ultraviolet inactivated bacteriophage particles. *Genetics*, *34*, 93 (1949).

113. Luria, S. E., and Latarjet, R. Ultraviolet irradiation during intracellular growth. *J. Bacteriol.*, *53*, 149 (1947).

114. Lwoff, A. Lysogeny. *Bacteriol. Rev.*, *17*, 269 (1953).

115. Lwoff, A. Bacteriophage as a model of host-virus relationship, in "The Viruses," F. M. Burnet and W. M. Stanley, eds. Vol. II, p. 187. Academic Press, New York, 1959.

116. Lwoff, A., and Gutmann, A. Recherches sur un *Bacillus megathérium* lysogène. *Ann. Inst. Pasteur*, *78*, 711 (1950).

117. Lwoff, A., Siminovitch, L., and Kjeldgaard, N. Induction de la lyse bactériophagique de la totalité d'une population microbienne lysogène. *Compt. rend.* *231*, 190 (1950).

118. Lwoff, A., Siminovitch, L., and Kjeldgaard, N. Induction de la production de bactériophages chez une bacterie lysogène. *Ann. Inst. Pasteur*, *79*, 815 (1950).

119. Maaløe, O., and Symonds, N. Radioactive sulfur tracer studies on the reproduction of T4 bacteriophage. *J. Bacteriol.*, *65*, 177 (1953).

120. Maaløe, O., and Watson, J. D. The transfer of radioactive phosphorus from parental to progeny phage. *Proc. Natl. Acad. Sci. U.S.*, *37*, 507 (1951).

121. McKinley, E. B. Sérum antilytique obtenu par immunisation contre une bactérie normale. *Compt. rend. Soc. Biol.*, *93*, 1050 (1925).

122. Meselson, M., and Stahl, F. W. The replication of DNA in *Escherichia coli*. *Proc. Natl. Acad. Sci. U.S.*, *44*, 671 (1958).

123. Meuli, H. Studien zum Bakteriophagen-problem. II. Die Konzentration des lytischen Prinzips und ihre Beziehung zum Ablauf der Bakteriophagenreaktion. *Z. Hyg. Infektionskrankh.*, *99*, 46 (1923).

124. Northrop, J. H. Increase in bacteriophage and gelatinase concentration in cultures of *Bacillus megatherium*. *J. Gen. Physiol.* *23*, 59 (1939).

125. Puck, T. T. The first steps of virus invasion. *Cold Spring Harbor Symp. Quant. Biol.*, *18*, 149 (1953).

126. Putnam, F. W. and Kozloff, L. M. Biochemical studies of virus reproduction. IV. The fate of the infecting virus particle. *J. Biol. Chem.*, *182*, 243 (1950).

127. Raettig, H. "Bakteriophagie, 1917 bis 1956." Gustav Fischer, Stuttgart, 1958.

128. Rubin, H., and Temin, H. M. A radiological study of cell-virus interaction in the Rous sarcoma. *Virology*, *7*, 75, (1959).

129. Schlesinger, M. Ueber die Bindung des Bakteriophagen an homologe Bakterien. I. Die Unterscheidung von Gruppen von verschiedener Bindungsaffinitaet innerhalb der Bakterien des selben Lysats. Die Frage der Reversibilitaet oder Irreversibilitaet der Bindung. *Z. Hyg. Infektionskrankh.*, *114*, 136 (1932).

130. Schlesinger, M. Ueber die Bindung des Bakteriophagen an homologe Bakterien. II. Quantitative Untersuchungen ueber die Bindungsgeschwindigkeit und die Saettigung. Berechnung der Teilchengroesse des Bakteriophagen aus deren Ergebnissen. *Z. Hyg. Infektionskrankh.*, *114*, 149 (1932).

131. Schlesinger, M. Reindarstellung eines Bakteriophagen in mit freiem Auge sichtbaren Mengen. *Biochem. Z.*, *264*, 6 (1933).

132. Schlesinger, M. Zur Frage der chemischen Zusammensetzung des Bakteriophagen. *Biochem. Z.*, *273*, 306 (1934).

133. Sertic, V. Procédé d'obtention de variantes de bactériophage adaptées a lyser des formes bactériennes secondaires. *Compt. rend. Soc. Biol.*, *100*, 612 (1929).

134. Siegel, A., Ginoza, W., and Wildman, S. G. The early events of infection with tobacco mosaic virus nucleic acid. *Virology, 3,* 554 (1957).

135. Siegel, A., and Wildman, S. G. The inactivation of the infectious centers of tobacco mosaic virus by ultraviolet light. *Virology, 2,* 69 (1956).

136. Stahl, F. W. Radiobiology of bacteriophage, in "The Viruses," F. M. Burnet and W. M. Stanley, eds., Vol. II, p. 353. Academic Press, New York, 1959.

137. Steinberg, C., and Stahl, F. The theory of formal phage genetics. *Cold Spring Harbor Symp. Quant. Biol., 23,* 42 (1958).

138. Stent, G. S. Decay of incorporated radioactive phosphorus during reproduction of bacteriophage T2. *J. Gen. Physiol., 38,* 853 (1955).

139. Stent, G. S. Mating in the reproduction of bacterial viruses. *Advances in Virus Research, 5,* 95 (1958).

140. Stent, G. S. Intracellular multiplication of bacterial viruses, in "The Viruses," F. M. Burnet and W. M. Stanley, eds., Vol. II, p. 237. Academic Press, New York, 1959.

141. Stent, G. S., and Fuerst, C. R. Inactivation of bacteriophages by decay of incorporated radioactive phosphorus. *J. Gen. Physiol., 38,* 441 (1955).

142. Stent, G. S., and Fuerst, C. R. Genetic and physiological effects of the decay of incorporated radioactive phosphorus in bacterial viruses and bacteria. *Advances in Biol. and Med. Physics, 7,* 1 (1960).

143. Stent, G. S., and Jerne, N. K. The distribution of parental phosphorus atoms among bacteriophage progeny. *Proc. Natl. Acad. Sci. U.S., 41,* 704 (1955).

144. Stent, G. S., and Maaløe, O. Radioactive phosphorus tracer studies on the reproduction of T4 bacteriophage. II. Kinetics of phosphorus assimilation. *Biochim. et Biophys. Acta., 10,* 55 (1953).

145. Stent, G. S., Sato, G. H., and Jerne, N. K., Dispersal of the parental nucleic acid of bacteriophage T4 among its progeny. *J. Mol. Biol., 1,* 134 (1959).

146. Stent, G. S., and Wollman, E. L., On the two-step nature of bacteriophage adsorption. *Biochim. et Biophys. Acta, 8,* 260 (1952).

147. Stocker, B. A. D., Zinder, N. D., and Lederberg, J. Transduction of flagellar characters in *Salmonella, J. Gen. Microbiol., 9,* 410 (1953).

148. Tolmach, L. J. Attachment and penetration of cells by viruses. *Advances in Virus Research, 4,* 63 (1957).

149. Twort, F. W. An investigation on the nature of the ultramicroscopic viruses. *Lancet, 1915,* II, 1241.

150. Visconti, N., and Delbrück, M. The mechanism of genetic recombination in phage. *Genetics, 38,* 5 (1953).

151. Watson, J. D., and Crick, F. H. C. The structure of DNA. *Cold Spring Harbor Symp. Quant. Biol., 18,* 123 (1953).

152. Watson, J. D., and Maaløe, O. Nucleic acid transfer from parental to progeny bacteriophage. *Biochim. et Biophys. Acta, 10,* 432 (1953).

153. Weidel, W. "Virus," Springer Verlag, Berlin, 1957. (University of Michigan Press, Ann Arbor, 1959.)

154. Weidel, W. Bacterial viruses (with particular reference to adsorption/penetration). *Ann. Rev. Microbiol. 12,* 27 (1958).

155. Williams, R. C., and Fraser, D. Structural and functional differentiation in T2 bacteriophage. *Virology, 2,* 289 (1956).

156. Wollman, E. Bactériophagie et processus similaires. Hérédité ou infection? *Bull. Inst. Pasteur, 26,* 1 (1928).

157. Wollman, E., and Wōllman, E. Régénération des bactériophages chez le *B. megatherium* lysogène. *Compt. rend. Soc. Biol., 122,* 190 (1936).

158. Wollman, E. L. Sur le determinisme génétique de la lysogenie. *Ann. Inst. Pasteur, 84,* 281 (1953).

159. Wollman, E. L., and Jacob, F. Lysogénie et récombinaison génétique chez *Escherichia coli* K12. *Compt. rend., 239,* 455 (1954).

160. Wollman, E. L., and Jacob, F. Sur les processus de conjugation et de récombinasion chez *Escherichia coli.* II. La localisation chromosomoqie du prophage et les conséquences de l'induction zygotique. *Ann. Inst. Pasteur, 93,* 323 (1957).

161. Wyatt, G. R., and Cohen, S. S. The bases of the nucleic acids of some bacterial and animal viruses: The occurrence of 5-hydroxymethylcytosine. *Biochem. J., 55,* 774 (1953).

162. Wyckoff, R. W. G. The electron microscopy of developing bacteriophage. II. Growth of T4 in liquid culture. *Biochim. et Biophys. Acta., 2,* 246 (1948).

163. Zinder, N. D. Infective heredity in bacteria. *Cold Spring Harbor Symp. Quant. Biol., 18,* 261 (1953).

164. Zinder, N. E., and Lederberg, J. Genetic exchange in *Salmonella. J. Bacteriol., 64,* 679 (1952).

PAPERS ON BACTERIAL VIRUSES

NINETIETH ANNUAL MEETING

OF THE

British Medical Association.

Held at Glasgow, July, 1922.

DISCUSSION ON THE BACTERIOPHAGE (BACTERIOLYSIN).

I.—THE NATURE OF BACTERIOPHAGE.

By Dr. F. D'HERELLE.
(From the Pasteur Institute, Paris.)

LET us record first, in a few words, the essential facts relating to the present discussion.

There exist in the intestinal contents of all living beings principles which have the property of dissolving certain bacteria. These principles pass porcelain filters; hence it is possible to separate them from intestinal bacteria.

Each filtering principle, isolated from intestinal contents of normal individuals, dissolves a certain number of bacterial species, belonging generally to the coli-typhoid-dysentery group. The action, therefore, of these principles is not strictly specific; but belongs, for a given filtrate, to a certain number of microbial species. In convalescents from an infectious disease a principle endowed with an energetic dissolving action on the bacterial species which causes the disease is always met with.

It is not only towards the intestinal bacteria that these lytic principles exist: for instance, one can isolate from the excreta of convalescents from bubonic plague a principle which dissolves *B. pestis*; the same phenomenon exists in various animal septicaemias.

I cannot enter here into an examination of all the facts relating to bacteriophage,[1] facts most of which have been already confirmed by the investigations of other workers. But if the facts themselves have not been contested, it is not so in regard to the hypothesis which I have put forward to explain the nature of the principle which brings about the dissolution of bacteria.

Reprinted by permission of the British Medical Association from the BRITISH MEDICAL JOURNAL, 2 (3216), 289-297, August 19, 1922.

A preliminary remark presents itself. Many authors who have formulated hypotheses as to the nature of the lytic principle have simply taken a particular fact supporting their own point of view and have neglected the whole assembly of experimental facts which renders such a thesis untenable, thereby forgetting that experiment is the final criterion of the truth of a theory. Let us try to resolve the question objectively.

The choice between the different hypotheses *a priori* possible to explain the origin of the lytic principle can only be made in accordance with a fundamental rule of logic — namely, in order that a hypothesis becomes admissible it is necessary that it should explain all the experimental facts and that it is not contradicted by any of them; further, in order that this admissible hypothesis may be considered as being in conformity with the nature of things, it must be proved that all the experimental facts cannot be explained if one abandons or modifies this hypothesis.

The bacteriolysis produced under the influence of the principle which we have named "bacteriophage" consists in a total dissolution of the microbial body; at the end of this action there remains no visible residue. A total dissolution of a microbial substance can only be due to a transformation or decomposition of the proteins of the microbe by proteolytic enzymes. Whence, it may be asked, come these proteolytic enzymes? Four hypotheses may be considered.

1. The enzymes may be derived from the animal organism which is attacked by the given bacteria. The enzymes would then be the result of a defensive reaction on the part of the organism.

This is the hypothesis of Kabeshima, Bordet and Ciuca, and Ann Kuttner. Kabeshima[2] does not specify the particular tissue of the animal from which the enzymes originate; Bordet and Ciuca[3] indicate the leucocytes; Ann Kuttner[4] incriminates any tissue.

2. The enzymes may come from intestinal bacteria as the result of a microbial antagonism. For instance, one knows the bacteriolytic action of filtrates of old cultures of *B. pyocyaneus*.

This is the hypothesis of Lisbonne et Carrère,[5] for whom the lytic enzymes are secreted by intestinal bacilli such as *B. coli, B. proteus*, etc.

3. The enzymes may be secreted by the bacterium itself which undergoes the lysis. These enzymes would therefore be autolysins.

This is the hypothesis of Weinberg and Aznar.[6] Under the action of a cause *x* the bacteria would acquire the property of secreting autolytic enzymes.

Bail[7] had already indicated a similar origin, but his hypothesis was more complicated, and that in order to harmonize his conception with certain experimental facts to which we shall refer later. The bacteria undergoing lysis would become fragmented into filtrable corpuscles (the "splitters" hypothesis of Bail). These corpuscles would secrete enzymes capable of dissolving the bacteria from which they spring.

With the same view, Otto and Winkler[8] have put forward a hypothesis closely related to that of Bail, but for them the question resolved itself into one of bacterial albuminoid micelles, which do not reproduce themselves, but which secrete the lytic enzymes.

4. The enzymes may be secreted by an ultramicroscopic virus, which is a parasite of bacteria. This is the hypothesis by which I have held since my first publication.[9]

Those four hypotheses cover all the possibilities. Let us now see which hypothesis conforms best with the experimental facts, at the same time eliminating those which fail to do so.

FIRST FACT: *The dissolution of bacteria under the influence of the bacteriophagic principle takes place in series.*

That is to say, a filtrate containing the bacteriophagic principle, when added to a culture in liquid medium of a bacterium towards which the principle manifests its lytic action, provokes the entire dissolution of the bacteria. A trace of the latter, inoculated into a second bacterial culture, leads to the latter in its turn undergoing total lysis. A trace of this second dissolved culture, inoculated into a third bacterial culture, produces the same phenomenon, and so on *ad infinitum.* After more than a thousand passages, the thousandth bacteriolysed culture contains a bacteriophagic principle as active as, and generally much more active than, that of the primitive filtrate.

The phenomenon goes on in series in the same way, whether the culture is inoculated with the previously dissolved non-filtered culture, or with the dissolved culture filtered through a porcelain filter: the filtrate contains the bacteriophagic principle as active as the lysed non-filtered culture.

A simple enzyme action would cease to show itself from the first tubes of the series, because of the greater and greater dilution of the enzyme solution in the course of the successive passages. One calculates easily that at the thousandth passage (each passage being carried out on 10 c.cm. of bacterial emulsion inoculated with 1/1000 c.cm. of the preceding dissolved culture) the titre of the dilution in the thousandth tube of the series is given in cubic kilometres by the the number 10^{3982}. To appreciate this incommensurable number it is interesting to note that, at the twenty-second passage only, the drop of primitive filtrate introduced into the first tube of the series finds itself diluted in 10^{70} cubic kilometres of liquid; such a cube of liquid is so great that a light ray would take one billion years to cross one edge of it. It is impossible to conceive of an enzyme, contained in a single drop of primitive filtrate, still existing, without any diminution of its activity, after being diluted to this extent.

That the action may become manifest, each dilution must be allowed sufficient time (four to six hours) to permit the development of the bacteriophagic principle. On the contrary, when the dilution is utilized immediately, the bacteriophagic action ceases about the fourth or fifth dilution.

These experiments establish clearly that a regeneration of the bacteriophagic principle occurs at each passage. Consequently the lytic enzymes are produced by a living being, which regenerates itself in the course of the successive passages.

It will be obvious, then, that this transmissibility in series eliminates hypotheses 1 and 2. The authors who have put forward these hypotheses must admit that the principle derived from the organism which is attacked by parasites (hypothesis 1), or from the foreign bacteria (hypothesis 2), plays solely the role of a transformer—that is to say, it gives rise in the bacteria which undergo the transmissible lysis to a special state of "autolysability." We come now to the third hypothesis. Only Bordet and Ciuca have attempted to give an explanation of this. For them the leucocytic principle would provoke in the bacteria a "hereditary vitiation of nutritional nature." I must say that I do not understand how a filtered liquid can transmit a hereditary property. Besides, the whole theory of Bordet and Ciuca is based on an experience entitled "leucocytic exudates," which I have elsewhere stated it is impossible to repeat—a statement which has not been challenged by Bordet.[10] The result obtained by him in one experiment would appear to be purely accidental.[11]

But it is to no purpose to discuss here, point by point, the different theories; it is sufficient to show that they are contrary to the facts. Hypotheses 1 and 2 being eliminated, there only remain to consider hypotheses 3 and 4.

Second Fact: *The lytic enzymes emanate from material corpuscles which traverse filters; these corpuscles multiply in the course of the bacteriolysis.*

Experiment A.

In a well-developed bacterial culture, showing a marked turbidity, let us add a small quantity (say 1/10,000,000 c.cm.) of a filtrate containing the bacteriophagic principle, shake, withdraw 1/20 c.cm. and spread it over the surface of an agar slope. Thus we spread over the agar a great number of bacteria and a very small quantity of bacteriophagic principle. After incubation (eighteen to twenty-four hours at 37°) we note that the surface of the agar shows a bacterial growth with a certain number of circular bare spaces here and there, where the agar presents no trace of growth. These vacant spaces once formed are unchangeable; they never spread, and they are never invaded by the surrounding culture.

It is the presence of these immutable bare spaces, which are perfectly circular, that characterizes what we have named "bacteriophage." Before concluding that any bacteriolytic phenomenon is bacteriophagic, it becomes necessary to verify if it gives rise to such bare spaces on agar culture. If not, the bacteriolysis is not of bacteriophagic nature.

The number of spaces depends simply on the quantity of filtrate added to the bacterial culture. If into various bacterial emulsions we introduce variable quantities of the filtrate, the number of bare spaces is strictly proportional to the quantity of filtrate added. On the other hand, the number of the bare spaces is independent of the number of bacteria contained in the medium; whether one introduces a given quantity of filtrate into a bacterial emulsion containing one hundred millions or ten billions of bacteria per cubic centimetre, the number of bare spaces on the agar is practically always the same.

The phenomenon of these vacant spaces is only comprehensible on the supposition that the bacteriophagic principle is of corpuscular nature. The following experiments give the proof thereof.

Experiment B.

Given a filtrate containing the bacteriophagic principle, let us determine its force in the production of bare spaces.

It is well known that to determine the number of living bacteria contained in an emulsion agar plates are inoculated with a dilution of this emulsion; after incubation, the number of colonies which develop multiplied by the titre of the dilution gives the number of bacteria per cubic centimetre of the primitive emulsion. The enumeration of the bacteriophagic corpuscles contained in a filtrate is estimated in exactly the same way. But as the bacteriophage only grows at the expense of living bacteria, we must make the dilutions of the filtrate in a bacterial emulsion. For this we pipette over agar the bacterial emulsion containing a given quantity of filtrate: after incubation we obtain a bacterial layer strewn with circular bare spaces, each of these spaces being a colony of bacteriophage issued from one corpuscle. The number of bare spaces multiplied by the titre of the dilution gives the number of ultramicroscopic bacteriophagic corpuscles contained in 1 c.cm. of the primitive filtrate.

This experiment shows that the behaviour of the bacteriophage is exactly the same as that of any ordinary microbe. But this last develops at the expense of the nutritive substances contained in the medium; the bacteriophage develops at the expense of the bacterial bodies which constitute its nutritive medium. The bare spaces represent places cleared up by the growth of the ultramicroscopic bacteriophagic corpuscles.

Experiment C.

Now dilute a filtrate so as to obtain a dilution such that 1 c.cm. contains one bacteriophagic corpuscle. Dilute this 1 c.cm. with 9 c.cm. of sterile water, and inoculate ten tubes of bacterial emulsion each with 1 c.cm. It will be obvious that only one of the ten tubes will contain the generator of a bare space; the nine others will not contain any. Place the ten tubes in the incubator at 37° for twenty-four to forty-eight hours; it will be seen that only one of the ten microbial emulsions shows bacteriolysis; the nine others will remain unchanged, the bacteria remain living, normal, and subculturable.

The lytic action, therefore, is complete when only *one* generator of a bare space is introduced into a bacterial emulsion; the action is *nil* in the contrary case. This experiment can only be explained on the supposition that the bacteriophagic principle, the source of the lytic enzymes, is a corpuscle; and that each corpuscle deposited on the agar in the midst of the bacteria gives rise to a colony of these ultramicroscopic corpuscles, such a colony being represented by a bare space.

Experiment D.

Inoculate a bacterial emulsion with a bacteriophagic filtrate of known corpuscular strength (that is, of known bare spaces forming force); make agar slopes every hour in the same way as in Experiment A. In this way, after six hours, we will have six agar slopes inoculated, and, on incubation, it will be seen that the number of bacteriophagic spaces (each bare space corresponding to a corpuscle) increases in proportion as the lytic action progresses in the emulsion. The maximum number of bare spaces is given when the lysis of the original emulsion is complete; at this moment there are no longer any living bacteria in the emulsion—it is a pure culture of the ultramicroscopic bacteriophagic corpuscles. The bacteriophagic power of such a lysed culture remains at its maximum level during many weeks—it is practically "fixed."

The foregoing experiments show that the lytic enzymes are originated by ultramicroscopic corpuscles which multiply and reproduce themselves. Hence those hypotheses explaining the phenomenon as being due to a *soluble* autolytic enzyme become eliminated.

Of all the hypotheses put forward, only that of Bail, and perhaps that of Otto and Winkler, could not be incompatible with these experiments, since they suppose that the element which secretes the lytic enzymes can be furnished by ultra-microscopic corpuscles, but derived from the bacteria. It is difficult to reconcile these hypotheses with the fact that the bacteriophagic action is not specific, and that the same strain of bacteriophage can dissolve bacteria of different species. Indeed, if one can understand how a principle originated by a species of bacteria can provoke the formation of a similar principle in a culture of the same bacterial species, it is hard to admit how this principle could provoke the formation of the bacteriophagic principle in a culture of a different bacterial species. Besides, these two hypotheses are rendered untenable by the following fact.

THIRD FACT: *All bacteriophagic ultramicroscopic corpuscles, grown at the expense of any bacterial species, constitute one and the same antigen.*

I have up to the present isolated various strains of bacteriophage active towards different bacteria: *B. typhosus, B. paratyphosus* A and B, *B. dysenteriae* (Shiga, Flexner, Hiss), *B. coli, B. pestis, B. proteus, B. gallinarum,* bacteria of haemorrhagic septicaemias, staphylococcus, etc.

We have seen above what constitutes a culture of the ultramicroscopic bacteriophagic corpuscles. Inoculate an emulsion of *B. dysenteriae* with a filtrate containing an active bacteriophage towards this bacterium; after a few hours the medium becomes limpid, the bacilli are dissolved, and the bacteriophage corpuscles have multiplied; the culture of the bacteria has become a culture of antidysenteric bacteriophage. Similarly, a culture of *B. pestis* dissolved under the action of the bacteriophagic principle (isolated from the intestinal contents of a convalescent from bubonic plague) becomes a culture of antipestic bacteriophage. And so on for any other microbe.

One knows that the serum of a rabbit prepared by injections of *B. dysenteriae* contains an amboceptor towards *B. dysenteriae,* but does not contain any amboceptor towards any other bacteria—for example, *B. pestis.*

Now prepare a rabbit with a culture of *B. dysenteriae* dissolved by bacteriophagic action; one verifies that its serum does not contain any amboceptor towards normal *B. pestis,* but contains an amboceptor for *B. pestis* dissolved by the action of the bacteriophage. And this is true for no matter what bacterial species; the serum of an animal prepared by a culture of any bacterial species dissolved by bacteriophage contains an amboceptor which fixes itself on any other bacteriophaged culture. Hence the amboceptor is specifically *antibacteriophagic*, and not *antibacterial*. Therefore the bacteriophage is an autonomous antigen, and consequently must be considered, in the present state of knowledge, as a definite ultramicroscopic virus constituted by corpuscles, such a virus being necessarily an ultramicrobe.

Only the hypothesis of a filtrable micro-organism which is an obligatory parasite of bacteria is compatible with the foregoing facts. It now remains to show that this only admissible hypothesis is not contradicted by any experimental fact.

FOURTH FACT: *The ultramicroscopic corpuscles possess a variable virulence.*

We have seen that the above ultramicroscopic organism, which we have designated by the name of "bacteriophage," is constituted by living corpuscles which multiply and which it is possible to count. Now, experience shows that the lytic activity of these corpuscles varies from one strain to another. For instance, certain strains recently isolated from the organism are unable to provoke the dissolution of a bacterial emulsion, and no matter what number of corpuscles are inoculated into this bacterial emulsion, one can only perceive the presence of these bacteriophagic corpuscles by the production of pin-point bare spaces on agar. On the contrary, with very active strains giving on agar large bare spaces (4 to 5 mm. in diameter), the inoculation of one corpuscle is sufficient to provoke a total dissolution of all the bacteria contained in the emulsion. It is easy to prove that this difference in action is due to a difference in the multiplication of the corpuscles inoculated. In the case of feeble strains reproduction is slow; in the case of strong strains it is rapid. The active particle, therefore, is endowed with a variable virulence, the term "virulence" being taken in its real bacteriological sense of "vegetative power *in vivo*." To explain this fact one must consider the active corpuscle as a microbe, because only a microbe possesses a variable virulence from strain to strain. Moreover, an enzyme only acts by its quantity; a microbe by its virulence and its toxicity combined.

FIFTH FACT: *By successive passages, it is possible to increase the virulence of a feeble strain of bacteriophage.*

For instance, inoculate a feeble strain of bacteriophage into a culture of *B. typhosus*; filter the mixture after incubation; introduce a drop of this filtrate into a fresh culture of *B. typhosus*, which is filtered in turn, and so on for a few passages. The virulence is found to increase little by little, and after a certain number of passages the virulence becomes such that a trace of the filtrate is sufficient to provoke the total dissolution of a fresh emulsion of this bacillus. The technique of the exaltation of virulence is really the same as for any microbe: we exalt the virulence of a bacterium for a given animal by serial passages in this animal species; we exalt the virulence of the bacteriophage for a given bacterial species by serial passages in this bacterium. This fact is only compatible with the hypothesis that bacteriophage is a microbial parasite, since adaptation is the prerogative of living beings.

SIXTH FACT: *Experience shows that bacteria attacked by bacteriophage do not remain passive; they defend themselves and are even capable, under certain conditions, of acquiring an immunity towards the parasite.*

This defence of the bacteria manifests itself by a double mechanism: the bacteria surround themselves with a capsule, and secrete "aggressines" capable of paralysing the lytic enzymes of the bacteriophage. Only the hypothesis of bacteriophage being a parasite of bacteria conforms with these facts.

SEVENTH FACT: *The behaviour of bacteriophage towards physical and chemical reagents is that of a living being, and does not agree with that of an enzyme.*

The resistance of bacteriophage to the action of physical and chemical reagents is intermediate between that of the vegetative and the spore forms of ordinary bacteria. The resistance is less than that of certain ultramicrobes, notably that of the tobacco mosaic. It is destroyed at 74°-75°C., but ceases to develop at 43°. Between 43° and 74° it possesses no lytic action. As to the action of the antiseptics, the bacteriophage is killed after twenty-four hours' contact with a 1 per cent. solution of a neutral salt of quinine, after forty-eight hours' contact with 95 per cent. alcohol, and by eight days' contact with glycerin. The last-named liquid is precisely the medium employed for preserving indefinitely an enzyme in soluble form.

EIGHTH FACT: *It is possible to extract the lytic enzymes free from the living bacteriophage mirco-organism.*

If to one part of a culture of bacteriophage is added nine parts of absolute alcohol and the mixture left forty-eight hours in contact, a precipitate is obtained which contains bacteriolytic enzymes, while the bacteriophagic germs are killed, which is proved by the failure of transmissibility in series of the phenomenon. One can only understand this fact on the supposition of an ultramicroscopic microbial parasite: the bacteria are dissolved by enzymes secreted by the living ultramicroscopic germs, hence the action in series. In the above experiment the ultramicroscopic germs are killed, while the enzymes already secreted are preserved intact; hence only a lytic action is obtained which is not transmissible in series.

NINTH FACT: *Bacteriophage is capable of adaptation.*

The bacteriophage is very sensitive to the action of acids—much more sensitive than ordinary microbes. It can be accustomed progressively to live in media containing quantities of an acid which would have been destructive beforehand. The same fact is observed with glycerin. Adaptation is a prerogative of living things.

TENTH FACT: *The properties of bacteriophage are essentially variable.*

It is impossible to isolate two strains of bacteriophage which are absolutely identical as to their range of action on different bacterial species, and as to their intensity of action towards each of these bacterial species. For a given strain of bacteriophage one can vary experimentally this intensity. Variability is an essential characteristic of life.

We have seen, first, that of all the possible hypotheses concerning the nature of the bacteriophage, the hypothesis of an ultramicroscopic parasite of bacteria is alone admissible. Moreover, we have just seen that this hypothesis is not contradicted by any of the facts of bacteriophagic phenomena; and, furthermore, all of the facts cannot be explained if this hypothesis is abandoned or modified. It follows logically, therefore, that such a hypothesis becomes a certitude.

Further, I would remark that I do not specify in any way the species to which the ultramicroscopic organism, which I have given the name of *Bacteriophagum intestinale,* belongs; the name simply recalls its characteristic property and the place where it was at first found. Is it a protozoon, a fungus, a bacterium? Does it belong to a kingdom which is neither the vegetable nor the animal—a still simpler form of life than any which we at present know? These are questions which cannot at present be answered. All that we know of it is that it is an ultramicroscopic organism, a filtrable being, parasite of bacteria, endowed with functions of assimilation and reproduction—functions which characterize the living nature of the being which possesses these properties. That is all that experiment actually shows us.*

The foregoing discussion can only apply to the phenomenon of bacteriolysis in series presenting the special characters that I have indicated. This being so, a final question arises—that of the plurality of the serial phenomena.

In 1915 Twort[12] described a bacterial transformation taking place in series, under the influence of a principle which passes through porcelain filters. His researches have been made chiefly with a micrococcus isolated from vaccine. In addition he observed an identical phenomenon with two other bacteria—a large indeterminate bacillus, and a bacillus of the coli-typhoid group. Twort isolated the active principle in the following manner.

"Some interesting results, however, were obtained with cultivations from glycerinated calf vaccinia. Inoculated agar tubes, after twenty-four hours at 37°, often showed watery-looking areas, and in cultures that grow micrococci it was found that some of these colonies could not be subcultured, but if kept became glassy and transparent. On examination of these glassy areas nothing but minute granules, staining reddish with Giemsa, could be seen."

The transforming principle is contained in this transparent material.

"The transparent material when diluted (one in a million) with water or saline was found to pass the finest porcelain filters with ease, and one drop of the filtrate, pipetted over an agar tube, was sufficient to make that tube unsuitable for the growth of the micrococcus. That is, if the micrococcus was inoculated down the tube as a streak, this would start to grow, but would soon become dotted with transparent points which would rapidly extend over the whole growth. If in an infected tube

* I will mention, in passing, the hypothesis of Salimbeni: the enzymes would be secreted by a myxobacteria, microscopically and even macroscopically visible, given filtrable spores. All the workers who have studied the question have failed to observe this would-be myxobacteria, which besides, according to the description of Salimbeni, presents a mycelium (?). That can only mean an impurity, as I have elsewhere pointed out.

small areas of micrococci are left—and this usually happens when the micrococcus has grown well before being infected—these areas will start to grow again and extend over the transparent portion. . . ."

According to this description of Twort, it is not a question of a real bacterial dissolution, but a transformation of a normal culture on agar into a glassy and transparent one. This phenomenon is totally different from that produced by *Bacteriophagum intestinale.* Indeed, under the influence of this latter—no matter what bacterial species is dealt with, no matter what virulence, feeble or strong, of the strain of the bacteriophage, operating exactly in the same experimental conditions as Twort—in no circumstances does one observe the formation of transparent material or anything presenting such an appearance.

Pipette over an agar tube a drop of a diluted filtrate containing a bacteriophage active towards staphylococcus; then inoculate this tube as a streak with a pure culture of staphylococcus; after incubation we obtain a surface growth of the organism, which macroscopically, microscopically, and biologically is normal. This normal bacterial culture is strewn here and there with circular clear spaces; in the interior of these spaces the agar is bare, without any visible trace of any material. These bare spaces never spread over the surrounding culture, even after months in the incubator. Furthermore, they never become invaded by the surrounding bacterial culture: once formed, the bare spaces remain immutable. Confusion, therefore, between the phenomenon observed by Twort and the phenomenon provoked by the bacteriophage is in no way possible.

What is the nature of the principle which acts in the phenomenon of bacterial transformation observed by Twort? From a consideration of the observations made on this phenomenon, and in view of the fact that the lytic agent and the bacteria are destroyed at the same temperature, it is probable that it is derived from the bacterium itself, which is capable of splitting up into fragments. Twort himself favours this view, but further experiments will be necessary to settle this question.

This conclusion, however, does not detract in any way from the interest attaching to the important researches of Twort. One can already see that the phenomenon observed by this author may play an important role in the etiology of the so-called filtrable virus diseases, as he indeed seems to have foreseen. On the other hand, the bacteriophage undoubtedly plays a part in the defence of the organism in the course of infectious diseases, as I have shown elsewhere.

From a survey of the results already arrived at in the domain of scientific investigation, it is easy to foresee that there exists a whole series of phenomena, quite unsuspected a few years ago, whose study should play a large part in the advance of scientific medicine.

References.

[1]For details see: *Le Bactériophage, son rôle dans l'immunité,* in the collection, Monographs of the Pasteur Institute (Masson, Paris), of which an English edition is in preparation (Williams and Wilkins, Baltimore, publishers). [2]Sur un ferment d'immunité bactériol-

ysant, *C.R. Soc. Biologie,* lxxxiii, February 28th, 1920, p. 219. [3]Le bactériophage de d'Herelle, sa reproduction, son interprétation, *C.R. Soc. Biologie,* lxxxiii, October 9th, 1920, p. 1296. [4]On the influence of the tissue enzymes on the bacteriophage principle, *Proceed. Exp. Biol. and Med.,* xviii, April 20th, 1 21, p. 222. [5]Antagonisme microbien et lyse transmissible, *C.R. Soc. Biologie,* lxxxvi, March 18th, 1922, p. 569 [6]Autobactériolysne et le phénomène de d'Herelle, *C.R. Soc.Biologie,* lxxxvi, April 29th, 1922, p. 833. [7]Bakeriophagen Wirkungen gegen Flexner- und Koli-Bakterien, *Wien. klin. Woch.,* xxxiv, No. 37, September 15th, 1921. [8]Über die Natur des d'Herelle'schen Bakteriophagen, *Deut. med. Woch.,* No. 21, 1922. [9]Sur un microbe invisible, antagoniste des bacilles dysentériques, *C.R. Acad. des Sciences,* clxv, September 10th, 1917, p. 373. [10]Exsudats leucocytaires et autolyse microbienne transmissible, *C.R. Soc. Biologie,* lxxxiii, October 9th, 1920, p. 1293. [11]L'ultramicrobe bactériophage, *C.R. Soc. Biologie,* October 29th, 1921, p. 721. [12]An investigation on the nature of ultramicroscopic viruses, *Lancet,* December 4th, 1915.

II.—THE BACTERIOPHAGE: THE BREAKING DOWN OF BACTERIA BY ASSOCIATED FILTER-PASSING LYSINS.

By F. W. TWORT, M.R.C.S., L.R.C.P.
(From the Laboratories of the Brown Institution, London.)

THIS phenomenon of bacteriolysis, which in France has been called the "bacteriophage," consists, as you know, of a breaking down and dissolving up of bacteria by a filter-passing material which in certain circumstances may be associated with pure cultures. My first experiments were carried out at the Brown Institution during 1914 and 1915, for the Local Government Board, and the results were published in the *Lancet* (December 4th, 1915) under the title of "An investigation on the nature of ultramicroscopic viruses." The condition, in my opinion, is distinct from the various degenerative changes which have been so often described in bacterial cultures, and it will be necessary for me to consider in detail experiments on degenerative changes. It is also impossible in the time at my disposal to discuss every aspect of the subject; moreover, other speakers will no doubt deal with the many interesting experiments which they have carried out. In this paper I propose to give you as shortly as possible my original experiments as they were published in 1915, and I shall pass on to consider certain aspects of the subject which have since become points of controversy between different workers, and shall then deal shortly with certain more recent experiments which I have been doing on the biology of bacteria, as these may throw some light on the use of the lytic material.

When starting the research my object was to discover, if possible, the nature and life-history of the ultramicroscopic group of viruses. The experiments were carried out with these views in my mind: In the first place we do not know for certain the nature of an ultramicroscopic virus. It may be a minute bacterium that will grow only on living material, or it may be a tiny amoeba which, like ordinary amoebae, thrives on living bacteria or animal tissue. On the other hand, it must be remembered that if the living organic world has been built up slowly in accordance with the theories of evolution, then an amoeba and a bacterium must be recognized as highly developed organisms in comparison with much more primitive forms which once existed, and probably still exist, in nature. It is quite possible that an ultramicroscopic virus belongs somewhere in this vast field of life where the organization is lower than that of the bacterium or amoeba. It may be living protoplasm that forms no definite individuals, or an enzyme with power of growth.

In the first instance attempts were made to demonstrate the presence of non-pathogenic filter-passing viruses. As is well known, in the case of ordinary bacteria, for every pathogenic micro-organism discovered many non-pathogenic varieties of the same type have been found in nature, and it seems highly probable that the same rule will be found to hold good in the case of ultra-microscopic viruses. It is difficult, however, to obtain proof of their existence, as pathogenicity is the only definite evidence we have at the present time of the presence of an ultramicroscopic virus. On the other hand, it seems probable that if non-pathogenic varieties exist in nature these should be more easily cultivated than the pathogenic varieties.

The first experiments were carried out with such materials as soil, dung, grass, hay, straw, and with water from ponds. Cultivations were made on a large number of special media and under special conditions. Experiments were also carried out with pathological material obtained from distemper in dogs, from vaccinia, and from various other sources. The first results of interest were obtained with vaccinia. Inoculations were made on to ordinary agar tubes, and on to tubes of special egg media such as I used in my experiments for the cultivation of Johnes's bacillus and the lepra bacilli of man and of rats. It will be impossible to describe all these in detail, but the essential part of one series consists in the incorporation in the media of the dead bodies of certain acid-fast bacilli such as *Bacillus phlei*, which proved to be so successful in the cultivation of Johnes's bacillus. The egg media usually grew a number of colonies of micrococci and diphtheroids, while the agar tubes grew only a few colonies of micrococci. In the case of the egg media it was noted that in a few days certain parts of the micrococcus growth sometimes became dull, and in appearance rather resembled bacterial growth in which amoebae were also growing. On the agar media the colonies of micrococci ocassionally showed a translucent or transparent change, which started as more or less clear spots at the margins of the colonies. It was also found that some of these colonies could not be subcultured, but if kept the transparent change extended over most of the colony.

On examination of these glassy areas nothing but minute granules, staining reddish with Giemsa, could be seen. Further experiments showed that if a colony of the white micrococcus that had started to become transparent was plated out instead of being subcultured as a streak, then the micrococcus grew and a pure streak culture from certain of these colonies could be obtained. On the other hand, if the plate cultures (made by inoculating the condensation water of a series of tubes and floating this over the surface of the medium) were left, the colonies, especially in the first dilution, soon started to turn transparent, and the micrococci were replaced by fine granules. This action, unlike an ordinary degenerative process, started from the edge of the colonies; and further experiments showed that when a pure culture of the white or the yellow micrococcus isolated from vaccinia is touched with a small portion of one of the glassy colonies the growth at the point touched soon starts to become transparent or glassy, sometimes killing out all the micrococci and replacing these by fine granules. Experiments showed that the action is more rapid and complete with vigorous growing young cultures than with old ones, and there is very little action on dead cultures or on young cultures that have been killed by heating to 60°C.

Anaerobia does not favour the action, although it appears best in tubes that are capped with gutta-percha tissue. The transparent growth when diluted (one in a million) with water or saline was found to pass the finest porcelain filters (Pasteur-Chamberland F. and B. and Doulton White) with ease, and one drop of the filtrate pipetted over an agar tube was sufficient to make that tube unsuitable for the growth of the micrococcus—that is, if the micrococcus was inoculated down the tube as a streak, this would start to grow, but would soon become dotted with transparent points which would rapidly extend over most of the growth. The number of points from which this starts depends upon the dilution of the transparent material, and in some cases it is so active that the growth is stopped and turned transparent almost directly it starts. This condition or disease of the micrococcus when transmitted to pure cultures of the micrococcus can be conveyed to fresh cultures for an indefinite number of generations; but the transparent material will not grow by itself on any medium.

If in an infected tube small areas of micrococci are left—and this usually happens when the micrococcus has grown well before becoming infected—these areas will start to grow again and extend over the transparent portions, which shows that the action of the transparent material is stopped or hindered in an overgrown tube; but it is not dead, for if a minute portion be transferred to another young culture of the micrococcus it soon starts to dissolve up the micrococci again. Although the transparent material shows no evidence of growth when placed on a fresh agar tube without micrococci, it will retain its power of activity for over six months. It also retains its activity when made into an emulsion and heated to 52°C., but when heated to 60°C. for an hour it appears to be destroyed. It has some action, but very much less on *Staphylococcus aureus* and *albus* isolated from boils of man, and it appears to have no action on members of the *coli* group or on streptococci, tuberc'e bacilli, yeasts, etc. The transparent material was inoculated into various animals, and was rubbed into the scratched skin of guinea-pigs, rabbits, a calf, a monkey, and a man, but all the results were negative.

When continuing my investigation of infantile diarrhoea and vomiting, for the Local Government Board in 1915, similar experiments were carried out with material obtained from the intestinal tract. After certain difficulties had been overcome it was found that in the upper third of the intestine, which contained numerous bacilli of the colon group, some larger forms were also present. In some cases these grew in far greater number than the ordinary types of bacteria, but this was only so when precautions were taken to eliminate the action of a dissolving substance which infected the colonies so rapidly that they were dissolved before attaining a size visible to the eye. Here, then, was a similar condition to that found in vaccinia, and the greatest difficulty was experienced in obtaining the bacilli free from the transparent dissolving material, so rapidly was the infection increased and carried from one colony to another. At first this bacillus was not believed to be a member of the dysentery-typhoid-coli group, but I have now no doubt that it was a special large form of a member of this group. Unfortunately I lost my cultures during the war before all the characters of the bacillus were completely worked out.

Similar though not such definite results were also obtained with a micrococcus and a member of the coli-typhoid group of bacilli which were obtained from the intestinal mucous membrane of a dog suffering from acute distemper, and I obtained some evidence that the difficulty often experienced in isolating certain known pathogenic micro-organisms might be due to the same cause. In my paper I also pointed out that results similar to those obtained with vaccinia and with bacilli from the intestinal tract would probably be obtained in cases of true dysentery; but I was unable at the time to investigate dysentery, as my scheme for research on this disease which was submitted to the War Office in 1914 was not accepted. Shortly after the publication of my work, however, I went to Salonica in charge of the base laboratory. While there in 1916 the subject was again discussed on several occasions with the English, French, and Canadian bacteriologists; but at the time the phenomenon was not accepted as one of much importance, and my fresh proposals for continuing the work on dysentery failed to meet with approval. As, however, I had predicted, a similar condition was later found to occur in cultures of true dysentery bacilli, particularly by Dr. d'Herelle, who carried out a series of important experiments on these bacilli. Dr. d'Herelle's published researches appear to me to confirm in the main my own results with micrococci and members of the coliform group of bacilli.

I will now pass on to consider the conclusions I drew from my experiments. In the case of vaccinia it is clear that the transparent material contains an enzyme, and this is destroyed on heating to 60°C. for one hour. It also increases in quantity when placed on an agar tube containing the micrococcus, and this can be carried on indefinitely from generation to generation. If it is part of the micrococcus it may be either a stage in its life-history which will not grow on ordinary media but stimulates fresh cultures of the micrococcus to pass into the same stage, or an enzyme secreted by the micrococcus which leads to its own destruction and the production of more enzyme. The fact that the transparent portion cannot be grown except on the micrococcus makes it impossible to obtain any definite evidence on these points. There is this, however, against the idea of a separate form of life: if the white micrococcus is repeatedly plated out a colony from the last plates may give a good white growth for months when subcultured at intervals on fresh tubes; eventually, however, most pure strains show a transparent spot, and from this the transparent material can be obtained once again. Of course, it may be that the micrococcus was never quite free from the transparent material, or this may have passed through the cotton-wool plug and contaminated the micrococcus, but it seems much more probable that the material was produced by the micrococcus. Incidentally, this apparent spontaneous production of a self-destroying material which, when started, increases in quantity, may be of interest in connexion with cancers. In any case, whatever explanation is accepted, I do not think my experiments definitely disproved the possibility of its being an ultramicroscopic virus, because we do not know for certain the nature of such a virus. If the transparent portion were a separate virus, it might be vaccinia, or it might be some contaminating non-pathogenic ultramicroscopic virus, for it is conceivable that whereas a non-pathogenic variety might grow on micrococci or bacilli, a pathogenic variety might grow only in the animal it infects. As the animal experiments were negative, there is no evidence that it is vaccinia, although such a virus might lose its virulence when grown outside the body. On the other hand, no evidence was obtained that it was a non-pathogenic variety. On the whole it seems probable, though by no means certain, that the active lytic material is produced by the micrococcus, and since it leads to its own destruction and can be transmitted to fresh healthy cultures, it might almost be considered as an acute infectious disease of micrococci.

I have now described my original experiments and conclusions, and I will pass on to consider the views of other workers in this field. Where differences of opinion exist the controversy has centred chiefly round the experiments that have been carried out to determine the source and nature of the lytic material. I have already pointed out that when this material is diluted and filtered and pipetted on to a tube of medium just before inoculating the tube with the micro-organism to be lysed, then the action starts at definite points throughout the growth. Dr. d'Herelle obtained a similar result in his experiments with dysentery bacilli, and he considers this a strong point in favour of the view that the lytic material is a separate living micro-organism. I cannot, however, for several reasons, agree that such experiments prove this. First, it is well known, notably in the case of certain starches, that the diastatic enzymes do not in every case dissolve up the grains evenly, but start at certain points, causing pitting and erosion of the grains; at the same time some grains are more susceptible to the enzyme than others. In this case no one has suggested that the unevenness of the action proves the diastatic enzyme to contain a living ultramicroscopic virus. I have noted also with bacteria that not only does the lytic agent attack some members of a culture before it attacks others, but individual members may be pitted and eroded, and particularly is this so with certain large forms of dysentery bacilli which I shall consider later. Again, it is well known in the case of all bacteria that certain members of a culture are more resistant to chemicals and to specific lysins produced in animals, and it may well be that the lytic action on the bacteria starts from a number of distinct points because these points happen to contain specially susceptible micro-organisms, and it is only when the action is started and the lytic substance increases in quantity and in concentration that the more resistant members become lysed.

Then there are the very interesting experiments of Professor Bordet and Dr. Ciuca. These workers found that when a lysin was produced by an animal against a coliform bacillus, this lysin not only dissolved up fresh cultures of the coliform bacillus, but the lytic effect could be transmitted from culture to culture. These results certainly do not favour the view that the lytic agent is a definite living micro-organism. Moreover, there are my own original experiments where, after obtaining normal growths of micrococci for a number of generations, eventually some fresh subcultures started to become lysed, apparently spontaneously. But these experiments appear to me to be evidence not only against the view that the lytic material is a definite living organism, but also against the view of Bordet and Ciuca that the lytic agent arises from an association of the bacterium with cells from the animal body. d'Herelle has also obtained the lytic agent by associating bacteria with filtrates of soil, etc., and I agree with him that these experiments do not support Bordet's view, although at the same time I do not think they support the view that the lytic agent is a definite living micro-organism. The apparent spontaneous production of the lytic agent in some of my pure cultures is, I think, evidence against both the views mentioned. It may, of course, be argued, as I mentioned at the time, that my cultures were never really quite free from the lytic agent, but if this view is accepted regarding my repeatedly plated cultures, then it is reasonable to suggest the same regarding the cultures used by d'Herelle and by Bordet.

Recent experiments, in fact, have in no way changed my views, and I repeat my original opinion regarding the lytic agent of the micrococcus—namely, that "the possibility of its being an ultramicroscopic virus has not been definitely disproved," and that "it seems probable, though by no means certain, that the active transparent material is produced by the micrococcus"; and I hold the same view regarding the lytic agent which various workers and myself have found associated with the dysentery-typhoid-coli group of bacilli.

However, as I have already pointed out, it is just possible that an ultramicroscopic virus may be of the nature of an enzyme, and if so, the original source of such a virus might be the cell it infects: in remote ages possibly a normal enzyme which has gradually developed to take on a pathological action as it has passed through an infinite number of generations of cells, either bacterial, vegetable, or animal, according to its source, and which possesses the powei either of directly increasing in quantity or of stimulating the cell to produce more pathological enzyme. On the other hand, it is conceivable that if this lytic agent be a pathological enzyme, it might bear the same relation to the normal enzyme that the cancer cell does to the normal cell. These possibilities may sound very improbable, but at the same time some such explanation would account for the extremely specific nature of many of the ultramicroscopic viruses, and it would certainly explain the absence of visibility and of growth on artificial media. After all, excluding such organisms as the lepto-spirillum of yellow fever, which probably belongs to an entirely different group, there are fundamental differences between the smallest micro-organisms known and the various ultramicroscopic viruses.

Cultivations of the minutest micro-organisms known show all the characteristics of ordinary bacteria. If these are obtained from the soil many of them grow well. On the other hand, if ultramicroscopic viruses are simply more minute members of the group of bacteria, there must be thousands of wild varieties in the soil, and yet no one has succeeded in obtaining a definite growth of a single variety on any solid medium. Minuteness of size might account for their being invisible, but it will not explain the absence of visible growth on artificial solid media. It is true that certain workers at one time claimed to have obtained growths of pathogenic varieties in Noguchi's medium, but in the absence of definite confirmation these experiments need not be considered here.

Professor Bordet and Dr. Ciuca have carried out some most important experiments with the dysentery-typhoid-coli group of bacilli on the specificity of the lytic material, and have obtained results which indicate not only that the lytic agent can be made to break down allied bacilli, but also that certain resisting and otherwise changed strains can be obtained. As I have already mentioned, my micrococcus lysin had little effect on *Staphylococcus aureus*; but I did not carry out many experiments of this nature after obtaining the apparent spontaneous production of the lytic agent in my pure cultures of micrococci, as this result appeared to me to make it difficult to draw definite conclusions from such experiments. Many other workers, but particularly Dr. d'Herelle and Dr. André Gratia, have also carried out important experiments in this branch of the subject, but I must leave other speakers to deal with it, as it is impossible in the space at my disposal to do justice to their work.

There is, however, another aspect of the subject which I should like to mention. As is well known, in pure cultures of such bacilli as dysentery, typhoid, and coli, one sometimes meets with forms which are considerably larger and longer than the average bacillus, and these may be found in pathological material containing these bacilli, being not uncommon in urine in cases of cystitis. Hort and others have described these large forms in considerable detail.

In certain experiments dealing with the lytic material I observed these long forms in greater number than usual, and it was thought that they might in some way be connected with the lytic agent associated with this group of bacilli. There was also the possibility that they might be distinct but symbiotic bacilli growing only with the dysentery or other bacilli forming the culture; they might be mutations, or, again, they might be special forms with special work to do, like bees in a swarm, and, alone or in association with the lytic agent, might prove to be of importance in connexion with the pathogenicity of cultures and the production of immunity in the host.

The work was interrupted by the war, but eventually the results were published in the *British Journal of Experimental Medicine* (October, 1920), and I shall do no more now than consider their possible relation to the lytic agent. In the first place, it must be noted that these large forms occur much more frequently in pathological material than they do in cultures on artificial media. In cases of infantile diarrhoea and vomiting I have found them in large number associated with a lytic agent in the upper part of the intestinal tract, and it is only after the action of the lytic agent is eliminated that they can be easily cultivated. The nature of the bacilli from such conditions is now being investigated.

Most of my experiments were carried out with the Shiga type of dysentery bacillus. The first point of importance to be noted is that the large or "special forms" occur in all pure cultures of bacilli belonging to the dysentery-typhoid-coli group, besides occurring in cultures of the influenza bacillus and other micro-organisms. Further, they are much more numerous in very young cultures than in older ones, and practically disappear in cultures that are twenty-four hours old. I observed also, in cultures that had been growing for six to twelve hours, that these "special forms" were often partially dissolved. From these early experiments I concluded that the bacilli normally produce "special forms," and that these, when presumably of no use to the bacterial community of a pure culture, are dissolved by a lytic agent which is also present, and that this lysin prevents the special forms from multiplying, and interferes with their isolation as growths free from the normal small bacilli. I found, however, two methods by which these "special forms" could be isolated. They may be obtained either by repeatedly plating out on litmus-maltose agar tubes, or by growing in an emulsion of dead coliform, typhoid, or some similar bacillus, and then plating out on the maltose agar medium. Three fairly distinct and stable types were isolated, but it will be unnecessary to consider these in detail. The chief points which I wish to bring to your notice are these: The large bacilli proved to be "special forms" of the bacterium from which they were obtained, and were easily agglutinated by the specific serums. I also obtained some evidence that they were more pathogenic when produced by the normal bacilli than after repeated multiplication by division. When isolated and grown they became more resistant to the lytic agent. In most of the cultures numerous free granules were present, while many of the bacilli contained similar looking granules in the fusiform and round swelling which they presented.

These researches seem to indicate another possible explanation of the lytic action of the substance under review. If this substance is, after all, not pathological to the bacterium, but is a normal product of its activity, then it must be produced for some special purpose which is advantageous to the life of that variety of bacterium. If the "special forms" of bacilli which are found in normal cultures and are so soon dissolved up are produced for the benefit of the bacterial community of a pure culture, then it may be that the lytic agent is formed for the purpose of carrying out this lytic action, and possibly setting free toxins contained in the special forms. Or it may be that it sets free "antitoxins," or substances that will neutralize the toxic substances of the host it infects, or such substances as are produced by other varieties of bacteria with which it struggles for existence when outside the animal body. Probably all bacteria produce substances of a toxic nature, but the possibility of their producing antibodies which will neutralize the toxins of other varieties is one that has interested me for some time. My experiments in this direction lead me to believe that this may be the case, but a research of this nature is rather difficult to carry out technically, and I shall do many more experiments before committing myself to this view. If, however, additional experiments should confirm my opinion, and if the special forms play some part in this process, one can quite understand that the special forms would be useless among the members of a pure culture growing on artificial media. In fact, they might be directly detrimental to the bacterial community, in that they would use up the food supply and overgrow the other bacilli which are necessary for a continuation of the life of that species or variety. In this case the lytic agent would perform a good purpose in getting rid of the useless special forms. It may be argued that this will not explain the lysis of the normal forms of bacilli, but then the conditions of cultivation on artificial media are not those of nature. In fact, in the process of evolution the bacterium did not develop its characters under the influence of cultivation in incubators, and an action that might be restrained to the limits of useful purposes in nature might very well extend beyond those limits under such an abnormal environment as that presented by an uncontaminated tube of agar.

Some of my views and the possibilities I have suggested are no doubt open to criticism, but I claim that the discovery of the filter-passing lytic agent in association with bacteria offers a large field for research, and I suggest that this field has been further extended by the isolation of "special forms" of bacteria and by the possibility of demonstrating the production of bacterial antitoxins for the neutralization of toxins produced by other varieties of bacteria. Moreover, it must be remembered that all the vital processes of a bacterium have some relation to each other, and it is therefore necessary to study these problems together, or the true significance of any one may not be fully appreciated.

III.—CONCERNING THE THEORIES OF THE SO-CALLED "BACTERIOPHAGE."

By J. Bordet, M.D.,
Director of the Pasteur Institute, Brussels.

[The following explanatory statement was read by Dr. Gratia for Professor Bordet.]

Through Dr. Gratia I obtained access to the paper Dr. d'Herelle intends to present on the lytic phenomenon due to the so-called "bacteriophage." I was not a little surprised to find that Dr. d'Herelle in this paper attributes to my co-worker, Dr. Ciuca, and to myself, as regards the intimate nature of this phenomenon, an opinion which is wholly different from what we felt entitled to uphold from the very beginning of our studies on the subject.[1] Dr. d'Herelle quotes our names next to Kabeshima's, and enlists us among the authors who assume that the lytic principle is a leucocytic secretion. In fact, this view seems to us altogether untenable, and is almost the reverse of the opinion we have constantly emphasized.

I think we were first to advocate the view that the lytic principle is produced by the microbe itself which shows the lysis—in other words, that the transmissible lysis is in reality an autolysis betraying a nutritive vitiation primarily started by external influences, an example of which may be the contact with a leucocytic exudate. No doubt it would be quite unnecessary to translate literally the many passages of our papers where this assumption is advocated. Some lines, however, may be quoted:

"External influences such as that of a leucocytic exudate modify the bacterium, inducing the latter to elaborate a lytic substance capable of diffusing itself and bringing about the same autolytic phenomenon through successive cultures. When the autolytic process occurs a large number of the microbes present may perish, but some of them, being more resistant, are, during a certain length of time, still capable of reproduction in spite of their producing the active principle, thus imparting to new cultures of the same microbe the same autolytic tendency."

In another paper we add:

"According to d'Herelle, the lysis is due to a living being, to a filtering virus. We, on the contrary, believe that the lytic principle originates from the bacteria themselves, which, when touched by this active substance, are capable of regenerating it, the factor responsible for the phenomenon being thus unceasingly reproduced—on the condition, however, that the bacteria be still living and provided with the alimentary substances necessary to their growth."

I wonder how Dr. d'Herelle could possibly give such an erroneous account of our work as in his paper. The many authors who have written on the subject did not, like Dr. d'Herelle, misinterpret a theory which we have so often and so distinctly outlined and explained. I shall allow myself to quote, for instance, the paper recently published by Dr. Bruynoghe,[2] who writes:

"According to Bordet and Ciuca, the microbes undergo—through the agency of a leucocytic exudate—a modification by which they are henceforth capable of elaborating an autolytic principle, this property being further transmitted to the following generations by the germs which were sufficiently resistant, and thus could multiply. This interesting view permits the understanding of the fact that the lytic principle is only regenerated when the bacteria are living, since the theory asserts that this principle is produced by the bacteria themselves."

I think there is no need to dwell longer on the subject. But one must agree that I could not refrain from correcting d'Herelle as regards our views, nor from presenting them again as they are expressed in all of our papers. The mere titles of these are clear enough; we always designate the phenomenon under the name of "the microbian transmissible autolysis."

References.

[1]*C.R. Soc. Biologie,* October, 1920. [2]*Le Scalpel,* March, 1922.

IV.—ANDRÉ GRATIA, M.D.,

Pasteur Institute, Brussels.

1. The Twort phenomenon and the d'Herelle phenomenon are identical. They are two different aspects of one and the same phenomenon: the transmissible lysis of bacteria.

When the "dissolving material" of Twort found in diseased agar cultures of micrococci obtained from vaccinia lymph is transplanted into a young broth culture of staphylococci a dissolution of the latter occurs, and the filtrate of the dissolved culture exhibits all the characteristics of a typical staphylococcus bacteriophage according to the definition of d'Herelle.

On the other hand, typical staphylococcus bacteriophage could be obtained also by other means—namely, by the leucocytic exudate technique of Bordet and Ciuca, or by the puncture of a subcutaneous abscess. When small amounts of this staphylococcus lytic agent are introduced in melted agar which is afterwards slanted and seeded with sensitive staphylococci a culture results, apparently normal at the beginning, but which, a little later, turns into the typical glassy transparent material of Twort. In other words, the Twort phenomenon leads to the d'Herelle phenomenon, and, inversely, the d'Herelle phenomenon leads to the Twort phenomenon.

2. There are no unquestionable proofs that the bacteriophage is a living organism.

The assumption of the bacteriophage being a filtrable virus for bacteria was suggested by two main facts: (*a*) The power of reproduction possessed by the lytic agent, and (*b*) the localization of the lysis to certain round spots of clarification when a very diluted lytic agent is poured over the surface of an agar culture of sensitive bacteria. Although easily explained by the virus theory, yet both facts are not unquestionable proofs of the living nature of the bacteriophage, because they are by no means exclusive features of living beings.

Fire is not living, and yet fire is endowed with power of reproduction. When once lighted, thanks to an initial impulsion such as an electric spark or the mere striking of a match, it can be indefinitely reproduced if fuel is provided. A still more striking, because more biological, example is found in blood coagulation. Suppose a series of tests tubes containing a stable plasma—bird's plasma, for instance—which will remain indefinitely fluid. To the first tube we add just a few cubic centimetres of distilled water. As a result of that initial thromboplastic action, which does not need to be repeated to the future, thrombin suddenly appears in the first tube and the plasma clots. If a few drops of the exudate serum in the first tube are pipetted off and poured in the next tube, this second tube clots, in its turn, with a new regeneration of thrombin, which, transferred in the third tube, brings about the coagulation of that tube with again a new production of thrombin, and so on indefinitely. In this way we realize the transmissible coagulation of blood in series, with the continuous regeneration of thrombin, and thrombin is not a living being.

The localization of the lytic action of diluted bacteriophage can be explained by the hypothesis of a chemical substance as well. It must be kept in mind that a culture is not a homogeneous whole, but made up of organisms showing all kinds of qualitative and quantitative individual differences—that is, as far as their susceptibility to the lytic agent is concerned. When a very concentrated lytic agent is poured over the surface of an agar culture an almost complete dissolution occurs, with the exception of just a few organisms resistant enough to overwhelm the strong action of the concentrated lytic agent. On the other hand, when a diluted lytic agent is used only the few extremely sensitive bacteria will be influenced, and each of them becomes a centre of regeneration of the lytic agent, which, diffusing evenly in every direction, produces perfectly round spots of clarification very often surrounded by a kind of halo of diffusion. Between these two extreme conditions all kinds of intermediate degrees exist. Further, any substance, living or not, is composed of particles, molecules, atoms, or ions. When we pour out a glass of soda water, there appear on the wall of the glass small round bubbles of gas, the size of which increases exactly as the so-called colonies of bacteriophage, and yet gas is not a virus.

3. The idea of the bacteriophage being a product of bacterial activity is suggested by the close parallelism existing between the regeneration of the lytic agent on the one hand, and the activity of growth of the bacteria on the other hand.

No regeneration ever occurs in dead cultures, nor in living cultures when put in such conditions that they cannot grow—in saline emulsions of bacteria, for instance, or at low temperature. A slight lysis, with but a small regeneration of lytic agent, is induced in the slow-growing culture of *B. coli* in a synthetic medium. On the contrary, an abundant regeneration occurs in a fast-growing culture in broth. A recently seeded broth culture to which is added just a trace of lytic agent will not be inhibited; but a few hours later, at the very moment the culture reaches its acme of growth, a rapid dissolution occurs with an abundant regeneration of lytic agent.

4. The conception of the bacteriophage being a chemical substance is favoured by the chemical-like affinity existing between a given lytic agent and the corresponding susceptible strain.

I first observed that small amounts of lytic agents lose a certain part of their activity when put together with too thick emulsions of sensitive bacteria. Bordet, with a different technique, could even obtain the complete disappearance of traces of lytic agent in the same condition. Still more convincing are the results of Yaumain and of Dà Costa, who observed the absorption of relatively important amount of lytic agent by dead emulsions of the corresponding sensitive bacteria. This specific affinity which is the necessary condition for a lytic agent for inducing the dissolution of a given bacterium is not favourable to the virus theory, because we question how a virus could be definitely fixed by dead bacilli, which, however, it is unable to attack.

5. The bacteriophage is not one and the same antigen. Several lytic agents showing antigenic specificity must be considered.

The *coli* lytic agent can be completely neutralized by proper amounts of corresponding *coli* antilytic serum, but is not at all affected by staphylococcus antilytic serum, which, on the other hand, is only able to neutralize staphylococcus lytic agent and not *coli* lytic agent. This neutralization reaction is thus specific, and demonstrates the plurality of the bacteriophage.

The non-specific results obtained with the alexin fixation reaction and advocated by d'Herelle in favour of the unicity of the bacteriophage, are of no value, because they are vitiated, as can be easily demonstrated, by the presence in the bacteriophage of bacterial dissolution products which have lost their specificity and play therefore the rôle of common antigen between different lytic agents.

Adsorption of Bacteriophages to Homologous Bacteria

II. Quantitative Investigations of Adsorption Velocity and Saturation. Estimation of the Particle Size of the Bacteriophage

By
M. SCHLESINGER
Institute for Colloid Research, Frankfurt A.M.

It was shown in the preceding communication that bacteriophages of a lysate do not represent a uniform population; instead they are composed of several classes of widely varying adsorbabilities. The following equation expressing the kinetics of adsorption of phages to homologous bacteria was derived:

$$2.3 \log \frac{n_o}{n_t} = kbt \,, \qquad (1)$$

where n_o represents the initial concentration of free phage, n_t the concentration after a reaction time t and b the concentration of bacteria per ml. However, this equation is applicable only to experimental conditions under which the observed change in the concentration of free bacteriophages is mainly due to the adsorption of a single class of particles of uniform adsorbability. Lysates of the coli 88 bacteriophage employed in our experiments were found to consist almost entirely of a uniform class of rapidly and irreversibly adsorbable phages when conditions were such that the concentration of sensitive bacteria and the reaction time was varied only within limits that allowed the decrease in concentration of free phage not to exceed 90 to 95%.

It shall be shown in this communication that under these conditions equation (1) is so well satisfied that wide variations of the different experimental parameters produce no change in the value of the velocity constant k calculated from the experimental results. After establishing the value of k for adsorption to dead as well as to living bacteria, experiments will be presented that are designed to determine the bacterial "saturation capacity", *i.e. the number of phage particles that a single bacterial cell can adsorb.* Finally, an attempt will be made to calculate the particle size of the phage from the adsorption velocity constant. Further insight shall be gained into the adsorption mechanism by a comparison of the values so calculated with the results of direct determinations of the particle size.

Translated from the German and reprinted by permission of the Springer Verlag from ZEITSCHRIFT FUR HYGENIE UND IMMUNITAETSFORSCHUNG, **114**, 149-160 (1932).

Measurement of the Adsorption Velocity.

In order to test equation (1), we shall determine, as a function of time, the infectivity of mixtures of known concentration of heat-killed bacteria and input bacteriophages, so that the value of the expression

$$k = \frac{2.3}{bt} \log \frac{n_o}{n_t},$$

whose constancy is demanded by equation (1), can be calculated.

These experiments are carried out in the following way. A heat-killed bacterial suspension of known concentration is diluted into broth, so that after addition of the phage the concentration of bacteria in the reaction mixture is b. After this dilution has been warmed to 37°, a measured amount of a lysate dilution of exactly known phage titer is added and the time noted. In order to keep the temperature constant, the reaction mixture is placed in an incubator, in the case of long experiments, or, otherwise, in a water bath. After various times have elapsed, a measured aliquot of the reaction mixture is quickly diluted 10 or 100-fold, so that for all practical purposes, the reaction is stopped[1]. In this manner, reaction times down to 2 minutes can be investigated, after some practice. For reaction times of more than 1 hour, in cases where the anticipated titer permits this procedure, the sample is plated directly on agar plates. Under the present experimental conditions it is unnecessary to separate the dead bacteria from the reaction mixture before plating, since only irreversible adsorption is involved.

The detailed results of one experiment, and the calculations based thereon, shall be presented here as an illustration. 0.25 ml of the heat-killed broth culture of coli bacteria, containing 4×10^8 bacteria ml, was added to 4.65 ml broth. After warming the bacterial suspension to 37°, 0.1 ml of a thousand-fold dilution of a lysate of titer 8.5×10^8 was added to it. The mixture was placed in the incubator; after 1, 2, and 3 hours, 0.1 ml aliquots were removed from the mixture and spread at once on agar plates. The initial titer of the mixture, n_o, was 1.7×10^4; the titers, after 1, 2, and 3 hours were found to be 5.8×10^3, 2.4×10^3, and 7.2×10^2. With the known value of $b = 2.0 \times 10^7$ and the time measured in seconds, k can be calculated.

After 1 hour

$$k = \frac{2.3}{bt} \log \frac{n_o}{n_t} = \frac{2.3}{2 \times 10^7 \times 3600} \log \frac{1.7 \times 10^4}{5.8 \times 10^3}$$

$$= 3.2 \times 10^{-11} \log 2.9 = 1.5 \times 10^{-11}$$

After 2 hours

$$k = \frac{3.2 \times 10^{-11}}{2} \log 7.1 = 1.4 \times 10^{-11}$$

After 3 hours

$$k = \frac{3.2 \times 10^{-11}}{3} \log 23.6 = 1.5 \times 10^{-11}$$

[1] A 100-fold dilution reduces the reaction velocity by a factor of 100.

The values of k (multiplied by 10^{11}), calculated on the basis of our most extensive experiments, are summarized in Table I.

For these experiments, a phage lysate of titer 6.5×10^8 and a heat-killed bacterial suspension (70° for 1 hour) were used. Prior to heating, the bacterial suspension was grown from a slant agar culture to a density of 5.8×10^8, as determined by colony count. However, the value of 6.5×10^8 used in the calculations was determined by microscopic cell count after heat-killing.

TABLE I

Time in Seconds		$b = 1.6 \times 10^8$		$b = 6.5 \times 10^7$		$b = 3.3 \times 10^7$			
	$b = 6.5 \times 10^8$, $n_o = 6.5 \times 10^5$	$n_o = 6.5 \times 10^5$	$n_o = 6.5 \times 10^4$	$n_o = 6.5 \times 10^4$	$n_o = 6.5 \times 10^3$	$n_o = 6.5 \times 10^4$	$n_o = 6.5 \times 10^3$	$b = 1.6 \times 10^7$, $n_o = 6.5 \times 10^3$	$b = 3.3 \times 10^6$, $n_o = 6.5 \times 10^3$
120	1.1	.	.	.	.	.	.	.	.
240	1.2	.	.	.	.	.	.	.	.
360	1.1	1.5	1.6	.	.	.	.	.	.
720	.	1.2	1.3	.	.	.	.	.	.
1080	.	1.1	1.1	.	.	.	.	.	.
1440	.	1.2	1.4	.	.	.	.	.	.
1800	.	.	.	1.0	1.2	.	.	.	.
3600	.	.	.	1.2	1.3	1.1	1.2	1.7	.
7200	.	.	.	.	.	1.2	1.2	1.3	.
10800	.	.	.	.	.	0.9	1.0	1.5	.
14400	.	.	.	.	.	.	.	1.3	1.1
28800	.	.	.	.	.	.	.	.	1.3
43200	.	.	.	.	.	.	.	.	1.5

It is apparent that, neglecting variations due to experimental error, the value of k remains virtually constant, in spite of the fact that in the different experiments the initial titer of phage has been varied by a factor of 100, the concentration of bacteria by a factor of 200 and the reaction time by a factor 360. The average value of the velocity constant in these experiments is 1.2×10^{-11}.

In five additional, less extensive, experiments, carried out with cultures of coli 88 grown either in broth or on agar, the following values of k were found: 1.0×10^{-11}, 1.4×10^{-11}, 1.6×10^{-11}, 1.0×10^{-11}, and 1.4×10^{-11} (average values of 3, 7, 9, 4, and 7 determinations). These fluctuations are no greater than the uncertainty in the determination of the bacterial concentrations[2]. The average value of the velocity constant k, computed on the basis of 58 single determinations for the binding to dead bacteria, was 1.3×10^{-11}.

[2]As has already been mentioned, the heat-killing was carried out by heating to 70° for 1 hour. This temperature treatment has no important effect on the binding capacity of the bacteria. In a series of experiments, aliquots from a single broth culture of coli were heat-killed at 70° for ½, 1, 2 and 3 hours; the adsorption velocity constants determined in experiments utilizing these suspensions were 1.7×10^{-11}, 1.6×10^{-11}, 1.3×10^{-11} and 1.4×10^{-11}.

The velocity of adsorption of phage to living bacteria was measured either directly, or by adding bacteriophages to a mixture of dead and living bacteria and then determining their distribution over the two components.

A 6-hour-old agar slant of coli 88 is suspended in broth and freed of larger clumps by short centrifugation; half of this suspension is placed on ice, and the other half is heated for 30 minutes in a water bath at 70°. The cell concentration in each of the cultures is then determined by microscopic counts. 0.9 ml aliquots of each culture, as well as equal volumes of a two-fold dilution, are placed in the water bath at 37° and infected with 0.1 ml of a 1000-fold dilution of the phage lysate. After 3 and 6 minutes, or after 6 and 12 minutes, aliquots of each mixture are diluted 10-fold and centrifuged at once at 8000 r.p.m. and the titer of the supernatant liquid determined. The values of k, calculated from the experimental results, are presented in Table II. (The uncentrifuged mixtures are also titrated; in the experiment with living bacteria, the infective titer remains equal to that of the original lysate; whereas, in the experiment with dead bacteria, the surviving infectivity is always equal to that of the infectivity of the supernatant liquid.)

The suspensions of living and dead bacteria are then mixed with one another in the following proportions: $5 + 5$, $3 + 7$, $2 + 8$, and $1 + 9$. To each of 0.9 ml of these mixtures, as well as to a suspension of only living bacteria, 0.1 ml of the lysate dilution is added and an aliquot of 0.1 ml of each mixture spread on agar plates after 15 minutes. During this time no multiplication of the bacteriophage takes place, whereas most of the phages are already adsorbed. Since any phage adsorbed to a living bacterium manifests itself by plaque formation, one may infer that any observed decrease in phage titer must represent phages adsorbed to dead bacteria. This decrease thus permits a calculation of the ratio of the adsorption velocity constants k (living) k (dead) which apparently indicates the distribution of phages over two competing components. The result of this experiment is presented in Table III.

Microscopic counts of the suspension of dead bacteria indicated a concentration of 4.7×10^8, of the suspension of living bacteria a count of 5.8×10^8/ml. These figures are reduced by 10% in the reaction mixture through dilution upon addition of the phage lysate.

The results of direct measurement of the adsorption velocity are presented in Table II.

TABLE II

Time in seconds	Heat-killed bacteria		Living bacteria	
	$b = 4.8 \times 10^8$	$b = 2.4 \times 10^8$	$b = 4.8 \times 10^8$	$b = 2.4 \times 10^8$
180	1.0×10^{-11}	.	2.4×10^{-11}	.
360	1.0×10^{-11}	1.0×10^{-11}	2.8×10^{-11}	2.7×10^{-11}
720	.	0.8×10^{-11}	.	2.3×10^{-11}

Thus, according to this experiment, with the ratio of the two velocity constants being 2.6, the average value of k is 1.0×10^{-11} for dead bacteria and 2.6×10^{-11}

for living bacteria. The distribution of bacteriophages in a mixture of living and dead bacteria is presented in Table III.

TABLE III

In 10 parts of the mixture		Plaques per 0.1 c.c.	k (living) / k (dead)
Living bacteria	Heat-killed bacteria		
10	.	1000	.
5	5	720	2.6
3	7	420	1.7
2	8	360	2.2
1	9	280	3.5
		Average	2.5

The results of this method are thus in agreement with those obtained from the first method. Hence adsorption of phages to young living bacteria proceeds 2 to 3 times more rapidly than adsorption to dead bacteria. If we multiply the value of k of 1.3×10^{-11}, determined in numerous experiments with dead bacteria, by the proportionality constant 2.6, we obtain the velocity constant of adsorption to living bacteria: $k = 3.4 \times 10^{-11}$.

Determination of the Saturation Capacity of Bacteria.

The following method was selected for determining the maximum number of bacteriophages, referred to as the saturation capacity of the bacterium, that the average heat-killed bacterium can adsorb: samples are prepared which contain exactly the same number of dead bacteria but to which increasing initial concentrations of bacteriophages are added. After a sufficient length of time has elapsed, all of the free bacteriophages capable of irreversible adsorption will have disappeared from each sample. The remaining phage titer will thus be independent of the absolute value of the initial phage concentration, or, at any rate, will represent only a small fraction of it. In fact, the approximate constancy of the relative decrease in free phage should persist even when the allowed reaction time is insufficient for the attainment of the final state; for both parameters important for the velocity of adsorption, the concentration of the bacteria and the relative proportion of phages of differing adsorbability, are constant for all of the samples. This picture will change, however, and change drastically, whenever the initial concentration of bacteriophages attains that multiple of the bacterial concentration which corresponds to the saturation capacity. For instance, when the initial concentration is only half of the saturation capacity, then the adsorption *velocity* could be reduced, but only near the end of the adsorption process; when, however, the initial concentration of phage is twice that of the total bacterial capacity, then irrespective of the length of time of the experiment, only half of the initial phage population can be adsorbed. The saturation range thus manifests itself by a rapid increase in the ratio of final to initial phage titer in such an adsorption experiment. This ratio will vary from a value of about 0.01 prior to a saturating phage concentration to a value of about 1.0, once saturation has been attained. If no saturation is observable in such a series of experiments, even with the highest initial concentrations of phages obtainable, then the concentration of bacteria must be decreased in a second series of experiments. In that event, of course, the reaction time must be correspondingly prolonged.

TABLE IV. Bacterial Concentration 5.0×10^7. Reaction Time: 1 Day.

Initial Titer	Final Titer	Ratio Phage/Bacteria	Relative Decrease
5.0×10^8	2.1×10^6	10:1	1:240
2.5×10^8	1.0×10^6	5:1	1:250
1.0×10^8	3.3×10^5	2:1	1:300
5.0×10^7	1.1×10^5	1:1	1:450
2.5×10^7	1.8×10^5	0.5:1	1:140
1.0×10^7	3.1×10^4	0.2:1	1:320

TABLE V. Bacterial Concentration 1.0×10^7. Reaction Time: 4 Days

Initial Titer	Final Titer	Ratio Phage/Bacteria	Relative Decrease
9.0×10^8	4.6×10^6	90:1	1:200
4.5×10^8	2.0×10^6	45:1	1:220
1.8×10^8	5.0×10^5	18:1	1:360
9.0×10^7	2.6×10^5	9:1	1:340

TABLE VI. Bacterial Concentration 1.0×10^6. Reaction Time: 8 Days (Two samples became unsterile)

Initial Titer	Final Titer	Ratio Phage/Bacteria	Relative Decrease
1.1×10^9	1.1×10^9	1100:1	1:1
5.5×10^8	.	550:1	.
2.2×10^8	8.4×10^7	220:1	1:2.6
1.1×10^8		110:1	.

TABLE VII. Bacterial Concentration 1.8×10^6. Reaction Time: 8 Days

Initial Titer	Final Titer	Ratio Phage/Bacteria	Relative Decrease
7.6×10^8	7.1×10^8	420:1	1:1.1
3.8×10^8	1.4×10^8	210:1	1:2.7
1.5×10^8	8.2×10^6	84:1	1:18
7.6×10^7	4.5×10^5	42:1	1:170
3.8×10^7	6.6×10^4	21:1	1:570
1.5×10^7	2.7×10^4	8.4:1	1:550

The experimental results are summarized in Tables IV to VII. The experiments were carried out with different dilutions of a three-hour broth culture of coli 88, heat-killed at 70°, containing 1.0×10^8 bacteria/ml (Table IV-VI) and with a dilution of a similar culture containing 1.8×10^8 bacteria ml (Table VII). As controls, samples or dilutions of the lysates were always placed in the incubator and their titers similarly determined at the conclusion of the experiments; these titers always agreed with the earlier assays of the lysates.

It follows from the data of Table IV that the saturation capacity must be at least 10, while the data of Table V show that this capacity must exceed at least 90. In the last two tables, the region of saturation has been attained, and their third and second lines, respectively, permit a more exact estimation. According to Table VI, 1.0×10^6 bacteria are saturated by $(2.2 - 0.8) \times 10^8$ bacteriophages. *Hence, one bacterium is saturated by 140 phage particles.* Similarly, it follows from the data of Table VII *that the saturation capacity has the value of 130.*

Therefore, a coli bacterium killed by heating to 70° is capable of irreversibly adsorbing an average maximum of 130 to 140 bacteriophages.

Calculation of the Particle Size of the Bacteriophage from the Adsorption Velocity and from the Saturation Capacity. Conclusions:

a) *Calculation of Particle Size from the Adsorption Velocity.* The assumption was made in the derivation of equation (1), a formal description of the adsorption kinetics, that contact between one phage and one bacterium occurs entirely by chance and without benefit of any orienting or attractive forces whatsoever. The collisions were thought to be mainly due to the Brownian movement of the particles[3], to which, obviously the movement of the much smaller bacteriophages made the principal contribution. Since there exist well-known relations between Brownian movement, the diffusion coefficient, and the particle size, it is thus possible theoretically to correlate the latter with the adsorption velocity of the phage. It is, however, first necessary to make an assumption concerning the relation which might exist between the Brownian movement collision frequency of phages and bacteria and the number of adsorptive events which actually ensue as a consequence of these collisions.

The simplest assumption in this connection is that every collision leads to an irreversible fixation. If this assumption is valid, then the relation of the adsorption velocity to the diffusion constant, D, of the phage follows at once from the formula on which M. v. Smoluchowsky has based his theory of the kinetics of coagulation[4]. This formula states that the quantity $J dt$ of a solute which diffuses in a time dt onto a sphere of radius R capable of fixing solute particles which touch it is

$$J dt = 4\pi DRc\, dt$$

where c is the concentration of the substance[5]. If we equate R to the radius of a supposedly spherical bacterial cell, substitute for c the number of free bacterio-

---

[3]It is also possible that convection or mechanical agitation of the fluid could play a certain role. The error arising from neglecting the Brownian movement of the bacteria depends on the ratio of the bacterial diameter to that of the phage, and probably causes the estimate of the phage diameter to be too small by 10% in the following calculation.

[4]*Z. Physik. Chem.*, *92*, 140 (1917). An attempt — though insufficient — to apply the formula of the v. Smoluchowsky coagulation theory to bacteriophage adsorption has already been made by v. Angerer [*Arch. f. Hyg.*, *92*, 312 (1924)].

[5]The complete formula is

$$J dt = 4DRc\left[1 + \frac{R}{\sqrt{\pi Dt}}\right] dt$$

where t indicates the time which has elapsed since the start of the experiment. As in the coagulation experiments of Zsigmondy analyzed by v. Smoluchowsky, so also, under our experimental conditions is the quantity $\frac{R}{\sqrt{\pi Dt}}$ small compared to unity, and can be neglected without significant error. Incidentally, $J dt$ represents in v. Smoluchowsky's application, as well as in ours, not the number of particles which actually diffuse onto the sphere in the time dt (after all, in our experiments there is only one bacteriophage for every hundredth or thousandth bacterial cell), but only the probability of an encounter of a particle with the adsorbing sphere.

phage particles n, replace Jdt by the decrease $-dn$ of the number of free phages which occurs in the time dt, and bear in mind that for the adsorption process there is available not one but simultaneously b adsorbing bacteria (referring our entire consideration to the unit of volume), then we can write

$$-dn = 4\pi DRbn\,dt.$$

If we compare this expression with the differential equation on which equation (1) was based

$$-dn = kbn\,dt$$

then it follows that

$$k = 4\pi DR \quad \text{or} \quad D = \frac{k}{4\pi R},$$

the desired relation between adsorption velocity and diffusion constant of the bacteriophage. Now it will be recalled that the values of the velocity constant for adsorption to living and dead bacteria are not the same, since k for living bacteria is 2.6 times greater than k for dead bacteria. The reduced adsorption velocity for heat-killed bacteria evidently implies that a smaller fraction of the contacts leads to adsorption, since the collision frequency is the same whether the bacteria are living or dead. The assumption that every collision leads to fixation can therefore be excluded *a priori* for dead bacteria, while it could still be valid for living bacteria. In the latter case, the number of collisions is probably greater than that estimated since the motion of the coli cell was neglected in the calculations. Nevertheless, the relatively slow motion of the bacteria is insufficient to explain the entire difference between the adsorption velocity to dead and to living bacteria, since the movement of the cells could hardly triple the collision frequency. Therefore, our comparison of the D values for living and dead bacteria will be based on our calculations of their respective k values.

For the purpose of our calculations we shall equate R to the radius of that sphere whose surface is equal to the surface of a cylinder of 1.2 μ length and 0.5 μ width, in which case R is equal to 4.3×10^{-5}. The diffusion coefficient of the phage at the experimental temperature of 37° thus is

$$D = \frac{3.4 \times 10^{-11}}{4 \times 4.3 \times 10^{-5}} = 6.3 \times 10^{-8}$$

if the time is reckoned in seconds, as in the calculation of k. If this value is reduced to the unit of time generally used in diffusion experiments, i.e., the day, it follows that D is equal to 0.0055. On the basis of this value of the diffusion coefficient, one estimates from Einstein's formula[6] a diameter of the bacterio-

[6]This formula is

$$\rho = \frac{CT}{6\pi NnD}$$

where ρ is the particle radius, C the gas constant (8.32×10^7 erg/degree), T the absolute temperature, N Avogadro's number (60.7×10^{22}), and n the viscosity. It thus follows that

$$\rho = \frac{8.32 \times 10^7\,(273 + 37)}{6\pi \times 60.7 \times 10^{22} \times 0.007 \times 6.3 \times 10^{-8}} = 5.1 \times 10^6 \text{ cm}$$

or that the diameter is 102 mμ.

phage of 100 mμ. On the other hand, utilizing k for killed bacteria (1.3×10^{-11}), one calculates a particle diameter of 260 mμ. This latter value is undoubtedly too high; thus, in the case of heat-killed bacteria, it seems certain that not every collision can lead to fixation. It follows from this calculation that the adsorption velocity of the bacteriophage is not too great to be fully explained by Brownian movement alone. If one reverses this calculation and estimates the adsorption velocity constant from the known particle size of the bacteriophage (80 to 90 mμ; see below), one obtains a value of approximately 4×10^{-11}. It seems probable that this agreement in order of magnitude of different, independent estimates of the particle diameter can be taken as confirmation of the essential validity of the concepts on which these estimates were based.

b) *Calculation of the Particle Size from the Saturation Capacity.* The particle size of the bacteriophage can be calculated from the saturation capacity, if it is assumed that the bacterial cell absorbs that maximum number of phages which can completely cover its surface with a monolayer of particles. The premise that the adsorption takes place in a single layer, i.e., that it results only from direct contact between phage and bacteria, is justified on the basis of the irreversible and specific nature of the adsorption process[7]. On the other hand, the assumption[8] that saturation occurs only after the entire surface of the bacterium has been covered by phages is inherent in the previous hypothesis that every contact between phage and bacterium leads to fixation. For every contact can lead to fixation only if the entire bacterial surface is capable of phage fixation[9].

In case of close-packing, 140 spheres of diameter δ cover a surface of $140\ \delta^2$. If this value is equal to the surface of the bacterial cell, that is to say $2.3\ \mu^2$, then it follows that $\delta = 127$ mμ. If one considers, however, that random collisions of phage particles will hardly cover the bacterial surface in the *closest* packing assumed here, and that the number 140 refers to the adsorption capacity of

---

[7]In the case of heat-killed bacteria, there can be no question of any penetration of the bacteriophage into the interior of the cell; at least there is no indication of such a possibility.

[8]Obviously, this hypothesis refers to conditions under which there can be no question of any interference with adsorption by partial saturation; that is to say, under conditions of great excess of bacteria. The assumption that this hypothesis is not fully applicable to heat-killed bacteria will be considered below.

[9]However, even if the entire surface of the bacterium were capable of phage fixation, it would not necessarily follow that every collision would lead to fixation; other prerequisites of fixation might be appropriate direction and adequate intensity of the collision. In the event that only a number of isolated points, instead of the entire surface, is capable of fixation, then only those collisions which bring the phages into contact with these "valence points" could lead to fixation. The saturation capacity (S) then represents the number of such points. This assumption also makes possible an estimate of the phage diameter δ, on the basis of the equation

$$k = 4\pi DR \frac{\delta^2 \pi S}{4R^2 \pi}$$

This equation states that the adsorption velocity is proportional to the fraction of the bacterial surface capable of adsorbing the phage. The calculation, for which k for heat-killed bacteria must be employed since S refers to the adsorption capacity of heat-killed bacteria, leads to a value of $\delta = 19$ mμ. If we assume the correctness of our direct determination of particle size of the phage (80-90 mμ) mentioned below, then this low estimate of the phage diameter indicates that almost the entire bacterial surface must be covered by "valence points."

heat-killed bacteria, whose 2.6-fold reduction in adsorption velocity possibly reflects in inactivation of the phage receptors of a corresponding fraction of the cell surface, then one might revise this estimate of the phage diameter down to values of 61 to 120 mμ.

Thus, two completely independent sets of data, the adsorption velocity and the saturation capacity, yield roughly the same value for the diameter of the bacteriophage: 100 mμ and 60-120 mμ respectively. These figures appear much too high when compared with most of the values for the particle diameter given in the literature. In recent months, however, we have succeeded in measuring the sedimentation velocity in a centrifuge run at 7000 to 8000 r.p.m., of phage particles from lysates of the same coli phage selected for the present adsorption experiments. These measurements, which no doubt exceed all others in reliability, allowed us to calculate a particle size of 80 to 90 mμ. By means of a successive series of repetitive centrifugations, we were finally able to sediment into a pellet up to 99.99% of the active particles without encountering any decrease in the sedimentation velocity, i.e., without detecting any particles of smaller diameter.[10]

The agreement of the values of the phage diameter calculated indirectly from the adsorption velocity and from the saturation capacity, and the similarity of these values to the phage diameter determined directly, substantiates the validity of our assumptions. In any case, the formal kinetics of the process as well as the actual numerical values of the relevant parameters can be integrated, without contradiction, into the following simple picture. In each suspension of a mixture of bacteria and bacteriophages collisions occur between the individual particles of the two components. These collisions are entirely random, and their frequency is mainly determined by the Brownian movement of the bacteriophages. In the case of bacteriophage particles of maximum adsorption affinity (and in our *coli* lysate most of the particles are of this nature), the first such random collision between phage and bacterial cell leads to an irreversible fixation. More precisely, in the case of young, living bacteria almost every collision leads to fixation and in the case of heat-killed bacteria approximately every third collision does[11]. In the case of phage particles of reduced affinity, only a fraction of the collisions leads to fixation; and here also the fixation is less stable and partially reversible. The bacteria conserve their ability to find additional bacteriophage particles as long as their surfaces are not completely covered by a monolayer of such particles. Investigations on the influence of the medium on the absorption process shall be communicated in a future paper.

Summary

1. The equation describing the adsorption kinetics derived in a previous paper

$$2.3 \log \frac{n_o}{n_t} = kbt$$

[10]The results of this investigation will be published in this journal.

[11]This statement refers only to the experimental conditions communicated here, that is to say, to a broth medium and to the temperature of the incubator.

is satisfied for very wide variations in the parameters n_o, b, and t (initial concentration of phage, concentration of bacteria, and reaction time), provided that these variations remain in such limits that the adsorption velocity is still determined by the same group of bacteriophages of maximal adsorptive affinity (i.e., n_t/n_o must not fall below 1/20).

2. The adsorption velocity constant k has the value of 1.3×10^{-11} for adsorption of phage to heat-killed bacteria; k has an approximately 2.5 times greater value for phage adsorption to living bacteria.

3. A heat-killed coli bacterium is capable of adsorbing, on the average, a maximum of 130 to 140 bacteriophage particles; this number is referred to as the saturation capacity.

4. On the basis of the simplest assumptions, two values for the diameter of the bacteriophage have been calculated; one from the adsorption velocity constant and the other from the saturation capacity; the former yields an approximate particle diameter of 100 mμ, the latter a value of 60 to 120 mμ. A direct size determination of the same bacteriophage from its sedimentation velocity leads to a particle diameter of 80 to 90 mμ.

THE GROWTH OF BACTERIOPHAGE

By EMORY L. ELLIS AND MAX DELBRÜCK*

(*From the William G. Kerckhoff Laboratories of the Biological Sciences, California Institute of Technology, Pasadena*)

(Accepted for publication, September 7, 1938)

INTRODUCTION

Certain large protein molecules (viruses) possess the property of multiplying within living organisms. This process, which is at once so foreign to chemistry and so fundamental to biology, is exemplified in the multiplication of bacteriophage in the presence of susceptible bacteria.

Bacteriophage offers a number of advantages for the study of the multiplication process not available with viruses which multiply at the expense of more complex hosts. It can be stored indefinitely in the absence of a host without deterioration. Its concentration can be determined with fair accuracy by several methods, and even the individual particles can be counted by d'Herelle's method. It can be concentrated, purified, and generally handled like nucleoprotein, to which class of substances it apparently belongs (Schlesinger (1) and Northrop (2)). The host organism is easy to culture and in some cases can be grown in purely synthetic media, thus the conditions of growth of the host and of the phage can be controlled and varied in a quantitative and chemically well defined way.

Before the main problem, which is elucidation of the multiplication process, can be studied, certain information regarding the behavior of phage is needed. Above all, the "natural history" of bacteriophage, *i.e.* its growth under a well defined set of cultural conditions, is as yet insufficiently known, the only extensive quantitative work being that of Krueger and Northrop (3) on an anti-*staphylococcus* phage. The present work is a study of this problem, the growth of another phage (anti-*Escherichia coli* phage) under a standardized set of culture conditions.

* Fellow of The Rockefeller Foundation.

Reprinted by permission of the authors and The Rockefeller Institute from The Journal of General Physiology, **22** (3), 365-384, January 20, 1939.

EXPERIMENTAL

Bacteria Culture.—Our host organism was a strain of *Escherichia coli*, which was kindly provided by Dr. C. C. Lindegren. Difco nutrient broth (pH 6.6–6.8) and nutrient agar were selected as culture media. These media were selected for the present work because of the complications which arise when synthetic media are used. We thus avoided the difficulties arising from the need for accessory growth factors.

Isolation, Culture, and Storage of Phage.—A bacteriophage active against this strain of *coli* was isolated in the usual way from fresh sewage filtrates. Its homogeneity was assured by five successive single plaque isolations. The properties of this phage remained constant throughout the work. The average plaque size on 1.5 per cent agar medium was 0.5 to 1.0 mm.

Phage was prepared by adding to 25 cc. of broth, 0.1 cc. of a 20 hour culture of bacteria, and 0.1 cc. of a previous phage preparation. After 3½ hours at 37° the culture had become clear, and contained about 10^9 phage particles.

Such lysates even though stored in the ice box, decreased in phage concentration to about 20 per cent of their initial value in 1 day, and to about 2 per cent in a week, after which they remained constant. Part of this lost phage activity was found to be present in a small quantity of a precipitate which had sedimented during this storage period.

Therefore, lysates were always filtered through Jena sintered glass filters (5 on 3 grade) immediately after preparation. The phage concentration of these filtrates also decreased on storage, though more slowly, falling to 20 per cent in a week. However, 1:100 dilutions in distilled water of the fresh filtered lysates retained a constant assay value for several months, and these diluted preparations were used in the work reported here, except where otherwise specified.

This inactivation of our undiluted filtered phage suspensions on standing is probably a result of a combination of phage and specific phage inhibiting substances from the bacteria, as suggested by Burnett (4, 5). To test this hypothesis we prepared a polysaccharide fraction from agar cultures of these bacteria, according to a method reported by Heidelberger *et al.* (6). Aqueous solutions of this material, when mixed with phage suspensions, rapidly inactivated the phage.

Method of Assay.—We have used a modification of the plaque counting method of d'Herelle (7) throughout this work for the determination of phage concentrations. Although the plaque counting method has been reported unsatisfactory by various investigators, under our conditions it has proven to be entirely satisfactory.

Phage preparations suitably diluted in 18 hour broth cultures of bacteria to give a readily countable number of plaques (100 to 1000) were spread with a bent glass capillary over the surface of nutrient agar plates which had been dried by inverting on sterile filter paper overnight. The plates were then incubated 6 to 24 hours at 37°C. at which time the plaques were readily distinguishable. The 0.1 cc. used for spreading was completely soaked into the agar thus prepared in

2 to 3 minutes, thus giving no opportunity for the multiplication of phage in the liquid phase. Each step of each dilution was done with fresh sterile glassware. Tests of the amount of phage adhering to the glass spreaders showed that this quantity is negligible.

The time of contact between phage and bacteria in the final dilution before plating has no measurable influence on the plaque count, up to 5 minutes at 25°C. Even if phage alone is spread on the plate and allowed to soak in for 10 minutes, before seeding the plate with bacteria, only a small decrease in plaque count is apparent (about 20 per cent). This decrease we attribute to failure of some phage particles to come into contact with bacteria.

Under parallel conditions, the reproducibility of an assay is limited by the sampling error, which in this case is equal to the square root of the number of plaques (10 per cent for counts of 100; 3.2 per cent for counts of 1000). To test the effect of phage concentration on the number of plaques obtained, successive dilutions of a phage preparation were all plated, and the number of plaques enumerated. Over a 100-fold range of dilution, the plaque count was in linear proportion to the phage concentration. (See Fig. 1.)

Dreyer and Campbell-Renton (8) using a different anti-*coli* phage and an anti-*staphylococcus* phage, and a different technique found a complicated dependence of plaque count on dilution. Such a finding is incompatible with the concept that phage particles behave as single particles, *i.e.* without interaction, with respect to plaque formation. Our experiments showed no evidence of such a complicated behavior, and we ascribe it therefore to some secondary cause inherent in their procedure.

Bronfenbrenner and Korb (9) using a phage active against *B. dysenteriae* Shiga, and a different plating technique found that when the agar concentration was changed from 1 per cent to 2.5 per cent, the number of plaques was reduced to 1 per cent of its former value. They ascribed this to a change in the water supplied to the bacteria. With the technique which we have employed, variation of the agar concentration from 0.75 per cent to 3.0 per cent, had little influence on the number of plaques produced, though the size decreased noticeably with increasing agar concentration. (See Table I.)

Changes in the concentration of bacteria spread with the phage on the agar plates had no important influence on the number of plaques obtained. (See Table I.) The temperature at which plates were incubated had no significant effect on the number of plaques produced. (See Table I.)

In appraising the accuracy of this method, several points must be borne in mind. With our phage, our experiments confirm in the main the picture proposed by d'Herelle, according to which a phage particle grows in the following way: it becomes attached to a susceptible bacterium, multiplies upon or within it up to a critical time, when the newly formed phage particles are dispersed into the solution.

In the plaque counting method a single phage particle and an infected bacterium containing any number of phage particles will each give only one plaque.

This method therefore, does not give the number of phage particles but the number of loci within the solution at which one or more phage particles exist. These loci will hereafter be called "infective centers." The linear relationship between phage concentration and plaque count (Fig. 1) does not prove that the number of plaques is equal to the number of infective centers, but only that it is proportional to this number. We shall call the fraction of infective centers which

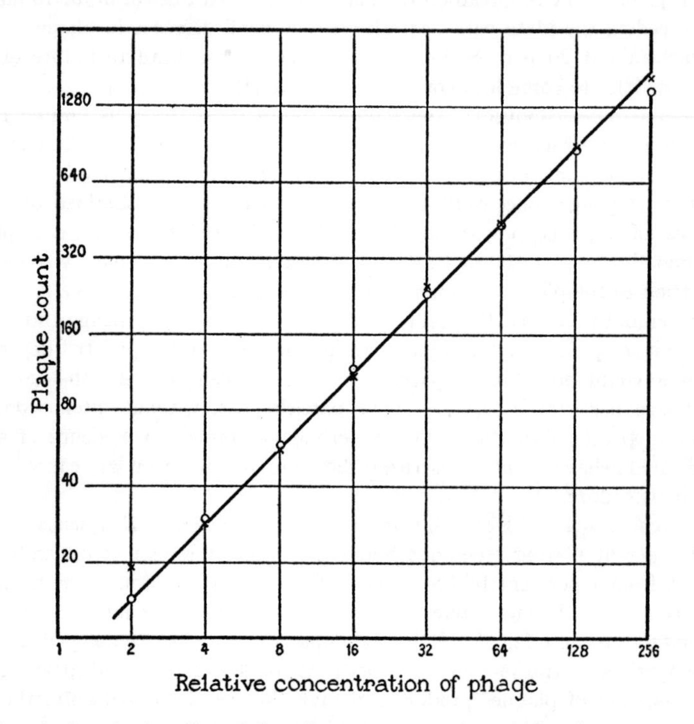

FIG. 1. Proportionality of the phage concentration to the plaque count.

Successive twofold dilutions of a phage preparation were plated in duplicate on nutrient agar; 0.1 cc. on each plate. The plaque counts from two such series of dilutions are plotted against the relative phage concentration, both on a logarithmic scale.

produces plaques the "efficiency of plating." With the concentrations of phage and bacteria which we have used this coefficient is essentially the fraction of infected bacteria in the suspension spread on the plate, which goes through to lysis under our cultural conditions on the agar medium. After plating, the phage particles released by this lysis infect the surrounding bacteria, increasing only the size, and not the number of plaques.

TABLE I

Independence of Plaque Count on Plating Method

Agar concentration

Plates were prepared in which the agar strength varied, and all spread with 0.1 cc. of the same dilution of a phage preparation. There is no significant difference in the numbers of plaques obtained.

Agar concentration, *per cent*	0.75	1.5	3.0
Plaque counts	394	373	424
	408	430	427
	376	443	455
	411	465	416
	373	404	469
Average	392	423	438
Plaque size, *mm*	2	0.5	0.2

Concentration of plating *coli*

A broth suspension of bacteria (10^9 bacteria/cc.) was prepared from a 24 hour agar slant and used at various dilutions, as the plating suspension for a single phage dilution. There are no significant differences in the plaque counts except at the highest dilution of the bacterial suspension, where the count is about 15 per cent lower.

Concentration	Plaque count
1	920
1/5	961
1/25	854
1/125	773

Temperature of plate incubation

Twelve plates were spread with 0.1 cc. of the same suspension of phage and bacteria, divided into three groups, and incubated at different temperatures. There were no significant differences in the plaque counts obtained.

Temperature, °*C*	37	24	10
Plaque count	352	384	405
	343	405	377
	386	403	400
	422	479	406
Average	376	418	397

The experimental determination of the efficiency of plating is described in a later section (see p. 379). The coefficient varies from 0.3 to 0.5. This means that three to five out of every ten infected bacteria produce plaques. The fact that the efficiency of plating is relatively insensitive to variations in the temperature of plate incubation, density of plating *coli*, concentration of agar, etc. indicates that a definite fraction of the infected bacteria in the broth cultures do not readily go through to lysis when transferred to agar plates. For most experiments only the relative assay is significant; we have therefore, given the values derived directly from the plaque counts without taking into account the efficiency of plating, unless the contrary is stated.

Growth Measurements

The main features of the growth of this phage in broth cultures of the host are shown in Fig. 2. After a small initial increase (discussed below) the number of infective centers (individual phage particles, plus infected bacteria) in the suspension remains constant for a time, then rises sharply to a new value, after which it again remains constant. Later, a second sharp rise, not as clear-cut as the first, and finally a third rise occur. At this time visible lysis of the bacterial suspension takes place. A number of features of the growth process may be deduced from this and similar experiments, and this is the main concern of the present paper.

The Initial Rise

When a concentration of phage suitable for plating was added to a suspension of bacteria, and plated at once, a reproducible plaque count was obtained. If the suspension with added phage was allowed to stand 5 minutes at 37°C. (or 20 minutes at 25°C.) the number of plaques obtained on plating the suspension was found to be 1.6 times higher. This initial rise is not to be confused with the first "burst" which occurs later and increases the plaque count 70-fold. After the initial rise, the new value is readily duplicated and remains constant until the start of the first burst in the growth curve (30 minutes at 37° and 60 minutes at 25°).

This initial rise we attribute not to an increase in the number of infective centers, but to an increase in the probability of plaque formation (*i.e.* an increase in the efficiency of plating) by infected bacteria in a progressed state; that is, bacteria in which the phage particle has commenced to multiply. That this rise results from a change in the efficiency of plating and not from a quick increase in the number of infective centers is evident from the following experiment. Bacteria were grown for 24 hours at 25°C. on agar slants, then suspended in broth. Phage was added to this suspension and to a suspension of bacteria grown in the usual way, and the concentration of infective

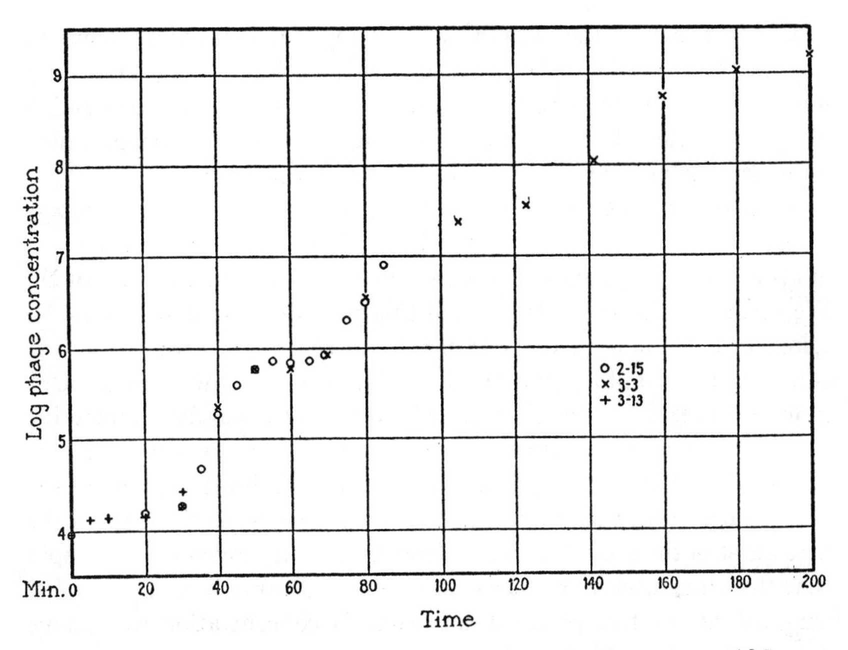

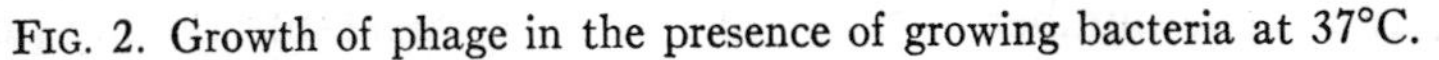

FIG. 2. Growth of phage in the presence of growing bacteria at 37°C.

A diluted phage preparation was mixed with a suspension of bacteria containing 2×10^8 organisms per cc., and diluted after 3 minutes 1 to 50 in broth. At this time about 70 per cent of the phage had become attached to bacteria. The total number of infective centers was determined at intervals on samples of this growth mixture. Three such experiments, done on different days, are plotted in this figure. The same curve was easily reproducible with all phage preparations stored under proper conditions.

centers was determined on both. The initial value was 1.6 times higher in the agar grown bacteria than in the control experiment, and remained constant until actual growth occurred. The initial rise was therefore absent in this case, clearly a result of an increase in the efficiency of plating. A sufficient number of experiments were performed with bacteria grown on agar to indicate that in other respects their behavior is similar to that of the bacteria grown in broth. The bacteria grown in this way on agar slants are in some way more susceptible to lysis than the broth cultured bacteria.

Adsorption

The first step in the growth of bacteriophage is its attachment to susceptible bacteria. The rate of this attachment can be readily measured by centrifuging the bacteria out of a suspension containing phage, at various times, and determining the amount of phage which remains unattached in the supernatant (*cf.* Krueger (10)).[1]

According to the picture of phage growth outlined above, phage cannot multiply except when attached to bacteria; therefore, the rate of attachment may, under certain conditions, limit the rate of growth. We wished to determine the rate of this adsorption so that it could be taken into account in the interpretation of growth experiments, or eliminated if possible, as a factor influencing the growth rate. Our growth curves show that there is no increase in the number of infective centers up to a critical time; we could therefore, make measurements of the adsorption on living bacteria suspended in broth, so long as the time allowed for attachment was less than the time to the start of the first burst in the growth curve. The adsorption proved to be so rapid that this time interval was ample to obtain adsorption of all but a few per cent of the free phage if the bacteria concentration was above 3×10^7. The number of bacteria remained constant; the lag phase in their growth was longer than the experimental period.

The rate of attachment was found to be first order with respect to the concentration of free phage (P_f) and first order with respect to the concentration of bacteria (B) over a wide range of concentrations, in agreement with the results reported by Krueger (10). That is, the concentration of free phage followed the equation

$$-\frac{d(P_f)}{dt} = k_a(P_f)(B)$$

[1] A very careful study of the adsorption of a *coli*-phage has also been made by Schlesinger (Schlesinger, M., *Z. Hyg. u. Infektionskrankh.*, 1932, **114**, 136, 149). Our results, which are less accurate and complete, agree qualitatively and quantitatively with the results of his detailed studies.

in which k_a was found to be 1.2×10^{-9} cm.^{3}/min. at 15° and 1.9×10^{-9} cm.^{3}/min. at 25°C. These rate constants are about five times greater than those reported by Krueger (10). With our ordinary 18 hour bacteria cultures (containing 2×10^8 *B. coli*/cc.) we thus obtain 70 per cent attachment of phage in 3 minutes and 98 per cent in 10 minutes. The adsorption follows the equation accurately until more than 90 per cent attachment has been accomplished, and then slows down somewhat, indicating either that not all the phage particles have the same affinity for the bacteria, or that equilibrium is being approached. Other experiments not recorded here suggest that, if an equilibrium exists, it lies too far in favor of adsorption to be readily detected. This equation expresses the rate of adsorption even when a tenfold excess of phage over bacteria is present, indicating that a single bacterium can accommodate a large number of phage particles on its surface, as found by several previous workers (5, 10).

Krueger (10) found a true equilibrium between free and adsorbed phage. The absence of a detectable desorption in our case may result from the fixation of adsorbed phage by growth processes, since our conditions permitted growth, whereas Krueger's experiments were conducted at a temperature at which the phage could not grow.

Growth of Phage

Following adsorption of the phage particle on a susceptible bacterium, multiplication occurs, though this is not apparent as an increase in the number of plaques until the bacterium releases the resulting colony of phage particles into the solution. Because the adsorption under proper conditions is so rapid and complete (as shown above) experiments could be devised in which only the influence of the processes following adsorption could be observed.

The details of these experiments were as follows: 0.1 cc. of a phage suspension of appropriate concentration was added to 0.9 cc. of an 18 hour broth bacterial culture, containing about 2×10^8 *B. coli* / cc. After standing for a few minutes, 70 to 90 per cent of the phage was attached to the bacteria. At this time, the mixture was diluted 50-fold in broth (previously adjusted to the required temperature) and incubated. Samples were removed at regular intervals, and the concentration of infective centers determined.

The results of three experiments at 37°C. are plotted in Fig. 2, and confirm the suggestion of d'Herelle that phage multiplies under a spatial constraint, *i.e.* within or upon the bacterium, and is suddenly liberated in a burst. It is seen that after the initial rise (discussed above) the count of infective centers remains constant up to 30 minutes, and then rises about 70-fold above the initial value. The rise corresponds to the liberation of the phage particles which have multiplied in the initial constant period. This interpretation was verified by measurements of the free phage by centrifuging out the infected bacteria, and determining the number of phage particles in the supernatant liquid. The free phage concentration after adsorption was, of course, small compared to the total and remained constant up to the time of the first rise. It then rose steeply and became substantially equal to the total phage.

The number of bacteria lysed in this first burst is too small a fraction of the total bacteria used in these experiments to be measured as a change in turbidity; the ratio of uninfected bacteria to the total possible number of infected bacteria before the first burst is 400 to 1, the largest number of bacteria which can disappear in the first burst is therefore only 0.25 per cent of the total.

The phage particles liberated in the first burst are free to infect more bacteria. These phage particles then multiply within or on the newly infected bacteria; nevertheless, as before, the concentration of infective centers remains constant until these bacteria are lysed and release the phage which they contain into the medium. This gives the second burst which begins at about 70 minutes from the start of the experiment. Since the uninfected bacteria have been growing during this time, the bacteria lysed in the second burst amount to less than 5 per cent of the total bacteria present at this time. There is again therefore, no visible lysis.

This process is repeated, leading to a third rise of smaller magnitude starting at 120 minutes. At this time, inspection of the culture, which has until now been growing more turbid with the growth of the uninfected bacteria, shows a rapid lysis. The number of phage particles available at the end of the second rise was sufficient to infect the remainder of the bacteria.

These results are typical of a large number of such experiments, at

37°, all of which gave the 70-fold burst size, *i.e.* an average of 70 phage particles per infected bacterium, occurring quite accurately at the time shown, 30 minutes. Indeed, one of the most striking features of these experiments was the constancy of the time interval from adsorption to the start of the first burst. The magnitude of the rise (70-fold) was likewise readily reproducible by all phage preparations which had been stored under proper conditions to prevent deterioration (see above).

Multiple Infection

The adsorption measurements showed that a single bacterium can adsorb many phage particles. The subsequent growth of phage in these "multiple infected" bacteria might conceivably lead to (*a*) an increase in burst size; (*b*) a burst at an earlier time, or (*c*) the same burst size at the same time, as if only one of the adsorbed particles had been effective, and the others inactivated. In the presence of very great excesses of phage, Krueger and Northrop (3) and Northrop (2) report that visible lysis of the bacteria occurs in a very short time. It was possible therefore, that in our case, the latent period could be shortened by multiple infection. To determine this point, we have made several experiments of which the following is an example. 0.8 cc. of a freshly prepared phage suspension containing 4×10^9 particles per cc. (assay corrected for efficiency of plating) was added to 0.2 cc. of bacterial suspension containing 4×10^9 bacteria per cc. The ratio of phage to bacteria in this mixture was 4 to 1. 5 minutes were allowed for adsorption, and then the mixture was diluted 1 to 12,500 in broth, incubated at 25°, and the growth of the phage followed by plating at 20 minute intervals, with a control growth curve in which the phage to bacteria ratio was 1 to 10. No significant difference was found either in the latent period or in the size of the burst. The bacteria which had adsorbed several phage particles behaved as if only one of these particles was effective.

Effect of Temperature on Latent Period and Burst Size

A change in temperature might change either the latent period, *i.e.* the time of the burst, or change the size of the burst, or both. In order to obtain more accurate estimates of the burst size it is desirable to minimize reinfection during the period of observation. This is obtained by diluting the phage-bacteria mixture (after initial contact to secure adsorption) to such an extent that the rate of adsorption then becomes extremely small. In this way, a single "cycle" of growth, (infection, growth, burst) was obtained as the following example

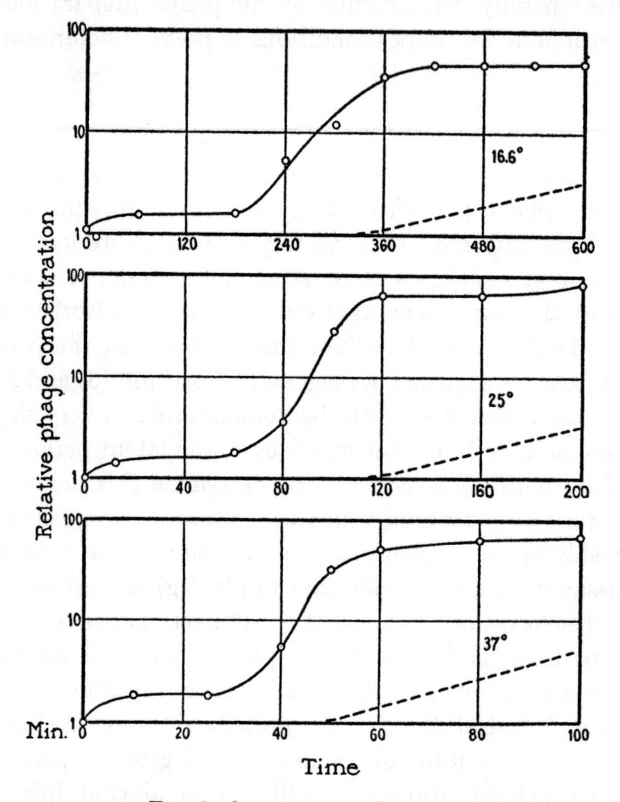

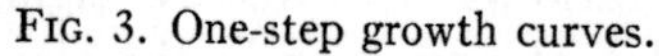
FIG. 3. One-step growth curves.

A suitable dilution of phage was mixed with a suspension of bacteria containing 2×10^8 organisms per cc. and allowed to stand at the indicated temperature for 10 minutes to obtain more than 90 per cent adsorption of the phage. This mixture was then diluted $1:10^4$ in broth, and incubated. It was again diluted 1:10 at the start of the first rise to further decrease the rate of adsorption of the phage set free in the first step. The time scales are in the ratio 1:2:6 for the temperatures 37, 25, and 16.6°C. Log P/P_0 is plotted, P_0 being the initial concentration of infective centers and P the concentration at time t. The broken line indicates the growth curve of the bacteria under the corresponding conditions.

shows. 0.1 cc. of phage of appropriate and known concentration was added to 0.9 cc. of an 18 hour culture and allowed to stand in this concentrated bacterial suspension for 10 minutes at the temperature of the experiment. This mixture was then diluted $1:10^4$ in broth and incubated at the temperature chosen. Samples of this diluted mixture were withdrawn at regular intervals and assayed. The results of three such experiments are plotted in Fig. 3. The rise corresponds to the average number of phage produced per burst, and its value can be appraised better in these experiments than in the complete growth curve previously given (Fig. 2) where there is probably some overlapping of the steps. In these experiments the rise is seen to be practically identical at the three temperatures, and equals about sixty particles per infected bacterium, but the time at which the rise occurred was 30 minutes at 37°, 60 minutes at 25°, and 180 minutes at 16.6°. This shows that the effect of temperature is solely on the latent period.

We have also made separate measurements of the rate of bacterial growth under the conditions of these experiments. They show that the average division period of the bacteria in their logarithmic growth phase varies in the same way with temperature, as the length of the latent period of phage growth. The figures are:

Temperature	Division period of *B*	Latent period of *P* growth
°*C*	*min.*	*min.*
16.6	About 120	180
25	42	60
37	21	30

There is a constant ratio (3/2) between the latent period of phage growth and the division period of the bacteria. This coincidence suggests a connection between the time required for division of a bacterium under optimum growth conditions, and the time from its infection by phage to its lysis.

Individual Phage Particle

The growth curves described above give averages only of large numbers of bursts. They can, however, also be studied individually, as was first done by Burnett (11).

If from a mixture containing many particles very small samples are withdrawn, containing each on the average only about one or less particles, then the fraction p_r of samples containing r particles is given by Poissons' (12) formula,

$$p_r = \frac{n^r e^{-n}}{r!} \tag{1}$$

where n is the average number of particles in a sample and e is the Napierian logarithm base. If the average number n is unknown, it can be evaluated from an experimental determination of any single

TABLE II

Distribution of Individual Particles among Small Samples

A suitably diluted phage preparation was added to 5 cc. of 18 hour bacteria culture and 0.1 cc. samples of this mixture were plated. The distribution of particles among the samples is that predicted by formula (1).

	p_r (experimental)	p_r (calculated)
0 plaques on 13 plates	0.394	0.441
1 plaque " 14 "	0.424	0.363
2 plaques " 5 "	0.151	0.148
3 " " 1 plate	0.033	0.040
4 " " 0 plates	0.000	0.008
27 " " 33 "	1.002	1.000

one of the p_r, for instance from a determination of p_0, the fraction of samples containing no particles:

$$n = -\ln p_0 \tag{2}$$

Let us now consider the following experiment. A small number of phage particles is added to a suspension containing bacteria in high concentration. Within a few minutes each phage particle has attached itself to a bacterium. The mixture is then diluted with a large volume of broth, in order to have the bacteria in low concentration so that after the first burst a long time elapses before reinfection, as in the one step growth curves. Samples (0.05 cc.) are removed from this mixture to separate small vials and incubated at the desired temperature. If these samples are plated separately (after adding a drop of bacterial suspension to each vial) before the occurrence of bursts, the fraction of the plates containing 0, 1, 2, *etc.* plaques is found to conform to formula (1) (see Table II). In this experiment we could also have inferred the average number of particles per sample, using formula (2), from the fraction of the plates showing no plaques (giving 0.93 per sample) instead of from the total number of plaques (27/33 = 0.82 per sample).

Experimental Measure of Efficiency of Plating

If the samples are incubated until the bursts have occurred, and then plated, the samples which had no particles will still show no plaques, those with one or more particles will show a large number, depending on the size of the burst, and on the efficiency of plating. In any case, if we wait until all bursts have occurred, only those samples which really contained no particle will show no plaques, quite independent of any inefficiency of plating. From this fraction of plates showing no plaques we can therefore evaluate the true number of particles originally present in the solution, and by comparison with the regular assay evaluate the efficiency of plating. In this way we have determined our efficiency of plating to be about 0.4. For instance, one such experiment gave no plaques on 23 out of 40 plates, and many plaques on each of the remaining plates. This gives $p_0 = \frac{23}{40}$ or 0.57 from which $n = 0.56$ particles per sample. A parallel assay of the stock phage used indicated 0.22 particles per sample; the plating efficiency was therefore $\frac{0.22}{0.56} = 0.39$. This plating efficiency remains fairly constant under our standard conditions for assay. The increase in probability of plaque formation which we suppose to take place following the infection of a bacterium by the phage particle, *i.e.* the initial rise, brings the plating efficiency up to 0.65.

The Burst Size

Single particle experiments such as that described above, revealed a great fluctuation in the magnitude of individual bursts, far larger than one would expect from the differences in size of the individual bacteria in a culture; indeed, they vary from a few particles to two hundred or more. Data from one such experiment are given in Table III.

We at first suspected that the fluctuation in burst size was connected with the time of the burst, in that early bursts were small and late bursts big, and the fluctuation was due to the experimental superposition of these. However, measurement of a large number of bursts, plated at a time when only a small fraction of the bursts had occurred, showed the same large fluctuation. We then suspected that the particles of a burst were not liberated simultaneously, but over an interval of time. In this case one might expect a greater homogeneity in burst size, if measurements were made at a late time when they are at their maximum value. This view also was found by experiment to be false.

TABLE III

Fluctuation in Individual Burst Size

97.9 per cent of phage attached to bacteria in presence of excess bacteria (10 minutes), this mixture diluted, and samples incubated 200 minutes, then entire sample plated with added bacteria.

	Bursts
25 plates show 0 plaques	130
1 plate shows 1 plaque	58
14 plates show bursts	26
Average burst size, taking account of probable doubles = 48	123
	83
	9
	31
	5
	53
	48
	72
	45
	190
	9
Total	882 plaques

The cause of the great fluctuation in burst size is therefore still obscure.

DISCUSSION

The results presented above show that the growth of this strain of phage is not uniform, but in bursts. These bursts though of constant average size, under our conditions, vary widely in individual size. A burst occurs after a definite latent period following the adsorption of the phage on susceptible bacteria, and visible lysis coincides only with the last step-wise rise in the growth curve when the phage particles outnumber the bacteria present. It seemed reasonable to us to assume that the burst is identical with the lysis of the individual bacterium.

Krueger and Northrop (3), in their careful quantitative studies of an anti-*staphylococcus* phage came to an interpretation of their results which differs in some important respects from the above:

1. Their growth curves were smooth and gave no indication of steps; they concluded therefore that the production of phage is a continuous process.

2. In their case, the free phage during the logarithmic phase of a growth curve was an almost constant small fraction of the total phage. This led them to the view that there is an equilibrium between intracellular and extracellular phage. With an improved technique, Krueger (10) found that the fraction of free phage decreased in proportion to the growth of the bacteria, in conformity with the assumption of an equilibrium between two phases.

3. Krueger and Northrop (3) found that visible lysis occurred when a critical ratio of total phage to bacteria had been attained, and they assumed that the·e was no lysis in the earlier period of phage growth.

To appreciate the nature of these differences it must be born in mind that their method of assay was essentially different from ours. They used, as a measure of the "activity" of the sample of phage assayed, the time required for it to lyse a test suspension of bacteria under standard conditions. This time interval, according to the picture of the growth process given here, is the composite effect of a number of factors: the average time required for adsorption of free phage, its rate of growth in the infected bacteria, the time and size of burst, and the average time required for repetition of this process until the number of phage particles exceeds the number of bacteria and infects substantially all of them. Then, after a time interval equal to the latent period, lysis occurs.

This lysis assay method tends to measure the total number of phage particles rather than the number of infective centers as the following considerations show. Let us take a sample of a growth mixture in which is suspended one infected bacterium containing fifty phage particles. If this sample is plated, it can show but a single plaque. However, if the sample is assayed by the lysis method, this single infective center soon sets free its fifty particles (or more, if multiplication is still proceeding) and the time required to attain lysis will approximate that for fifty free particles rather than that for a single particle.

Since the burst does not lead to an increase in the number of phage particles, but only to their dispersion into the solution, the lysis method cannot give any steps in the concentration of the *total* phage in a growth curve. On the other hand one might have expected a step-wise increase in the concentration of *free* phage. However, the adsorption rate of the phage used by Krueger (10) is so slow that the infection of the bacteria is spread over a time longer than the presumed latent period, and therefore the bursts would be similarly spread in time, smoothing out any steps which might otherwise appear. Moreover, their measurements were made at 30 minute intervals, which even in our case would have been insufficient to reveal the steps.

The ratio between intracellular and extracellular phage would be determined, according to this picture of phage growth, by the ratio of the average time of adsorption to the average latent period. The average time of adsorption would decrease as the bacteria increased, shifting the ratio of intracellular to extracellular phage in precisely the manner described by Krueger (10).

As we have indicated in the description of our growth curves, lysis of bacteria should become visible only at a late time. Infection of a large fraction of the bacteria is possible only after the free phage has attained a value comparable to the number of bacteria, and visible lysis should then set in after the lapse of a latent period. At this time the total phage (by activity assay) will be already large compared to the number of bacteria, in agreement with Krueger and Northrop's findings.

It appears therefore that while Krueger and Northrop's picture does not apply to our phage and bacteria, their results do not exclude for their phage the picture which we have adopted. It would be of fundamental importance if two phages behave in such a markedly different way.

SUMMARY

1. An anti-*Escherichia coli* phage has been isolated and its behavior studied.

2. A plaque counting method for this phage is described, and shown to give a number of plaques which is proportional to the phage concentration. The number of plaques is shown to be independent of agar concentration, temperature of plate incubation, and concentration of the suspension of plating bacteria.

3. The efficiency of plating, *i.e.* the probability of plaque formation by a phage particle, depends somewhat on the culture of bacteria used for plating, and averages around 0.4.

4. Methods are described to avoid the inactivation of phage by substances in the fresh lysates.

5. The growth of phage can be divided into three periods: adsorption of the phage on the bacterium, growth upon or within the bacterium (latent period), and the release of the phage (burst).

6. The rate of adsorption of phage was found to be proportional to the concentration of phage and to the concentration of bacteria. The rate constant k_a is 1.2×10^{-9} cm.^{3}/min. at 15°C. and 1.9×10^{-9} cm.^{3}/min. at 25°.

7. The average latent period varies with the temperature in the same way as the division period of the bacteria.

8. The latent period before a burst of individual infected bacteria varies under constant conditions between a minimal value and about twice this value.

9. The average latent period and the average burst size are neither increased nor decreased by a fourfold infection of the bacteria with phage.

10. The average burst size is independent of the temperature, and is about 60 phage particles per bacterium.

11. The individual bursts vary in size from a few particles to about 200. The same variability is found when the early bursts are measured separately, and when all the bursts are measured at a late time.

One of us (E. L. E.) wishes to acknowledge a grant in aid from Mrs. Seeley W. Mudd. Acknowledgment is also made of the assistance of Mr. Dean Nichols during the preliminary phases of the work.

REFERENCES

1. Schlesinger, M., *Biochem. Z.*, Berlin, 1934, **273**, 306.
2. Northrop, J. H., *J. Gen. Physiol.*, 1938, **21**, 335.
3. Krueger, A. P., and Northrop, J. H., *J. Gen. Physiol.*, 1930, **14**, 223.
4. Burnet, F. M., *Brit. J. Exp. Path.*, 1927, **8**, 121.
5. Burnet, F. M., Keogh, E. V., and Lush, D., *Australian J. Exp. Biol. and Med. Sc.*, 1937, **15**, suppl. to part 3, p. 227.
6. Heidelberger, M., Kendall, F. E., and Scherp, H. W., *J. Exp. Med.*, 1936, **64**, 559.
7. d'Herelle, F., The bacteriophage and its behavior, Baltimore, The Williams & Wilkins Co., 1926.
8. Dreyer, C., and Campbell-Renton, M. L., *J. Path. and Bact.*, 1933, **36**, 399.
9. Bronfenbrenner, J. J., and Korb, C., *Proc. Soc. Exp. Biol. and Med.*, 1923, **21**, 315.
10. Krueger, A. P., *J. Gen. Physiol.*, 1931, **14**, 493.
11. Burnet, F. M., *Brit, J. Exp. Path.*, 1929, **10**, 109.
12. Poisson, S. D., Recherches sur la probabilité des jugements en matière criminelle et en matière civile, précédées des règles générales du calcul des probabilités, Paris, 1837.

THE GROWTH OF BACTERIOPHAGE AND LYSIS OF THE HOST

By M. DELBRÜCK*

(*From the William G. Kerckhoff Laboratories of the Biological Sciences, California Institute of Technology, Pasadena*)

(Received for publication, January 29, 1940)

Introduction and Statement of Main Result

Bacteriophage grows in the presence of living susceptible bacteria. In many but not all cases the growth of phage leads finally to a lysis of the bacterial cells, a phenomenon which in dense cultures manifests itself to the naked eye as a clearing of the bacterial culture. The exact nature of the connection between the growth of the phage and the dissolution of the cells has been a subject of controversy since the original discoveries of d'Herelle in 1917.

D'Herelle believed that lysis is the process by which the phage, which has grown within the bacterium, is liberated from the cell and dispersed in solution. Many later authors, notably Burnet, have concurred with him on this point. Last year Ellis and Delbrück (1) published detailed evidence that phage liberation in *B. coli* occurs in sudden bursts and showed that all the evidence was compatible with the assumption that in sensitive strains the bursts of phage liberation occurred only if and when a cell is lysed.

Northrop and Krueger (3–5) on the other hand have developed ideas along a somewhat different line in the course of their extensive research with a strain of *Staphylococcus aureus* and a bacteriophage active against it. Bordet (2) had put forward the conception that phage production followed by lysis is a more or less normal physiological function of the bacteria. In lysogenic strains where visible lysis never occurs it can be put into close analogy with the production of an extra-cellular enzyme. Northrop's and Krueger's work served to substantiate this view also in their case where the phage growth leads finally to the dissolution of the bacteria. In their view lysis of the bacteria is a secondary and incidental activity of the phage.

Krueger and Northrop (3) found first that clearing, if it occurs at all, begins when a certain threshold value in the ratio total phage/bacteria is

* Fellow of The Rockefeller Foundation.

Reprinted by permission of the author and The Rockefeller Institute from THE JOURNAL OF GENERAL PHYSIOLOGY, **23** (5), 643-660, May 20, 1940.

overstepped. A considerable *loss in total phage* parallels the clearing of the culture. If sufficient phage is added so that the ratio phage/bacteria is greater than the threshold value lysis begins almost at once. This experiment was later repeated and confirmed by Northrop (4, 5) with purified concentrates of phage.

Recently Northrop (5) found with a susceptible *megatherium* strain and homologous phage that the bulk of the phage was liberated *before* the culture began to clear. He found further with a lysogenic strain which never showed clearing but produced phage lysing the sensitive strain, that the yield in phage from this lysogenic strain was large compared to the number of bacteria present in the culture.

All these results indicate that in these strains lysis, if it occurs at all, is brought about by a mass attack of the phage on the bacteria *after* the phage have grown and been liberated into solution.

We have now studied in more detail the relation between phage growth and lysis in a new sensitive strain of *B. coli* and homologous phage and have obtained results which may offer a basis for reconciling the two diverging lines of interpretation.

We have found in this strain two entirely different types of lysis, which we designate as "Lysis from within" and "Lysis from without."

Lysis from without is brought about almost instantly by adsorption of phage at a threshold limit, which is equal to the adsorption capacity of that bacterium. No phage are liberated in this case, on the contrary, the adsorbed phage are lost. The phage attack the cell wall in such a way as to permit swelling of the cell, and its deformation into a spherical body.

Lysis from within is brought about by adsorption of *one* (or few) phage particle(s). Under favorable conditions this one phage particle multiplies during a latent period within the bacterium up to a threshold value (which is equal to the adsorption capacity). When the threshold value is reached, and not before, the phage is liberated by a sudden destruction of the protoplasmic membrane, which permits a rapid exudation of the cell contents without deformation of the cell wall.

It would seem that the results of other observers may be explained by postulating that

(*a*) In the case of *Staphylococcus aureus* the observable clearing is caused by lysis from without. Lysis from within either does not exist here and is replaced by continuous phage secretion; or it exists but leads only to a slow equalization of the refractive indices of the cell interior and the *milieu*. The decrease of total phage during lysis is caused by the adsorption of phage in the process of lysis from without.

(*b*) In the case of *B. megatherium* 36, sensitive, (Northrop (5)) the same relations hold.

(*c*) In the case of *B. megatherium* 899, lysogenic, (Northrop (5)), lysis from without does not occur, although the bacteria can adsorb a few phage particles each. Both the phage production capacity and the phage adsorption capacity are far smaller than the corresponding value for the same phage acting on the sensitive strain.

The equation

$$\text{Adsorption capacity} = \text{maximum yield of phage per bacterium}$$

was found to hold true both for bacteria in the phase of rapid growth, and for saturated bacterial cultures that had been aerated for 24 hours and consisted only of very small bacteria.

This equality points to a material connection between the bacterial constituents which can adsorb the phage and the new phage formed when it grows. These bacterial constituents we shall call *b*. It might be assumed that *b*, which the bacterium constantly produces without the help of phage (and in some cases also secretes), is part of the precursor which under favorable conditions is transformed into phage after combination of the bacterium with a phage particle from without. The complex *bP* might be the catalyst which *in the cell* transforms uncombined *b* into phage. The difference between a sensitive strain and a lysogenic strain would consist in this: in the sensitive strain the reaction

$$b \xrightarrow{\text{catalyzed by } bP} \text{phage (in the cell)}$$

would be faster than the production of *b* (in the cell). In the lysogenic strain *b* would be produced faster than it is converted into phage. This permits the bacterium *and* the phage to grow.

The extremely interesting but puzzling observations of Burnet and McKie (6) on lysogenesis of different variants of one strain of *B. enteriditis* Gaertner, and of Burnet and Lush (7) on induction of resistance and lysogenesis by the phage in a strain of *Staphylococcus albus* may perhaps allow further analysis in the light of these speculations.

EXPERIMENTAL

The strains of B. coli and of homologous phage used in this work were obtained from the Pasadena Junior College, through the courtesy of Mr. F. Gardner. They have not been studied before and will be designated as B_2 and P_2, in distinction to the strains B_1 and P_1 used last year by Ellis and Delbrück (1).

Growth curves of B_2 in Difco nutrient broth at 37° (by colony counts) are shown in Fig. 1. The maximum division rate is considerably smaller than that of B_1.

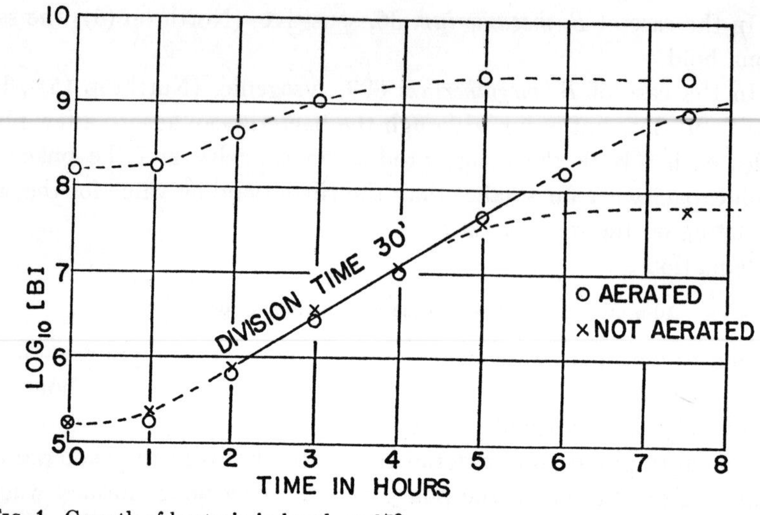

FIG. 1. Growth of bacteria in broth at 37°.

The inoculating bacteria were taken from an 18 hour not aerated broth culture. Without aeration the growth reaches saturation at 10^8 B/cc. With aeration the growth proceeds further beyond 10^9 B/cc. The maximum growth rate is in both cases equal and corresponds to an average division time of 30 minutes. The cessation of growth in the unaerated culture is therefore caused by lack of air. This is further supported by the top curve, which shows how the unaerated 18 hour culture, without the addition of fresh broth, proceeds to grow, when aerated, and reaches about 2×10^9 B/cc.

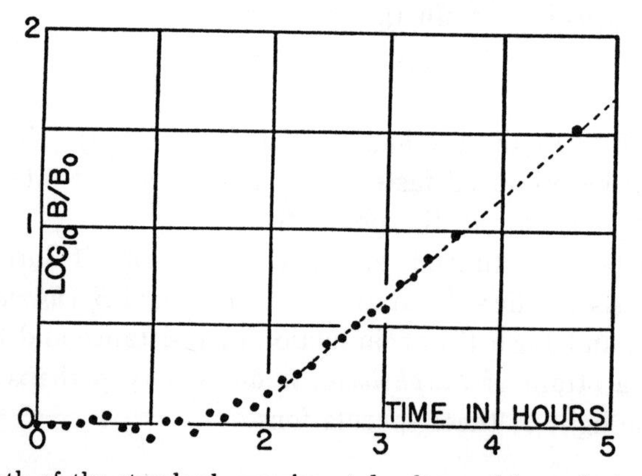

FIG. 2. Growth of the standard experimental culture of bacteria in broth at 37°.

At time zero 0.1 cc. of a 24 hour stock culture was added to 25 cc. broth. Every 7.5 minutes platings were made for colony counts. The plotted values show complete agreement with Hershey's (11) finding that such aerated bacteria exhibit a sudden transition from the phase of cell enlargement (lag period) to the phase of cell division. The lag period is 2 hours, if defined as the time required for increase in cell number by a factor 1.5 (compare Hershey's discussion (11)).

Synthetic Medium.—The bacteria and phage were also grown with aeration in a synthetic medium, consisting of

l-Asparagine	2 gm.
Glucose	4 gm.
Na_2HPO_4 (anhydrous)	6 gm.
KH_2PO_4	3 gm.
$MgSO_4$	0.05 gm.
NaCl	0.05 gm.
Distilled H_2O	1000 cc.

The bacteria in this medium grow more slowly than in broth but attain a higher final concentration. The phage also grow well on bacteria in this medium and cause lysis. But the growth rates of both the bacteria and the phage are only approximately reproducible with different batches of medium. These irregularities must be eliminated before the medium can be used for quantitative studies.

Bacteria transferred from this medium into broth grow at once. Transferred from broth to this medium they require a period of about 24 hours of adaptation before growth begins.

The bacteria were therefore carried on slants of synthetic medium agar and transferred into broth only for the specific experiments.

Stock phage was obtained by lysis in broth and filtration through Jena sintered glass filters. No measurable decrease in titer in periods over 6 months (in contrast to P_1, compare (1)).

Phage assay by plaque count on Difco nutrient agar plates, as described previously (1). The plaques are large (2 mm. diameter) and are countable after 4 hours incubation at 37°.

Turbidity was determined by visual comparison with turbidity standards, in most cases taken from the same culture. Such turbidity determinations are of course very rough, but a refinement of technique in this respect did not seem profitable. The turbidity in any event would not be proportional to the lysis, which in dense cultures, as we have seen, is a complex phenomenon, in which changes in shape, size, and refractive index occur. Each of these factors contributes to the turbidity change.

Preparation of Phage Concentrates.—For the experiments with large excess of phage over bacteria stock phage of very high titer were needed. These were obtained in the following way.

It was observed that lysates obtained from *synthetic medium* cultures (in contrast to broth lysates) lost all their phage on filtration through Jena sintered glass filters. The phage is not inactivated by the filter but simply adsorbed, and it can be eluted with good yields by small volumes of distilled water. An example is given in Table I.

These concentrates could be further concentrated by adding phosphate buffer to restore the original salt concentration and repeating the adsorption-elution procedure.

Filters of the coarser grade 4 were also tried and though effective gave less reliable yields.

Ground glass, silica, and fullers' earth were tried as adsorbents. These also gave good adsorption but the elution was again often unsatisfactory.

The phosphate buffer was replaced by 1 per cent $MgCl_2$ solution and by a 1 per cent

NaCl solution. Both were as effective as phosphates in causing the phage to be adsorbed by the filter.

Finally various concentrations of phosphate buffer were tried in order to determine the lower limit at which adsorption would take place. It was found that reduction of the buffer concentration to one half practically eliminated the adsorption.

By this method several concentrates were obtained with titers between 10^{11}/cc. and 10^{12}/cc. These concentrates were clear in transmitted light and showed intense blue Tyndall scattering. When kept in the ice box they showed no measurable decrease of titer over periods of more than 5 months.

Standard Cultural Conditions.—The cultural conditions of the bacteria were standardized in the following way. A stock culture was kept going for about a week by daily transfers into fresh synthetic medium. At the time the transfer was made, the culture contained about 2.5×10^9 bacteria/cc. These 24 hour aerated bacteria were used for phage assay. They will be referred to as the *stock culture.*

TABLE I

Adsorption and Elution of Phage from Jena Sintered Glass Filters

	Assay	Total phage
25 cc. fresh lysate	1.4×10^{10}	35×10^{10}
Filter lysate through Jena sintered glass filter grade 5 on 3, filtrate	0.001×10^{10}	0.025×10^{10}
Follow with 2 cc. distilled water	6.4×10^{10}	12.8×10^{10}
Follow with 5 cc. distilled water	0.19×10^{10}	0.95×10^{10}

At the time of the transfer of the stock culture a sample of 0.1 cc. was also transferred into 25 cc. *broth* and aerated at 37°. This culture was used for growing the phage, and will be referred to as the *experimental culture.*

Fig. 2 shows the growth of this experimental culture as determined by colony counts in 7.5 minute intervals. It is seen that the bacteria do not start to divide in the first 90 minutes and divide at maximum rate after 3 hours. It can therefore be used to study phage growth either on bacteria that are small and have a long period of growth in size without divisions ahead of them, or on bacteria that have attained their maximum average size and divide at a maximum rate.

Microscopic Observations

We have made some microscopic studies of the lysis of our bacteria under various conditions, both in hanging drop preparations and on nutrient agar plates. The hanging drop preparations have the advantage that one can study changes in mobility of the bacteria and also that the bacteria are subjected to more uniform conditions, while on the agar plate one can follow the history of individual bacteria over a stretch of time. These observations were made at room temperature, the time schedule is therefore retarded in comparison with the growth curves at 37°C.

Great differences in behavior were found depending on whether the bacteria were infected with about an equal number of phage or with a large excess of phage (200 to 1 or still higher ratios) and these will be described separately.

1. $P/B = 1$

(*a*) *Hanging Drop*

No changes in the shape of the bacteria were observed, only a gradual diminution in the number of bacteria.

(*b*) *On Nutrient Agar Plates*

The bacteria were first mixed with phage in broth and aerated at 37° for 10 minutes, as in an ordinary growth curve set up. At 10 minutes a 0.1 cc. sample was spread on an agar plate and observed under the microscope (magnification 600). A map was drawn of about 100 bacteria in the field of vision and these were checked every 5 minutes for changes. Up to about 30 minutes (now at room temperature, 25°) only a few bacteria disappeared, the others showed no change. Between 30 and 70 minutes 70 per cent of the bacteria disappeared. They disappeared by a process of fading out, *without noticeable change in shape.* The fading out takes about 2 minutes, a faint outline of the rod remaining visible for a long time afterwards. There appeared to be no correlation between the size of the bacterium and the inception of its fading. Many bacteria which at the beginning had a constriction as if they were on the point of dividing behaved as one bacterium on lysis. Sometimes the fading appeared to start at one end of the rod and then to proceed gradually through its entire length.

Discussion.—The bacteria are visible without staining under the microscope by virtue of a difference in the refractive index between their interior and the surrounding medium. The fading out without change of shape means then that the refractive index of its contents becomes equal to that of its *milieu,* while the cell wall retains its form. Inside and outside must suddenly become capable of free exchange. This must be due to a sudden disruption of the protoplasmic membrane. A change in permeability could hardly be so drastic as to permit complete equalization in so short a time.

2. $P/B = 200$ or greater

(*a*) *Hanging Drop*

The bacteria kept their normal size and rod shape up to about 20 minutes. Then suddenly within 1 or 2 minutes the large majority was transformed into spherical bodies of about the same volume and small refractive power. These spherical bodies were visible for a long time and only gradually decreased in number, some could be seen much distended and of oval shape.

Besides these spherical bodies there appeared a few very minute rods that were extremely motile.

Also some of the spherical bodies showed great motility.

(*b*) *On Nutrient Agar Plates*

The bacteria were mixed with a 200-fold excess of phage in broth for 5 minutes to permit time for adsorption. Then a 0.1 cc. sample was plated and observation began at 10 minutes. No changes in size or shape were observable up to 18 minutes. Then first few and soon many of the bacteria exhibited a variety of changes in form with parallel slow fading out. In most cases the rod simply swelled to an oval or spherical shape. Sometimes the swelling began at one end giving the impression of a rod attached to a little sphere, gradually the rod shortened and the sphere grew until only the sphere was left, which later assumed an irregular shape and finally faded out. Often the swelling began in the middle at the constriction of a dividing cell

TABLE II

	No. of bacteria lysed by	
P/B	Fading	Swelling
1.3	83	0
1	66	0
1	59	0
25	43	9
150	3	15
250	0	12
300	1	43

and then extended to both ends until only one sphere was visible. The whole process from the inception of swelling to the attainment of a spherical shape took between 2 and 10 minutes. The spheres then fade out very slowly.

Also a few minute rods are seen on the agar plate. They are never lysed. Their genesis has not been observed.

Discussion.—It is clear from the above description that lysis under the influence of many external phage particles is an entirely different phenomenon from lysis under influence of one external phage particle which has grown within the bacterium to a large number. We must distinguish between lysis from within and lysis from without. In the latter case apparently the phage *en masse* attack the cell wall and so alter its elastic properties as to permit swelling of the cell and the uptake of water. Possibly the cell wall is actually dissolved and only the protoplasm remains and swells up freely.

3. P/B between 1 and 200

For these intermediate cases observations on agar plates showed not an intermediate type of lysis but a gradual shift of the *fractions* of bacteria that are lysed by fading or by swelling respectively. Table II illustrates this point.

There is no ambiguity regarding the type of lysis a particular bacterium has undergone, except in rare cases when the fading has proceeded too far by the time of the next inspection, so that the form cannot be ascertained any more.

Bronfenbrenner, Muckenfuss, and Hetler in 1927 (12) and Bayne-Jones and Sandholzer in 1933 (13) have published very interesting photomicrographic moving pictures of lysing bacteria. They describe essentially the same morphological types of lysis which we find. In their experiments, however, the conditions of infection were not systematically varied and the ratio phage/bacteria was in no case determined. The significance of variations in the lytic process was therefore not recognized.

One Step Growth Curves

Phage growth curves with these strains of phage and bacteria show the same general features as those described by Ellis and Delbrück (1) for the strains B_1 and P_1. If phage is added at time zero to an excess of bacteria the plaque count stays constant for 17 minutes, then rises, at first sharply and then more gently (on the logarithmic plot!) until about 30 minutes. At that time the first step is nearly completed. If the growth mixture has not been diluted before the beginning of this first rise another sharp rise begins at about 34 minutes (Fig. 3). If reinfection has been prevented by extreme dilution there is very little further increase in plaque count (see Fig. 2 of the preceding paper).

It was decided to study in more detail this first step. The condition of extreme dilution under which the one step growth curve has to be measured facilitates an accurate analysis, because the samples which have to be plated at definite intervals need only be mixed with bacteria and plated, without further dilution. The time to which the assay is to be referred can then be defined within a fraction of a minute.

Fig. 4 shows the values obtained from three such growth curves. It should be noted that since the plaque count is plotted directly (instead of logarithmically as in most plots of this kind) the sampling error (which is proportional to the measured value) is more conspicuous near the upper end of the growth curve. The actual percentage deviations are experimentally larger near the beginning of the rise, because here the plaque count increases by a factor of twenty in 3 minutes and very slight inaccuracies in timing will entail huge percentage deviations in the plaque count. During the process of plating a bacterium may liberate the phage which it contains and thus add the full number of a "burst" to the normal sample value. This will place the point too high; it was probably the case in the 17 minute point of the first growth curve.

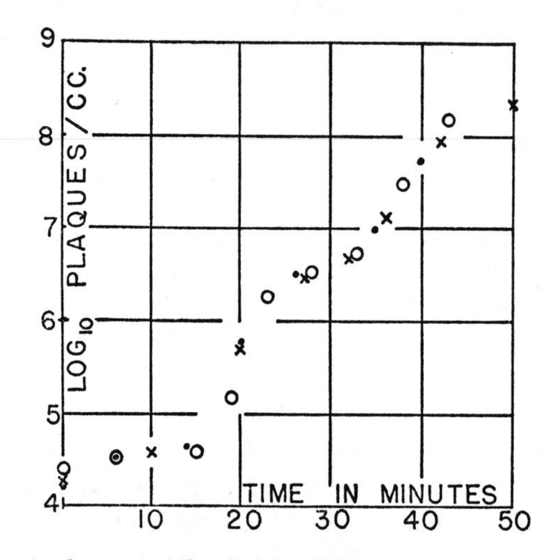

FIG. 3. Phage growth on rapidly dividing bacteria.

At time zero phage were added to the experimental culture of bacteria in its optimal growth phase (3 hours after inoculation) and well below its maximum concentration of bacteria (5×10^7 against 2.5×10^9). The initial phage concentration was 2×10^4, so that even after the first step the bacteria were still much in excess and no multiple infection occurred. After the second step the phage were in excess. The course of events resulting from this situation will be discussed separately.

Dates of experiments: ● 9–13, ○ 9–15, × 9–22.

Fig. 4 brings out very clearly one point which was not recognizable in the logarithmic plots: Phage liberation starts suddenly after the latent period of 17 minutes and continues *at a constant rate* for about 16 minutes, at which point it ceases almost equally abruptly. In this interval from 17 to 33 minutes the plaque count increases by a factor 170.

These characteristics of phage growth, namely the latent period, the spread of the latent period, and the step size depend on the physiological state of the bacteria. For example, if, instead of using the above defined experimental culture after 3 hours when the bacteria are large and divide rapidly we had taken the bacteria from the stock culture directly, the one step phage growth curve under the same conditions (in broth at 37°C.)

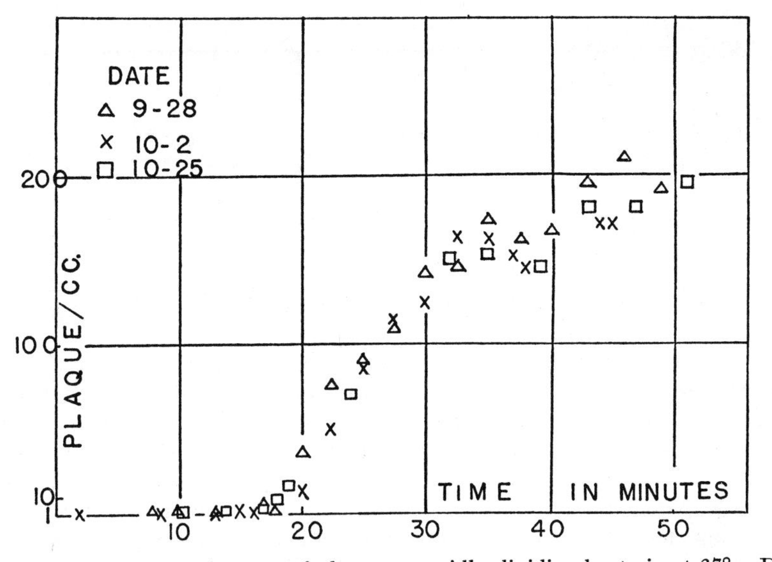

FIG. 4. One step growth curve of phage on rapidly dividing bacteria at 37°. Direct plot.

At time zero about 10^7 phage/cc. were added to 25 cc. of a rapidly growing broth culture of bacteria, that had been aerated for 3 hours and contained about 5×10^7 bacteria/cc. After 5 minutes, 10^3-, 10^4-, and 10^5-fold dilutions of this growth mixture were made in broth of 37° and these were further aerated and incubated. At 1 or 2 minute intervals samples from these mixtures were plated for plaque counts.

It is seen that the plaque count stays constant for 17 minutes, then increases *linearly* with time till 33 minutes when it reaches 170 times the original value. After 33 minutes it stays nearly constant. Phage liberation takes place uniformly during 16 minutes.

It should be noted that on a logarithmic plot the rise would appear to be much more sudden. In fact on such a plot more than half of the step would be accomplished within 3 minutes, when the plaque count has risen to twenty times the original value.

TABLE III

Characteristics of Phage Growth on Rapidly Dividing Bacteria and on 24 Hour Aerated Bacteria, Both Measured in Broth at 37°C., with Aeration

	Minimum latent period	Spread of latent period	Step size	Saturation value
	min.	*min.*		
Rapidly dividing bacteria	17	16	170	250
24 hrs. aerated bacteria	30	22	20	20

would have been qualitatively the same but quantitatively quite different (see Fig. 5). Table III lists the respective values.

The constant rate of phage liberation in the best one step growth curves

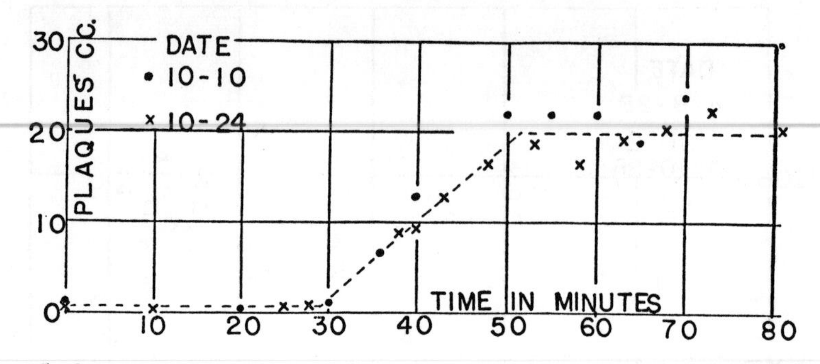

FIG. 5. One step phage growth on 24 hour aerated bacteria. Direct plot.

At time zero 2 × 10^8 phage/cc. were added to 1 cc. of a 24 hour stock culture of bacteria, containing 2 × 10^9 bacteria/cc. After 5 minutes free phage were determined and suitable high dilutions in broth were further incubated at 37° with aeration. At intervals samples from these mixtures were plated for plaque count.

It is seen that the plaque count stays constant for 30 minutes, then increases linearly with time till about 50 minutes when it reaches twenty times the original value. After 50 minutes it stays nearly constant. Phage liberation takes place uniformly during 20 minutes.

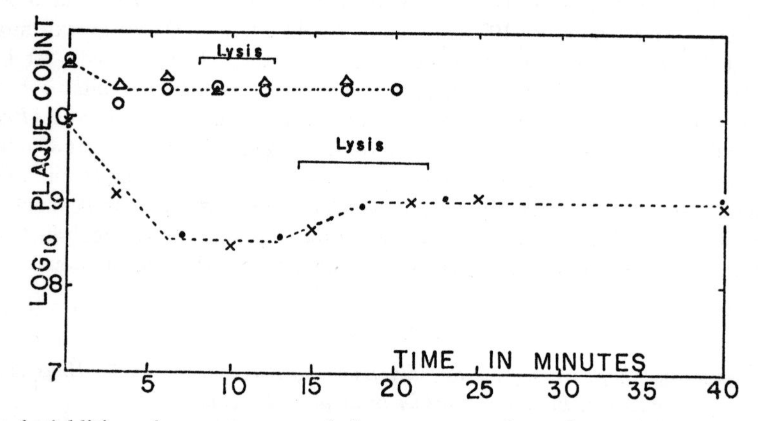

FIG. 6. Addition of a great excess of phage to a growing culture of bacteria, at 37°

	Date	P/B	log P/B	P bound/B	Free phage after adsorption
					per cent
●	9–13	120	2.08	115	4
×	9–22	60	1.78	57	5
○	10–26	500	2.70	250	50
△	11–20	700	2.85	270	60

(Fig. 4) permits a closer analysis. Since the liberation of phage from the *individual bacterium* probably occurs quite suddenly when the bacterium is lysed our result means that the infected bacteria represent a mixture of groups with latent periods ranging between 17 and 33 minutes and that there is a uniform distribution of bacteria over this whole range of latent periods.

The question arises as to what causes a bacterium to have a shorter or longer latent period. Several hypotheses might be suggested, either by ascribing the cause to statistical fluctuations of reactions involving a small number of particles (10), or by connecting it in one way or another with the bacterial cycle. The latter view seems to the author the more likely one but since it has not yet been worked out, further discussion will be deferred.

Multiple Infection

It was reported by Ellis and Delbrück (1) that if a bacterial suspension is infected with an excess of phage no changes occur in the latent period or in the burst size. At that time no phage concentrates were available and the maximum ratio of phage to bacteria attained in that work was only four to one.

We have repeated this work with our new strains and with the concentrates and have been able to work with much higher ratios of phage/bacteria, up to 700 to 1.

Fig. 6 shows some of the results obtained with the high ratios. Samples were assayed every 3 or 5 minutes. Since the assays here require several dilution steps these growth curves are less accurate both with respect to assay values and with respect to timing.

The results show an initial decrease in plaque count because many phage particles are bound to one bacterium which then gives only one plaque. For instance, starting with 10^{10} phage/cc. and a hundred times less bacteria, one finds initially 10^{10} plaques/cc. After 10 minutes only 5 per cent of the phage will be left free; these will give 5×10^8 plaques/cc. In addition the 10^8 bacteria/cc., each having adsorbed on the average 95 phage particles, will give 10^8 plaques/cc., bringing the total plaques to 6×10^8/cc. If the initial ratio phage/bacteria is greater than a certain critical value the bacteria show saturation. This saturation value depends on the physiological state of the bacteria. For instance, for rapidly growing bacteria, if the ratio is 500, the plaque count decreases only by a factor two. The saturation value is therefore 250. On the other hand, for 24 hour aerated bacteria, the saturation value is only about 20. (See Table III, last column.)

We have indicated in the figure the time during which clearing of the mixture occurs. If the initial ratio of phage/bacteria is smaller than the saturation value, clearing occurs only slightly earlier than in a one to one mixture, and it is accompanied by a noticeable increase in the plaque count.

On the other hand if the initial ratio of phage/bacteria is greater than the saturation value, clearing occurs much earlier and is not accompanied by an increase in plaque count.

In both cases the final plaque count is considerably smaller than the initial one; we have, in effect, a phage destruction by the adsorption that causes lysis.

One can see the difference between the two types of lysis with the naked eye. A culture of rod shaped bacteria, like *B. coli*, shows flow lines on shaking due to the orientation of the rods under the influence of the shearing forces of unequal flow. In lyses under the influence of great excess of phage these flow lines disappear before the culture clears up, because the rods are transformed into spherical bodies before they disappear, as described in the section on microscopic observations.

Growth of Phage and Lysis of Bacteria When Equivalent Numbers Are Mixed

It can be predicted that a disturbance must arise when equivalent amounts of phage and bacteria are mixed, due to the fact that the phage that are liberated from the first lysing bacteria will cause an excess of phage over bacteria to be present. These phage will be adsorbed on bacteria that are already infected and will therefore not show up in a plaque count assay. They will moreover interfere with the phage growth in these bacteria and in some of them cause a lysis from without.

Qualitatively the following can be predicted. We have seen that the phage will be liberated at a constant rate (after the lapse of the minimum latent period of 17 minutes). They will be adsorbed at a rate that is proportional to the phage concentration and to the bacterial concentration. The phage concentration is constantly increasing and the bacterial concentration is constantly decreasing (due to lysis). The adsorption rate will therefore pass through a maximum and the net free phage production rate will pass through a minimum. The net result is the appearance of a point of inflection, *i.e.* a secondary step in the phage growth curve, in some cases even a temporary decrease in the free phage if the rate of adsorption at any time exceeds the rate of phage liberation. Because of the loss of phage by adsorption and partial lysis from without the total step size must be smaller than in a one step growth curve where the bacteria are in excess and where multiple adsorption is prevented by extreme dilution, after adsorption of the parent phage.

These predictions are borne out by the experimental results. Fig. 7 shows three such growth curves where nearly equivalent amounts of phage and bacteria were mixed at time zero. The diminished yield is very pronounced and the secondary step is discernible in two sets of observational points. The condition of single infection of all bacteria at zero time can of course be realized only approximately. Even if exactly equivalent amounts

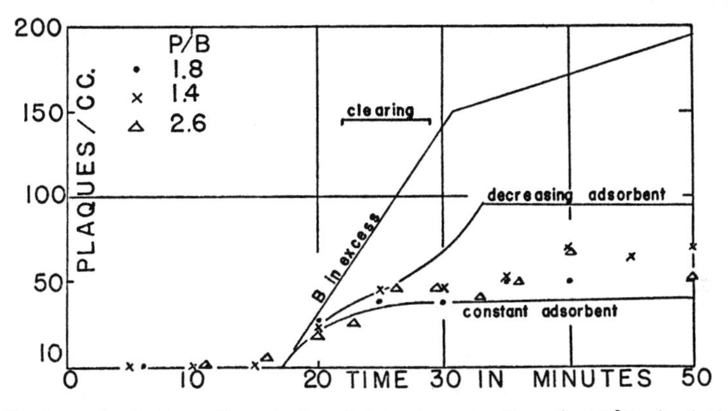

FIG. 7. Growth of phage if equivalent high concentrations (~10^8/cc.) of phage and bacteria are mixed at time zero. Direct plot.

Besides the experimental points from three growth curves three theoretical curves are drawn in the figure. These are

1. A one step growth curve with B in excess, taken from Fig. 4.
2. A calculated growth curve, assuming inactivation of the liberated phage on bacteria not yet lysed.
3. Same, but assuming that the adsorbing power of the bacterial constituents responsible for it is unimpaired till the completion of phage liberation and then vanishes abruptly.

The time interval from the beginning of clearing to its completion is indicated. It falls well on the ascending part of the one step growth curve. In the one-to-one growth curves this ascending part is soon counter-balanced by the multiple adsorption loss, so that clearing *seems* to occur during a phase of little phage liberation.

were mixed, the phage would not infect all the bacteria, but distribute themselves according to the probability formulas derived by Poisson. If $P/B = n$ there will be a fraction e^{-n} of the bacteria uninfected. On the other hand our phage assays, though fully reliable as far as relative values go, are not as certain with respect to absolute value, because of the difficulty of obtaining an accurate determination of the efficiency of plating (*cf.* Ellis and Delbrück (1)).

It is not possible to make a complete quantitative prediction of the growth curve because it is not known in detail how the adsorption *en masse* of phage to a bacterium that is already near a lysis from within will interfere with this process. It is also not quite certain whether those parts of the surface of the bacterium that adsorb the phage will lose their capacity of binding phage immediately upon lysis. In the strains used previously a slow decrease of phage assay after lysis could be ascribed to the continued "adsorption" of phage onto those scattered surface elements. No such decrease of phage assay was ever observed with the new strain. But such observations refer only to inactivation long after lysis and do not tell us whether the adsorbent is instantly destroyed upon lysis.

We have therefore calculated growth curves on the basis of two extreme assumptions.

(*a*) The amount of adsorbent decreases linearly from its initial value to zero during the 16 minutes in which the bacteria are lysed.

(*b*) The amount of adsorbent stays constant at its initial value throughout the course of lysis.

Case (*a*) is described by the differential equation

$$dP/dt = A - kB_0\,(1-t/T)\,P$$

In case (*b*) we have

$$dP/dt = A - kB_0P$$

In these equations the first term, A, represents the phage liberation by lysis during the interval T, as determined in the one step growth curves, the second term is the decrease of phage due to adsorption either on the unlysed bacteria only (case *a*) or on the unlysed bacteria plus the adsorbent from the lysed bacteria (case *b*).

These equations can be integrated explicitly.

We obtain in case (*a*)

$$P = \tfrac{1}{2}A\sqrt{\pi}\,\tau e^{2(T/\tau)^2-(T-t)^2/\tau^2}[G(T/\tau) - G([T - t]/\tau)]$$

with

$$\tau = \sqrt{2T/kB_0}$$

and $G(x)$ the Gaussian integral

$$G(x) = \frac{2}{\sqrt{\pi}}\int_0^x e^{-x^2}\,dx$$

In case (*b*), with constant adsorbent, the adsorption rate grows continuously with the free phage concentration. In this case we have therefore no point of inflection but a continuous asymptotic approach to the final titre

$$P = \frac{A}{kB_0}(1 - e^{-kB_0t}).$$

Since all required constants are known from independent experiments, the particular solutions applying to our case can be evaluated quantitatively. These have been plotted in Fig. 6. The experimental values fall between the limits set by these two cases.

We have also plotted the curve obtained in an ordinary one step growth curve, with B in excess (taken from Fig. 4). The difference between this curve and the experimental values is the amount of phage lost by adsorption. The data show that about one hundred phage are lost per bacterium. It is clear that this loss depends entirely on the rate of adsorption, which is determined by the product kB_0. If we wish to increase the yield per bacterium we have to decrease either B_0 or k. Reduction of B_0 brings us to the condition employed in the one step growth curves. Here the maximum yield of phage growth per bacterium is obtained, but the actual concentrations of phage are of course very small.

A promising way of increasing the end titre of phage would be to reduce k, the adsorption rate constant. The very interesting experiments of Krueger and his coworkers (8, 9) on the influence of the addition of salts (NaCl and Na_2SO_4) to a growth mixture of phage and bacteria would seem to be completely in accord with the assumption that the adsorption rate constant is diminished in the presence of salt.

In fact, a diminished adsorption rate constant should manifest itself in several ways in a phage growth curve, in which one starts with low concentrations of both phage and bacteria. Namely

1. Delayed clearing, due to delayed adsorption, and therefore delayed phage growth.
2. Higher maximum concentration of bacteria, due to delayed lysis.
3. Higher end titre of phage, due to
(*a*) higher number of bacteria producing phage
(*b*) reduced loss of phage by multiple adsorption.
4. Higher ratio of free to bound phage during the stationary growth phase, due to the fact, that every phage particle spends a longer time in the free state between liberation and adsorption.
5. A period of constant bacterial concentration preceding lysis, when all bacteria are infected and cease to divide but when the phage concentration is not yet sufficient for lysis.

Precisely these five differences from the normal course and no others were noted by Krueger and Strietmann (9) in their study of the influence of the addition of Na_2SO_4.

SUMMARY

1. A new strain of *B. coli* and of phage active against it is described, and the relation between phage growth and lysis has been studied. It has been found that the phage can lyse these bacteria in two distinct ways, which have been designated lysis from within and lysis from without.

2. Lysis from within is caused by infection of a bacterium by a single phage particle and multiplication of this particle up to a threshold value.

The cell contents are then liberated into solution without deformation of the cell wall.

3. Lysis from without is caused by adsorption of phage above a threshold value. The cell contents are liberated by a distension and destruction of the cell wall. The adsorbed phage is not retrieved upon lysis. No new phage is formed.

4. The maximum yield of phage in a lysis from within is equal to the adsorption capacity.

5. Liberation of phage from a culture in which the bacteria have been singly infected proceeds at a constant rate, after the lapse of a minimum latent period, until all the infected bacteria are lysed.

6. If the bacteria are originally not highly in excess, this liberation is soon counterbalanced by multiple adsorption of the liberated phage to bacteria that are already infected. This leads to a reduction of the final yield.

The author wishes to express his appreciation for the hospitality extended to him by the Biology Department of the California Institute of Technology during the tenure of a Fellowship of The Rockefeller Foundation. In particular he wishes to record his indebtedness to Dr. E. L. Ellis for constant help and advice and to Mr. F. Gardner for technical assistance.

REFERENCES

1. Ellis, E. L., and Delbrück, M., *J. Gen. Physiol.*, 1939, **22,** 365.
2. Bordet, J., *Proc. Roy. Soc. London, Series B*, 1931, **107,** 398.
3. Krueger, A. P., and Northrop, J. H., *J. Gen. Physiol.*, 1930, **14,** 223.
4. Northrop, J. H., *J. Gen. Physiol.*, 1937, **21,** 335.
5. Northrop, J. H., *J. Gen. Physiol.*, 1939, **23,** 59.
6. Burnet, F. M., and McKie, M., *Australian J. Exp. Biol. and Med. Sc.*, 1929, **6,** 277.
7. Burnet, F. M., and Lush, D., *Australian J. Exp. Biol. and Med. Sc.*, 1936, **14,** 27.
8. Scribner, E. J., and Krueger, A. P., *J. Gen. Physiol.*, 1937, **21,** 1.
9. Krueger, A. P., and Strietmann, W. L., *J. Gen. Physiol.*, 1939, **22,** 131.
10. Delbrück, M., *J. Physic. Chem.*, 1940, **8,** 120.
11. Hershey, A. D., *J. Gen. Physiol.*, 1939, **23,** 11.
12. Bronfenbrenner, J., Muckenfuss, R. S., and Hetler, D. M., *Am. J. Path.*, 1927, **3,** 562.
13. Bayne-Jones, S., and Sandholzer, L. A., *J. Exp. Med.*, 1933, **57,** 279.

THE INTRACELLULAR GROWTH OF BACTERIOPHAGES

I. Liberation of Intracellular Bacteriophage T4 by Premature Lysis with Another Phage or with Cyanide

By A. H. DOERMANN*, ‡

(*From the Department of Genetics, Carnegie Institution of Washington, Cold Spring Harbor*)

(Received for publication, August 20, 1951)

Direct studies of bacteriophage reproduction have been handicapped by the fact that the cell wall of the infected bacterium presents a closed door to the investigator in the period between infection and lysis. As a result it was impossible to demonstrate the presence of intracellular phage particles during this so called latent period, and, much less, to estimate their number or to describe them genetically. This barrier has now been penetrated. It is the purpose of the first two papers of this series to describe two methods for disrupting infected bacteria in such a way that the intracellular phage particles can be counted and their genetic constitution analyzed.

The first method used to liberate intracellular bacteriophage depends on the induction of premature lysis in infected bacteria by "lysis from without" which occurs when a large excess of phage particles is adsorbed on bacteria (1). It was found by nephelometric tests that T6 lysates are efficient in disrupting cells when moderately high multiplicities are used (2). The further observation was made that the addition of a large number of T6 particles to bacteria previously infected with T4, would, under some conditions, cause liberation of T4 particles before the expiration of the normal latent period of these cells. It therefore seemed hopeful that a method of reproducibly disrupting infected bacteria could be developed on the basis of this preliminary knowledge.

* The experiments described here were carried out while the author was a fellow of the Carnegie Institution of Washington. The author is indebted to Dr. M. Demerec and the staff of the Department of Genetics of the Carnegie Institution of Washington for providing facilities for this work. In particular the stimulating discussions with Dr. Barbara McClintock are gratefully acknowledged. The manuscript was prepared while the author held a fellowship in the Department of Biology of the California Institute of Technology. He is grateful to Dr. G. W. Beadle and the staff of that department for their interest in this work, and especially to Dr. Max Delbrück for criticism of the manuscript.

‡ Present address: Biology Division, Oak Ridge National Laboratory, Oak Ridge, Tennessee.

Reprinted by permission of the author and The Rockefeller Institute from The Journal of General Physiology, **35** (4), 645-656, March 20, 1952.

The first experiments in devising a method of this kind were made with phage T5 (3). It was found that T5 is liberated before the end of the latent period if the infected cells are exposed to a high excess of T6. However, the extremely low rate of adsorption of T5 coupled with difficulties in inactivation of unadsorbed phage by specific antisera indicated that this phage was a poor choice. Hence T4 was chosen because of its fast rate of adsorption and because of the availability of high titer antisera against it. The first experiments with T4, along with the T5 results, showed conclusively that, by itself, lysis from without is not sufficiently rapid for the purpose of this investigation. It is likely that phage growth continues after the addition of the lysing agent T6. Therefore the attempt was made to stop phage growth while T6 was allowed to accomplish lysis from without. Low temperature could not be used for this purpose

TABLE I

Composition of the Growth Medium

Material	Amount
	gm. per liter
KH_2PO_4	1.5
Na_2HPO_4(anhydrous)	3.0
NH_4Cl	1.0
$MgSO_4 \cdot 7HOH$	0.2
Glycerol	10.0
Acid-hydrolyzed casein	5.0
dl-Tryptophan	0.01
Gelatin*	0.02
Tween-80	0.2

* To reduce surface inactivation of free phage particles (4).

since it also inhibits lysis from without. A search for a suitable metabolic inhibitor was therefore undertaken, and cyanide was eventually chosen as the most suitable one.

Materials and Methods

The experiments described here were carried out with the system $T4r_{48}$[1] growing at 37°C. in *Escherichia coli*, strain B/r/1. The latter is a T1 resistant, tryptophan-dependent mutant of B/r obtained from Dr. E. M. Witkin.

Two media were used in these experiments, namely the growth medium and the lysing medium. The composition of the growth medium used for both bacterial and phage cultures, is given in Table I. The lysing medium consists of growth medium with

[1] The subscript refers to a particular *r* mutant of T4 which arose by mutation and was numbered after the system of Hershey and Rotman (12) using the high subscript number to avoid confusion with the mutants already described by Hershey and Rotman.

the addition of one part in ten of a high titer T6 phage filtrate (concentration of T6 in lysing medium was *ca.* 4×10^9 particles per ml.) and cyanide brought to a final concentration of 0.01 M. Specially designed experiments showed that at this concentration the cyanide does not inactivate free phage particles, nor does the amount which reaches the plate affect titration by interference with plaque development.

T6 was used as the lysing phage because in several experiments it proved to be a more effective lysing agent than any of the other T phages tested. Since only single stocks of the phages were compared in the early experiments, the superiority of T6 over the other phages may have been due to a difference in the particular stock used, and not to an inherent difference among the phages. In fact, later experiments with different T6 stocks showed marked differences in lysing efficiency, and phage titer proved to be a poor criterion of lysing ability. The experiments described here were made with T6 stocks selected for their ability to induce lysis from without. The selections were made on the basis of nephelometric comparisons.

Platings were made in agar layer (0.7 per cent agar) poured over nutrient agar plates (1.3 per cent agar), and in order to assay T4 in the presence of high titer T6, the indicator strain, B/6, was used. B/6 is completely resistant to T6 (no host range mutants have so far been found which will lyse the strain used here) and gives full efficiency of plating (compared to B) with T4.

EXPERIMENTAL

Experiments with the Standard Lysing Medium.—The experimental procedure used consisted essentially of a one-step growth experiment (5) with certain modifications. B/r/1 cells in the exponential growth phase were concentrated by centrifugation to about 10^9 cells per ml. To these concentrated bacteria T4r_{48} was added and this adsorption mixture was incubated for 1 to 2 minutes with aeration, allowing at least 80 per cent of the phage to be adsorbed to the bacteria. Then a 40-fold or larger dilution was made into growth medium containing anti-T4 rabbit serum. The serum inactivated most of the residual unadsorbed phage. After several minutes' incubation in the serum tube, a further dilution was made to reduce the serum concentration to one of relative inactivity. The resulting culture will be referred to as the *source culture* (SC). The entire experiment was carried out with the infected bacteria from SC. The titer of infected B/r/1 in this tube was approximately 10^5 cells per ml.

Simultaneously with the dilution into the tube containing serum, another dilution from the adsorption tube was made. From the latter an estimation of the unadsorbed phage was made by assaying the supernatant after sedimentation of the cells. This step permits calculation of the multiplicity of infection (5).

From SC a further dilution of 1:20 was made at some time before the end of the latent period. The resulting culture, containing approximately 5×10^3 infected bacteria per ml., was used for determining the normal end of the latent period and for estimating the average yield of phage per infected cell. It will be called the *control growth tube* (GT). In addition, a number of precisely timed 20-fold dilutions were made from SC into lysing medium. These were titrated after they had been incubated in the lysing medium for 30 minutes or longer. Serial platings from the lysing medium cultures over a longer period of time have shown that the phage titer remained constant after 30 minutes' incubation. The titer calculated from these platings, divided by the titer of infected bacteria given by the preburst control platings, gives the average yield per infected cell. As a working hypothesis, this yield was considered to be the average number of intracellular phage particles per bacterium at the time of dilution into the lysing medium. Dividing these numbers by the control burst size gives the fraction of the control yield found in the experimental lysing medium tubes.

The results of several typical experiments are shown in Fig. 1 in which the data are plotted on semilogarithmic coordinates. The fraction of the control yield found in a given experimental culture is plotted against the time at which the dilution is made into lysing medium. Curve 1 shows the results from a single experiment in which the bacteria were infected with an average of 7 phage particles each. Curve 2 is the composite result of four experiments in which the bacteria were infected with single phage particles. Curve 3 is the control one-step growth curve derived from the control growth tube platings in the four experiments of curve 2.

Several striking results can be seen in these experiments. First, it is clearly seen that during the early stages of the latent period the virus-host complex is inactivated by the cyanide-T6 mixture, and that not even the infecting particles are recovered. Even when 7 phage particles were adsorbed on each bacterium, less than two are recovered per cell at the earliest stage tested, and the shape of the curve suggests that if earlier stages had been tested, still fewer would have been recovered. In experiments with singly infected bacteria, the earliest tests indicated that less than one infected bacterium in 80 liberated any phage at all. A second point to be noted is that the multiplicity of infection appears to influence slightly the time at which phage particles can be recovered from the cell, and it continues to affect the fraction found in the bacteria at a given time. That this difference is a real one seems clear from the consistency among the points of curve 2. This result has been observed in each experiment, although the effect appeared to be less pronounced in some experiments made at the lower temperature of 30°C. Attention should also be drawn to the fact that the shape of the curves is clearly not exponential. In fact, it parallels with a delay of several minutes the approximately linear DNA increase observed in this system (6).

In connection with the preceding experiments a test was made to establish whether the cyanide concentration chosen was maximally effective in inhibiting phage synthesis. Using the described technique, but changing the cyanide concentration of the lysing medium from 0.01 M to 0.004 M and 0.001 M in parallel aliquots, no difference was detectable in the three lysing media. Thus 0.01 M cyanide is well beyond the minimum concentration necessary and was considered to be adequate for these experiments.

Action of Cyanide in the Absence of the Lysing Agent T6.—Cohen and Anderson (7) reported a loss of infectious centers when infected bacteria were incubated in the presence of the antimetabolite 5-methyltryptophan. Although the details

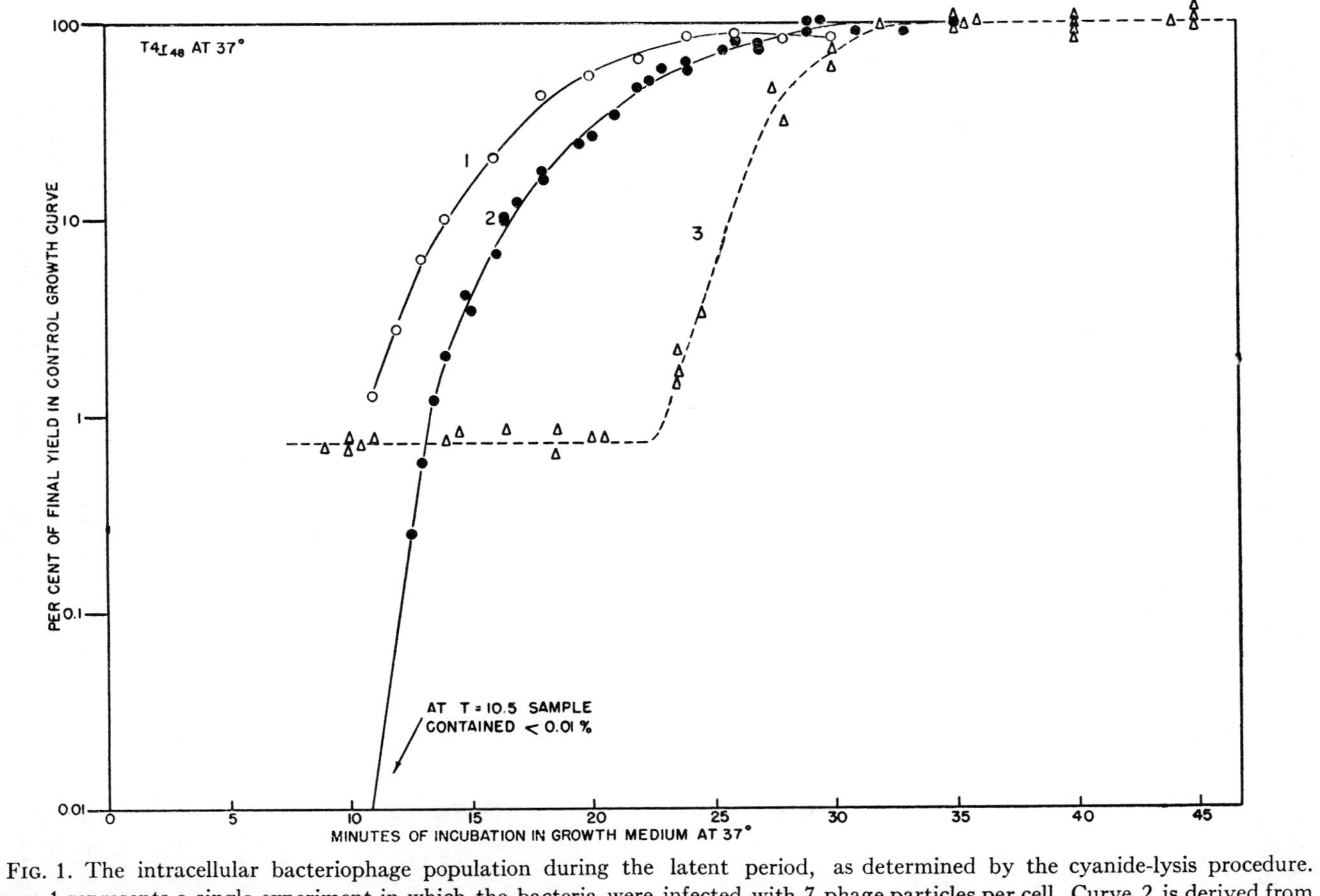

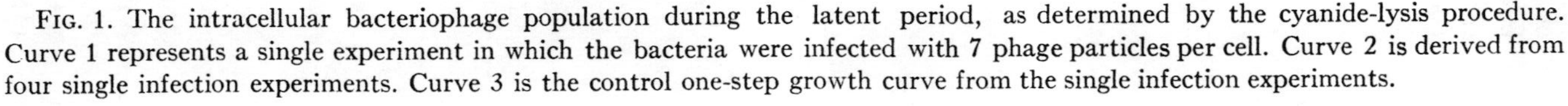

FIG. 1. The intracellular bacteriophage population during the latent period, as determined by the cyanide-lysis procedure. Curve 1 represents a single experiment in which the bacteria were infected with 7 phage particles per cell. Curve 2 is derived from four single infection experiments. Curve 3 is the control one-step growth curve from the single infection experiments.

of their experiments differed somewhat from those presented here, the loss of infectious centers in their experiments suggested testing whether cyanide could cause a similar loss of infected bacteria in the present procedure. An experiment was made which was identical with the standard cyanide lysis experiment

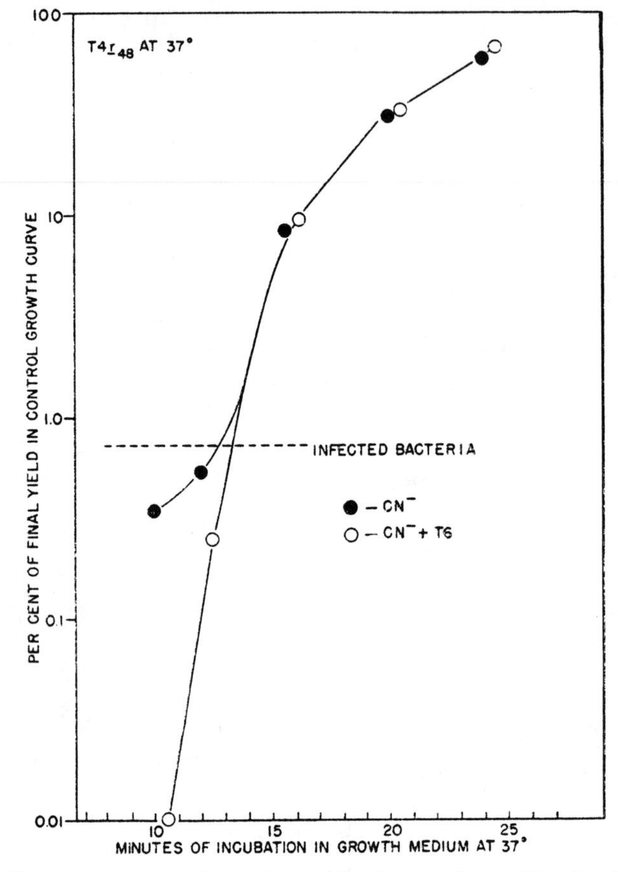

FIG. 2. The comparative effect of cyanide alone and cyanide plus T6 on singly infected bacteria at various stages in the latent period.

except that T6 was omitted from one set and included in a parallel set of lysing medium cultures (Fig. 2). As in the case of 5-methyltryptophan, it is seen that cyanide alone caused a loss of infectious centers when added in the early stages of phage growth, although the loss is less than that produced by cyanide and T6 together. Furthermore, in the second half of the latent period, comparison of the two media showed clearly and surprisingly that a definite *rise* in titer of infective centers occurred even when the lysing agent, T6, was omitted from the lysing medium. In fact, during the second half of the latent period, phage liberation is identical in the two media.

In order to see whether lysis is actually occurring and can account for the liberation of phage, a nephelometric experiment was made introducing CN^- at two points in the latent period. Three cultures of B/r/1 growing exponentially in growth medium were infected with T4r_{48} (*ca.* fivefold multiplicity). One culture served as a control for normal lysis. To the second culture cyanide (0.01 M final concentration) was added 7.5 minutes after addition of the virus and to

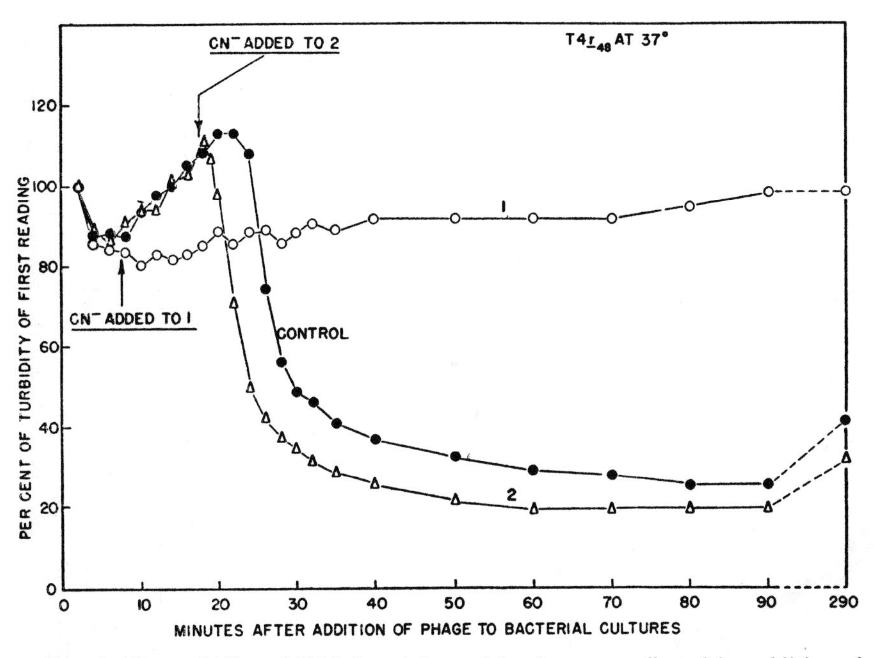

FIG. 3. The turbidity of T4-infected bacterial cultures as affected by addition of cyanide at two stages in the latent period.

the third tube 17.5 minutes after addition of the T4r_{48}. The turbidities of these three cultures were followed with a nephelometer designed like that described previously by Underwood and Doermann (8), but with four separate units which permit independent readings on the four tubes without removing any of them from the instrument. The results indicate that CN^- added to infected bacteria early during the latent period does not induce lysis (Fig. 3). From the plaque count experiment (Fig. 2) it is seen that a loss of infective centers does occur. This loss must therefore be due to some cause other than lysis of these cells. In the later stages of the latent period, the turbidimetric experiment indicates that lysis occurs promptly upon the addition of CN^- to the culture

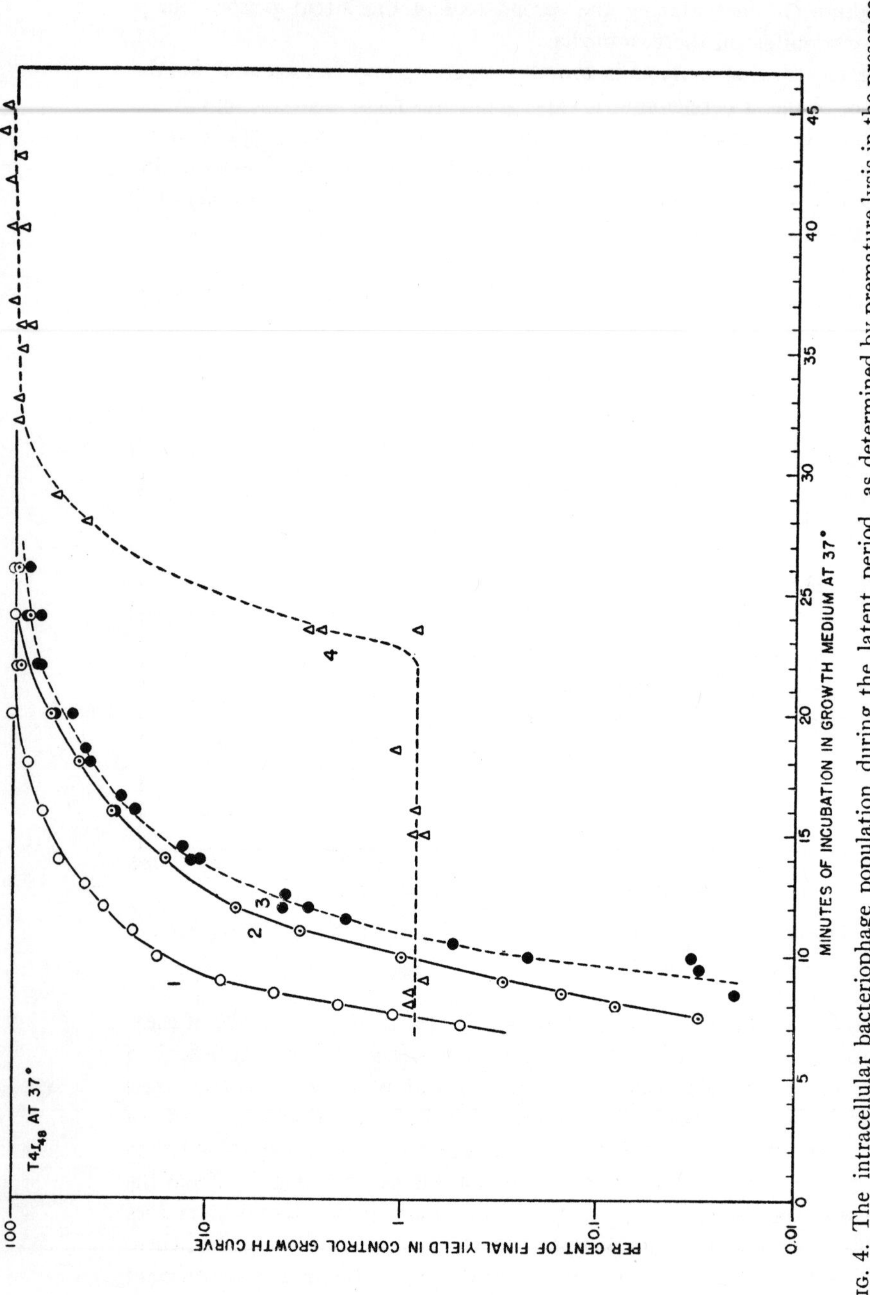

FIG. 4. The intracellular bacteriophage population during the latent period, as determined by premature lysis in the presence of 5-methyltryptophan. Curve 1 represents a multiple (fivefold) infection and curve 2 a single infection experiment with a different T4*r* mutant than that used in the other experiments described here. Curve 3 is a composite of three single infection experiments made with the same phage as was used in the cyanide experiments. Curve 4 is the standard one-step growth curve from the experiments which gave the data for curve 3.

(Fig. 3). The increase of infective centers in comparable cultures (Fig. 2) at these later stages is probably brought about by liberation of phage particles concurrent with this lysis.

Experiments Using 5-Methyltryptophan as the Metabolic Inhibitor.—In trying to find a suitable metabolic inhibitor for instantaneously stopping phage growth, a large number of experiments was done using the antimetabolite 5-methyltryptophan (5MT)[2] whose bacteriostatic action is blocked by tryptophan (9). The technique used was similar to the cyanide lysis procedure except that tryptophan was omitted from the lysing medium and 5MT was used in place of cyanide. The results (Fig. 4) are quite similar to the cyanide results in all respects except one. They are similar in failure to recover any phage particles during the early stages of the latent period, in the difference between single and multiple infection, and in the shapes of the curves. They are different, however, in that both the single and the multiple infection curves are moved to the left along the time scale by 3 to 4 minutes. This indicates that more phage is liberated per cell if lysis is induced in the presence of 5MT than if it is brought about in the presence of CN^-. This difference may be interpreted on the basis of two alternative hypotheses.

First, it might be suspected that CN^- penetrates the cell and reaches its site of inhibition more quickly than 5MT. This would allow more phage reproduction to go on between the time of exposure to the 5MT and the time at which the cell breaks open. In this event, a higher concentration of 5MT would enable penetration of an inhibitory amount in a shorter period of time, thus reducing the amount of phage found. To test this, the concentration of 5MT in the lysing medium was increased fivefold. No difference in the amount of phage liberated was found, suggesting that the rate of penetration of the poison is not limiting its effectiveness.

A second hypothesis is that the reaction blocked by 5MT may be one of the earlier ones involved in the synthesis of phage constituents. At the time of addition of 5MT many individual phages may already have acquired these constituents and thus be able to go on to maturity before lysis disperses the enzyme equipment of the infected cell. Cyanide, on the other hand, may block one of the terminal reactions in phage production, with the result that at a given time fewer individuals will have passed this reaction than will have passed the 5MT-inhibitable step. Consequently, fewer particles will be liberated when using cyanide than when 5MT is used.

DISCUSSION

Earlier experiments (2) and tests made of the lysing efficiency of the T6 stocks used here indicate that rapid lysis occurs when T6 stocks are added in

[2] Obtained through the courtesy of Dr. M. L. Tainter, Sterling-Winthrop Research Institute, Rensselaer, New York.

sufficient concentration to bacterial cultures. The very first experiments with bacteria infected with T5 (3) left no doubt that lysis from without by T6 will liberate T5 particles prematurely from infected bacteria. From the evidence contained in the present paper it cannot be definitely established whether the combined action of T6 and cyanide liberates all of the mature phage present in the cells. However, the fact that, during the terminal stages of intracellular development, the cyanide-lysis method yields as much phage as does spontaneous lysis, suggests that the cyanide method liberates all of the mature phage. Furthermore, during the second half of the latent period, exactly the same amount of phage is liberated by cyanide alone as by cyanide plus T6. This suggests that cyanide acts promptly in arresting phage growth. Otherwise one would expect to find a consistently higher number of phage particles in the cyanide medium than in the medium in which cyanide and T6 are combined. The experiments presented here therefore warrant the working hypothesis that mature intracellular phage is effectively liberated by the treatment described, and that the method gives a true picture of the intracellular phage population. The validity of this working hypothesis will be conclusively demonstrated for the phage T3 in the second paper of this series (10).

The bearing of the present experiments on our concept of phage reproduction might be discussed here. The finding that the original infecting particles are not recoverable from the cells during the first stages of the latent period appears at first sight surprising. Nevertheless some indirect evidence indicates that this is to be expected. The discovery that yields from mixedly infected bacteria may contain new combinations of the genetic material of the infecting types (11–13) suggests that some alteration of the infecting particles may occur. Furthermore, in mixed infections of bacteria with unrelated phages only one type is reproduced. The other type, although adsorbed on the cells, it not only prevented from multiplying but the infecting particle of that type is lost (5, 14). On the basis of multiple infection experiments with ultraviolet-inactivated phage particles, Luria (15) has proposed that reproduction of phage occurs by reproduction of subunits which are at some later stage assembled into complete virus particles. The failure to find infective phage particles within the infected cell in the early stages of reproduction agrees with what would have been predicted from these experiments.

The results of our experiments agree quite well with the scheme which Latarjet (16) suggested on the basis of x-ray inactivation studies of phage inside infected bacteria. Latarjet differentiated three segments of the latent period of phage growth. Using T2 he found that during the first segment of 6 to 7 minutes' duration, singly infected bacteria show the same inactivation characteristics as do unadsorbed phage particles. In the second period, from time 7 to time 13 minutes, the phage in infected cells became more resistant to x-rays, even during the first 2 minutes of this segment in which the inactivation curves still retain a single hit character. During the last 4 minutes of this period the curves take on a multiple hit character. In the final segment, from time 13 minutes to the end of the latent period, the curves retain the multiple hit character, but gradually regain the original x-ray sensitivity characteristic of free phage. These x-ray experiments suggest again that a rather drastic alteration occurs to the infecting particle, and that particles with the original characteristics are not found in the cell until the second half of the latent period. This is precisely what is observed in the results presented here. Our experiments were done with T4, but comparison seems legitimate since the two viruses are quite closely related (17).

Results of a similar nature to those discussed here were published by Foster (18). In studying the effect of proflavine on the growth of phage T2, Foster found that the time at which this poison was added influenced the amount of phage liberated by the bacteria. No phage is liberated from T2-infected cells (latent period 21 minutes) if proflavine is added during the first 12 minutes after infection even though lysis of the cells does occur at the normal time. When proflavine is added at later points in the latent period, lysis yields phage particles, the number depending on the time of proflavine addition. When the results of these single infection experiments are compared to the cyanide single infection experiments (Fig. 1) the results are seen to be quite similar. From other experiments Foster concluded that proflavine inhibits one of the final stages in the formation of fully infective phage. These facts, taken together, suggests that proflavine experiments were, in fact, measuring intracellular phage.

SUMMARY

A method is described for liberating and estimating intracellular bacteriophage at any stage during the latent period by arresting phage growth and inducing premature lysis of the infected cells. This is brought about by placing the infected bacteria into the growth medium supplemented with 0.01 M cyanide and with a high titer T6 lysate. It was found in some of the later experiments that the T6 lysate is essential only during the first half of the latent period. Cyanide alone will induce lysis during the latter part of the latent period.

Using this method on T4-infected bacteria it is found that during the first half of the latent period no phage particles, not even those originally infecting the bacteria, are recovered. This result is in agreement with the gradually emerging concept that a profound alteration of the infecting phage particle takes place before reproduction ensues. During the second half of the latent period mature phage is found to accumulate within the bacteria at a rate which is parallel to the approximately linear increase of intracellular DNA in this system. However, the phage production lags several minutes behind DNA production.

When 5-methyltryptophan replaced cyanide as the metabolic inhibitor, similar results were obtained. The curves were, however, displaced several minutes to the left on the time axis.

The results are compared with Latarjet's (16) data on x-radiation of infected bacteria and with Foster's data (18) concerning the effect of proflavine on infected bacteria. Essential agreement with both is apparent.

BIBLIOGRAPHY

1. Delbrück, M., *J. Gen. Physiol.*, 1940, **23,** 643.
2. Doermann, A. H., *J. Bact.*, 1948, **55,** 257.
3. Doermann, A. H., *Ann. Rep. Biol. Lab., Long Island Biol. Assn.*, 1946, 22.
4. Adams, M. H., *J. Gen. Physiol.*, 1948, **31,** 417.
5. Delbrück, M., and Luria, S. E., *Arch. Biochem.*, 1942, **1,** 111.
6. Cohen, S. S., *Bact. Rev.*, 1949, **13,** 1.
7. Cohen, S. S., and Anderson, T. F., *J. Exp. Med.*, 1946, **84,** 525.
8. Underwood, N., and Doermann, A. H., *Rev. Scient. Instr.*, 1947, **18,** 665.
9. Anderson, T. F., *Science*, 1945, **101,** 565.
10. Anderson, T. F., and Doermann, A. H., *J. Gen. Physiol.*, 1952, **35,** 657.
11. Delbrück, M., and Bailey, W. T., Jr., *Cold Spring Harbor Symp. Quant. Biol.*, 1946, **11,** 33.
12. Hershey, A. D., and Rotman, R., *Proc. Nat. Acad. Sc.*, 1948, **34,** 89.
13. Hershey, A. D., and Rotman, R., *Genetics*, 1949, **34,** 44.
14. Delbrück, M., *J. Bact.*, 1945, **50,** 151.
15. Luria, S. E., *Proc. Nat. Acad. Sc.*, 1947, **33,** 253.
16. Latarjet, R., *J. Gen. Physiol.*, 1948, **31,** 529.
17. Adams, M. H., *in* Methods in Medical Research, (J. H. Comroe, editor), Chicago, The Yearbook Publishers, Inc., 1950, **2,** 1.
18. Foster, R. A. C., *J. Bact.*, 1948, **56,** 795.

INDEPENDENT FUNCTIONS OF VIRAL PROTEIN AND NUCLEIC ACID IN GROWTH OF BACTERIOPHAGE*

By A. D. HERSHEY and MARTHA CHASE

(*From the Department of Genetics, Carnegie Institution of Washington, Cold Spring Harbor, Long Island*)

(Received for publication, April 9, 1952)

The work of Doermann (1948), Doermann and Dissosway (1949), and Anderson and Doermann (1952) has shown that bacteriophages T2, T3, and T4 multiply in the bacterial cell in a non-infective form. The same is true of the phage carried by certain lysogenic bacteria (Lwoff and Gutmann, 1950). Little else is known about the vegetative phase of these viruses. The experiments reported in this paper show that one of the first steps in the growth of T2 is the release from its protein coat of the nucleic acid of the virus particle, after which the bulk of the sulfur-containing protein has no further function.

Materials and Methods.—Phage T2 means in this paper the variety called T2H (Hershey, 1946); T2*h* means one of the host range mutants of T2; UV-phage means phage irradiated with ultraviolet light from a germicidal lamp (General Electric Co.) to a fractional survival of 10^{-5}.

Sensitive bacteria means a strain (H) of *Escherichia coli* sensitive to T2 and its *h* mutant; resistant bacteria B/2 means a strain resistant to T2 but sensitive to its *h* mutant; resistant bacteria B/2*h* means a strain resistant to both. These bacteria do not adsorb the phages to which they are resistant.

"Salt-poor" broth contains per liter 10 gm. bacto-peptone, 1 gm. glucose, and 1 gm. NaCl. "Broth" contains, in addition, 3 gm. bacto-beef extract and 4 gm. NaCl.

Glycerol-lactate medium contains per liter 70 mM sodium lactate, 4 gm. glycerol, 5 gm. NaCl, 2 gm. KCl, 1 gm. NH_4Cl, 1 mM $MgCl_2$, 0.1 mM $CaCl_2$, 0.01 gm. gelatin, 10 mg. P (as orthophosphate), and 10 mg. S (as $MgSO_4$), at pH 7.0.

Adsorption medium contains per liter 4 gm. NaCl, 5 gm. K_2SO_4, 1.5 gm. KH_2PO_4, 3.0 gm. Na_2HPO_4, 1 mM $MgSO_4$, 0.1 mM $CaCl_2$, and 0.01 gm. gelatin, at pH 7.0.

Veronal buffer contains per liter 1 gm. sodium diethylbarbiturate, 3 mM $MgSO_4$, and 1 gm. gelatin, at pH 8.0.

The HCN referred to in this paper consists of molar sodium cyanide solution neutralized when needed with phosphoric acid.

---

* This investigation was supported in part by a research grant from the National Microbiological Institute of the National Institutes of Health, Public Health Service. Radioactive isotopes were supplied by the Oak Ridge National Laboratory on allocation from the Isotopes Division, United States Atomic Energy Commission.

Reprinted by permission of the authors and The Rockefeller Institute from THE JOURNAL OF GENERAL PHYSIOLOGY, **36** (1), 39-56, September 20, 1952.

Adsorption of isotope to bacteria was usually measured by mixing the sample in adsorption medium with bacteria from 18 hour broth cultures previously heated to 70°C. for 10 minutes and washed with adsorption medium. The mixtures were warmed for 5 minutes at 37°C., diluted with water, and centrifuged. Assays were made of both sediment and supernatant fractions.

Precipitation of isotope with antiserum was measured by mixing the sample in 0.5 per cent saline with about 10^{11} per ml. of non-radioactive phage and slightly more than the least quantity of antiphage serum (final dilution 1:160) that would cause visible precipitation. The mixture was centrifuged after 2 hours at 37°C.

Tests with DNase (desoxyribonuclease) were performed by warming samples diluted in veronal buffer for 15 minutes at 37°C. with 0.1 mg. per ml. of crystalline enzyme (Worthington Biochemical Laboratory).

Acid-soluble isotope was measured after the chilled sample had been precipitated with 5 per cent trichloroacetic acid in the presence of 1 mg./ml. of serum albumin, and centrifuged.

In all fractionations involving centrifugation, the sediments were not washed, and contained about 5 per cent of the supernatant. Both fractions were assayed.

Radioactivity was measured by means of an end-window Geiger counter, using dried samples sufficiently small to avoid losses by self-absorption. For absolute measurements, reference solutions of P^{32} obtained from the National Bureau of Standards, as well as a permanent simulated standard, were used. For absolute measurements of S^{35} we relied on the assays (± 20 per cent) furnished by the supplier of the isotope (Oak Ridge National Laboratory).

Glycerol-lactate medium was chosen to permit growth of bacteria without undesirable pH changes at low concentrations of phosphorus and sulfur, and proved useful also for certain experiments described in this paper. 18-hour cultures of sensitive bacteria grown in this medium contain about 2×10^9 cells per ml., which grow exponentially without lag or change in light-scattering per cell when subcultured in the same medium from either large or small seedings. The generation time is 1.5 hours at 37°C. The cells are smaller than those grown in broth. T2 shows a latent period of 22 to 25 minutes in this medium. The phage yield obtained by lysis with cyanide and UV-phage (described in context) is one per bacterium at 15 minutes and 16 per bacterium at 25 minutes. The final burst size in diluted cultures is 30 to 40 per bacterium, reached at 50 minutes. At 2×10^8 cells per ml., the culture lyses slowly, and yields 140 phage per bacterium. The growth of both bacteria and phage in this medium is as reproducible as that in broth.

For the preparation of radioactive phage, P^{32} of specific activity 0.5 mc./mg. or S^{35} of specific activity 8.0 mc./mg. was incorporated into glycerol-lactate medium, in which bacteria were allowed to grow at least 4 hours before seeding with phage. After infection with phage, the culture was aerated overnight, and the radioactive phage was isolated by three cycles of alternate slow (2000 *G*) and fast (12,000 *G*) centrifugation in adsorption medium. The suspensions were stored at a concentration not exceeding 4 μc./ml.

Preparations of this kind contain 1.0 to 3.0×10^{-12} μg. S and 2.5 to 3.5×10^{-11} μg. P per viable phage particle. Occasional preparations containing excessive amounts of sulfur can be improved by absorption with heat-killed bacteria that do not adsorb the phage. The radiochemical purity of the preparations is somewhat uncertain, owing to the possible presence of inactive phage particles and empty phage membranes. The presence in our preparations of sulfur (about 20 per cent) that is precipitated by antiphage serum (Table I) and either adsorbed by bacteria resistant to phage, or not adsorbed by bacteria sensitive to phage (Table VII), indicates contamination by membrane material. Contaminants of bacterial origin are probably negligible for present purposes as indicated by the data given in Table I. For proof that our principal findings reflect genuine properties of viable phage particles, we rely on some experiments with inactivated phage cited at the conclusion of this paper.

The Chemical Morphology of Resting Phage Particles.—Anderson (1949) found that bacteriophage T2 could be inactivated by suspending the particles in high concentrations of sodium chloride, and rapidly diluting the suspension with water. The inactivated phage was visible in electron micrographs as tadpole-shaped "ghosts." Since no inactivation occurred if the dilution was slow

TABLE I

Composition of Ghosts and Solution of Plasmolyzed Phage

Per cent of isotope]	Whole phage labeled with		Plasmolyzed phage labeled with	
	P^{32}	S^{35}	P^{32}	S^{35}
Acid-soluble	—	—	1	—
Acid-soluble after treatment with DNase	1	1	80	1
Adsorbed to sensitive bacteria	85	90	2	90
Precipitated by antiphage	90	99	5	97

he attributed the inactivation to osmotic shock, and inferred that the particles possessed an osmotic membrane. Herriott (1951) found that osmotic shock released into solution the DNA (desoxypentose nucleic acid) of the phage particle, and that the ghosts could adsorb to bacteria and lyse them. He pointed out that this was a beginning toward the identification of viral functions with viral substances.

We have plasmolyzed isotopically labeled T2 by suspending the phage (10^{11} per ml.) in 3 M sodium chloride for 5 minutes at room temperature, and rapidly pouring into the suspension 40 volumes of distilled water. The plasmolyzed phage, containing not more than 2 per cent survivors, was then analyzed for phosphorus and sulfur in the several ways shown in Table I. The results confirm and extend previous findings as follows:—

1. Plasmolysis separates phage T2 into ghosts containing nearly all the sulfur and a solution containing nearly all the DNA of the intact particles.

2. The ghosts contain the principal antigens of the phage particle detectable by our antiserum. The DNA is released as the free acid, or possibly linked to sulfur-free, apparently non-antigenic substances.

3. The ghosts are specifically adsorbed to phage-susceptible bacteria; the DNA is not.

4. The ghosts represent protein coats that surround the DNA of the intact particles, react with antiserum, protect the DNA from DNase (desoxyribonuclease), and carry the organ of attachment to bacteria.

5. The effects noted are due to osmotic shock, because phage suspended in salt and diluted slowly is not inactivated, and its DNA is not exposed to DNase.

TABLE II

Sensitization of Phage DNA to DNase by Adsorption to Bacteria

Phage adsorbed to		Phage labeled with	Non-sedimentable isotope, *per cent*	
			After DNase	No DNase
Live bacteria		S^{35}	2	1
" "		P^{32}	8	7
Bacteria heated before infection		S^{35}	15	11
" " " "		P^{32}	76	13
Bacteria heated after infection		S^{35}	12	14
" " " "		P^{32}	66	23
Heated unadsorbed phage: acid-soluble P^{32}	70°	P^{32}	5	
	80°	P^{32}	13	
	90°	P^{32}	81	
	100°	P^{32}	88	

Phage adsorbed to bacteria for 5 minutes at 37°C. in adsorption medium, followed by washing.

Bacteria heated for 10 minutes at 80°C. in adsorption medium (before infection) or in veronal buffer (after infection).

Unadsorbed phage heated in veronal buffer, treated with DNase, and precipitated with trichloroacetic acid.

All samples fractionated by centrifuging 10 minutes at 1300 *G*.

Sensitization of Phage DNA to DNase by Adsorption to Bacteria.—The structure of the resting phage particle described above suggests at once the possibility that multiplication of virus is preceded by the alteration or removal of the protective coats of the particles. This change might be expected to show itself as a sensitization of the phage DNA to DNase. The experiments described in Table II show that this happens. The results may be summarized as follows:—

1. Phage DNA becomes largely sensitive to DNase after adsorption to heat-killed bacteria.

2. The same is true of the DNA of phage adsorbed to live bacteria, and then

heated to 80°C. for 10 minutes, at which temperature unadsorbed phage is not sensitized to DNase.

3. The DNA of phage adsorbed to unheated bacteria is resistant to DNase, presumably because it is protected by cell structures impervious to the enzyme.

Graham and collaborators (personal communication) were the first to discover the sensitization of phage DNA to DNase by adsorption to heat-killed bacteria.

The DNA in infected cells is also made accessible to DNase by alternate freezing and thawing (followed by formaldehyde fixation to inactivate cellular enzymes), and to some extent by formaldehyde fixation alone, as illustrated by the following experiment.

Bacteria were grown in broth to 5×10^7 cells per ml., centrifuged, resuspended in adsorption medium, and infected with about two P^{32}-labeled phage per bacterium. After 5 minutes for adsorption, the suspension was diluted with water containing per liter 1.0 mM $MgSO_4$, 0.1 mM $CaCl_2$, and 10 mg. gelatin, and recentrifuged. The cells were resuspended in the fluid last mentioned at a concentration of 5×10^8 per ml. This suspension was frozen at −15°C. and thawed with a minimum of warming, three times in succession. Immediately after the third thawing, the cells were fixed by the addition of 0.5 per cent (*v/v*) of formalin (35 per cent HCHO). After 30 minutes at room temperature, the suspension was dialyzed free from formaldehyde and centrifuged at 2200 *G* for 15 minutes. Samples of P^{32}-labeled phage, frozen-thawed, fixed, and dialyzed, and of infected cells fixed only and dialyzed, were carried along as controls.

The analysis of these materials, given in Table III, shows that the effect of freezing and thawing is to make the intracellular DNA labile to DNase, without, however, causing much of it to leach out of the cells. Freezing and thawing and formaldehyde fixation have a negligible effect on unadsorbed phage, and formaldehyde fixation alone has only a mild effect on infected cells.

Both sensitization of the intracellular P^{32} to DNase, and its failure to leach out of the cells, are constant features of experiments of this type, independently of visible lysis. In the experiment just described, the frozen suspension cleared during the period of dialysis. Phase-contrast microscopy showed that the cells consisted largely of empty membranes, many apparently broken. In another experiment, samples of infected bacteria from a culture in salt-poor broth were repeatedly frozen and thawed at various times during the latent period of phage growth, fixed with formaldehyde, and then washed in the centrifuge. Clearing and microscopic lysis occurred only in suspensions frozen during the second half of the latent period, and occurred during the first or second thawing. In this case the lysed cells consisted wholly of intact cell membranes, appearing empty except for a few small, rather characteristic refractile bodies apparently attached to the cell walls. The behavior of intracellular P^{32} toward DNase, in either the lysed or unlysed cells, was not significantly different from that shown in Table III, and the content of P^{32} was only slightly less after lysis. The phage liberated during freezing and thawing was also titrated in this experiment. The lysis occurred without appreciable liberation of phage in suspensions frozen up to and including the 16th minute, and the 20 minute sample yielded only five per bacterium. Another sample of the culture formalinized at 30 minutes, and centrifuged without freezing, contained 66 per cent of the P^{32} in non-sedimentable form. The yield of extracellular phage at 30 minutes was 108 per bacterium, and the sedimented material consisted largely of formless debris but contained also many apparently intact cell membranes.

TABLE III

Sensitization of Intracellular Phage to DNase by Freezing, Thawing, and Fixation with Formaldehyde

	Unadsorbed phage frozen, thawed, fixed	Infected cells frozen, thawed, fixed	Infected cells fixed only
Low speed sediment fraction			
Total P^{32}	—	71	86
Acid-soluble	—	0	0.5
Acid-soluble after DNase	—	59	28
Low speed supernatant fraction			
Total P^{32}	—	29	14
Acid-soluble	1	0.8	0.4
Acid-soluble after DNase	11	21	5.5

The figures express per cent of total P^{32} in the original phage, or its adsorbed fraction.

We draw the following conclusions from the experiments in which cells infected with P^{32}-labeled phage are subjected to freezing and thawing.

1. Phage DNA becomes sensitive to DNAse after adsorption to bacteria in buffer under conditions in which no known growth process occurs (Benzer, 1952; Dulbecco, 1952).

2. The cell membrane can be made permeable to DNase under conditions that do not permit the escape of either the intracellular P^{32} or the bulk of the cell contents.

3. Even if the cells lyse as a result of freezing and thawing, permitting escape of other cell constituents, most of the P^{32} derived from phage remains inside the cell membranes, as do the mature phage progeny.

4. The intracellular P^{32} derived from phage is largely freed during spontaneous lysis accompanied by phage liberation.

We interpret these facts to mean that intracellular DNA derived from phage is not merely DNA in solution, but is part of an organized structure at all times during the latent period.

Liberation of DNA from Phage Particles by Adsorption to Bacterial Fragments.—The sensitization of phage DNA to specific depolymerase by adsorption to bacteria might mean that adsorption is followed by the ejection of the phage DNA from its protective coat. The following experiment shows that this is in fact what happens when phage attaches to fragmented bacterial cells.

TABLE IV

Release of DNA from Phage Adsorbed to Bacterial Debris

	Phage labeled with	
	S^{35}	P^{32}
Sediment fraction		
Surviving phage	16	22
Total isotope	87	55
Acid-soluble isotope	0	2
Acid-soluble after DNase	2	29
Supernatant fraction		
Surviving phage	5	5
Total isotope	13	45
Acid-soluble isotope	0.8	0.5
Acid-soluble after DNase	0.8	39

S^{35}- and P^{32}-labeled T2 were mixed with identical samples of bacterial debris in adsorption medium and warmed for 30 minutes at 37°C. The mixtures were then centrifuged for 15 minutes at 2200 *G*, and the sediment and supernatant fractions were analyzed separately. The results are expressed as per cent of input phage or isotope.

Bacterial debris was prepared by infecting cells in adsorption medium with four particles of T2 per bacterium, and transferring the cells to salt-poor broth at 37°C. The culture was aerated for 60 minutes, M/50 HCN was added, and incubation continued for 30 minutes longer. At this time the yield of extracellular phage was 400 particles per bacterium, which remained unadsorbed because of the low concentration of electrolytes. The debris from the lysed cells was washed by centrifugation at 1700 *G*, and resuspended in adsorption medium at a concentration equivalent to 3×10^9 lysed cells per ml. It consisted largely of collapsed and fragmented cell membranes. The adsorption of radioactive phage to this material is described in Table IV. The following facts should be noted.

1. The unadsorbed fraction contained only 5 per cent of the original phage particles in infective form, and only 13 per cent of the total sulfur. (Much of this sulfur must be the material that is not adsorbable to whole bacteria.)

2. About 80 per cent of the phage was inactivated. Most of the sulfur of this phage, as well as most of the surviving phage, was found in the sediment fraction.

3. The supernatant fraction contained 40 per cent of the total phage DNA (in a form labile to DNase) in addition to the DNA of the unadsorbed surviving phage. The labile DNA amounted to about half of the DNA of the inactivated phage particles, whose sulfur sedimented with the bacterial debris.

4. Most of the sedimentable DNA could be accounted for either as surviving phage, or as DNA labile to DNase, the latter amounting to about half the DNA of the inactivated particles.

Experiments of this kind are unsatisfactory in one respect: one cannot tell whether the liberated DNA represents all the DNA of some of the inactivated particles, or only part of it.

Similar results were obtained when bacteria (strain B) were lysed by large amounts of UV-killed phage T2 or T4 and then tested with P^{32}-labeled T2 and T4. The chief point of interest in this experiment is that bacterial debris saturated with UV-killed T2 adsorbs T4 better than T2, and debris saturated with T4 adsorbs T2 better than T4. As in the preceding experiment, some of the adsorbed phage was not inactivated and some of the DNA of the inactivated phage was not released from the debris.

These experiments show that some of the cell receptors for T2 are different from some of the cell receptors for T4, and that phage attaching to these specific receptors is inactivated by the same mechanism as phage attaching to unselected receptors. This mechanism is evidently an active one, and not merely the blocking of sites of attachment to bacteria.

Removal of Phage Coats from Infected Bacteria.—Anderson (1951) has obtained electron micrographs indicating that phage T2 attaches to bacteria by its tail. If this precarious attachment is preserved during the progress of the infection, and if the conclusions reached above are correct, it ought to be a simple matter to break the empty phage membranes off the infected bacteria, leaving the phage DNA inside the cells.

The following experiments show that this is readily accomplished by strong shearing forces applied to suspensions of infected cells, and further that infected cells from which 80 per cent of the sulfur of the parent virus has been removed remain capable of yielding phage progeny.

Broth-grown bacteria were infected with S^{35}- or P^{32}-labeled phage in adsorption medium, the unadsorbed material was removed by centrifugation, and the cells were resuspended in water containing per liter 1 mM $MgSO_4$, 0.1 mM $CaCl_2$, and 0.1 gm. gelatin. This suspension was spun in a Waring blendor (semimicro size) at 10,000 R.P.M. The suspension was cooled briefly in ice water at the end of each 60 second running period. Samples were removed at intervals, titrated (through antiphage serum) to measure the number of bacteria capable of yielding phage, and centrifuged to measure the proportion of isotope released from the cells.

The results of one experiment with each isotope are shown in Fig. 1. The data for S^{35} and survival of infected bacteria come from the same experiment, in which the ratio of added phage to bacteria was 0.28, and the concentrations

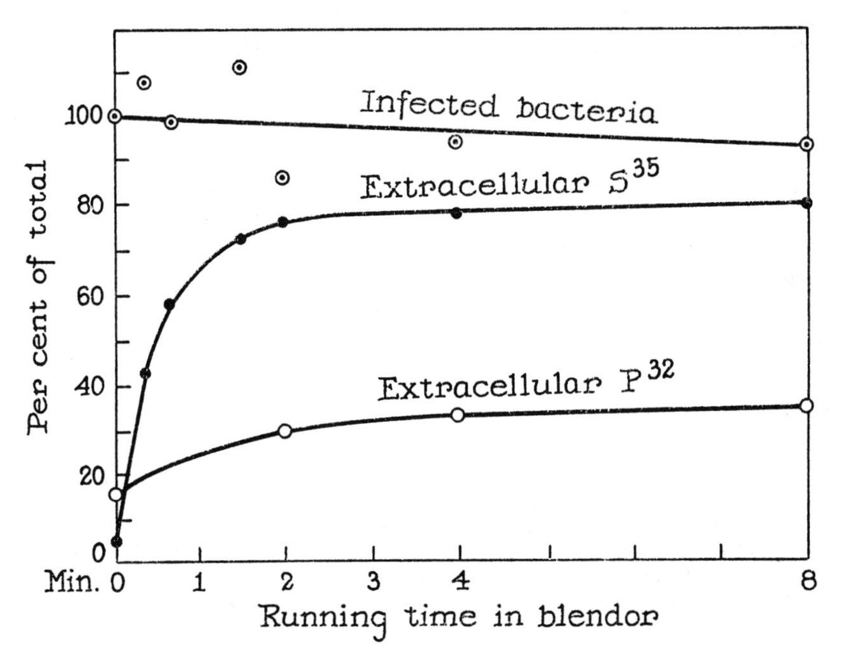

FIG. 1. Removal of S^{35} and P^{32} from bacteria infected with radioactive phage, and survival of the infected bacteria, during agitation in a Waring blendor.

of bacteria were 2.5×10^8 per ml. infected, and 9.7×10^8 per ml. total, by direct titration. The experiment with P^{32}-labeled phage was very similar. In connection with these results, it should be recalled that Anderson (1949) found that adsorption of phage to bacteria could be prevented by rapid stirring of the suspension.

At higher ratios of infection, considerable amounts of phage sulfur elute from the cells spontaneously under the conditions of these experiments, though the elution of P^{32} and the survival of infected cells are not affected by multiplicity of infection (Table V). This shows that there is a cooperative action among phage particles in producing alterations of the bacterial membrane which weaken the attachment of the phage. The cellular changes detected in this way may be related to those responsible for the release of bacterial components from infected bacteria (Prater, 1951; Price, 1952).

A variant of the preceding experiments was designed to test bacteria at a later stage in the growth of phage. For this purpose infected cells were aerated in broth for 5 or 15 minutes, fixed by the addition of 0.5 per cent (*v/v*) commercial formalin, centrifuged, resuspended in 0.1 per cent formalin in water, and subsequently handled as described above. The results were very similar to those already presented, except that the release of P^{32} from the cells was slightly less, and titrations of infected cells could not be made.

The S^{35}-labeled material detached from infected cells in the manner described possesses the following properties. It is sedimented at 12,000 *G*, though less completely than intact phage particles. It is completely precipitated by

TABLE V

Effect of Multiplicity of Infection on Elution of Phage Membranes from Infected Bacteria

Running time in blendor	Multiplicity of infection	P^{32}-labeled phage		S^{35}-labeled phage	
		Isotope eluted	Infected bacteria surviving	Isotope eluted	Infected bacteria surviving
min.		*per cent*	*per cent*	*per cent*	*per cent*
0	0.6	10	120	16	101
2.5	0.6	21	82	81	78
0	6.0	13	89	46	90
2.5	6.0	24	86	82	85

The infected bacteria were suspended at 10^9 cells per ml. in water containing per liter 1 mM $MgSO_4$, 0.1 mM $CaCl_2$, and 0.1 gm. gelatin. Samples were withdrawn for assay of extracellular isotope and infected bacteria before and after agitating the suspension. In either case the cells spent about 15 minutes at room temperature in the eluting fluid.

antiphage serum in the presence of whole phage carrier. 40 to 50 per cent of it readsorbs to sensitive bacteria, almost independently of bacterial concentration between 2×10^8 and 10^9 cells per ml., in 5 minutes at 37°C. The adsorption is not very specific: 10 to 25 per cent adsorbs to phage-resistant bacteria under the same conditions. The adsorption requires salt, and for this reason the efficient removal of S^{35} from infected bacteria can be accomplished only in a fluid poor in electrolytes.

The results of these experiments may be summarized as follows:—

1. 75 to 80 per cent of the phage sulfur can be stripped from infected cells by violent agitation of the suspension. At high multiplicity of infection, nearly 50 per cent elutes spontaneously. The properties of the S^{35}-labeled material show that it consists of more or less intact phage membranes, most of which have lost the ability to attach specifically to bacteria.

2. The release of sulfur is accompanied by the release of only 21 to 35 per

cent of the phage phosphorus, half of which is given up without any mechanical agitation.

3. The treatment does not cause any appreciable inactivation of intracellular phage.

4. These facts show that the bulk of the phage sulfur remains at the cell surface during infection, and takes no part in the multiplication of intracellular phage. The bulk of the phage DNA, on the other hand, enters the cell soon after adsorption of phage to bacteria.

Transfer of Sulfur and Phosphorus from Parental Phage to Progeny.—We have concluded above that the bulk of the sulfur-containing protein of the resting phage particle takes no part in the multiplication of phage, and in fact does not enter the cell. It follows that little or no sulfur should be transferred from parental phage to progeny. The experiments described below show that this expectation is correct, and that the maximal transfer is of the order 1 per cent

Bacteria were grown in glycerol-lactate medium overnight and subcultured in the same medium for 2 hours at 37°C. with aeration, the size of seeding being adjusted nephelometrically to yield 2×10^8 cells per ml. in the subculture. These bacteria were sedimented, resuspended in adsorption medium at a concentration of 10^9 cells per ml., and infected with S^{35}-labeled phage T2. After 5 minutes at 37°C., the suspension was diluted with 2 volumes of water and resedimented to remove unadsorbed phage (5 to 10 per cent by titer) and S^{35} (about 15 per cent). The cells were next suspended in glycerol-lactate medium at a concentration of 2×10^8 per ml. and aerated at 37°C. Growth of phage was terminated at the desired time by adding in rapid succession 0.02 mM HCN and 2×10^{11} UV-killed phage per ml. of culture. The cyanide stops the maturation of intracellular phage (Doermann, 1948), and the UV-killed phage minimizes losses of phage progeny by adsorption to bacterial debris, and promotes the lysis of bacteria (Maaløe and Watson, 1951). As mentioned in another connection, and also noted in these experiments, the lysing phage must be closely related to the phage undergoing multiplication (*e.g.*, T2H, its *h* mutant, or T2L, but not T4 or T6, in this instance) in order to prevent inactivation of progeny by adsorption to bacterial debris.

To obtain what we shall call the maximal yield of phage, the lysing phage was added 25 minutes after placing the infected cells in the culture medium, and the cyanide was added at the end of the 2nd hour. Under these conditions, lysis of infected cells occurs rather slowly.

Aeration was interrupted when the cyanide was added, and the cultures were left overnight at 37°C. The lysates were then fractionated by centrifugation into an initial low speed sediment (2500 *G* for 20 minutes), a high speed supernatant (12,000 *G* for 30 minutes), a second low speed sediment obtained by recentrifuging in adsorption medium the resuspended high speed sediment, and the clarified high speed sediment.

The distribution of S^{35} and phage among fractions obtained from three cultures of this kind is shown in Table VI. The results are typical (except for the excessively good recoveries of phage and S^{35}) of lysates in broth as well as lysates in glycerol-lactate medium.

The striking result of this experiment is that the distribution of S^{35} among the fractions is the same for early lysates that do not contain phage progeny, and later ones that do. This suggests that little or no S^{35} is contained in the mature phage progeny. Further fractionation by adsorption to bacteria confirms this suggestion.

Adsorption mixtures prepared for this purpose contained about 5×10^9 heat-killed bacteria (70°C. for 10 minutes) from 18 hour broth cultures, and

TABLE VI

Per Cent Distributions of Phage and S^{35} among Centrifugally Separated Fractions of Lysates after Infection with S^{35}-Labeled T2

Fraction	Lysis at $t = 0$ S^{35}	Lysis at $t = 10$ S^{35}	Maximal yield	
			S^{35}	Phage
1st low speed sediment	79	81	82	19
2nd " " "	2.4	2.1	2.8	14
High speed "	8.6	6.9	7.1	61
" " supernatant	10	10	7.5	7.0
Recovery	100	100	96	100

Infection with S^{35}-labeled T2, 0.8 particles per bacterium. Lysing phage UV-killed *h* mutant of T2. Phage yields per infected bacterium: <0.1 after lysis at $t = 0$; 0.12 at $t = 10$; maximal yield 29. Recovery of S^{35} means per cent of adsorbed input recovered in the four fractions; recovery of phage means per cent of total phage yield (by plaque count before fractionation) recovered by titration of fractions.

about 10^{11} phage (UV-killed lysing phage plus test phage), per ml. of adsorption medium. After warming to 37°C. for 5 minutes, the mixtures were diluted with 2 volumes of water, and centrifuged. Assays were made from supernatants and from unwashed resuspended sediments.

The results of tests of adsorption of S^{35} and phage to bacteria (H) adsorbing both T2 progeny and *h*-mutant lysing phage, to bacteria (B/2) adsorbing lysing phage only, and to bacteria (B/2*h*) adsorbing neither, are shown in Table VII, together with parallel tests of authentic S^{35}-labeled phage.

The adsorption tests show that the S^{35} present in the seed phage is adsorbed with the specificity of the phage, but that S^{35} present in lysates of bacteria infected with this phage shows a more complicated behavior. It is strongly adsorbed to bacteria adsorbing both progeny and lysing phage. It is weakly adsorbed to bacteria adsorbing neither. It is moderately well adsorbed to bacteria adsorbing lysing phage but not phage progeny. The latter test shows that the S^{35} is not contained in the phage progeny, and explains the fact that the S^{35} in early lysates not containing progeny behaves in the same way.

The specificity of the adsorption of S^{35}-labeled material contaminating the phage progeny is evidently due to the lysing phage, which is also adsorbed much more strongly to strain H than to B/2, as shown both by the visible reduction in Tyndall scattering (due to the lysing phage) in the supernatants of the test mixtures, and by independent measurements. This conclusion is further confirmed by the following facts.

TABLE VII

Adsorption Tests with Uniformly S^{35}-Labeled Phage and with Products of Their Growth in Non-Radioactive Medium

Adsorbing bacteria	Per cent adsorbed				
	Uniformly labeled S^{35} phage		Products of lysis at t = 10	Phage progeny (Maximal yield)	
	+ UV-*h*	No UV-*h*			
	S^{35}	S^{35}	S^{35}	S^{35}	Phage
Sensitive (H)......................	84	86	79	78	96
Resistant (B/2)....................	15	11	46	49	10
Resistant (B/2*h*)..................	13	12	29	28	8

The uniformly labeled phage and the products of their growth are respectively the seed phage and the high speed sediment fractions from the experiment shown in Table VI.

The uniformly labeled phage is tested at a low ratio of phage to bacteria: +UV-*h* means with added UV-killed *h* mutant in equal concentration to that present in the other test materials.

The adsorption of phage is measured by plaque counts of supernatants, and also sediments in the case of the resistant bacteria, in the usual way.

1. If bacteria are infected with S^{35} phage, and then lysed near the midpoint of the latent period with cyanide alone (in salt-poor broth, to prevent readsorption of S^{35} to bacterial debris), the high speed sediment fraction contains S^{35} that is adsorbed weakly and non-specifically to bacteria.

2. If the lysing phage and the S^{35}-labeled infecting phage are the same (T2), or if the culture in salt-poor broth is allowed to lyse spontaneously (so that the yield of progeny is large), the S^{35} in the high speed sediment fraction is adsorbed with the specificity of the phage progeny (except for a weak non-specific adsorption). This is illustrated in Table VII by the adsorption to H and B/2*h*.

It should be noted that a phage progeny grown from S^{35}-labeled phage and containing a larger or smaller amount of contaminating radioactivity could not be distinguished by any known method from authentic S^{35}-labeled phage, except that a small amount of the contaminant could be removed by adsorption to bacteria resistant to the phage. In addition to the properties already mentioned, the contaminating S^{35} is completely precipitated with the phage by antiserum, and cannot be appreciably separated from the phage by further fractional sedimentation, at either high or low concentrations of electrolyte. On the other hand, the chemical contamination from this source would be very small in favorable circumstances, because the progeny of a single phage particle are numerous and the contaminant is evidently derived from the parents.

The properties of the S^{35}-labeled contaminant show that it consists of the remains of the coats of the parental phage particles, presumably identical with the material that can be removed from unlysed cells in the Waring blendor. The fact that it undergoes little chemical change is not surprising since it probably never enters the infected cell.

The properties described explain a mistaken preliminary report (Hershey *et al.*, 1951) of the transfer of S^{35} from parental to progeny phage.

It should be added that experiments identical to those shown in Tables VI and VII, but starting from phage labeled with P^{32}, show that phosphorus is transferred from parental to progeny phage to the extent of 30 per cent at yields of about 30 phage per infected bacterium, and that the P^{32} in prematurely lysed cultures is almost entirely non-sedimentable, becoming, in fact, acid-soluble on aging.

Similar measures of the transfer of P^{32} have been published by Putnam and Kozloff (1950) and others. Watson and Maaløe (1952) summarize this work, and report equal transfer (nearly 50 per cent) of phosphorus and adenine.

A Progeny of S^{35}-Labeled Phage Nearly Free from the Parental Label.—The following experiment shows clearly that the obligatory transfer of parental sulfur to offspring phage is less than 1 per cent, and probably considerably less. In this experiment, the phage yield from infected bacteria from which the S^{35}-labeled phage coats had been stripped in the Waring blendor was assayed directly for S^{35}.

Sensitive bacteria grown in broth were infected with five particles of S^{35}-labeled phage per bacterium, the high ratio of infection being necessary for purposes of assay. The infected bacteria were freed from unadsorbed phage and suspended in water containing per liter 1 mM $MgSO_4$, 0.1 mM $CaCl_2$, and 0.1 gm. gelatin. A sample of this suspension was agitated for 2.5 minutes in the Waring blendor, and centrifuged to remove the extracellular S^{35}. A second sample not run in the blendor was centrifuged at the same time. The cells from both samples were resuspended in warm salt-poor broth at a concentration of 10^8 bacteria per ml., and aerated for 80 minutes. The cultures were then lysed by the addition of 0.02 mM HCN, 2×10^{11} UV-killed T2, and 6 mg. NaCl per ml. of culture. The addition of salt at this point causes S^{35} that would otherwise be eluted (Hershey *et al.*, 1951) to remain attached to the bacterial debris. The lysates were fractionated and assayed as described previously, with the results shown in Table VIII.

The data show that stripping reduces more or less proportionately the S^{35}-content of all fractions. In particular, the S^{35}-content of the fraction containing most of the phage progeny is reduced from nearly 10 per cent to less than 1 per cent of the initially adsorbed isotope. This experiment shows that the bulk of the S^{35} appearing in all lysate fractions is derived from the remains of the coats of the parental phage particles.

Properties of Phage Inactivated by Formaldehyde.—Phage T2 warmed for 1 hour at 37°C. in adsorption medium containing 0.1 per cent (*v/v*) commercial formalin (35 per cent HCHO), and then dialyzed free from formaldehyde, shows a reduction in plaque titer by a factor 1000 or more. Inactivated phage of this kind possesses the following properties.

TABLE VIII

Lysates of Bacteria Infected with S^{35}-Labeled T2 and Stripped in the Waring Blendor

Per cent of adsorbed S^{35} or of phage yield:	Cells stripped		Cells not stripped	
	S^{35}	Phage	S^{35}	Phage
Eluted in blendor fluid	86	—	39	—
1st low-speed sediment	3.8	9.3	31	13
2nd " " "	(0.2)	11	2.7	11
High-speed "	(0.7)	58	9.4	89
" " supernatant	(2.0)	1.1	(1.7)	1.6
Recovery	93	79	84	115

All the input bacteria were recovered in assays of infected cells made during the latent period of both cultures. The phage yields were 270 (stripped cells) and 200 per bacterium, assayed before fractionation. Figures in parentheses were obtained from counting rates close to background.

1. It is adsorbed to sensitive bacteria (as measured by either S^{35} or P^{32} labels), to the extent of about 70 per cent.
2. The adsorbed phage kills bacteria with an efficiency of about 35 per cent compared with the original phage stock.
3. The DNA of the inactive particles is resistant to DNase, but is made sensitive by osmotic shock.
4. The DNA of the inactive particles is not sensitized to DNase by adsorption to heat-killed bacteria, nor is it released into solution by adsorption to bacterial debris.
5. 70 per cent of the adsorbed phage DNA can be detached from infected cells spun in the Waring blendor. The detached DNA is almost entirely resistant to DNase.

These properties show that T2 inactivated by formaldehyde is largely incapable of injecting its DNA into the cells to which it attaches. Its behavior in the experiments outlined gives strong support to our interpretation of the corresponding experiments with active phage.

DISCUSSION

We have shown that when a particle of bacteriophage T2 attaches to a bacterial cell, most of the phage DNA enters the cell, and a residue containing at least 80 per cent of the sulfur-containing protein of the phage remains at the cell surface. This residue consists of the material forming the protective membrane of the resting phage particle, and it plays no further role in infection after the attachment of phage to bacterium.

These facts leave in question the possible function of the 20 per cent of sulfur-containing protein that may or may not enter the cell. We find that little or none of it is incorporated into the progeny of the infecting particle, and that at least part of it consists of additional material resembling the residue that can be shown to remain extracellular. Phosphorus and adenine (Watson and Maaløe, 1952) derived from the DNA of the infecting particle, on the other hand, are transferred to the phage progeny to a considerable and equal extent. We infer that sulfur-containing protein has no function in phage multiplication, and that DNA has some function.

It must be recalled that the following questions remain unanswered. (1) Does any sulfur-free phage material other than DNA enter the cell? (2) If so, is it transferred to the phage progeny? (3) Is the transfer of phosphorus (or hypothetical other substance) to progeny direct—that is, does it remain at all times in a form specifically identifiable as phage substance—or indirect?

Our experiments show clearly that a physical separation of the phage T2 into genetic and non-genetic parts is possible. A corresponding functional separation is seen in the partial independence of phenotype and genotype in the same phage (Novick and Szilard, 1951; Hershey *et al.*, 1951). The chemical identification of the genetic part must wait, however, until some of the questions asked above have been answered.

Two facts of significance for the immunologic method of attack on problems of viral growth should be emphasized here. First, the principal antigen of the infecting particles of phage T2 persists unchanged in infected cells. Second, it remains attached to the bacterial debris resulting from lysis of the cells. These possibilities seem to have been overlooked in a study by Rountree (1951) of viral antigens during the growth of phage T5.

SUMMARY

1. Osmotic shock disrupts particles of phage T2 into material containing nearly all the phage sulfur in a form precipitable by antiphage serum, and capable of specific adsorption to bacteria. It releases into solution nearly all

the phage DNA in a form not precipitable by antiserum and not adsorbable to bacteria. The sulfur-containing protein of the phage particle evidently makes up a membrane that protects the phage DNA from DNase, comprises the sole or principal antigenic material, and is responsible for attachment of the virus to bacteria.

2. Adsorption of T2 to heat-killed bacteria, and heating or alternate freezing and thawing of infected cells, sensitize the DNA of the adsorbed phage to DNase. These treatments have little or no sensitizing effect on unadsorbed phage. Neither heating nor freezing and thawing releases the phage DNA from infected cells, although other cell constituents can be extracted by these methods. These facts suggest that the phage DNA forms part of an organized intracellular structure throughout the period of phage growth.

3. Adsorption of phage T2 to bacterial debris causes part of the phage DNA to appear in solution, leaving the phage sulfur attached to the debris. Another part of the phage DNA, corresponding roughly to the remaining half of the DNA of the inactivated phage, remains attached to the debris but can be separated from it by DNase. Phage T4 behaves similarly, although the two phages can be shown to attach to different combining sites. The inactivation of phage by bacterial debris is evidently accompanied by the rupture of the viral membrane.

4. Suspensions of infected cells agitated in a Waring blendor release 75 per cent of the phage sulfur and only 15 per cent of the phage phosphorus to the solution as a result of the applied shearing force. The cells remain capable of yielding phage progeny.

5. The facts stated show that most of the phage sulfur remains at the cell surface and most of the phage DNA enters the cell on infection. Whether sulfur-free material other than DNA enters the cell has not been determined. The properties of the sulfur-containing residue identify it as essentially unchanged membranes of the phage particles. All types of evidence show that the passage of phage DNA into the cell occurs in non-nutrient medium under conditions in which other known steps in viral growth do not occur.

6. The phage progeny yielded by bacteria infected with phage labeled with radioactive sulfur contain less than 1 per cent of the parental radioactivity. The progeny of phage particles labeled with radioactive phosphorus contain 30 per cent or more of the parental phosphorus.

7. Phage inactivated by dilute formaldehyde is capable of adsorbing to bacteria, but does not release its DNA to the cell. This shows that the interaction between phage and bacterium resulting in release of the phage DNA from its protective membrane depends on labile components of the phage particle. By contrast, the components of the bacterium essential to this interaction are remarkably stable. The nature of the interaction is otherwise unknown.

8. The sulfur-containing protein of resting phage particles is confined to a

protective coat that is responsible for the adsorption to bacteria, and functions as an instrument for the injection of the phage DNA into the cell. This protein probably has no function in the growth of intracellular phage. The DNA has some function. Further chemical inferences should not be drawn from the experiments presented.

REFERENCES

Anderson, T. F., 1949, The reactions of bacterial viruses with their host cells, *Bot. Rev.*, **15,** 464.

Anderson, T. F., 1951, *Tr. New York Acad. Sc.*, **13,** 130.

Anderson, T. F., and Doermann, A. H., 1952, *J. Gen. Physiol.*, **35,** 657.

Benzer, S., 1952, *J. Bact.*, **63,** 59.

Doermann, A. H., 1948, *Carnegie Institution of Washington Yearbook, No. 47*, 176.

Doermann, A. H., and Dissosway, C., 1949, *Carnegie Institution of Washington Yearbook, No. 48*, 170.

Dulbecco, R., 1952, *J. Bact.*, **63,** 209.

Herriott, R. M., 1951, *J. Bact.*, **61,** 752.

Hershey, A. D., 1946, *Genetics*, **31,** 620.

Hershey, A. D., Roesel, C., Chase, M., and Forman, S., 1951, *Carnegie Institution of Washington Yearbook, No. 50*, 195.

Lwoff, A., and Gutmann, A., 1950, *Ann. Inst. Pasteur*, **78,** 711.

Maaløe, O., and Watson, J. D., 1951, *Proc. Nat. Acad. Sc.*, **37,** 507.

Novick, A., and Szilard, L., 1951, *Science*, **113,** 34.

Prater, C. D., 1951, Thesis, University of Pennsylvania.

Price, W. H., 1952, *J. Gen. Physiol.*, **35,** 409.

Putnam, F. W., and Kozloff, L.,1950, *J. Biol. Chem.*, **182,** 243.

Rountree, P. M., 1951, *Brit. J. Exp. Path.*, **32,** 341.

Watson, J. D., and Maaløe, O., 1952, *Acta path. et microbiol. scand.*, in press.

NUCLEIC ACID TRANSFER FROM PARENTAL TO PROGENY BACTERIOPHAGE

by

J. D. WATSON*, ** AND O. MAALØE

Institute for Cytophysiology and State Serum Institute, Copenhagen (Denmark)

INTRODUCTION

In recent years several investigators have used isotopic markers to determine the transfer of P or N atoms from parental to progeny virus particles. PUTNAM AND KOZLOFF[1] using the bacteriophage T6 labelled with ^{32}P, found that 20–40% of the label appeared in material identified as progeny phage by differential centrifugation. LESLIE *et al.*[2] found similar, or lower, values with ^{32}P-labelled T2 bacteriophage. KOZLOFF[3] extended his original observations by studying P and N transfer from normal as well as radiation damaged phage particles. All these experiments show incomplete transfer varying greatly from one experiment to the other.

To determine the true transfer values, two technical problems must be solved: (1) adsorption of the labelled phage must be complete within about 2 minutes because later adsorbing particles are broken down before entering the cells (LESLIE *et al.*[2]), (2) means must be found to prevent progeny particles from adsorbing onto bacterial debris or unlysed cells. Failure to control either of these processes will result in underestimation of the transfer values.

In our first experiments (MAALØE AND WATSON[4]), although the second factor was well controlled, the first was not, and our ^{32}P transfer values of about 30% were, therefore, like those of PUTNAM AND KOZLOFF[1], LESLIE *et al.*[2], and KOZLOFF[3], too low. In this paper, we present experiments in which both factors are controlled, and which indicate that T2 and T4 phages transfer about 50%, T3 phages about 40% of their phosphorus to the progeny. Identical values are found when, instead of ^{32}P, ^{14}C-labelled adenine is used to label the parental phage. The ^{32}P experiments show that the transferred material goes predominantly to the early formed phages, and that the transfer values of about 50% are maximum values. Our finding that the early completed phages receive most of the parental material confirms similar observations by DOERMANN (personal communication) and WEED AND COHEN[5] (unpublished).

In agreement with KOZLOFF[3], we have also demonstrated that considerable amounts of ^{32}P may be transferred from labelled particles which do not participate in reproduction, either because of radiation damage or because they are excluded by another phage. These "abnormal" cases show that infecting particles may be broken down

* Merck Fellow in the Natural Sciences of the National Research Council at the Institute for Cytophysiology, Copenhagen.
** Present address; Cavendish Laboratory, Cambridge, England.

References p. 442.

Reprinted by permission of the authors and Elsevier Publishing Co.
from BIOCHIMICA ET BIOPHYSICA ACTA, **10**, 432-442 (1953).

extensively before[3] their constituents are used for synthesis of new phage particles. We do not, however, think that this evidence excludes the possibility that under normal conditions the infecting and reproducing particle remains essentially unbroken. We shall return to this important point in the discussion.

MATERIALS AND METHODS

The phages T2, T3 and T4, and their common host *E. coli*, strain B/1, have been used: the latter because contamination of cultures with phage T1 occurs in our laboratory. Most of the techniques used in this study have been described in detail by ADAMS[6]. All cultures were grown at 37° C: centrifugations were done in a Servall Angle centrifuge at 10° C.

Media. The nutrient broth is an aqueous extract of minced meat enriched with 1% peptone and containing 0.02% Tween 80 and 0.5% NaCl: pH is adjusted to 7.4. For experiments with T3, the concentration of NaCl was reduced to 0.05% to obtain rapid adsorption. In this medium, at 37° C the latent period of T4r is 22–23 minutes. and the burst size about 150. ^{32}P-labelled phage was prepared using the synthetic g-medium described earlier (MAALØE AND WATSON[4]).

Anti-sera. Rabbit anti-phage sera were prepared, using highly purified and concentrated phage suspensions as antigens. All sera had k-values (ADAMS[6]) of 500–1000 when tested against phage suspended in broth (*cf.* JERNE[7]). These sera showed no agglutination of *E. coli*, strain B/1, in dilution 1 to 10. Samples of anti-phage sera were absorbed with large amounts of live B/1, and used in parallel with unabsorbed serum for phage precipitation: no evidence for the presence of antibacterial antibodies was found. Serum against *E. coli*, strain B/1, was obtained after series of subcutaneous and intravenous injections of heat-killed and subsequently of live cultures. This serum had no anti-phage activity.

X-ray technique. The X-ray source was a Holbeck-Beaudouin tube operating at 33 kv and 36 mA. A cooled molybdenum target produced radiation with an average wave-length of 0.9 A. On the surface of the samples the intensity of radiation was 66,000 r.p.m. The irradiation was done by Dr R. LATARJET on samples sent to Paris by airmail. No decrease in titer was observed in control samples as a result of the shipment.

Isotope technique. Carrier-free orthophosphoric acid was obtained from the Isotope Division of the Oak Ridge National Laboratory, United States Atomic Energy Commission. Adenine labelled with ^{14}C in position 8 was also used: this preparation was synthesized by CLARK AND KALCKAR[8], and had a specific activity of 0.8 mC per mMole. All samples containing ^{14}C were evaporated to dryness and self-absorption due to solids in the suspension medium was made uniform by diluting into nutrient broth before counting. Variation between counts on duplicate ^{14}C samples was less than 10%. The counting equipment was the same as previously described.

Preparation of ^{32}P-labelled T4r. Washed B/1 bacteria from a 24-hour broth culture were inoculated into 10 ml of g-medium containing 20 μC ^{32}P. After two and a half hours of aeration, the bacterial density was about 10^8 cells per ml, and the culture was then infected with about 10 T4r particles per cell. Aeration was continued, and 2–3 minutes before the onset of lysis 0.5 ml of undiluted antibacterial serum was added. If antibacterial serum is not added, the titer of a crude T4r lysate will drop appreciably during the first 24 hours and a fraction of the remaining phages will adsorb slowly. Both effects are presumably due to phage particles absorbing on bacterial debris (MAALØE AND STENT[9]). The antibacterial serum proved completely effective in blocking adsorption of T3 and T4 on B/1, but was not fully effective for T2r$^+$. T2r$^+$ stocks may, therefore contain inactive as well as slowly adsorbing particles even when antibacterial serum is used. It is possible to restore infectivity and full adsorbability to these particles by diluting into distilled water for several hours at 37° C: presumably because adsorbed particles dissociate from the debris at low salt concentrations (PUCK, GAREN, AND CLINE[10] and HERSHEY, personal communication). This treatment was first used by BERTANI (personal communication) to raise the titer of T2r$^+$ broth lysates.

The crude radioactive lysates were centrifuged at 5000 g for 5 minutes to remove bacterial debris and at 12,000 g for one hour to sediment the phage. Three cycles of low and high speed centrifugation reduced the concentration of inorganic ^{32}P by a factor of about 10^5. Further purification was achieved by adding heat-killed resistant bacteria (B/3, 4, 7 heated to 58° C for 1 hour) at a concentration of $5 \cdot 10^8$ per ml. After 30 minutes at 37° C, about 5% of the radioactivity had adsorbed to the resistant cells, which were removed by centrifugation. A similar number of sensitive B/1 cells adsorbed 95–98% of the activity. An additional test of the purity of the virus stock was obtained by precipitation with antiphage serum, as previously described; with anti-T4 serum, 94% of the radioactivity was precipitated, while in a control sample in which T3 phage was precipitated with anti-T3 serum, the precipitate contained less than 2% of the activity.

Assuming that about 95% of the ^{32}P in the final preparation was present as phage phosphorus, the initial specific activity was 10^{-6} counts per minute per particle. From this we can calculate

References p. 442.

that each virus particle contained an average of 0.25 ^{32}P atoms. Since the inactivation efficiency of nuclear decay is only 1/12 (HERSHEY, KAMEN, KENNEDY AND GEST[11]). the fraction of labelled particles which will lose infectivity during an experiment is negligible.

With minor variation indicated by adsorption requirements, etc., the procedure just described was also used to prepare ^{32}P-labelled stocks of the phages T2r+, T3, and T4r+. Phage labelled with ^{14}C adenine was grown on a purine requiring mutant of *E. coli*, strain B, which was obtained from Dr A. H. DOERMANN of the Oak Ridge National Laboratory. For this purpose the g-medium was supplemented with 5 γ ^{14}C adenine per ml. The specific activity of phages grown on the purine requiring strain was ten times that of phages grown similarly on B/1.

EXPERIMENTAL

The basic experimental procedure is unchanged throughout this study. It will, therefore, suffice to describe one typical and simple experiment in detail; more complex experiments can then be introduced briefly and the results summarized in tables.

Distribution of ^{32}P following infection of unlabelled B/1 with labelled T4r:

Exponentially growing bacteria from an unlabelled broth culture were collected by centrifugation and resuspensed in unlabelled broth at 37° C at a concentration of $2 \cdot 10^9$ cells per ml. ^{32}P-labelled T4r phage was added at a ratio of 4.5 particles per bacterium and one and one-half minutes allowed for adsorption. The culture was then chilled and centrifuged at 5000 *g* for 5 minutes. The supernatant was carefully siphoned off and samples for phage assay and radioactivity measurement were taken. The pellet was resuspended in broth at 37° C to give a suspension of infected bacteria with about 10^8 cells/ml; this figure was determined by a separate assay. Aeration was then started, and 25 minutes after infection one volume of undiluted antibacterial serum was added to 19 volumes of culture to prevent adsorption of progeny phage particles to bacterial debris. The cooling and centrifugation retarded phage growth by about 8 minutes. The assays and radioactivity measurements showed that in this experiment over 99.5% of the phages and 96% of the input radioactivity were adsorbed on the bacteria.

About 30 minutes after lysis, the culture was centrifuged at 5000 *g* for 5 minutes to remove bacterial debris and then at 12,000 *g* for one hour to sediment the progeny phage. The material collected during these centrifugations will be referred to as the "low speed pellet" and the "high speed pellet", respectively. The latter was resuspended in broth and again centrifuged at low speed to remove remaining bacterial debris. The

TABLE I

DISTRIBUTION OF ^{32}P AFTER INFECTION OF B/1 WITH LABELLED T4r

Growing bacteria were concentrated to $2 \cdot 10^9$ cells per ml and infected with labelled T4r at a concentration of $9 \cdot 10^9$ particles per ml. Following an adsorption period of 1½ minutes the bacteria were centrifuged for 4 minutes at 5000 *g* to remove unadsorbed phage and then resuspended in nutrient broth at a concentration of $1.1 \cdot 10^8$ cells per ml. Approximately 99.5% of the phage and 96% of ^{32}P adsorbed to the bacteria.

Material	*Phage titer/ml*	*^{32}P distribution (% of radioactivity adsorbed on bacteria)*
Crude lysate	$1.5 \cdot 10^{10}$	100%
Low Speed Pellets	$.027 \cdot 10^{10}$	8.4%
High Speed Pellet	$1.45 \cdot 10^{10}$	42.1%
High Speed Supernatant	$.11 \cdot 10^{10}$	49.5%

References p. 442.

two low speed pellets were resuspended in broth and all fractions assayed for ^{32}P and phage. Table I shows that 42.1% of the ^{32}P which initially adsorbed to the bacteria and about 95% of the progeny phage was recovered in the high speed pellet.

The radioactivity of the high speed pellet was characterized as belonging to phage particles by precipitation with an excess of anti-T4 serum and by adsorption to sensitive bacteria. Native as well as B/1 adsorbed serum was used and in both cases 93% of the ^{32}P was precipitated with the phage. Adsorption tests showed that over 90% of the radioactivity adsorbed on B/1 cells while less than 5% adsorbed on the resistant strain B/3, 4, 7 on which T4 does not itself adsorb. These tests show that 90–95% of the radioactivity in the high speed pellet is somehow associated with the phage particles.

Before asserting that this ^{32}P is truly incorporated into the progeny phages, the following possibilities must be considered: (1) degraded parental nucleic acids might stay attached to the surface of the progeny particles, or (2) non-infective parental particles might be adsorbed to the bacteria initially, released during lysis, and later sediment together with the progeny particles.

Both these possibilities are ruled out by the fact that the progeny particles from an experiment like the one just described transfer their ^{32}P in exactly the same way as did their uniformly labelled parents (MAALØE AND WATSON[4]). We, therefore, conclude that about 95% of the ^{32}P in the high speed pellet is incorporated into the progeny particles. Using this estimate in correcting for the phage present in the low speed pellets and in the high speed supernatant, the fraction of the parental ^{32}P which has become incorporated into the progeny particles is 45% in this experiment.

Table II shows a series of similar experiments involving different stocks of labelled T4r; it is notable that the differences in transfer are very small, usually less than 5%. These values are not changed by varying the number of infective particles from 1 to 10 (the highest number tested). The amount of ^{32}P remaining attached to bacterial debris is uniformly about 5 to 10%. If the different phage stocks had contained greatly varying fractions of adsorbing but non-infecting phages, this would have caused the low speed pellet values to fluctuate greatly.

TABLE II

EXPERIMENTAL VARIATION IN ^{32}P TRANSFER VALUES FOR T4r

Experiment	*Burst size*	*% of parental radioactivity in*		
		Low speed pellets	*Progeny phage*	*High speed supernatant*
1	122	6	47	47
2	141	7	46	47
3	150	6	45	49
4	126	3	45	52
5	160	9	43	48
6	155	10	42	48

^{32}P transfer from secondarily adsorbed phage

The experiments given in Table III show that particles which adsorb on a bacterium more than two minutes after a primary infection with T4r transfer insignificant amounts of ^{32}P. This was demonstrated by infecting bacteria with an average of 5 non-labelled phages per cell and at various times later reinfecting with labelled phage. Column 1

References p. 442.

of Table III further shows that with increasing intervals between primary and secondary infection, the amount of ^{32}P which stays attached to the bacteria decreases. Since the labelled phages adsorb at the normal rate, most of the ^{32}P in the supernate of the infected cells must initially have been adsorbed onto the cells. The observed increase in unadsorbed material is probably an expression of the breakdown of secondarily adsorbed particles described by LESLIE, FRENCH, GRAHAM, AND VAN ROOYEN[2]. These authors observed that a primary infection stimulates within a few minutes the infected cell in such a way that, if a new phage particle adsorbs, it is broken down extensively on the surface of the bacterium, releasing about 50% of its phosphorus into the medium in the form of material soluble in 5% trichloroacetic acid.

This stimulation phenomenon is of further importance for transfer experiments, since we must assume that early released progeny particles which adsorb on unlysed cells will be broken down and release half their phosphorus into the medium. In most of the previous work adsorption of progeny particles was not prevented and the breakdown effect presumably decreased the transfer values. Since in our experiments adsorption was blocked by antibacterial serum, the 50% transfer values can be taken as a good estimate of the transfer to *all* the progeny particles.

TABLE III

DISTRIBUTION OF ^{32}P FOLLOWING SECONDARY INFECTION OF B/1 BY LABELLED T4r

Growing bacteria concentrated to $1.3 \cdot 10^9$ cells/ml in broth were infected at $t = 0$, with an average of 5 unlabelled T4r particles. At various intervals, labelled T4r was added at a ratio of 1 particle per bacterium. Several minutes after the addition of the labelled phage, unadsorbed ^{32}P was removed by low speed centrifugation and the infected bacteria resuspended in nutrient broth at a concentration of 10^8 cells/ml.

Minutes between primary and secondary infection	*Unadsorbed* ^{32}P*	*% of parental radioactivity in*		
		Low speed pellet	*Progeny phage*	*High speed supernatant*
0	5	6	44	45
0.5	6	4	48	42
2	23	15	18	44
4	48	23	4	25
6	45	20	3	32

* This material must initially have been adsorbed but has been released again because of the breakdown effect described by LESLEY *et al.*[2].

Isotope transfer from parental to progeny T3

At the salt concentration usually employed in growth media, T3 phage adsorbs rather slowly. To ensure the necessary rapid adsorption of the labelled T3 particles, the NaCl concentration in the adsorption tube had to be lowered to 0.05%. At this low salt concentration, over 99% of the infecting particles adsorbed within two minutes. Except for this modification, the experiments were like the T4 experiments and included characterization of the progeny by serum precipitation and adsorption on sensitive bacteria. Table IV shows that about 40% of the parental ^{32}P was transferred. Since nearly simultaneous adsorption of the infecting phage particles and isolation of the entire progeny were achieved, we may consider the transfer value of about 40% as a maximum value. As in the case of the phages T2 and T4, the transfer of phosphorus is incomplete.

References p. 442.

TABLE IV

DISTRIBUTION OF ^{32}P FOLLOWING INFECTION OF B/1 BY LABELLED T3

Experiment	*Burst size*	*% of parental radioactivity in*		
		Low speed pellet	*Progeny phage*	*High speed supernatant*
1	195	9	46	45
2	234	8	38	54

Purine transfer from parental to progeny phage

Over 95% of the phage phosphorus is located in DNA, and it is therefore desirable to know whether other nucleic acids constituents such as the purine bases are transferred incompletely like the phosphorus. Phages T2, T3 and T4 were grown in purine requiring bacteria in the presence of adenine labelled with ^{14}C in position 8 (see page 433 *et seq.*). Paper chromatography shows that in this way both the phage adenine and guanine is labelled with ^{14}C. Table V presents a series of experiments with the purine labelled phages. They all show incomplete transfer with values not significantly different from those obtained with ^{32}P; T3 again seems to transfer a little less than do T2 and T4.

TABLE V

DISTRIBUTION OF ^{14}C FOLLOWING INFECTION OF B/1 WITH PURINE LABELLED PHAGE

Experiment	*Phage*	*Burst size*	*% of parent radioactivity in*		
			Low speed pellet	*Progeny phage*	*High speed supernatant*
1	T2r+	322	12	55	33
2	T2r+	238	16	54	30
3	T2r+	162	18	43	39
4	T2r+	360	14	48	38
5	T3	180	14	38	48
6	T3	276	11	38	51
7	T3	210	14	32	54
8	T4r	115	12	44	44
9	T4r	122	14	40	46

Isotope transfer as a function of burst size

In experiments with T3 and T4r spontaneous lysis always occurs when the burst size is relatively low. It is known, however, that the r+-phages behave differently, and that lysis can be delayed by a secondary infection (DOERMANN[12]). At the time of normal lysis the infected cells have not exhausted their capacity for phage production. During the last ten minutes before normal lysis, large amounts of phosphorus-containing phage material is produced in the cells which is not developed into mature phage before lysis (MAALØE AND STENT[9]). After normal lysis, this material cannot be recovered by centrifugation. The incompleteness of the phosphorus and purine transfers might, therefore, be due to our failure to detect parental material transmitted to the immature phage particles formed late in the latent period.

This hypothesis was tested by infecting bacteria with labelled T4r+-phage and inhibiting lysis artificially by reinfection with unlabelled phage. The burst size in this

References p. 442.

experiment was 350, or 2 or 3 times greater than in the experiment with T4r. Despite this increase in phage yield, the transfer was again about 50%, showing that the late formed particles received very little, if any, of the parental phosphorus.

The experiment reported in Table VI shows directly that the transferred ^{32}P goes predominantly to the early formed particles. In this experiment, bacteria infected with labelled T2r+-phage were lysed prematurely by addition of *M*/1000 KCN and a large number of ultraviolet inactivated phage, as previously described[4]. The excess of added phage served as carrier material during centrifugation, and insured that the labelled progeny particles were effectively isolated even when the yield was low. Several identical experiments were carried out, all showing the same trend. Thus the material which an infecting particle transfers to the progeny usually goes to one or more of the early formed particles, while the later formed ones virtually never receive any of it. We therefore conclude that our transfer values of about 50% are true maximum values. Table VI also shows that bacteria lysed before the appearance of the first progeny particles contain insignificant amounts of radioactivity sedimentable at high speed. This is additional evidence that our results are not affected by spurious measurements of non-infective but still sedimentable parental particles released upon lysis.

TABLE VI

DISTRIBUTION OF PARENTAL ^{32}P AMONG PROGENY PARTICLES FROM PREMATURELY LYSED BACTERIA

Concentrated B/1 were infected with an average of 5 ^{32}P-labelled T2r+ particles per bacterium. Two minutes after infection the culture was chilled and centrifuged at 5000 g for 4 minutes to remove unadsorbed radioactivity. The pellet was resuspended in broth at 37° C at a bacterial concentration of 10^8 cells/ml. The progress of phage growth was retarded about 8 minutes by the cooling and centrifugation. Ten minutes after infection ultraviolet (UV) inactivated T2r+ at the average multiplicity of 5 particles was added to inhibit lysis. Samples of the infected bacteria were then broken open at various times by the addition of *M*/1000 KCN and approximately 2000 UV inactivated T2r+ particles per cell. Readsorption of the progeny particles was prevented by saturation of the bacterial surface with the UV treated phage (MAALØE AND WATSON[4]).

Time of premature lysis	*Burst size*	*% of parental ^{32}P in*		
		Low speed pellet	*High speed pellet*	*High speed supernatant*
19 minutes	0	13	2	85
25	34	15	15	70
28	100	14	26	60
34	210	15	38	47
48	275	16	37	47

Isotope transfer in the absence of genetic transfer

The "second generation experiment" (MAALØE AND WATSON[4]) referred to earlier in this paper permits the conclusion that the transmitted phosphorus is distributed in the progeny particles in the same uniform way as in the parental particles. It leaves open the question whether transfer occurs via large blocks carrying biological specificity or via highly degraded material. In this study we have tried to answer a complementary question: Does isotope transfer occur under conditions where no genetic transfer is possible? *i.e.*, can material from an infecting particle be broken down to genetically unspecific structures which are then incorporated into new phage particles?

References p. 442.

TABLE VII

TRANSFER OF ^{32}P FROM X-RAY INACTIVATED T4r

Bacteria were mixedly infected with unlabelled T4r+ and X-ray irradiated ^{32}P-labelled T4r. The adsorption of ^{32}P to bacteria was similar in the mixtures containing irradiated phage and in control mixtures containing non-irradiated phage, being approximately 93% in both cases.

Tube contents	*% of parental ^{32}P in*		
	Low speed pellet	*Progeny phage*	*High speed supernatant*
Unlabelled T4r+ + labelled T4r (non-irradiated)	11	43	46
Unlabelled T4r+ + labelled T4r (e^{-3} survival)	31	24	45
Unlabelled T4r+ + labelled T4r (e^{-6} survival)	45	22	33
Unlabelled T4r+ + labelled T4r (e^{-10}survival)	42	30	28

To answer this question we first carried out experiments with labelled phage heavily irradiated with X-rays. Such particles retain the ability to adsorb to bacteria while the majority of them have lost not only their infectivity, but also the ability to kill the host cell and to transfer genetic specificity (WATSON[13]). The experiments presented in Table VII show, however, that heavy X-ray damage reduces the transfer values only from the normal 40 to 50% to about 25%. Thus, substantial amounts of phosphorus may be transferred from particles which do not participate in genetic exchange. It should be noted that nearly 50% of the phosphorus of the irradiated particles remain attached to the bacterial debris. This value is significantly greater than the values of 5 to 15% found when active phage reproduces. It is possible that as many as 50% of the irradiation damaged phages remains passively attached to the cell surfaces; if so, the transfer value per transferring particle is again about 50%.

Transfer of parental isotope without simultaneous genetic transfer can also be demonstrated in bacteria in which one of the infecting phages does not multiply because of the presence of an unrelated phage. This "mutual exclusion" (DELBRÜCK[14]) is well illustrated by the unrelated phages T3 and T4; if a bacterium is infected simultaneously by both phages, T3 multiplication is completely suppressed and only T4 progeny particles appear; even the infecting T3 particles are lost. In Table VIII are shown the results of an experiment in which bacteria were simultaneously infected with ^{32}P-labelled T3 particles and unlabelled T4 particles. After lysis, the progeny particles were isolated and tested for radioactivity, the specificity of which was shown by the extent of its precipitation with anti-T3 and anti-T4 serum. It can be seen that approximately 25% of the ^{32}P originally present in the T3 particles was transferred to the T4 progeny, another 25% was associated with bacterial debris, while the remaining 50% cannot be sedimented at high speed. The excluded phage thus does not sit passively on the bacterial surface but must penetrate to the interior of the cell where it is broken down into its simpler components. Our experiment, therefore, supports the conclusion of WEIGLE AND DELBRÜCK[15] that mutual exclusion must involve some mechanism other than the establishment of a barrier to penetration.

References p. 442.

TABLE VIII

TRANSFER OF ^{32}P FROM EXCLUDED PHAGE

Bacteria were mixedly infected with an average of 5 particles of T4r and 1 particle of labelled T3 per bacterium. Following lysis the progeny particles were isolated and tested for radioactivity.

Experiment No.	*Burst size*		*% of parental (T3) radioactivity in*				
	T3	*T4r*	*Low speed pellet*	*High speed pellet*	*% of high speed pellet radioactivity precipitated by*		*High speed supernatant*
					anti T3 serum	*anti T4 serum*	
1	2	145	20	21	—	—	59
2	4	162	24	27	4	92	49
3	5	148	19	16	—	—	65

DISCUSSION

We shall now discuss the results of the seven different types of experiments described in the preceding section in relation to the problem of virus reproduction. First it must be stressed, however, that in all our experiments only the nucleic acid portion of the phage has been labelled; entirely different results are obtained if a specific protein labelling isotope, like ^{35}S, is used, (HERSHEY AND CHASE[16]).

1. Infection of unlabelled bacteria with ^{32}P-labelled T4r phage results in the transfer of 40 to 50% of the label to the progeny particles. The transmitted phosphorus is truly incorporated into the new phage. When the infected bacteria lyse, 5 to 10% of the parental ^{32}P remain associated with the bacterial debris; this may mean that 5 to 10% of the adsorbing particles stay passively attached to the bacterial surfaces. In our experiments the transfer value is an extremely reproducible figure and must be close to the maximum value since (a) nearly all the adsorbed particles participate in the reproduction process, and (b) all the progeny particles are recovered. The transfer value is constant for different preparations of labelled phage.

2. For maximum ^{32}P transfer to occur, all the phage particles which adsorb on a bacterium must do so within about two minutes. Particles which adsorb more than two minutes after the primary infection of the cell do not transfer significant amounts of ^{32}P. Half the ^{32}P of such late adsorbing particles remains attached to the bacterial debris; the rest appears within a few minutes in the medium as material soluble in 5% trichloroacetic acid. In contrast, over 95% of the ^{32}P of the early adsorbing phage is retained in the infected cells until lysis. Under conditions of almost simultaneous infection, the transfer value per infecting particle is constant for multiplicities of infection up to ten.

3. ^{32}P-labelled T2 phage shows the same transfer as T4, and, according to PUTNAM AND KOZLOFF[1] and KOZLOFF[3], similar maximum values are obtained with the related phage T6. The unrelated phage T3 transfers about 40% of its phosphorus to the progeny. Thus an incomplete ^{32}P transfer of 40 to 50% may be a general characteristic of phage reproduction in *E. coli*.

4. If the purines of T2, T3 and T4 phages are labelled with ^{14}C, transfer values are obtained which do not differ from those obtained with ^{32}P. This suggests that the purine bases and the phosphorus are not transferred independently but as the constituents of nucleotides or larger units.

References p. 442.

5. Most of the transmitted ^{32}P is incorporated into the early finished phage. An increase by a factor 2 to 3 in the phage yield per infected cell can be obtained in lysis inhibited cultures; such an increase in yield does not significantly increase the transfer.

6. The "second generation experiments" previously published (MAALØE AND WATSON[4]) show that uniformly labelled parental particles transmit phosphorus to all parts of the progeny particles which in turn become uniformly labelled.

7. Phage heavily damaged by X-rays or excluded from growth by the simultaneous presence of an unrelated phage transfer part of their nucleic acid. Isotope transfer is, therefore, not necessarily connected with the transfer of genetic specificity.

It is well known that infecting particles cannot be recovered by artificial lysis at any time during the first half of the latent period (DOERMANN[17]), and it is now firmly established that the nucleic acid components, phosphorus, adenine and guanine, are incompletely transferred from the infecting particle to the progeny. The transfer experiments, and especially the observation that chemical transfer may occur in the absence of genetic transfer, might, therefore, be viewed as evidence for an obligate and extensive breakdown of the infecting particle soon after adsorption. There is no doubt that such a breakdown can occur as evidenced by the unspecific transfer from radiation damaged or excluded phage (7). In both these cases, however, transfer takes place under abnormal conditions where the transferring particle does not participate in the reproduction processes. It is therefore unwarranted to conclude from these experiments that phosphorus is always transferred via genetically unspecific structures.

As they have turned out, the existing data on nucleic acid transfer, including the second generation experiments, do not decide whether transfer occurs via extensively degraded parental material or via large, genetically specific units. The data even fit with the assumption that nucleic acid structure of the infecting phage remains intact during replication and with a probability of about 50% becomes infective again and reappears among the progeny.

ACKNOWLEDGEMENTS

This investigation has been generously assisted by funds from the Danish Society for Infantile Paralysis and by the William Waterman Fund for the Combat of Dietary Diseases. The synthesis of the ^{14}C-adenine by Drs. M. CLARK AND H. M. KALCKAR was made possible by a grant to Dr KALCKAR from the Lederle Laboratories Division of the American Cyanamid Company. We are also grateful to Dr A. H. DOERMANN for supplying us with the purine requiring strain of *E. coli*, to Dr DEAN FRASER for a most generous gift of anti-T3 rabbit serum, and to Dr R. LATARJET for putting the X-ray facilities of the Laboratoire Pasteur de l'Institut du Radium, Paris, at our disposal.

SUMMARY

a. When ^{32}P-labelled phage reproduce in unlabelled coli bacteria a maximum of 40–50% of their label is transmitted to the phage progeny. Only 5–10% of the label stay associated with bacterial debris after lysis: the remaining about 40% appear as non-sedimentable material in the lysate.

b. The maximum transfer-values are very reproducible provided that all phages adsorbing on a given cell do so within about 2 minutes, and that the entire progeny is accounted for.

c. Experiments with T2, T3 and T4 all show a maximum ^{32}P transfer of 40–50%. The same phages labelled with ^{14}C in the purines yield identical transfer-values.

References p. 442.

d. The transmitted ^{32}P is found predominantly in the early formed phages. The latest formed progeny particles receive no ^{32}P from the parental particles.

e. Damaged or excluded phage particles which do not participate in reproduction or in genetic exchange nevertheless transmit considerable amounts of ^{32}P to the phage progeny.

RÉSUMÉ

a. Lorsque des phages marqués par ^{32}P se reproduisent dans des colibactéries non marquées, le 40–50% au maximum de leur ^{32}P est transmis aux phages nouveaux. Le 10% du ^{32}P seulement reste dans les débris bactériens après la lyse: le reste, 40% environ, apparaît comme matière non sédimentable dans le lysat.

b. Les valeurs maxima de transfert sont bien reproductibles pourvu que l'adsorption de tous les phages d'une même cellule ait lieu en moins de 2 minutes environ et que l'on tienne compte de tous les phages nouveaux.

c. Des expériences faites avec T2, T3 et T4 donnent toutes, pour le transfert de ^{32}P, un maximum de 40–50%. Les mêmes phages, marqués par ^{14}C dans les purines, donnent des valeurs de transfert identiques.

d. Le ^{32}P transmis se trouve surtout dans les phages formés les premiers. Les phages de la nouvelle génération formés les derniers ne reçoivent pas de ^{32}P des particules mères.

e. Des particules de phages endommagées ou "exclues" (c.à d., dont la croissance est empêchée par un autre phage) qui ne prennent pas part à la reproduction ou à l'échange génétique, transmettent tout de même des quantités considérables de ^{32}P à la nouvelle génération.

ZUSAMMENFASSUNG

a. Bei der Vermehrung von mit ^{32}P markierten Phagen in nicht markierten Colibakterien wird ein Maximum von 40–50% des markierten Phosphors auf die Phagennachkommenschaft übertragen. Nur 5–10% des markierten Phosphors bleiben mit den Bakterienresten nach der Lysis verbunden, die übrigen 40% erscheinen als nicht sedimentierbares Material im Lysat.

b. Die Maximumübertragungswerte sind sehr gut reproduzierbar, vorausgesehen, dass die Adsorption bei allen Phagen einer gegebenen Zelle innerhalb von zwei Minuten stattfindet und dass die gesamte Nachkommenschaft berücksichtigt wird.

c. Versuche mit T2, T3 und T4 zeigen alle ein Maximum der ^{32}P-Übertragung von 40–50%. Die gleichen, mit ^{14}C in den Purinen markierten Phagen ergeben identische Übertragungswerte.

d. Der übertragene ^{32}P findet sich überwiegend in den zuerst gebildeten Phagen wieder. Die zuletzt gebildeten Nachkommenteilchen erhalten keinen ^{32}P von den Elternteilchen.

e. Beschädigte oder von der Vermehrung ausgeschlossene Phagenteilchen, die nicht an der Vermehrung oder dem genetischen Austausch teilnehmen, übertragen trotzdem beträchtliche Mengen ^{32}P an die Phagennachkommenschaft.

REFERENCES

[1] F. W. PUTNAM AND L. KOZLOFF, *J. Biol. Chem.*, 182 (1950) 243.
[2] S. M. LESLIE, R. C. FRENCH, A. F. GRAHAM AND C. E. VAN ROOYEN, *Can. J. Med. Sci.*, 29 (1951) 128.
[3] L. M. KOZLOFF, *J. Biol. Chem.*, 194 (1952) 95.
[4] O. MAALØE AND J. D. WATSON, *Proc. Natl. Acad. Sci.*, 37 (1951) 507.
[5] L. WEED AND S. S. COHEN, 1951, unpublished.
[6] M. H. ADAMS, In *Methods in Medical Research*, Vol. ii, Year Book Publishers, Chicago, 1950.
[7] N. K. JERNE, *Nature*, 169 (1952) 117.
[8] M. M. CLARK AND H. M. KALCKAR, *J. Chem. Soc.*, (1950) 1029.
[9] O. MAALØE AND G. S. STENT, *Acta Path. Microbiol. Scand.*, (in press).
[10] T. T. PUCK, A. GAREN AND J. CLINE, *J. Exptl Med.*, 93 (1951) 65.
[11] A. D. HERSHEY, M. D. KAMEN, J. W. KENNEDY AND H. GEST, *J. Gen. Physiol.*, 23 (1951) 643.
[12] A. H. DOERMANN, *J. Bact.*, 55 (1948) 257.
[13] J. D. WATSON, *J. Bact.*, 60 (1950) 697.
[14] M. DELBRÜCK, *J. Bact.*, 50 (1945) 137, 151.
[15] J. J. WEIGLE AND M. DELBRÜCK, *J. Bact.*, 62 (1951) 301.
[16] A. D. HERSHEY AND M. CHASE, *J. Gen. Physiol.*, in press.
[17] A. H. DOERMANN, *Carnegie Inst. Year Book*, 47 (1948) 176.

Received April 24th, 1952

THE SYNTHESIS OF BACTERIAL VIRUSES*

II. THE ORIGIN OF THE PHOSPHORUS FOUND IN THE DESOXYRIBONUCLEIC ACIDS OF THE T_2 AND T_4 BACTERIOPHAGES

By SEYMOUR S. COHEN

(From the Children's Hospital of Philadelphia (Department of Pediatrics) and the Department of Physiological Chemistry, School of Medicine, University of Pennsylvania, Philadelphia)

(Received for publication, August 28, 1947)

It has been shown that *Escherichia coli* B infected by T_2 bacteriophage in a synthetic medium, F, synthesizes protein-bound constituents containing phosphorus and nitrogen at a constant rate (1). Evidence was presented that suggests that the virus-infected cell synthesizes virus constituents solely. This was most clearly indicated in the phosphorus metabolism, since the only phosphorylated protein-bound constituent synthesized in the infected cell was that characteristic of virus; *i.e.*, desoxyribonucleic acid (DNA). The ribonucleic acid (RNA) content of infected cells did not increase.

Although the data presented suggested that the materials formed during infection were derived from the medium as in normal cells, it had not been proved that the nucleic acid phosphorus found in virus was not derived from cellular substance existing prior to infection, or had not been in normal host constituents during infection prior to appearance in virus. It seemed unlikely that the virus nucleic acid was derived from the host DNA, since several times more DNA was synthesized after infection than was originally present. However, it was possible that the RNA of the infected cell possessed an active turnover yielding its phosphorus to DNA nucleotides, while the RNA was continually replaced with nucleotides whose phosphorus was derived from the medium.

Two basic problems were therefore posed. (1) Was the DNA-P of virus derived from the phosphorus in the host prior to infection? (2) Was RNA a precursor of DNA? These hypotheses were tested by means of radioactive phosphorus, P^{32}.

EXPERIMENTAL

Conditions for Optimal Virus Yield—A single generation of virus multiplication was studied under conditions of multiple infection. The possibility was therefore eliminated that the generations of virus produced after the first generation in a medium of known composition would be affected by the

*The work described in this paper was aided by the Office of Naval Research.

appreciable amounts of complex products, radioactive and otherwise, liberated by lysed cells. Some of the chemical phenomena and basic biological aspects of this system have been described in Paper I (1).

The yield of virus from infected cells under conditions of multiple infection in the aerated F medium at 37° was studied at concentrations of 5×10^7, 10^8, 2×10^8, and 5×10^8 bacteria per cc. It was found that with both T_2 and T_4 maximal titers were obtained with 2×10^8 bacteria per cc. in about 4 to 6 hours. After this time, titers generally decreased markedly, and to a greater extent in T_2 lysates than in T_4 lysates. This was due probably to a combination of several factors, readsorption to cellular débris, spontaneous thermal inactivation, surface denaturation, etc. In view of this marked loss of titer, it was considered desirable to prepare virus lysates by a single generation in infected cells for a 6 hour period, to minimize the destruction of virus activity.

Distribution of DNA and Protein-Bound P in T_2 and T_4 Lysates—Two types of experiments were done. (1) Bacteria were grown in media containing radioactive P, washed several times, and infected in media containing non-radioactive P; (2) bacteria were grown in media free of P^{32} and infected in the presence of P^{32}.

The following typical control experiments were performed to indicate whether (1) the experimental conditions employed would permit the isolation of sufficient virus for analytical purposes, (2) virus isolated by these procedures would be very low in inorganic P and otherwise possess the proper chemical properties, (3) the newly synthesized DNA appeared in the virus fraction. Bacteria were grown to 2×10^8 per cc. in F medium. Two 125 cc. aliquots were sedimented and the bacteria washed twice with 0.85 per cent NaCl. Each aliquot was resuspended in 125 cc. portions of F medium to which were added an adsorption cofactor, 12 cc. of 5×10^{-3} M tryptophan in F (2). To these bacterial suspensions (A and C) were added small volumes of purified concentrates of T_4r^+-F and T_2r^+-F to give cultures T_4A and T_2C containing 6×10^8 virus particles per cc. The virus concentrates were also added to unwashed bacterial cultures (B and D) in F medium at the same concentrations to yield T_4B and T_2D; B contained 5×10^{-4} M tryptophan. The four infected cultures were assayed periodically; the titers followed the course described previously.

After 5 hours at 37°, the T_2 and T_4 lysates were stored for 13 hours at 4°. Very little inactivation occurred; the final titers were T_4A 2.0×10^{10}, T_4B 4.0×10^{10}, T_2C 1.5×10^{10}, T_2D 1.5×10^{10} active virus particles per cc. The lysates were analyzed for total protein-bound P and DNA (1). They were sedimented at 4000 R.P.M. for 30 minutes and the sediments were washed twice with cold 0.85 per cent NaCl. The supernatant fluids were sedimented at 10,000 R.P.M. for 2 hours, and the supernatant fluids from this high speed centrifugation, containing more than 5 per cent of the activity of the lysate, were analyzed for protein-bound P and DNA. Virus was isolated from the high speed sediments as described previously (3, 4). The distribution of these substances in the four lysates is given in Table I.

It may be seen that the largest amounts of DNA and P appear in the virus-containing fraction; *i.e.*, the high speed sediment. When this fraction was resuspended in 5 cc. of 0.85 per cent NaCl and centrifuged at 4000 R.P.M. for 30 minutes, approximately 25 per cent of the DNA of the fraction had become insoluble. After dialysis of this supernatant fluid against running water overnight, the once sedimented virus concentrate had DNA-P to total P ratios which were very close to 1.0. These values for isolated dialyzed virus after one differential centrifugation cycle were

TABLE I

Distribution of Protein-Bound P and DNA in Lysates of Infected Bacteria

Virus lysate	Analyses	Initial total	Total lysate	Low speed sediment	High speed supernatant fluid	High speed sediment containing virus
		mg.	*mg.*	*per cent*	*per cent*	*per cent*
T_4A, 97 cc.	P		0.210	31	29	40
	DNA	0.213	1.49	25	37	38
T_4B, 105 "	P	0.141	0.263	19	21	60
	DNA	0.220	1.80	17	21	62
T_2C, 96 "	P	0.161	0.275	27	22	51
	DNA	0.275	1.63	29	20	51
T_2D, 92 "	P	0.148	0.260	33	17	50
	DNA	0.221	1.36	35	16	49

T_4A 1.05, T_4B 1.00, T_2D 1.02. Thus the conditions described above yielded fractions with the characteristics of virus whose inorganic P contents were so low as to be undetectable.

Infected cells may synthesize as much as 7 to 8 times as much DNA as was originally present. In many cases, at least 3 times as much DNA was isolated in the virus as was present in the bacteria at the onset of infection. It is considered probable that DNA formed after infection and not recovered in isolated virus was nevertheless originally part of the virus and was lost either by adsorption to débris or by becoming insoluble as a result of high speed centrifugation. No indication has been obtained in preparations of either T_2r^+ or T_4r^+ bacteriophage from F lysates that a phosphorylated compound other than DNA is present in either virus. Furthermore, in contrast to the observations of Taylor (5), preparations of these viruses from nutrient broth lysates prepared from infected cells as described above also possessed DNA-P to total P ratios of 1.0 (6). Hence no evidence has been obtained to confirm the report of Taylor that T_2r^+ virus contains ribonucleic acid (5). It is considered possible that the method of isolating virus from 5 to 6 hour lysates described above assists in the removal in the low speed sediment of bacterial components containing RNA. Since proteolysis in r^+ systems is relatively weak, the prolonged period used by Hook *et al.* (7) in the preparation of lysates may have assisted the degradation of bacterial débris to a size which would not sediment at a low speed but would at high speeds. Proteolysis in r^+ systems in F medium seems even less pronounced than in broth.

Synthesis of Virus in Labeled Host Cells—Small inocula of bacteria were grown to 2×10^8 per cc. in 125 aliquots of F medium containing 0.02 to 0.05 millicurie of P^{32} in 13.7 mg. of inorganic phosphate. More than 99 per cent

TABLE II

Radioactivity of Virus Isolated after Synthesis in P^{32}-Labeled Cells in Media Free of P^{32}

Virus isolated	DNA-P / Total P in virus	Bacteria	Virus	Relative radioactivity, virus P / host P
		counts per 10 γ P per min.	*counts per 10 γ P per min.*	*per cent*
T_2r^+*	1.00	222	33	14
T_2r^+†	1.00	293	53.5	18
T_4r^+*	1.01	37.8	5.9	16
T_4r^+†	1.06	293	53.3	18

*Virus to cell ratio 3.0.
†Virus to cell ration 5.0.

of the P of the bacteria was derived from the P of the medium. The cells were washed twice with 0.85 per cent NaCl. The second washing contained less than 0.1 per cent of the radioactivity of the original medium, as determined on a Geiger-Müller counter, kindly loaned by Dr. H. D. Brunner of the Department of Pharmacology of the University of Pennsylvania.

The radioactive cells were resuspended in 131 cc. of F medium containing 2.5×10^{-4} M tryptophan. Purified T_2r^+ or T_4r^+ virus was added and the infected cultures were incubated for 5 hours and regularly assayed for virus during this interval. The lysates were stored at 4° overnight and virus was isolated as previously described.

The DNA contents of the initial cultures, final lysates, and isolated virus were determined. The radioactivity of the virus was compared with the radioactivity of the uninfected host cell per unit weight of P. Samples of known P content were digested in 1.2 cc. of 60 per cent perchloric acid and diluted to 10 cc. after the solutions were neutralized to pH 4. The counting chamber was filled by perfusion and held identical aliquots of slightly more than 3 cc. The background was determined between samples and yielded 8 to 11 counts per minute. This was subtracted from the count on the sample. Samples and the time of counting were adjusted to yield 100 to 1000 counts. Comparisons of samples were made at similar total counts.

In Table II are presented data on four experiments of this type, in which the increments in DNA in the infected bacteria and the yields of isolated virus were comparable to the data presented previously. The radioactivity of the virus isolated after synthesis under these conditions was far lower than the radioactivity of the host P. It has therefore been concluded that most of the P organized into virus is derived from the medium after infection.

TABLE III

Radioactivity of Virus Synthesized in Unlabeled Cells in Media Containing P^{32}

Virus isolated	DNA-P / Total P in virus	F medium	Virus	Relative radioactivity virus P / medium P
		counts per 10 γ P per min.	*counts per 10 γ P per min.*	*per cent*
T_2r^+*	1.04	443	315	71
T_4r^+†	1.00	840	633	75
T_4r^+*		422	291	69

*Virus to cell ratio 5.0.
†Virus to cell ratio 3.0.

Synthesis of Virus in Unlabeled Host Cells in Media Containing Radioactive Phosphate—Bacteria were grown in the absence of radioactive P. Virus was added immediately after the addition of 0.02 to 0.05 millicurie of inorganic phosphate and tryptophan for the adsorption of T_4. The cultures were incubated, and the DNA increments, rates of virus liberation, and isolated virus were studied as described previously.

In Table III are presented some data on experiments of this type. The radioactivity of the virus isolated after synthesis under these conditions was 70 to 75 per cent of that of the inorganic phosphate of the medium. These data confirm the previous conclusion that most of the P organized into virus is derived from the medium after infection.

Nucleic Acid Turnover after Infection—Since the P^{32} added to the F medium was assimilated in DNA after infection, the distribution of the radioactivity in the infected cell was studied. In a typical experiment bacteria were grown to 2×10^8 per cc. in 1 liter of F medium. The cells were centrifuged and resuspended in 100 cc. of F medium. To the culture were added

4.5 cc. of T_2r^+ at 2.2×10^{11} per cc. and 1.5 mg. of P in inorganic phosphate containing about 0.05 millicurie of P^{32}. The infected culture was aerated vigorously at 37° for 1 hour. At zero time and at 1 hour, aliquots were analyzed for protein-bound P, DNA, and radioactivity.

The counts per minute of the medium were 93 per microgram of P. In 1 hour, the bacterial protein-bound P increased from 0.0109 mg. per cc. to 0.0163 or 5.4 γ per cc. Newly assimilated P had a radioactivity of 98 counts per microgram. The DNA had increased from 24 to 72 γ per cc., or the ratio of newly formed DNA to original DNA was 2:1.

Following the removal of aliquots after 1 hour, the entire culture was precipitated with 5 per cent trichloroacetic acid (TCA) and the sediment was washed twice in the centrifuge with TCA. The supernatant fluids were pooled. The sediment was washed twice with 95 per cent alcohol and twice with ether. These supernatant fluids were combined with lipide extracts prepared by three extractions of this sediment with boiling alcohol-ether (1:1). The pooled lipide extracts were taken to dryness *in vacuo* and dissolved in 10 cc. of $CHCl_3$.

The dried lipide-free sediment was fractionated according to Schmidt and Thannhauser (8). It was incubated with 2 cc. of N KOH at 37° for 20 hours and chilled. To the solution containing a very slight flocculent precipitate were added 0.4 cc. of 6 N HCl and 2 cc. of 5 per cent TCA. After 30 minutes at 0°, the sediment, containing DNA, was removed by centrifugation and washed with several cc. of water. The DNA fraction was dissolved in 0.1 N NaOH. The combined supernatant fluids were precipitated according to Delory (9); essentially no P was found in this sediment and this fraction was discarded. The supernatant fluid contained ribose-3-phosphate nucleotides and comprised the RNA fraction.

Both the DNA and RNA fractions prepared above were analyzed for DNA. The former contained 6.9 mg. and the latter 0.6 mg. of DNA, or a total of 7.5 mg. of DNA was recovered. The total DNA content of the culture was 7.4 mg. Radioactivity measurements of the RNA fraction were corrected for the radioactivity of the DNA it contained. This comprised 10 per cent of the P of this fraction. The radioactivities of the nucleic acid fractions are summarized in Table IV.

One-half of the P in the RNA fraction consisted of ribose-3-phosphate nucleotides reactive in the Bial reaction (10). Pyrimidine nucleotides derived from RNA and comprising one-half of the total P would not be expected to react. Thus the RNA fraction with the exception of a small amount of DNA contained ribose nucleotides of the expected characteristics.

It may be seen from Table IV that the newly synthesized DNA contained P of essentially similar radioactivity to that in the medium, while the RNA fraction contained essentially no radioactive P. It may be concluded from this experiment and others which yielded the same result that not more than 2 per cent of the RNA could have been undergoing synthesis involving P of the medium. It is highly improbable that the turnover of this much RNA, if any synthesis actually occurred, could have produced the synthesis of the DNA found. Therefore it appears that RNA nucleotides are not precursors to DNA synthesis in this system.

Since special precautions were not taken to purify the nucleotides of the RNA fraction before estimating the radioactivity, it is possible that even the low radioactivity found (2 per cent) was due to some contaminant, and was not truly significant. In this experiment the lipide P was found to have a radioactivity of about 26 per cent of the P of the medium. Reprecipitation of phospholipide in the presence of carrier sphingomyelin derived

TABLE IV

Inclusion of Radioactive P into Nucleic Acids of Escherichia coli B Infected with T_2r^+ Bacteriophage

Nucleic acid	Total Protein-bound P	Lipide-free bacterial residue	Counts per γ P per min.	Corrected counts per γ P per min.
	per cent	*per cent*		
DNA	48	13.8	60	90
RNA	36.5	10.5	8.8	2

DNA, counts corrected for presence of original bacterial DNA; RNA, counts corrected for presence of traces of DNA in RNA fraction.

from beef lung readily reduced the radioactivity sufficiently to suggest the inactivity of the phospholipide fraction.

Fractionation of Non-Protein P—It was not found possible to isolate organic phosphate from the TCA supernatant fluids in this experiment, owing to the large excess of inorganic P of the medium. In another experiment, the bacteria were first sedimented to remove the inorganic P of the medium before fractionation. 10 cc. of TCA extract contained 66 γ of organic P and 183 γ of inorganic P. To this solution, adjusted to pH 8.3 with NH_4OH, were added 1 cc. of 2.5 per cent $CaCl_2$ and 2 cc. of a 0.5 per cent suspension of $MgCO_3$. After being chilled, the mixture was centrifuged and the sediment was discarded. The supernatant fluid was precipitated with 4 volumes of alcohol and stored overnight in the ice box. The alcohol precipitate was placed in 3 cc. of water. It contained 44 γ of organic P, of which ribose-5-phosphate in some form comprised 75 per cent of the total organic P of the fraction (10). The water-soluble fraction of the alcohol precipitate contained 16.5 γ of pentose P in 25 γ of organic P. The radioactivity per microgram of P of this fraction was 37 per cent of that of the inorganic

P of the medium. It is not known in what compounds the radioactivity resided.

DISCUSSION

It may be seen from the data presented in this paper that the hypotheses suggested in Paper I have been verified by means of the isotope technique. These are (1) that phosphorylated virus constituents are synthesized in the main from P assimilated from the medium after infection, and (2) that RNA after infection has a very low, if any, turnover rate, and is not a precursor of virus DNA.

Nevertheless the radioactivity of the virus P was significantly different from that of the P of the medium. It has been observed that a very small amount of virus multiplication may occur in the absence of external P (11). Therefore it appears that some of the P of the host may be incorporated into virus. It is considered likely that this small amount of P is derived from the intracellular pool of inorganic P or low molecular weight organic P which can equilibrate with P assimilated after infection. This intracellular metabolic pool would be used for the synthesis of DNA after infection and possibly even before the P assimilated after infection. Thus in short term experiments involving r strains the percentage of host P appearing in virus may conceivably be greater than that observed in these long term experiments with r^+ type virus. This remains to be tested.

Many workers have found that protein and DNA syntheses are accompanied by a vigorous RNA metabolism in a wide variety of tissues. In addition it has been reported that there is apparently a conversion of ribose nucleotides to desoxyribonucleotides in the early stages of cleavage of the fertilized sea-urchin egg (12). These data are ably reviewed by Brachet (13). In the system described in these papers, none of these phenomena are to be observed. It appears possible to study the precursors of DNA in this system uncomplicated by the metabolism of RNA.

I am indebted to Dr. Samuel Gurin of this University and Dr. M. Kamen of Washington University for their advice and assistance in the course of these studies. I wish to thank Miss Catherine Fowler for her technical assistance.

SUMMARY

The preparation and properties of bacterial lysates after multiple infection have been described. As a result certain isotope experiments requiring viral isolation could be performed. The distribution of the bacterial and viral components in these lysates has been studied. It has been found possible to recover in a purified concentrate of virus much of the P assimilated and the DNA synthesized after infection. The newly synthesized DNA greatly exceeded the starting DNA of the bacterial culture.

With P^{32} in the labeled host or labeled medium, the DNA of the virus has been found to be built in the main from the inorganic P of the medium. Ribonucleic acid was not a precursor in the synthesis of this DNA and was essentially inert in infected cells.

BIBLIOGRAPHY

1. Cohen, S. S., *J. Biol. Chem.*, **174,** 281 (1948).
2. Anderson, T. F., *J. Cell. and Comp. Physiol.*, **25,** 17 (1945).
3. Cohen, S. S., and Anderson, T. F., *J. Exp. Med.*, **84,** 511 (1946).
4. Cohen, S. S., *J. Biol. Chem.*, **168,** 511 (1947).
5. Taylor, A. R., *J. Biol. Chem.*, **165,** 271 (1946).
6. Cohen, S. S., Cold Spring Harbor symposia on quantitative biology, Cold Spring Harbor, **12,** 35 (1947).
7. Hook, A. E., Beard, D., Taylor, A. R., Sharp, D. G., and Beard, J. W., *J. Biol. Chem.*, **165,** 241 (1946).
8. Schmidt, G., and Thannhauser, S. J., *J. Biol. Chem.*, **161,** 83 (1945).
9. Delory, G. E., *Biochem. J.*, **32,** 1161 (1938).
10. Albaum, H. G., and Umbreit, W. W., *J. Biol. Chem.*, **167,** 369 (1947).
11. Fowler, C. B., and Cohen, S. S., *J. Exp. Med.*, in press.
12. Brachet, J., *Arch. Biol.*, **48,** 520 (1937).
13. Brachet, J., Embryologie chimique, Liége (1944).

*ENZYMATIC SYNTHESIS OF DEOXYRIBONUCLEIC ACID. VI. INFLUENCE OF BACTERIOPHAGE T2 ON THE SYNTHETIC PATHWAY IN HOST CELLS**

By Arthur Kornberg, Steven B. Zimmerman,[†] S. R. Kornberg, and John Josse[‡]

DEPARTMENT OF MICROBIOLOGY, WASHINGTON UNIVERSITY SCHOOL OF MEDICINE, ST. LOUIS

Communicated April 20, 1959

Information now available about DNA[1] synthesis by *Escherichia coli* enzymes[2–4] has encouraged an inquiry into the biochemical basis for the observation that a phage-infected *E. coli* cell ceases to produce its own DNA and makes instead the DNA characteristic of the infecting phage.[5] This general problem poses several rather specific questions which may be summarized as follows:

1. T2, T4, and T6 DNA differ from the DNA of *E. coli*, as well as from that of other sources which have been examined, in containing hydroxymethylcytosine (HMC) but no cytosine.[6] Flaks and Cohen[7] have already shown that within several minutes after infection by phage T2, T4, or T6, a new enzyme which hydroxymethylates deoxycytidine 5′-phosphate is produced. Is there an enzyme for converting the resulting dHMC-5-P to the triphosphate level in order to provide a functional substrate for DNA synthesis?
2. With respect to the exclusion of cytosine from the DNA of phage T2, T4, and T6, is there a mechanism in the infected cell for removal of deoxycytidine triphosphate from the site of polymerase action?
3. The DNA's of T2, T4, and T6 contain glucose linked to the hydroxymethyl groups of the HMC in characteristic ratios,[8, 9, 10] although it is clear that in T2 and T6 some of the HMC groups contain no glucose.[9] According to our present understanding of DNA synthesis,[4] it is difficult to conceive how these constant ratios are achieved if the incorporation were to occur via glucosylated and non-glucosylated HMC nucleotides. Is there an alternative mechanism involving direct glucosylation of the DNA even though direct substitutions on intact DNA have been hitherto unknown?
4. Following phage T2 infection there is a temporary halt followed by a resumption of DNA synthesis at about 5 times the rate shown by the uninfected cell.[11] However, measurements with extracts of infected cells, using standard substrates, revealed much diminished rather than the anticipated augmented levels of DNA-synthesizing activity.[12] What are the altered conditions for assay of DNA synthesis in infected cell extracts which would elicit the high levels of activity expected from the physiologic studies?

We have explored these questions and have found that following infection with phage T2 several new enzymes appear.[13] These are (1) an enzyme which phosphorylates dHMC-5-P, leading to the synthesis of hydroxymethyldeoxycytidine triphosphate (dHMC-TP), (2) an enzyme which removes the terminal pyrophosphate group from dCTP, and (3) an enzyme which transfers glucose from UDPG directly to the HMC in DNA. Measurements of DNA synthesis, using dHMC-TP in place of dCTP, revealed about a 12-fold increase in activity in extracts of infected cells over the levels observed in uninfected cell extracts.

Reprinted by permission of the authors and the National Academy of Sciences from the Proceedings of the National Academy of Sciences, 45 (6), 772-785, June, 1959.

METHODS AND MATERIALS

Preparation of Cell Extracts.—*E. coli* B was grown at 37° with vigorous aeration in M-9 medium[14] modified to contain per liter: KH_2PO_4, 3 gm, Na_2HPO_4, 6 gm, NH_4Cl, 1 gm, $MgSO_4 \cdot 7H_2O$, 0.49 gm, glucose, 5.0 gm, $FeSO_4 \cdot 7H_2O$, 0.5 mg, $CaCl_2$, 55 mg. Growth at a logarithmic rate continued to 4–5 $\times$ 10^9 cells per ml with a generation time of about 50 min.

Cell extracts were prepared in two ways:

Method I: Cultures grown to 2 $\times$ 10^8 cells per ml were chilled, centrifuged, and the cells resuspended at 4 $\times$ 10^9 cells per ml in cold growth medium. Five $T2r^+$[15] or T5 per cell were added and after a 4-min adsorption period at 0°, the culture was diluted twenty-fold into fresh growth medium at 37° and aeration continued. The time of dilution was taken as "zero minutes." 50-ml aliquots were pipetted rapidly onto crushed ice at intervals. The cells were sedimented by centrifuging for 5 min at 10,000 $\times$ g, were resuspended in 1 ml. of 0.5 *M* glycylglycine buffer, pH 7.0, containing 0.001 *M* glutathione, and were stored for 1 to 3 days at −15°. The cells were disrupted in a 10 kc Raytheon sonic oscillator. After removal of a small amount of debris by centrifugation, the extracts contained about 2 mg of protein per ml.

Method II: Cultures were grown to 2 $\times$ 10^9 cells per ml, in the modified medium without $CaCl_2$ and four $T2r^+$ per cell added ("zero minutes"). 50-ml aliquots were pipetted rapidly onto crushed ice at intervals. The cells were sedimented and resuspended in 4 ml of 0.05 *M* glycylglycine buffer, pH 7.0, containing 0.001 *M* glutathione and disrupted as above. Extracts containing about 6 mg of protein per ml were obtained after centrifugation.

All results refer to extracts prepared by Method I unless otherwise stated. While Method II was less effective for phage multiplication (see below), a description of this method is included since it provided an alternative and efficient technique for obtaining concentrated extracts in kinetic studies. The activities per mg protein for the several enzymes studied were found to be at levels similar to those obtained by Method I.

Bacteriophage Determinations.—Bacteriophage was assayed by standard techniques.[16] Intracellular phage was measured after "lysis from without" essentially as described by Doermann.[17] The formation of infectious units in both $T2r^+$ and T5 infected cells (Fig. 1) was found to proceed in normal fashion in cells infected as described in Method I. $T2r^+$-infections produced by Method II yielded only about 2 phage per original cell at 25 min when measured after "lysis from without," although after clearing of the culture a yield of several hundred phage per original cell was obtained.

Enzyme Assays and Preparations.—Phosphorylation of the deoxynucleoside monophosphates (kinase activities) was measured, as described before,[2] by using a $5'$-P^{32}-labeled mononucleotide as substrate and assaying the amount of label which becomes resistant to the action of semen phosphatase.[18] Formation of dHMC-5-P from dC-5-P (hydroxymethylase) was assayed according to Flaks and Cohen.[7] The assay of DNA synthesis ("polymerase") was measured by the conversion of a C^{14}-labeled deoxynucleoside triphosphate into an acid-insoluble product.[2] "Polymerase" fraction VII from uninfected *E. coli* was prepared as previously described.[2]

Substrates.—Deoxynucleotides and samples of native and enzymatically synthesized DNA were prepared as in earlier studies.[2, 4] dHMC-5-P was synthesized according to Flaks and Cohen[7] using a 230-fold purified hydroxymethylase[19]; C^{14}-dHMC-5-P was obtained by using C^{14}-formaldehyde (Volk Radiochemical Co.) in the hydroxymethylation reaction, and P^{32}-dHMC-5-P was prepared by using P^{32}-dC-5-P. The E_m value determined for the nucleotide in this preparation was 13.5×10^3 at 284 mμ at pH 1. Since this value conflicts with that of 11.7×10^3 given by Flaks and Cohen,[7] it is regarded as provisional and requires further

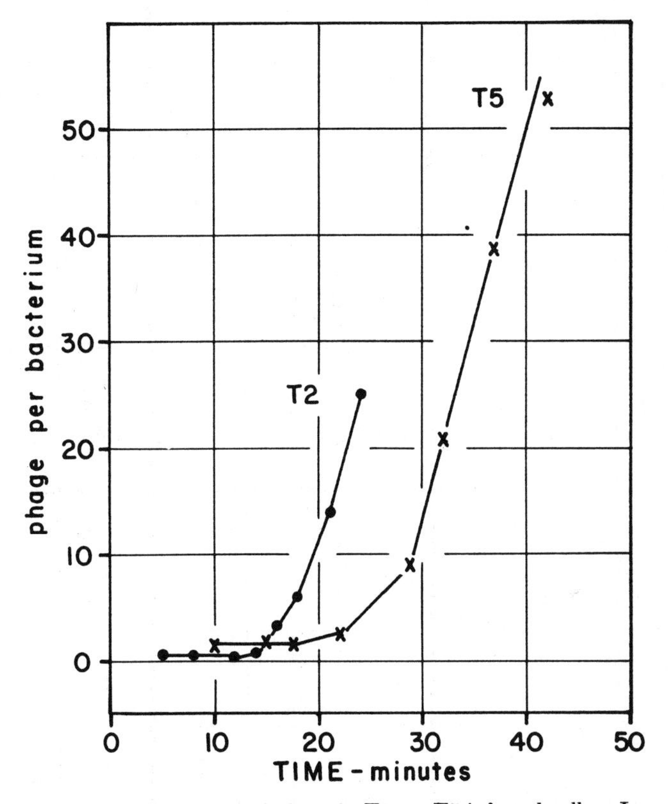

FIG. 1.—Appearance of phage in T2- or T5-infected cells. Infected cultures were prepared by Method I. Infectious units were measured after "lysis from without."

checking. C^{14}-glucose 6-phosphate was prepared by hexokinase action on uniformly labeled C^{14}-glucose (Isotope Specialties Co.). C^{14}-UDPG was prepared from C^{14}-glucose 6-phosphate and uridine triphosphate by the action of phosphoglucomutase and UDPG pyrophosphorylase as outlined by Glaser and Brown.[20] Unlabeled UDPG was a product of the Sigma Chemical Company.

RESULTS

An Enzyme which Phosphorylates dHMC-5-P.—At about 4 min after infection of *E. coli* with phage T2, it was possible to detect in the extracts an enzyme which catalyzes the phosphorylation by ATP of dHMC-5-P (Fig. 2 *A*). This reaction was undetectable (<0.5 per cent of the maximal value after infection with T2) in normal cells or in extracts of cells infected with T5 (Fig. 2 *A*), a phage without HMC in its DNA. The maximal level of phosphorylating ("kinase") activity for dHMC-5-P was of the same order as that of the kinases for the other deoxynucleotides in-

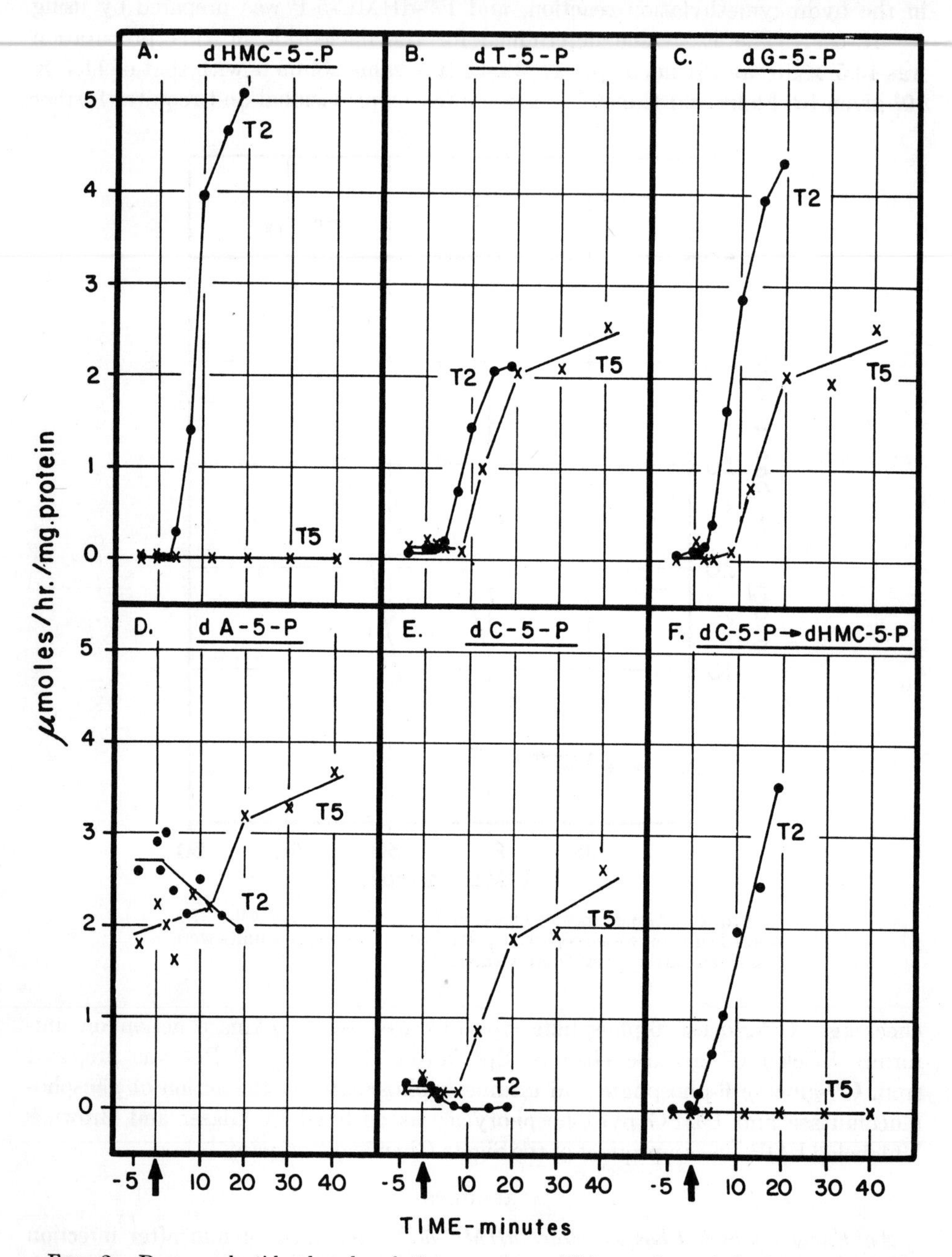

FIG. 2.—Deoxynucleotide-phosphorylating enzymes ("kinases") and hydroxymethylating enzyme levels before and after infection with phage T2 or T5. The arrow indicates the start of infection ("zero minutes," see Method I). Assays were as referred to in Methods.

corporated into viral DNA (see below) and was essentially similar in extracts prepared by either Method I or Method II.

The product of the dHMC-5-P kinase action (with the presumed participation of nucleoside diphosphate kinase in the preparation) was shown to be the triphosphate. Using a 20-fold purified kinase preparation,[19] 25 μmoles of dHMC-TP were prepared and isolated by ion-exchange chromatography, a yield of 92 per cent based on the starting dHMC-5-P. Theoretical specific radioactivity values were found in the isolated dHMC-TP when P^{32}- or C^{14}-labeled dHMC-5-P was the

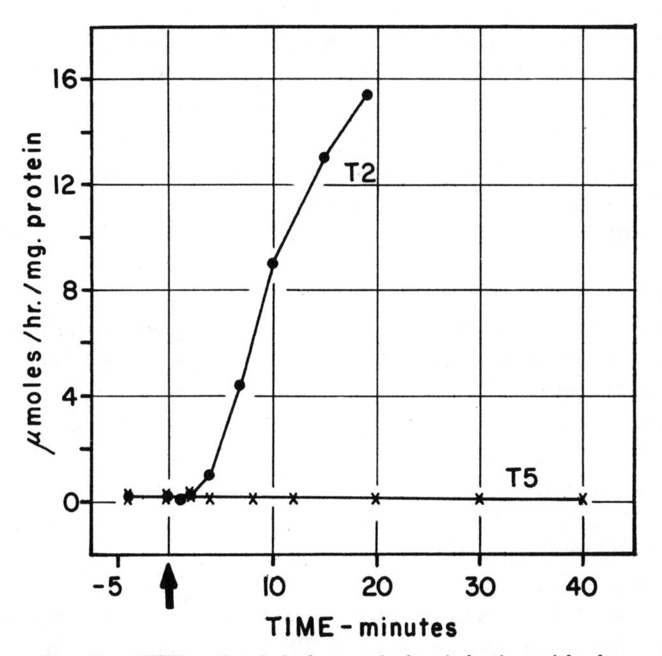

FIG. 3.—dCTPase levels before and after infection with phage T2 or T5. The arrow indicates the start of infection ("zero minutes," see Method I). The incubation mixtures (0.25 ml) contained: 6.0 mμmoles of dCTP labeled with P^{32} in the terminal pyrophosphate group (10^3 cpm per mμmole), glycine buffer, pH 9.2 (0.04 *M*), $MgCl_2$ (0.008 *M*), 2-mercaptoethanol (0.01 *M*) and a quantity of extract containing about 0.3 μg of protein. After 20 min of incubation at 37°, the reaction was terminated by adding 0.5 ml of 0.1 *N* HCl, followed by 0.2 ml of a mixture (containing per ml: 5 mg of crystalline bovine serum albumin, 25 μmoles of sodium pyrophosphate and 25 μmoles of potassium phosphate, pH 7), and 0.1 ml of a Norit suspension (20 per cent packed volume). The Norit was removed by centrifugation and the supernatant fluid was assayed for radioactivity.

starting material. After concentration with Norit, analysis revealed a ratio of HMC: total P: acid-labile P of 1.0: 3.2: 2.2, using an E_m value of 13.5×10^3 at 284 mμ at pH 1.

Kinase Levels for the Other Deoxynucleotides and Levels of the Hydroxymethylating Enzyme.—It is noteworthy that after T2 infection, the kinase levels for dT-5-P and dG-5-P were increased approximately 20 and 45 times, respectively, while that for dA-5-P was essentially unaltered (Fig. 2 *B*, *C*, *D*). Bessman has made similar observations independently.[21] As mentioned above, the kinase levels for each of the four deoxynucleotides incorporated into phage T2 DNA reach values of about the same magnitude. By contrast, only traces of dC-5-P kinase were detected (Fig. 2 *E*). Furthermore, extracts of T2-infected cells were found to inhibit the dC-5-P kinase activity of normal cell extracts when equal amounts of infected and non-infected extracts were mixed. As will be described below, this inhibitory effect is due to an enzyme (dCTPase) which splits dCTP. By use of fluoride (8×10^{-3} *M*), which inhibits dCTPase more than 98 per cent, but the dC-5-P kinase by 15 per cent or less, it was possible to show that there was actually little or no change in the dC-5-P kinase levels upon infection. Extracts prepared by Method II showed the same kinase patterns after T2 infection.

Infection with phage T5, which contains cytosine rather than HMC, showed increased kinase activities for the four deoxynucleotides which are present in its DNA (Fig. 2 *B*, *C*, *D*, *E*). The 10-fold increase in dC-5-P kinase activity in the extracts of T5-infected cells may be contrasted with the absence of any increase in this activity in the extracts of T2-infected cells.

Hydroxymethylating activity was first detected at 4 min after T2 infection, and, as predicted from the results of Flaks and Cohen,[7] was absent from T5-infected cell extracts (Fig. 2 *F*).

An Enzyme which Destroys Deoxycytidine Triphosphate (dCTPase).—The inhibitor of dC-5-P kinase that develops upon T2 infection has been identified as an enzyme which splits dCTP by removal of the terminal pyrophosphate group (Fig. 3). Extracts of uninfected cells have 1 per cent or less of the dCTPase activity observed in extracts of T2-infected cells; the level of dCTPase activity of T5-infected cells was the same as in normal cells. The relative insensitivity to fluoride of the dCTPase activity in normal cells makes it doubtful that it represents the same enzyme found in the T2-infected cells.

After partial purification of the dCTPase,[19] which reduced the level of an inorganic pyrophosphatase to 2 per cent of the dCTPase, it was demonstrated that the complete splitting of 0.92 μmole of dCTP was accompanied by the appearance of 0.74 μmole of inorganic pyrophosphate identified as Norit-nonadsorbable, acid-labile P and 0.15 μmole of orthophosphate. With the purified enzyme preparation, the rates of cleavage of cytidine triphosphate and ATP were less than 1 per cent of that of dCTP; the splitting of dHMC-TP was 1–2 per cent of that of dCTP. The K_m of dCTP for the enzyme is in the region of 10^{-6} *M*. In view of this high affinity for dCTP and of the high level of enzyme activity compared to the dC-5-P kinase in the extract (cf. Fig. 2 *E* and Fig. 3), it is reasonable to suppose that the dCTP concentrations in the infected cell are reduced to an extremely low level.

An Enzyme which Glucosylates the HMC of DNA.—An enzyme which transfers glucose from UDPG to DNA containing HMC was observed in extracts of T2-infected but not T5-infected or normal cells (Fig. 4). With the partially purified enzyme[19] UDPG could not be replaced by glucose, glucose 1-phosphate or glucose 6-phosphate (Table I); similar results were also obtained with the crude extracts. The reaction requires HMC-containing DNA, which for these experiments was enzymatically synthesized from dHMC-TP, dATP, dGTP, dTTP, purified polymerase, and primer DNA derived from any one of several sources (calf thymus, *E. coli*, phage T2, phage ϕX174[22]). When DNA enzymatically synthesized with dCTP in place of dHMC-TP, or when the glucosylated DNA from phage T2 itself were used, no glucose fixation in DNA was detectable (Table 1). dHMC-5-P and dHMC-TP failed to substitute for HMC-containing DNA as glucose acceptors. For example, in an incubation mixture containing these three types of HMC compounds with 30-fold purified enzyme, the HMC-DNA fixed 46 per cent of the glucose of the UDPG, while dHMC-5-P and dHMC-TP fixed none (<0.5 per cent).

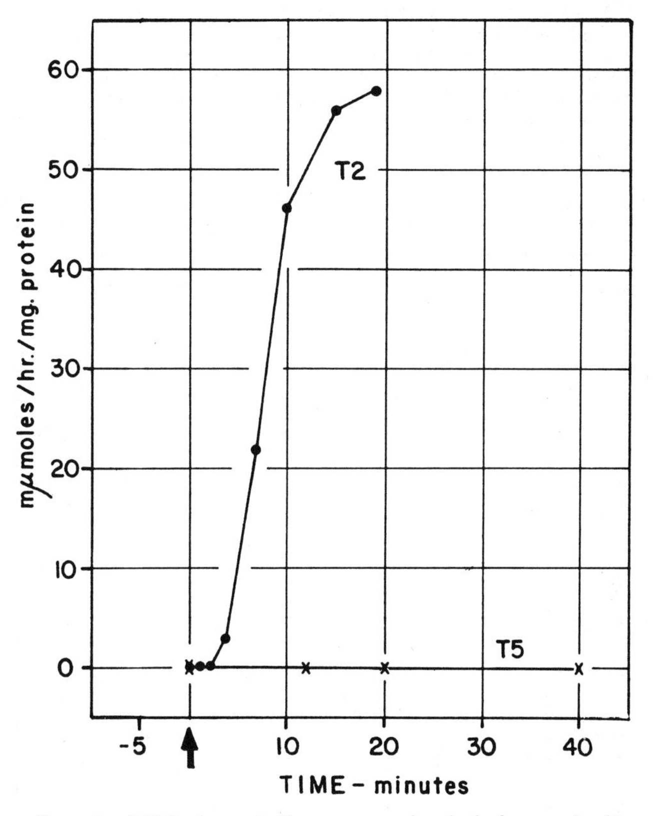

Fig. 4.—DNA-glucosylating enzyme levels before and after infection with phage T2 or T5. The arrow indicates the start of infection ("zero minutes," see Method I). The incubation mixtures (0.20 ml) contained: 10 mμmoles of UDPG labeled uniformly with C^{14} in the glucose residue (2×10^3 cpm per mμmole), Tris buffer, pH 7.5 (0.1 *M*), glutathione (0.02 *M*), DNA synthesized enzymatically (using thymus or phage T2 DNA as primer) and containing about 1 mμmole of HMC, and extract containing 10–50 μg of protein. After 15 min of incubation at 30°, the mixture was treated as in the "polymerase" assay of incorporation of a labeled deoxynucleotide into an acid-insoluble product (see Methods).

In the presence of an excess of HMC-DNA, the glucose of UDPG is transferred completely to the DNA. With an excess of UDPG and enzyme, the fixation of glucose in DNA reaches a limiting value, which is a function of the HMC-DNA present (Fig. 5). The number of glucose residues fixed in this experiment was approximately 60 per cent of the number of HMC residues in the added DNA. At this point it may be premature to regard the glucosylation limit observed with

TABLE 1

SPECIFICITY OF THE ENZYME WHICH GLUCOSYLATES DNA

Expt. No.	Conditions	Glucose fixed in DNA, mμmoles
1	Complete system (10 mμmoles of C^{14}-UDPG)	0.69
	Add C^{12}-UDPG (10 mμmoles)	0.65*
	Add C^{12}-glucose (200 mμmoles)	0.53
	Add C^{12}-glucose 1-P (200 mμmoles)	0.59
	Add C^{12}-glucose 6-P (250 mμmoles)	0.59
	Replace UDPG with C^{14}-glucose (10 mμmoles)	0.00
	Replace UDPG with C^{14}-glucose 6-P (12 mμmoles)	0.00
2	Complete system (DNA containing 0.46 mμmole of HMC)	0.28
	Replace HMC-DNA with cytosine-DNA (containing 0.75 mμmole cytosine)	0.00
	Replace HMC-DNA with T2 DNA (containing 2 mμmoles HMC)	0.00

The complete system had the composition and was treated as described in Figure 4, using a 30-fold purified enzyme, 0.3 μg in Expt. 1 and 1.5 μg in Expt. 2. In each case the DNA was glucosylated to its limit (see Fig. 5).

* The glucose fixed is calculated on the basis of the specific radioactivity of the UDPG after dilution of the C^{14} sample with C^{12}-UDPG.

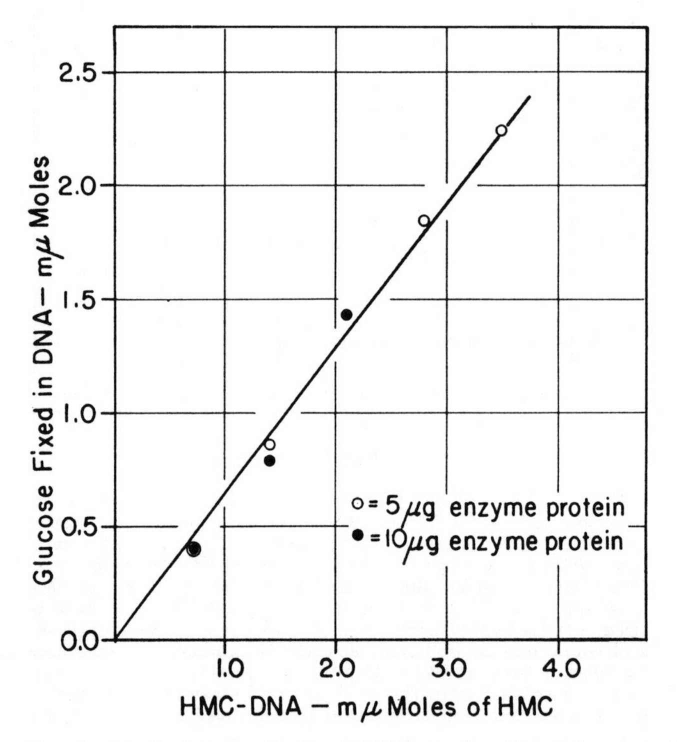

FIG. 5.—Limit of glucose fixation in DNA as a function of the amount of DNA added. The experimental details were as in Fig. 4, using the partially purified enzyme. The HMC-DNA was prepared with thymus DNA as primer.

a given sample of HMC-DNA as distinctive for the type of primer used in the enzymatic synthesis of the HMC-DNA. Further studies are required to determine how conditions of enzymatic polymerization, as well as the isolation of the DNA, may influence the glucose/HMC ratios obtained.

The C^{14}-glucose fixed in DNA was rendered acid-soluble by crystalline pancreatic deoxyribonuclease. When 52 per cent of the nucleotides were no longer acid-precipitable, 88 per cent of the glucose had been made acid-soluble. When the C^{14}-glucosylated HMC-DNA was digested to completion under conditions which Lehman has found[23] to yield a quantitative conversion of phage T2 DNA to 5′-mononucleotides, over 95 per cent of the radioactivity was found in the HMC deoxynucleotide fractions of the ion-exchange chromatogram.

Increase Rate of DNA Synthesis upon Infection.—DNA synthesis, measured by the standard assay,[2] but with dHMC-TP instead of dCTP, is increased 12-fold in extracts prepared 19 min after infection with T2 (Fig. 6). Little or no DNA synthesis can be measured in these extracts when dCTP replaces dHMCTP. However,

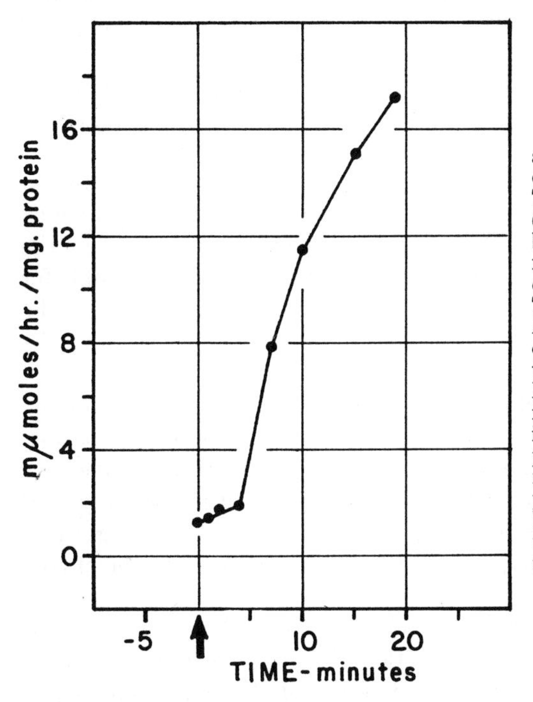

FIG. 6—DNA "polymerase" levels before and after infection with phage T2 with dHMC-TP as substrate in place of dCTP. The arrow indicates the start of infection ("zero minutes," see Method I). The incubation mixtures (0.30 ml) contained: 10 mμmoles each of dGTP, dATP, dTTP and dHMC-TP (C^{14}, 1 × 10^3 cpm per mμmole), Tris buffer, pH 7.5 (0.07 *M*), $MgCl_2$ (0.007 *M*), 2-mercaptoethanol (0.001 *M*), 0.04 ml. of "heated DNA" and sonic extract containing 10–50 μg of protein. The "heated DNA" was prepared by heating at 100° for 5 min, at pH 9.2, an extract of T2-infected cells; this preparation could be purified without loss of activity by treatment with ribonuclease, Norit, dialysis and precipitation with acid; it was inactivated by treatment with deoxyribonuclease. Further details of procedure were as referred to in Methods.

using 0.005 *M* F^- to inhibit dCTPase, DNA synthesis was elevated to levels near those observed in assays with dHMC-TP.

It should be emphasized that these measurements of rates of DNA synthesis with dHMC-TP were made with heated DNA as primer; when unheated DNA was used, there was no demonstrable increase in rate in the infected cell extracts. Heated DNA of phage T2 or calf thymus origin served as well as that used in Figure 6. The basis for this requirement for heated DNA with infected cell extracts requires further investigation.

DISCUSSION

In addition to the interest inherent in understanding the nature of viral infection of a cell, studies of the pathway of DNA synthesis in infected cells provide a means of testing and expanding our conceptions about the mechanism of DNA replication in normal cells.

Control of DNA Synthesis at the Level of Deoxynucleotide Phosphorylation.—It appears from studies with various analogues of the naturally occurring purines and pyrimidines[3] that an analogue in the form of a deoxynucleoside triphosphate is incorporated into DNA when its structure has the hydrogen-bonding properties of the base it replaces. For example, uracil and 5-bromouracil are both effective substitutes for thymine. Yet, uracil is never found in DNA[24] while bromouracil, when supplied to the cell, readily replaces thymine in the DNA.[25] The reason appears to be the absence of any mechanism for phosphorylating deoxyuridylate as contrasted with the availability of an enzyme for phosphorylating 5-bromodeoxyuridylate or 5-methyldeoxyuridylate (thymidylate).[3]

The present studies of phage-infected cells provide additional examples of control at the phosphorylation level. Earlier observations with 5-methyldeoxycytidylate[3] had suggested the lack of an enzyme for phosphorylation of a 5-substituted cytosine deoxynucleotide, and posed the problem of how 5-hydroxymethylcytosine deoxynucleotide becomes a substrate for phage T2 DNA synthesis. This problem seems to be solved by the development of a new enzyme after phage T2 infection of the cell. According to our studies, and those of Flaks and Cohen,[7] the synthesis of a compound novel for the cell is carried out by a new enzyme, the formation of which is presumably induced by the phage DNA. Another example of control at the phosphorylation level is provided by the device which appears to be responsible for the absence of cytosine in T2 DNA. For lack of a mechanism to eliminate the dCTP-synthesizing enzyme system, the evolution of an enzyme to destroy the dCTP provides an effective alternative.

Direct Substitution on DNA.—Genetic studies indicate that the glucose contents of DNA of phages T2, T4, and T6, and strains derived from them by recombination, are a fixed property resembling other phenotypic characters of these phages.[9, 10] It appears plausible, therefore, that the precise arrangement of these glucosylated HMC residues in the DNA may be a source of genetic information, and insight into the nature of the replication of these types of phage DNA would clearly be of considerable value.

The incorporation of a fixed proportion of non-, mono-, and polyglucosylated derivatives of dHMC-TP during the polymerization of the DNA chain is difficult to conceive because it is likely that these derivatives would all behave similarly in hydrogen-bonding to guanine. It becomes even more difficult to conceive the incorporation of these various HMC residues in a precise sequence in DNA on the basis of selection of the triphosphate derivatives. The existence of an enzymatic system for direct glucosylation of DNA offers an alternative which seems to circumvent these difficulties. At this stage, the information is still too fragmentary to determine whether this glucosylating enzyme, and perhaps an additional one for polyglucosylation, will be sufficient to explain the replication of various phage DNA's. It is apparent that further studies with T4- and T6-, as well as T2-infected cell enzyme systems are essential.

Superficially analogous to the partial glucosylation of the HMC residues in phage DNA is the partial methylation of the cytosine residues in certain plant and animal DNA's, such as wheat germ and calf thymus.[24] In the light of our findings, it would be interesting to look for an enzymatic mechanism for direct methylation of DNA in these tissues.

Kinetics of Enzyme Development and Enzyme Reactions.—The temporal pattern of development of all the enzymes studied in this report that were either "new," or the levels of which were significantly raised, was similar. The first traces of change were apparent at four minutes after T2 infection and about ten minutes after T5 infection. While the precision of measurement of these time intervals is not great, it is clear that there is a time lag before significant levels of these enzyme activities appear. Several groups of investigators[26, 27, 28] have shown that 5-methyltryptophan and chloramphenicol administered to cells at levels sufficient to inhibit protein synthesis also blocked DNA synthesis when given before or up to about 5 min after infection. When given 10 min or later following T2 infection, the inhibition of protein synthesis had only a small or even no effect on the rate of DNA synthesis. It seems reasonable to consider that the time lag we have observed may be related to the chloramphenicol-sensitive interval required for development of the enzymatic machinery for DNA synthesis, as well as other protein components vital to virus information. There have been indications of non-phage protein synthesis immediately upon infection[29] and it remains to be determined what fraction of this protein can be identified with the enzymes described here.

The multiplicity of enzyme changes described in this study along with the findings on the hydroxymethylating[7] and deoxyuridylate-methylating[30] enzymes, are all directly related to DNA synthesis. Enzyme measurements related to other metabolic pathways in infected cells have as yet disclosed few significant changes.[31] It would be surprising if further exploration of the phage-infected cell failed to reveal additional examples of new or augmented enzyme activities related to the requirements imposed by rapid phage synthesis.

In view of the pitfalls inherent in assaying the level of an enzyme activity in a cell extract, let alone in the cell itself, a detailed evaluation of the various enzyme values in terms of virus DNA synthesis does not seem warranted. However, it is interesting to note that the rates of the kinases and the glucosylating enzyme are all greater than that found for the DNA polymerizing activity and, further, that the increase in the latter activity over levels found in uninfected cell extracts is about the same as the increase in DNA synthesis in whole cells following T2 infection. Also it is remarkable that the dA-5-P kinase activity (very likely identical to adenylate kinase) is about 10 times that of the other deoxynucleotide kinases in the uninfected cell extract and does not change upon T2 infection, while after infection the other kinases and hydroxymethylase reach levels comparable to the dA-5-P kinase. Finally, it is noteworthy that the dC-5-P kinase activity does not increase upon T2 infection but remains at the relatively low level observed in the uninfected cell, whereas it increases about 10-fold upon T5 infection.

References to increases in level of a preexisting enzyme carry no implication that the additional enzyme activity is identical to the old or even that more enzyme has been synthesized "*de novo.*" To resolve this important point, it will be necessary to characterize isolated preparations of the normal- and infected-cell enzymes and to establish by tracer techniques that the enzymes developed after infection have, like induced enzymes,[32] been synthesized from the amino acid pool.

Control of DNA Synthesis by the Nature of the DNA Primer.—Perhaps the most interesting question regarding T2 infection of *E. coli* is how the T2 DNA seems to preempt from the host DNA the primer function for the polymerase system. The present studies can explain why DNA synthesized by the phage T2-*E. coli* system contains hydroxymethylcytosine rather than cytosine, but not why the base composition is that of phage rather than that of host DNA. An observation reported in this paper which may bear on this question is the dependence of the augmented polymerase activity of the infected cell extracts on a physically altered DNA primer. When "native" calf thymus or phage T2 DNA was used, the polymerase values of infected and normal cell extracts were similar. However, with DNA samples heated at pH 9, the values for dHMC-TP incorporation with infected cell extracts were increased 12-fold, while the normal cell values were unaffected or even depressed. It is not clear as yet whether infection has resulted in formation of a new type of polymerase or in an increase of the normal polymerase and new factors which modify it. Further studies to clarify this question may lead to a better insight into how the injected phage DNA proves to be the chosen primer for this system.

SUMMARY

1. Extracts of *E. coli* infected with bacteriophage T2 have been shown to contain three enzymes which are undetectable in extracts of uninfected or in T5-infected cells. These are: (*a*) an enzyme which phosphorylates hydroxymethyldeoxycytidine 5-phosphate, leading to the synthesis of the triphosphate, (*b*) an enzyme which removes the terminal pyrophosphate group specifically from deoxycytidine triphosphate, and (*c*) an enzyme which transfers glucose from uridine diphosphate glucose directly to the hydroxymethylcytosine of certain DNA's.

2. These new enzymes can account for (*a*) the availability of the triphosphate of hydroxymethyldeoxycytidine for the enzymatic synthesis of T2 DNA, (*b*) the absence of deoxycytidylate from T2 DNA, and (*c*) the presence of glucose on a fixed fraction of the hydroxymethylcytosine residues in DNA.

3. The DNA-polymerizing enzyme assayed with hydroxymethyldeoxycytidine triphosphate in place of deoxycytidine triphosphate reveals about a 12-fold increase in activity after T2 infection. Increases, after T2 infection, in the levels of thymine and guanine deoxynucleotide phosphorylating enzymes (by 20–45 fold) bring their activities up to the level of the adenine deoxynucleotide phosphorylating enzyme which is unchanged; the level of the cytosine deoxynucleotide phosphorylating enzyme remains at a low level.

4. After T5 infection, levels of the thymine, guanine, and cytosine deoxynucleotide phosphorylating enzymes increase by 10–40 fold, bringing their activities up to the level of the adenine deoxynucleotide phosphorylating enzyme, which increases about 2-fold.

5. The new enzymes and the increases in level of the enzymes occurring in normal cells are first detectable about 4 min after infection with phage T2 and about 10 min after infection with phage T5. These results are consistent with previously published studies which have indicated with the use of inhibitors of protein synthesis that viral DNA synthesis requires a preliminary period of protein synthesis.

* This investigation was supported by research grants from the National Institutes of Health of the Public Health Service and the National Science Foundation.

† National Science Foundation Predoctoral Fellow.

‡ Fellow of the National Foundation.

[1] The abbreviations used in this report are: cpm, counts per minute; ATP, adenosine triphosphate; dA-5-P, deoxyadenosine 5′-phosphate; dC-5-P, deoxycytidine 5′-phosphate; dG-5-P, deoxyguanosine 5′-phosphate; dHMC-5-P, hydroxymethyldeoxycytidine 5′-phosphate; dT-5-P, deoxythymidine 5′-phosphate; dATP, deoxyadenosine triphosphate; dCTP, deoxycytidine triphosphate; dGTP, deoxyguanosine triphosphate; dHMC-TP, hydroxymethyldeoxycytidine triphosphate; dTTP, deoxythymidine triphosphate; DNA, deoxyribonucleic acid; HMC, 5-hydroxymethylcytosine; UDPG, uridine diphosphate glucose; Tris, tris-(hydroxymethyl)aminomethane; KPO_4, potassium phosphate buffer; PRPP, 5-phosphoryl α-D-ribofuranose 1-pyrophosphate; E_m, molar extinction coefficient.

[2] Lehman, I. R., M. J. Bessman, E. S. Simms, and A. Kornberg, *J. Biol. Chem.*, **233,** 163 (1958).

[3] Bessman, M. J., I. R. Lehman, J. Adler, S. B. Zimmerman, E. S. Simms, and A. Kornberg, these PROCEEDINGS, **44,** 633 (1958).

[4] Bessman, M. J., I. R. Lehman, E. S. Simms, and A. Kornberg, *J. Biol. Chem.*, **233,** 171 (1958); Adler, J., I. R. Lehman, M. J. Bessman, E. S. Simms, and A. Kornberg, these PROCEEDINGS, **44,** 641 (1958); Lehman, I. R., S. B. Zimmerman, J. Adler, M. J. Bessman, E. S. Simms, and A. Kornberg, these PROCEEDINGS, **44,** 1191 (1958); Kornberg, A., *Harvey Lectures*, **53,** 83 (1957–1958).

[5] Hershey, A. D., J. Dixon, and M. Chase, *J. Gen. Physiol.*, **36,** 777 (1952–1953).

[6] Wyatt, G. R., and S. S. Cohen, *Biochem. J.*, **55,** 774 (1953).

[7] Flaks, J. G., and S. S. Cohen, *Biochim. et Biophys. Acta*, **25,** 667 (1957); *Federation Proc.*, **17,** 220 (1958).

[8] Sinsheimer, R. L., *Science*, **120,** 551 (1954); Volkin, E., *J. Am. Chem. Soc.*, **76,** 5892 (1954).

[9] Sinsheimer, R. L., these PROCEEDINGS, **42,** 502 (1956); Jesaitis, M. A., *J. Exp. Med.*, **106,** 233 (1957); *Federation Proc.*, **17,** 250 (1958).

[10] Streisinger, G., and J. Weigle, these PROCEEDINGS, **42,** 504 (1956).

[11] Cohen, S. S., *J. Biol. Chem.*, **174,** 281 (1948).

[12] Kornberg, A., I. R. Lehman, and E. S. Simms, *Federation Proc.*, **15,** 291 (1956), and more recent unpublished observations.

[13] An abstract of this work has appeared [Zimmerman, S. B., S. R. Kornberg, J. Josse, and A. Kornberg, *Federation Proc.*, **18,** 359 (1959)], as have abstracts regarding an enzyme which phosphorylates dHMC-5-P (R. Somerville and G. R. Greenberg, *Ibid.*, 327), dHMC-TP incorporation into DNA, and a suggested dCTP-degrading enzyme (J. F. Koerner and M. S. Smith, *Ibid.*, 264) in T2-infected *E. coli.*

[14] Anderson, E. H., these PROCEEDINGS, **32,** 120 (1946).

[15] We are indebted to Dr. Helen Van Vunakis for a generous gift of phage T2r$^+$.

[16] Adams, M. H., in *Methods in Medical Research*, ed. J. H. Comroe, Jr. (Chicago: Yearbook Publishers, Inc., 1950), **2,** 1.

[17] Doermann, A. H., *J. Gen. Physiol.*, **35,** 645 (1952).

[18] When fluoride was present in the kinase assays, the nucleotides were adsorbed to and eluted from Norit before phosphatase treatment in Stage II of the assay.

[19] For large-scale enzyme preparations, 50-liter cultures at the late exponential phase (2×10^9 cells/ml), in modified M-9 medium (see Methods) but lacking $CaCl_2$, were treated with 3–4 T2r$^+$ per cell and 10 min later with 50 γ of chloramphenicol per ml. The culture was then chilled to 0° with ice over a 10-min period and harvested by centrifugation. The initial steps in the purification of the dHMC-5-P kinase, dCTPase, glucosylating enzyme, and hydroxymethylating enzyme were the same. Sonic extracts, prepared in 5 volumes of 0.05 *M* glycylglycine buffer, pH 7.0, were centrifuged and the supernatant fluid diluted with buffer to contain 10 mg of protein per ml. Streptomycin sulfate (5 per cent solution), equal to 0.3 volume of the diluted extract, was added; the supernatant fluid collected after centrifugation contained 3 to 4 mg of protein per ml. It was adjusted to pH 8 with KOH and applied to a diethylaminoethylcellulose (Brown Co.) column [Peterson, E. A., and H. A. Sober, *J. Am. Chem. Soc.*, **78,** 751 (1956)], equi-

librated with 0.02 *M* KPO_4, pH 8.0, containing 0.01 *M* 2-mercaptoethanol. Linear gradients were applied and the purifications obtained are expressed relative to the supernatant fluid of the sonic extract; all solutions contained 0.01 *M* 2-mercaptoethanol. Glucosylating enzyme: gradient of 0.08 to 0.32 *M* NaCl in 0.02 *M* KPO_4, pH 8.0–30× purification; dCTPase: gradient of 0.08 *M* to 0.32 *M* NaCl in 0.02 *M* KPO_4, pH 8.0–24× purification, rechromatographed with a gradient of 0.06–0.32 *M* KPO_4, pH 6.5–85× purification; dHMC-5-P kinase: gradient of 0.06 to 0.32 *M* KPO_4, pH 6.5–20× purification; hydroxymethylating enzyme: gradient of 0.3 *M* KPO_4, pH 6.5 to 1.0 *M* KPO_4, pH 6.1–230× purification. Fractions containing 2-mercaptoethanol were not frozen. Active fractions were concentrated by precipitation with solid $(NH_4)_2SO_4$. Further details of the purification procedures will be published elsewhere.

[20] Glaser, L., and D. Brown, these PROCEEDINGS, **41,** 253 (1955); Glaser, L., *J. Biol. Chem.*, **232,** 627 (1958).

[21] Personal communication from Dr. M. J. Bessman.

[22] We are indebted to Dr. R. L. Sinsheimer for the sample of ϕX174 DNA.

[23] Personal communication from Dr. I. R. Lehman.

[24] Chargaff, E., in *Nucleic Acids*, ed. E. Chargaff and J. N. Davidson (New York: Academic Press, Inc., 1955), **1,** 307.

[25] Dunn, D. B., and J. D. Smith, *Nature*, **174,** 305 (1954); S. Zamenhof and G. Griboff, *Nature*, **174,** 306 (1954).

[26] Burton, K., *Biochem. J.*, **61,** 473 (1955).

[27] Tomizawa, J., and S. Sunakawa, *J. Gen. Physiol.*, **39,** 553 (1956).

[28] Hershey, A. D., and N. E. Melechen, *Virology*, **3,** 207 (1957).

[29] Watanabe, I., *Biochim. et Biophys. Acta*, **25,** 665 (1957); Watanabe, I., and Y. Kiho, *Proc. Int'l. Symp. Enzyme Chemistry* (Tokyo-Kyoto, 1958), p. 418; Hershey, A. D., A. Garen, D. K. Fraser, and J. D. Hudis, *Carnegie Insitution of Washington Year Book*, **53,** 210 (1953–1954).

[30] Cohen, S. S., Abstracts of the American Chemical Society, Meeting, September, 1958, p. 22C.

[31] Pardee, A. B., and R. E. Kunkee, *J. Biol. Chem.*, **199,** 9 (1952). Dr. Fred Bergmann has found no changes, following T2 infection of *E. coli* B, in amino acid "activation" levels for valine, isoleucine, methionine, leucine, phenylalanine, tryptophan, and tyrosine. We have observed that levels of the following activities did not change (± 20 per cent) within 15 min after *E. coli* B infection with phage T2: PRPP synthetase, orotate + PRPP conversion to uridylate, inorganic pyrophosphatase, adenine + PRPP conversion to adenylate, and adenylate kinase.

[32] Hogness, D. S., M. Cohn, and J. Monod, *Biochim. et Biophys. Acta*, **16,** 99 (1955); Rotman, B., and S. Spiegelman, *J. Bacteriol.*, **68,** 419 (1954).

THE FREQUENCY DISTRIBUTION OF SPONTANEOUS BACTERIOPHAGE MUTANTS AS EVIDENCE FOR THE EXPONENTIAL RATE OF PHAGE REPRODUCTION[1]

S. E. Luria

University of Illinois, Urbana, Illinois

The phage geneticist is faced with the task of constructing a satisfactory model of phage reproduction, in the absence of direct morphological evidence similar to the one available to the macro-geneticist. Cell division, mitosis, meiosis, fertilization have a solid basis of morphological observation that the modern geneticist takes for granted. The virologist, on the other hand, begins where the cytogeneticist ends; in a sense, he deals directly with the units of genetic material whose existence the macro-geneticists (including the bacterial geneticists) must infer. Here lies his weakness, since little is known of the performance of such units — and also his strength, since he can manipulate this subcytological world. He is not limited to dealing with integrated units of reproduction at the cellular level, but can control to a certain extent what goes into his cells. Because of this, virology's methods may lead more directly to solving the problem of the mode of replication of genetic material.

Penetration of one phage particle into a susceptible bacterium leads to production of a large number of similar particles. The intervening steps are unknown. We conjecture a reorganization of the viral material, because of its nonrecoverability in infectious form early after penetration (Doermann, 1948). We conjecture an integration of the viral material into the cell machinery at the genetic level (Luria and Human, 1950), because cell syntheses are redirected toward the production of virus specific substances. The genetic complexities of bacteriophage tell us that the viral specificities to be replicated are multiple (Hershey, 1946b) and that the new virus may receive imprints from more than one viral ancestor within the same cell (Delbrück and Bailey, 1946; Hershey, 1946b). There is evidence suggesting a discrete and regularly assorted nature of the material determinants of these specificities (Hershey and Rotman, 1948).

---

[1]Aided by grants from the American Cancer Society (upon recommendation of the Committee on Growth) and from the Research Board, University of Illinois. The competent assistance of Miss Martha R. Sheek is gratefully acknowledged.

Reprinted by permission of the author and the Long Island Biological Association from Cold Spring Harbor Symposia on Quantitative Biology, 16, 463-470 (1951).

A theory proposed by this writer (Luria, 1947) assumed independent replication of these determinants (or groups of determinants) followed by their assembly into mature virus particles. This theory originally aimed at accounting for the reactivation of ultraviolet inactivated phage inside multiple-infected bacteria (Luria and Dulbecco, 1949) and was extended to account for some features of genetic recombination (Hershey and Rotman, 1949). The main ground for proposing the theory, namely, the belief that the reactivation resulted from genetic exchange, has been weakened by new evidence (Dulbecco, 1952), and the theory has as little left to support it as to disprove it.

Yet, all this concerns the organization of virus material during reproduction, not the elementary process of replication. The latter cannot yet be attacked at the chemical level by any tool except speculation. It can be attacked on a limited front, however, by strictly genetic means. The experiments described in this paper were done to investigate the rate of replication of individual genetic determinants of the virus. They indicate that reproduction is exponential, each replica acting as a source of new replicas.

Theory

Phage mutations occur only in the intracellular state, presumably during replication. If a phage mutation occurs in a bacterium, that bacterium will liberate one or more mutants (assuming that no loss occurs intracellularly). Delbrück pointed out several years ago that the actual numbers of mutants would depend on the mode of phage replication — more specifically, on the mode of replications of the determinant or "gene" involved (see Luria, 1945b). We shall analyze a few possible mechanisms; other mechanisms may be proposed, but do not seem to lead to any simple picture.

I. *Exponential Reproduction*

One gene produces n genes, each of which in turn gives n genes, and so on. After r generations, the number will be n^r. For $n = 2$ (duplication mechanism), the situation is analogous to bacterial reproduction. Let us assume this to be the case. N gene copies will derive from one gene by N-1 acts of replication. Let the last generation have the order number 0, the second last the order number 1, the third last 2, and so on. Suppose a mutation occurs at generation k, either as an "error of replication" affecting one of the two products of duplication, or as a change in one gene during interphase. If the replication process is completely synchronized (the consequences of nonsynchronization can, if necessary, be analyzed), the resulting clone of mutants will at generation 0 consist of 2^k individuals. If the total number of individuals (at generation 0) in the population is N, at generation k there were $N/2^k$ individuals. Assuming a constant probability m of mutation per individual, the number of mutations occurring at generation k is $mN/2^k$. The relation between the number x of mutants in a clone and the frequency y_x of such clones will then be obtained as follows:

$$y_x = \frac{mN}{2^k};\ x = 2^k;\ y_x = \frac{mN}{x}. \qquad (1)$$

Synchronization is expressed by the requirement that for $x \neq 2^k$, $y_x = 0$.

The frequency distribution (1) is, of course, identical to that of bacterial mutants in a series of similar populations (Luria and Delbrück, 1943; Lea and Coulson, 1949). If we limit our observation to one intracellular cycle of phage production, the maximum clone size will be the maximum "burst size." Each phage burst with 2^K particles represents a population. For $m \gg 2^{-K}$, there will practically never be more than one mutation per bacterium; the frequency distribution (1) will then be that of the mutant clones among a large number of bacterial yields, with limitations imposed by the inequality of burst size from cell to cell.

II. *Independent Successive Replications*

Let us suppose that each new replica of a gene is produced independently of the preceding one, for example, by a series of successive acts of replication controlled by the initial gene brought in by the infecting phage particle.

(a) If one of the copies mutates (at the time of its formation or later) the probability of mutation in other copies produced in the same cell should not be affected. Assuming a uniform mutation probability m, the mutants will be distributed at random among phage bursts (Poisson distribution).

(b) If the initial gene, the pattern, mutates while turning out replicas, we may assume that afterwards it produces only mutants. If the mutation rate is constant in successive replications, there will occur as many cases of mutation just before the production of the last viable gene copy as before the production of the second last, the third last, and so on. The mutants will be in clones, and the frequency of clones of different sizes will be uniform, at least up to the value of the minimum burst size.

Experimental Work

Previous data on the number of host range mutants in individual phage cultures (Luria, 1945a; Hershey, 1946a) did not allow the desired type of analysis, because the quantitative detection of the mutants was uncertain and because their low frequency made it necessary to look for them in mass cultures, where more than one cycle of intrabacterial growth of some mutants could take place.

The experiments here reported consisted in making single infection of *Escherichia coli* B with phage T2L (Hershey, 1946a; for the experimental methods used, see Adams, 1950) and counting the mutants *r* or *w* produced in phage bursts from individual bacteria. These mutant phenotypes (Hershey, 1946b) were chosen because they occur with suitable frequency, can be recognized and scored efficiently, and can be tested for genetic allelism or nonallelism (Hershey and Rotman, 1948). Previous extensive tests by Dulbecco (1949) and other tests made in the course of this work established the following technical points.

1. Mutant plaques *r* and *w* can be detected and scored without difficulty after six to eight hours of incubation at 37°C on nutrient agar plates under standard conditions (plating in a 0.6% agar layer over 24 hour old 1% agar plates, with about 2×10^8 young bacteria per plate). Over 100 single plaque isolations and replatings confirmed the scorings made by plaque type.

2. A plaque of *r* type can be distinguished without difficulty from a "mottled plaque" stemming from a bacterium infected with a mixture of *r* and wild-type, even when *r* is in moderate excess. Thus, it is possible to distinguish a plaque originating from an *r* particle from one resulting from a mutation that occurs on the plate during the development of a wild type plaque, unless the *r* mutation occurred in the first bacterium infected after plating and produced within that bacterium a large majority of *r* mutants — an improbable occurrence, as the results of the present work will show.

3. As for the *w* mutants, mixed plaques of *w* and wild type closely resemble the plaques of wild type, so that the chances of mistaking a mixed plaque for a pure *w* one are rather small.

Several single burst experiments of T2L on B, with single infection in Difco nutrient broth, gave average yields per bacterium around 60–100; the burst size distributions are shown in Table 1. The reasons for the lower average yield of T2L in Difco nutrient broth, as compared with the yields obtained several years ago in the same system (Delbrück and Luria, 1942), are unknown; they may have to do with changes in medium composition, in the bacterial host, or in the virus itself.

Mass phage lysates often contain more phage particles than plaque-forming units; most of the particles can be caused to form plaques by treatment with distilled water or Zn^{++} before plating (Bertani, unpub.). Electron micrographic counts give, for carefully assayed lysates of T2L, ratios "particles/plaques" between 1.0 and 2.0 (Luria, Williams and Backus, 1951 and unpub.). The failure of some phage particles to form plaques is apparently a peculiarity of phage in mass lysates, probably due to a combination between phage and inhibitors of bacterial origin. Repeated attempts to reveal, by various treatments, any increase in the plaque count of dilute lysates similar to those used in the experiments here reported, constantly failed. It is likely that plaque counts reveal nearly 100 per cent of the phage particles plated.

In our experiments, we plated the full content of tubes in which one or several bacteria had lysed. The loss of phage remaining in each tube after plating is of the order of five per cent or less. Thus, we feel that we recovered and examined practically the totality of the active phage produced by the bacteria.

Preliminary experiments indicated that mutants were present in about one burst out of 200. This made it possible to examine on each plate the phage yields from several infected bacteria, and yet to have almost never more than one mutant clone per plate. As many as 20 bursts per plate were examined in some experiments, particularly when only the *r* mutants were scored, since these are more easily recognized than the *w* mutants.

Independently isolated *r* mutants are generally found to be nonallelic, yielding wild-type recombinants in mixed infection (Hershey and Rotman, 1948). To test for allelism among *r* mutants isolated in our experiments, stocks were prepared from individual mutant plaques and used, separately or in mixtures, to infect bacteria. The yields were examined for wild-type plaques. Similar tests with *w* mutants are technically more difficult and were therefore not attempted.

TABLE 1. BURST SIZE DISTRIBUTION, T2L ON B, SINGLE INFECTION

Date	Number of plates	Average number of bursts per plate	Average yield per burst	Median	Range*
12/7/50	96	0.93	69	101	13–472
12/8/50	105	0.89	71	84	5–347
4/10/51	96	0.73	92	106	9–477
4/23/51	48	0.85	87	111	10–254

*The maximum values are almost certainly too high, since they probably represent plates with two or more bursts.

The Frequency Distribution of Mutants

A total of 16 experiments, done between April 1949 and April 1951, yielded the data to be reported. In five experiments, only the *r* mutants were scored. The results are presented in Tables 2 and 3. A total of 90 plates with mutants *r* and 103 plates with mutants *w* were observed. The expected number of plates with both *r* and *w* mutants (calculated from the assumption of independent incidence of *r* mutations and *w* mutations, either in the same bacterium or in different bacteria whose bursts were pooled on one plate) was seven; six were found.

TABLE 2. SYNOPSIS OF EXPERIMENTS ON DISTRIBUTION OF *r* AND *w* MUTANTS

Date	Stock phage, number	Number of plates	Number of bursts	Average number of bursts per plate	Number of plates with *r* mutants	Number of plates with *w* mutants
4/26/49	33	144	660	4.6	3	10
5/6/49	"	144	660	4.6	7	9
3/9/50	44	142	1120	7.9	12	7
3/14/50	"	143	1180	8.25	4	15
3/31/50	"	144	2020	14	6	18
5/2/50	"	143	250	1.75	2	3
5/19/50	46	144	1060	7.5	9	12
5/26/50	"	144	1800	13	15	9
12/18/50	51	605	540	0.89	2	1
1/11/51	"	144	800	5.5	7	10
2/12/51	"	144	820	5.7	4	9
3/1/51	"	192	1500	7.9	1	..*
3/8/51	"	192	2400	17.5	1	..
3/20/51	"	180	3400	19	7	..
3/29/51	"	173	4400	25.5	9	..
4/10/51	"	96	70	0.73	1	..
		Totals	22620		90	103

*Mutants *w* not scored.

Let us observe the frequency distributions of the numbers of mutants (Table 3). The total number of mutants observed in all experiments (Table 3; total clone frequency) was 766, distributed among 2874 plates containing about 1.8×10^6 normal phages. The proportion of mutants is about 4×10^{-4}, and their average number per plate is about 2.5×10^{-1}. If the mutants were distributed at random, there would be about 550 plates with one mutant, about 90 with two or three mutants, and only four with four mutants or more. There is no doubt that the distributions are not random, but clonal.

As a test of the nature of the mutants appearing on the same plate, 11 pairs of *r* mutants were isolated from 11 plates, which contained between 2 and 59 mutants. In all cases, the mutants in each pair proved allelic (probably identical); no wild-type recombinant was observed among at least 1000 plaques of the yield from mixed infected bacteria. In 11 out of 12 crosses between mutants isolated from different plates we observed wild-type recombinants; the twelfth cross failed to show recombinants. It may have represented either a case of repeated occurrence of the same mutation or a case of two mutations with recombination frequency lower than 0.2 per cent, the lowest frequency detectable in our rather crude tests. These results, then confirm the clonal nature of the mutants produced within a given bacterium. We will now consider the clonal distributions.

Inspection of Table 3 shows that the mutant distribution, though clonal, fails to fit the uniform frequency predicted for small clones of various sizes by the hypothesis of independent gene replication, with mutations occurring in the pattern.

Let us turn next to the distribution predicted by the hypothesis of exponential duplication.

Inspection of the data shows: (a) there are clones with two mutants; therefore, if exponential reproduction occurs, the elementary process is probably one of duplication (from 1 to 2) rather than triplication or quadruplication; (b) there are clones with 3, 5, 6, 7, . . . in addition to clones with 1, 2, 4, 8, . . . mutants. Thus, exponential reproduction, if present, must be nonsynchronized, a conclusion also suggested by the well-known distribution of the total burst size.

For a quantitative test of the hypothesis of exponential reduplication we shall use, instead of Equation (1), the following expression (accumulated distribution) suggested by Dr. Howard Levene:

$$Y_x = \sum_{\gg x} y_x = \Sigma \frac{mN}{x} = \Sigma \frac{mN}{2^k} = mN\Sigma \frac{1}{2^k} \approx \frac{mN}{2^{k-1}} = \frac{2mN}{x} \text{ (for } N = 2^K \gg x). \qquad (2)$$

Y_x is the number of clones with x or more mutants. The product $Y_x \times x$ is constant and a plot of log Y versus log x gives a straight line with slope -1; the vertical intercept for $x = 1$ is the logarithm of the total number of mutant clones. This plot has the advantage that it is hardly affected by nonsynchronization. A clone with three mutants can be considered either as a clone that should have had two mutants and underwent one extra reduplication, or as a four-mutant clone that lagged one reduplication behind. In either case, the clone will contribute to the value Y_2 and will be deducted from the value Y_4.

A correction should be made before comparing the results with the theoretical expectation. The stocks of phage used to infect bacteria contained small, known

TABLE 3. THE DISTRIBUTION OF MUTANTS IN INDIVIDUAL PLATES

Clone size	Clone frequency, *r* mutants		Clone frequency, *w* mutants		Clone frequency, total, corrected for full mutant clones
	All plates	Corrected for full mutant clones	All plates	Corrected for full mutant clones	
1	47	47	46	46	93
2	9	9	18	18	27
3	11	11	11	11	22
4	2	2	4	4	6
5	2	2	1	1	3
6			7	7	7
7	2	2	2	2	4
8	1	1	1	1	2
9					
10	2	2	1	1	3
11			1	1	1
12	1	1			1
13					
14	1	1	1	1	2
15	1	1	1	1	2
16			1	1	1
20			2	1	1
22	2	2			2
25			1		
26			1	1	1
30	1	1			1
34			1	1	1
37			1		
39	1				
40	1		1		
41	2	1			1
47	1	1	1		1
53	1				
59	1	1			1
100	1				
Total	90	85	103	98	183

numbers of *r* and *w* mutants. Since we plated more than one burst per plate, some of the mutant clones observed may have stemmed from bacteria infected solely with one mutant particle. These clones ought to be eliminated (since they derive from mutant particles originated in a mass lysate, where different conditions obtain) but they cannot be recognized. The expected number of such "full mutant" clones was 10. Assuming that a "full mutant" clone would be at least as large as the minimum burst size, we eliminated from the experiments where such clones were expected to be present an appropriate fraction of the largest clones (see Table 3). This correction is indeed a small one.

Figure 1 compares the experimental distribution of clones with one or more mutants with the expected distribution from the hypothesis of exponential reduplication. The data corresponding to the "corrected" columns in Table 3 are plotted for *r* mutants, for *w* mutants and for the two together. They fit well the expected relationship (linear relation between log Y_x and log x with slope -1) for low clone size, up to mutant clone sizes of the order of 10–15. Above that point, the frequency of mutant clones falls below the theoretical values. This behavior is precisely what we should expect. The linear relation between log y and log x — see Equation (1) — should only obtain for clones so small that they have equal chances to be formed in all bacteria. For clone sizes of the order of the burst size, a limitation is placed on the frequency with which these clones can be observed. In the curve log Y_x versus log x this limitation will manifest itself as a downward concavity, which becomes appreciable around the value corresponding to the lowest class of frequent burst sizes (about 20 phages per bacterium in our experiments) and progressively more pronounced as the median burst size is approached. Of course, there cannot be any clone larger than the maximum burst size. An additional factor (suggested by Dr. S. Dancoff) that works in the same direction is nonsynchronization itself; in fact, this results in the existence, within each burst, of subclones that have originated at the same generation but have different sizes, thus producing effects similar to those of the burst size differences.

No closer analysis of the concave portion of the distribution frequency curve is feasible beyond these qualitative considerations, since the clones in this region are few and fluctuations affect the results strongly. Altogether, our results fit quite well the hypothesis that the genes responsible for the investigated phenotypes reproduce exponentially by successive reduplications. Let us now analyze some of the factors that might affect the experimental results.

1. Failure to recognize mutants. This cause of error is difficult to assess; we believe the error to be very small. All plates were scored by the same observer after the optimum incubation period, and every plate that might have presented difficulties in scoring, because of crowding or of faulty layering, was discarded before examination. All the doubtful plaques were picked and replated for the phenotype test. Any residual error from this source would probably result in underestimation of the frequency of clones with one mutant, since the finding of the first mutant on a plate might sharpen the alertness of the observer, thereby increasing the chances of detecting other mutants on the same plate; the classes of clones with more than one mutant might thus have been favored in our observations.

2. A more definite and more easily evaluated source of error is the coincidence of more than one clone of a given mutant type (*r* or *w*) on the same plate because of coincidence of two mutations, either in the same bacterium or in the group of bacterial bursts examined on one plate. The expected coincidences ("doubles") were calculated to be 2.6 *r* and 4.3 *w*. It is not easy to correct for these "doubles,"

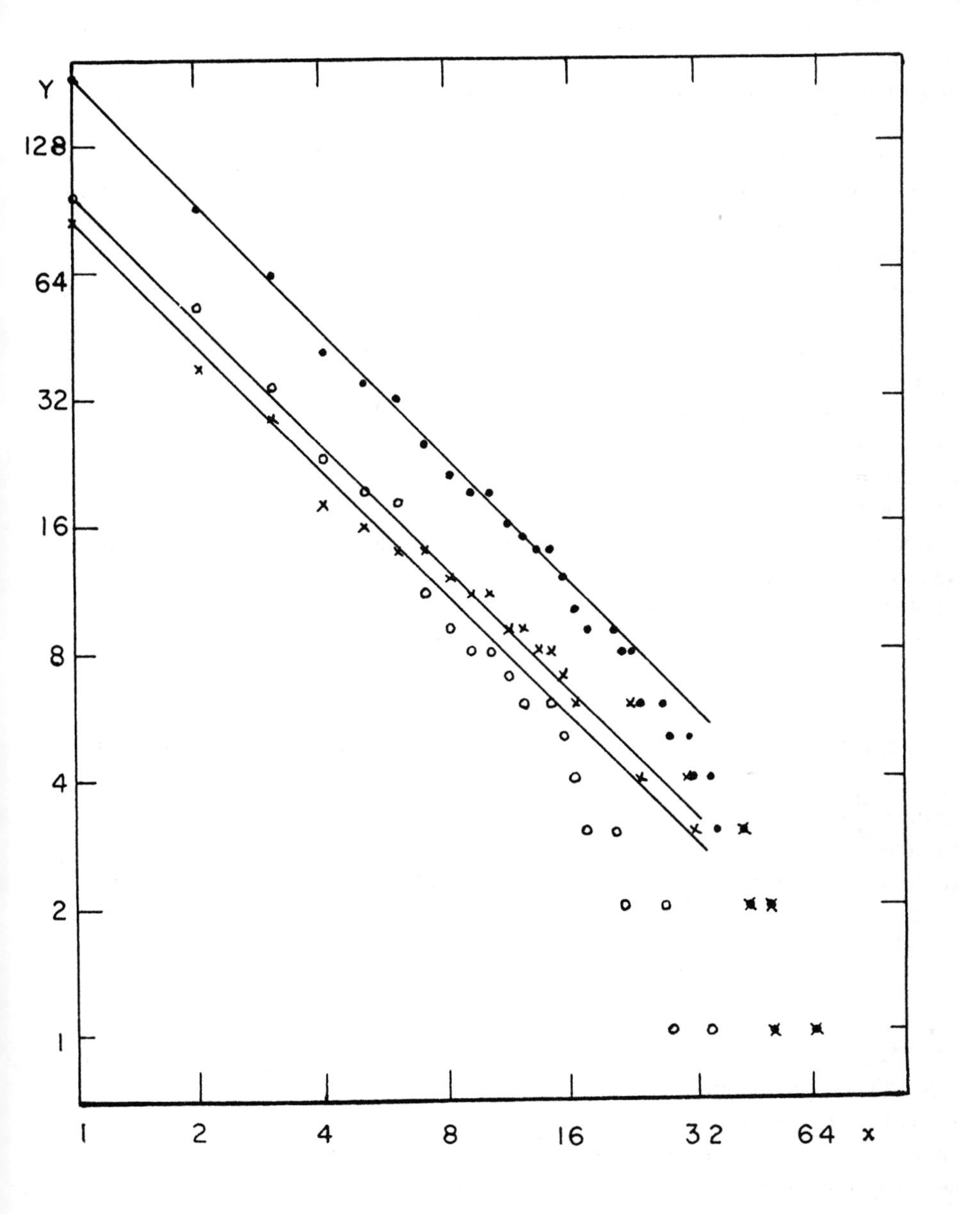

FIG. 1. The distribution of mutant clones. x = number of mutants in a clone. Y = number of clones with x or more mutants. X : *r* mutants. C : *w* mutants. ●: *r* and *w* mutants. The solid lines represent the theoretical distributions, with slope −1.

which cannot be recognized by inspection. A first approximation can be made by assuming that all "doubles" include a clone of one mutant, and that they all occur among the most frequent clone size classes observed (plates with 2, 3, 4 mutants). The resulting corrected distribution has a slight excess of ones, but does not deviate significantly from Equation (2), in spite of the fact that the correction is an extreme one, which concentrates all the distortion in the initial, most critical portion of the frequency distribution curve.

3. Failure of the plaque count method to reveal the full number of mutants is unlikely to result from technical reasons, but might be due to intrinsic properties of phage reproduction. For example, only a fraction of the gene copies produced might appear in active phage particles because of loss or inactivation of a certain proportion of phage within the bacteria before liberation. Such "sampling losses," superimposed on a logarithmic distribution, would make the initial slope of log Y versus log x steeper; a sampling loss of 50 per cent would give a quite appreciable deviation from the initial slope of -1. This is in conflict with our results. Sampling losses could be superimposed on any other distribution, but it is hard to visualize how the results could simulate those of an exponential distribution.

A variety of alternate hypotheses was considered in an attempt to find one, besides that of exponential reproduction, that could lead to the results found experimentally. No sensible hypothesis could be devised. Altogether, the hypothesis of mutations occurring at a constant rate in the course of exponential nonsynchronized gene reduplication appears adequate to account for our results.

Mutation Rates

Our results permit fairly accurate estimations of mutation rates. A total of 87.6 *r* mutations (85 mutant clones plus 2.6 coincidences) occurred in 23,000 bursts, producing approximately 1,850,000 active phage particles. The mutation frequency per reduplication is around 5×10^{-5}. 102.3 *w* mutations in 11,000 bursts, or 880,000 particles, correspond to a mutation frequency of 1.2×10^{-4}. These mutation rates, of course, are the sums of the mutation rates at all the individual loci that can mutate to give either the *r* or the *w* phenotype.

Incidental Observations

1. The mutants of T2L classified as *r* or *w* are generally clearly recognizable as such. The *r* phenotype, however, is not uniform; different *r* mutations give plaque types often distinguishable from one another. The *w* phenotype, though generally sharply distinct from *r* and from wild-type, is even more variable. Only one clone (consisting of one plaque), even after repeated replatings, could not be classified with certainty as either *w* or *r*; since at any rate it seemed to represent a novel phenotype, it was excluded from the analysis.

2. Several other types of mutants were observed in the course of our experiments, mainly "minute" or "sharp" plaque types. These were not included in the results.

3. Mottled plaques were often seen on our plates. They generally derive from mutations occurring during plaque formation. In several cases, mottled plaques were present on the same plate with *r* mutants. Three such mottled plaques were replated and the *r* component strain was isolated and crossed with a strain from a pure *r* plaque on the same plate. In two cases wild-type recombinants appeared, indicating that the mottled plaque probably stemmed from an independent *r* mutation that occurred on the plate; in the third case no recombinant was found. The latter type of mottled plaque could appear in the yield of a bacterium containing a clone of *r* mutants, owing to some limitations to the complete segregation of virus particles or of their genetic components (Hershey and Chase, 1951).

Discussion

The exponential rate of gene reproduction in phage, suggested by our analysis of the clonal distribution of spontaneous phage mutants, simply means that the initial gene copy brought in by the infective virus does not possess the monopoly of replication. Its copies act in turn as sources for new replications and the elementary replication process is a reduplication. This conclusion, if correct, represents a step further in our analysis of phage reproduction.

Our results do not contribute any information as to whether the mutations occur only at reduplication or between reduplications, in the "interphase." They are compatible both with production of phage particles as such and of individual genetic components, although the apparent lack of "sampling losses" is more easily reconciled with the former.

There is some interest in comparing the clonal distribution of spontaneous mutants with the almost random distribution of recombinant phage from mixed-infected bacteria (Hershey and Rotman, 1949). The very first active phage particles that appear inside mixed-infected bacteria include recombinants (Doermann and Dissosway, 1949), whose distribution is also intermediate between a clonal, reduplicational one and a random one. The facts suggest the following conclusions:

1. Recombination occurs late in reproduction of the genetic material of phage. This may be due either to the coincidence of recombination with some terminal step in phage maturation or to an increased probability of recombination when large numbers of phage elements are present in a cell.

2. Recombinants detectable as mature particles around the middle of the intracellular growth period do not reduplicate as such; otherwise, by giving rise to clones, they would cause the later population of recombinants to be distributed more and more like spontaneous mutants, contrary to experimental finding (terminal distribution of recombinants almost random).

3. Reproduction of the genetic material of phage, therefore, takes place mainly by reduplication of elements that are not yet in the form of mature phage particles.

References

ADAMS, M. H., 1950, Methods of study of bacterial viruses. In: Methods in Medical Research. *2*: 1–73.

DELBRÜCK, M., and BAILEY, W. T., Jr., 1946, Induced mutations in bacterial viruses. Cold Spring Harb. Symposium Quant. Biol. *11*: 33–37.

DELBRÜCK, M., and LURIA, S. E., 1942, Interference between bacterial viruses. I. Arch. Biochem. *1*: 111–141.

DOERMANN, A. H., 1948, Intracellular growth of bacteriophage. Yearb. Carneg. Instn. *47*: 176–182.

DOERMANN, A. H., and DISSOSWAY, C. F.-R., 1949, Intracellular growth and genetics of bacteriophage. Yearb. Carneg. Instn. *48*: 170–176.

DULBECCO, R., 1949, The number of particles of bacteriophage T2 that can participate in intracellular growth. Genetics *34*: 126–132.

1952, A critical test of the recombination theory of multiplicity reactivation. J. Bact. (in press).

HERSHEY, A. D., 1946a, Mutations of bacteriophage with respect to type of plaque. Genetics *31*: 620–640.

1946b, Spontaneous mutations in bacterial viruses. Cold Spring Harb. Symposium Quant. Biol. *11*: 67–76.

HERSHEY, A. D., and CHASE, M., 1951, Genetic recombination and heterozygosis in bacteriophage. Cold Spring Harb. Symposium Quant. Biol. *16*.

HERSHEY, A. D., and ROTMAN, R., 1948, Linkage among genes controlling inhibition of lysis in a bacterial virus. Proc. Nat. Acad. Sci. Wash. *34*: 89–96.

1949, Genetic recombination between host-range and plaque-type mutants of bacteriophage in single bacterial cells. Genetics *34*: 44–71.

LEA, D. E., and COULSON, C. A., 1949, The distribution of the numbers of mutants in bacterial populations. J. Genet. *49*: 264–285.

LURIA, S. E., 1945a, Mutations of bacterial viruses affecting their host range. Genetics *30*: 84–99.

1945b, Genetics of bacterium-bacterial virus relationships. Ann. Missouri Bot. Gard. *32*: 235–242.

1947, Reactivation of irradiated bacteriophage by transfer of self-reproducing units. Proc. Nat. Acad. Sci. Wash. *33*: 253–264.

LURIA, S. E., and DELBRÜCK, M., 1943, Mutations of bacteria from virus sensitivity to virus resistance. Genetics *28*: 491–511.

LURIA, S. E., and DULBECCO, R., 1949, Genetic recombinations leading to production of active bacteriophage from ultraviolet inactivated bacteriophage particles. Genetics *34*: 93–125.

LURIA, S. E., and HUMAN, M. L., 1950, Chromatin staining of bacteria during bacteriophage infection. J. Bact. *59*: 551–560.

LURIA, S. E., WILLIAMS, R. C., and BACKUS, R. C., 1951, Electron micrographic counts of bacteriophage particles. J. Bact. *61*: 179–188.

DISCUSSION

ALTENBURG: I suggest that the conclusion to be drawn from Dr. Luria's experiments is that the reproduction cycle of viruses conforms with that of organisms in general, and that therefore viruses are to be considered organisms.

GENETIC RECOMBINATION BETWEEN HOST-RANGE AND PLAQUE-TYPE MUTANTS OF BACTERIOPHAGE IN SINGLE BACTERIAL CELLS[1,2]

A. D. HERSHEY AND RAQUEL ROTMAN[3]

Department of Bacteriology and Immunology, Washington University Medical School, St. Louis, Missouri

Received June 28, 1948

WE HAVE previously shown that any two of several independently arising plaque-type (*r*) mutants of the bacterial virus *T2H* interact with each other, in bacterial cells infected with both, to give rise to wild type and double mutant genetic recombinants (HERSHEY and ROTMAN 1948). In this paper we describe comparable interactions between host-range and *r* mutants of the same virus. The experiments furnish new information because it has proved possible to count the numbers of all four types of virus found in yields from the mixedly infected bacteria.

MATERIALS AND METHODS

The types of viral mutant to which we shall refer in this paper may be summarized in terms of the mutational pattern illustrated in fig. 1. In this diagram, *h* refers to a host-range mutant, *r* to any one of the rapidly lysing mutants (HERSHEY and ROTMAN 1948), and *m* ("minute") to a mutant not previously described which is characterized by a very small haloless plaque. The *h* mutant is one which forms plaques identical in appearance and number on typically sensitive strains of *Escherichia coli*, and on an indicator strain (No. 2 B/2H, 2K) resistant to h^+ forms of the virus (HERSHEY 1946a). All the steps indicated in the diagram by arrows can be observed either as spontaneous mutations, or by making the appropriate crosses. Only one example of the mutant *m*, obtained by crossing wild type with an *rm* arising in a stock of the mutant *r13*, has been studied. The plaques of *m* and *rm* are different, but are not easily distinguishable, as shown in the photograph (fig. 2).

In principle, the experimental technique we have to describe is very similar to that of genetic crossing, and will be referred to in this paper in genetic terms. One starts with a pair of mutants, each corresponding to a mutant haploid germ cell differing from wild type by a different unit change. Bacterial cells are infected with both members of the pair, and during viral growth the pair interact to produce viral progeny corresponding to germ cells of a new

[1] Aided by a grant from the U. S. PUBLIC HEALTH SERVICE.

[2] The manuscript was prepared while the senior author held a temporary appointment in the Department of Biology of the CALIFORNIA INSTITUTE OF TECHNOLOGY. It is a pleasure for him to acknowledge material and intellectual aid received from members of the staff of that department.

[3] Present address: University of Minnesota, Minneapolis, Minn.

Reprinted by permission of the authors and Genetics, Inc. from GENETICS, 34, 44-71, January, 1949.

generation, but now including some individuals differing from wild type by both unit changes, and other individuals differing from wild type not at all.

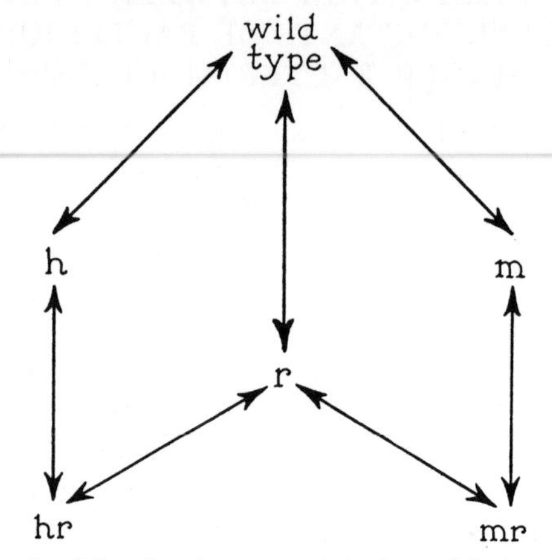

FIGURE 1.—Mutational pattern of the bacterial virus *T2H*.

The analogy to other genetic recombinations is obvious, and it is natural to look for a common mechanism.

The procedure of making a cross consists essentially in infecting a measured number of growing bacteria with larger measured numbers of two kinds of virus, diluting the culture before lysis begins to prevent readsorption of viral progeny to bacteria not yet lysed, and plating samples of the total yield of

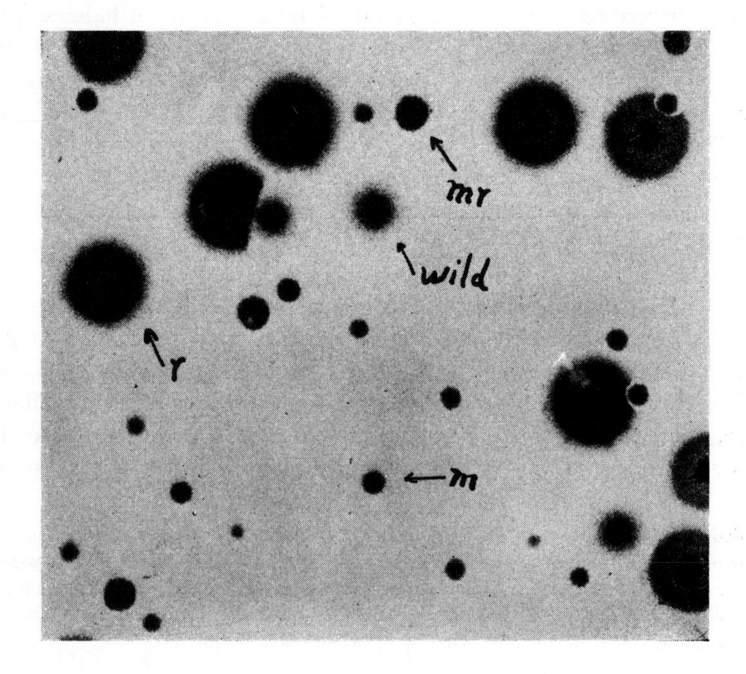

FIGURE 2.—Progeny of the cross *m*×*r1*.

virus for a differential count of its component types. This procedure was first used, for another purpose, by DELBRÜCK and LURIA (1942).

The advantage of the $h \times r$ cross is that all the genetic types of virus to which it gives rise can be recognized in a single plating on a mixture of bacterial strains (fig. 3). This makes possible the analysis of viral yields from single bacterial cells. For this purpose the procedure already described is modified

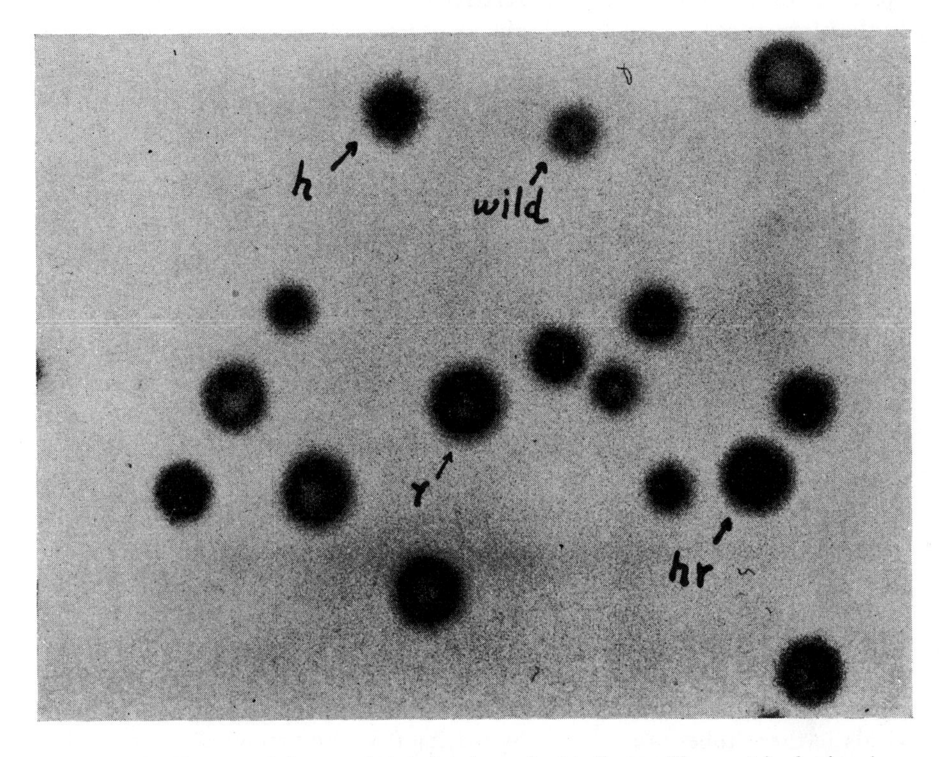

FIGURE 3.—Progeny of the cross $h \times r1$ plated on mixed indicator. The acentric clearings in the h^+r plaques result from secondary h mutations.

by increasing the factor of dilution to obtain only one infected bacterium to about three ml of nutrient broth. The culture is then divided up into samples of one ml, most of which will contain either no bacteria at all, or a single one. A large number of these samples are plated out after the bacteria lyse, and the elementary yields, averaging about 500 particles of virus in our experiments, are analyzed in toto. Both the mixed indicator method for differential counting of viral mixtures, and the single burst technique as here employed, were first used by DELBRÜCK (1945a, b).

The remaining portion of this discussion of materials and methods is of technical interest only.

Viral stocks are prepared by seeding nutrient broth cultures of *E. coli* strain S with material taken directly from a single plaque. Stocks of wild type and h mutant usually have titers exceeding 10^{10}/ml; r mutant titers are always a little less. Many of the stocks, particularly of the *r* mutants, contain unknown substances inhibiting adsorption of the virus if the dilution into bacterial suspension is less than 1:100 or so. There is no difference in the adsorption of different stocks at high dilutions of the virus. If a mixed infection is attempted with an *r* stock which contains inhibitor, and an *h* or wild type stock which does not, the adsorption of both viruses in the mixture is prevented equally. No undesirable disturbance of the relative multiplicity of infection in mixtures is therefore encountered. To obtain satisfactory levels of adsorption, all *r* mutant stocks are sedimented in a refrigerated International centrifuge with Multispeed head, and resuspended in a solution containing 1 percent Bacto-peptone and 0.5 percent NaCl. Very little loss of virus occurs during sedimentation, and probably no permanent aggregation, since sedimented mixtures of *r* and wild type virus do not yield mixed plaques. The resuspended virus is stable for at least several weeks.

To make a cross, a two hour culture of *E. coli* strain H in nutrient broth, containing 2×10^7 bacteria per ml, is infected at 37°C in an aerated culture tube (the "adsorption tube") with $\frac{1}{10}$ volume of a mixture of diluted viral stocks containing 2×10^9 plaque forming particles of each kind per ml. After five minutes, during which equal numbers (about 50 percent) of each virus are adsorbed, a 10^4 dilution is made into broth (the "growth tube") for further incubation, and a second diluted sample is spun for the assay of unadsorbed virus. Sixty minutes after infection, an assay from the growth tube gives the average yield of virus from about 40,000 mixedly infected bacteria.

For the single burst experiments, an additional dilution from the adsorption tube into antiserum to neutralize the unadsorbed virus (Delbrück 1945c), is made at the end of the adsorption period. Five minutes later, a further dilution from the antiserum tube is made into broth to contain about one infected bacterium per three ml. Before the 20th minute after infection, samples measuring one ml are distributed into a series of small tubes. The virus yields in these tubes are assayed by plating 0.3 ml 60 minutes or more after infection. The remainder of each sample, excepting those containing no virus or unmixed yields, is plated on two additional plates the next day. About 10 percent of each sample is mechanically lost. An important feature of these experiments is the guard against contamination of materials provided by the fact that about $\frac{3}{4}$ of the samples contain no virus, whereas the remainder contain more than 100 particles.

Viral yields from the growth tube are plated on sensitive bacteria (strain S), on the indicator strain (No. 2 B/2H, 2K), and on a mixture containing one volume S and two volumes indicator (day-old broth cultures). On the mixed indicator all four types of virus can be recognized (fig. 3), and their sum equals the count on S. Mixed indicators plates always show a few doubtful plaques which can be identified only by sampling and retesting, but their number is too small to be of importance, and mixtures of pure stocks can be counted with satisfactory accuracy. The counts on the single indicator, giving only the *h* mutants, are also satisfactory with mixtures of pure stocks. These counts tend to be low, however, for mixed yields of *h* and h^+ virus. The cause of this "mixed indicator effect," similar to that observed by DELBRÜCK and BAILEY (1946), remains obscure. It does not appear to be the result of segregation of multiple *h* factors, because no intermediate genetic types can be found in crosses between *h* and wild type. In $h \times r$ crosses, it affects equally counts of parental and recombinant virus.

The validity of the mixed indicator count itself rests on three lines of evidence. First, plaques sampled and retested always conform to the genetic type deduced from inspection. Second, the ratio of *h* to h^+ virus in the yield following mixed infection, measured by the mixed indicator count, is the same as the corresponding ratio of infecting viruses, with minor exceptions to be mentioned below. Third, the yield of the two recombinants in either $h \times r$ or $hr \times$ wild type crosses is very nearly equal, and the slight bias (actually of doubtful significance) correlates not with the *h*, but with the *r* pair of alleles.

For these reasons, and because of its statistical efficiency, only the mixed indicator plating is used for counting single bursts. The reproducibility of the counts so obtained may be judged from the examples shown in table 1.

TABLE 1

Mixed Indicator Counts of Viral Types in the First Eight Bursts Examined from the Cross $h \times r7$.

The counts shown are for 3 aliquots of 0.3 ml from each tube. The volumes are not measured very accurately, owing to the effort made to plate the entire sample. In computing results, it was assumed that totals of counts for each tube represented 90 percent of the actual virus content, 10 percent of the fluid being lost mechanically.

TUBE	h^+r^+	hr^+	h^+r	hr	TUBE	h^+r^+	hr^+	h^+r	hr
2	9	57	46	19	35	21	80	71	23
	9	77	56	20		24	74	65	18
	11	50	47	18		14	68	39	15
10	18	17	95	13	36	9	136	30	9
	10	14	73	8		7	100	22	7
	10	22	118	15		14	120	18	9
26	9	84	51	8	38	9	139	30	9
	10	124	53	5		9	130	19	13
	8	78	34	7		4	102	31	4
34	2	20	58	17	40	1	24	54	1
	6	26	78	32		3	38	83	10
	6	33	55	16		3	24	66	7

The nutrient broth referred to above is composed of Bacto-peptone 10 g, Bacto-beef extract 3 g, NaCl 5 g, glucose 1 g, per liter distilled water. The pH (unadjusted) is about 6.8. An occasional batch of broth prepared according to this formula proves unfavorable to the adsorption of the virus.

Nutrient agar plates are poured with a minimum of 35 ml per 9 cm Petri dish of Bacto-agar 10 g, Bacto-Tryptose 10 g, NaCl 8 g, sodium citrate crystals 2 g, glucose 1 g, per liter distilled water. The pH of the agar is adjusted to 6.8 to 7.0. Contrary to an early experience, we have recently found that Bacto-Tryptone can be substituted for Tryptose. Poured plates are stored in the refrigerator. Agar for layer plating has the same nutrient composition, but contains only 0.5 to 0.6 percent agar, the optimal concentration depending on the age of the plates and on other variables.

All platings of virus are made by the agar layer method, by adding an aliquot of virus measuring 0.1 to 0.5 ml and about 0.1 ml of a day old unaerated broth culture of bacteria, to 2 ml of melted soft agar at 45°C, and pouring the mixture over the surface of an agar plate at room temperature. The plates are incubated 18 to 24 hours at 37°C without inverting, during which time fluid collects on the agar surface without undesirable effects if conditions are optimal.

Bacterial counts are made by spreading 0.1 ml aliquots on the surface of dried agar plates.

THE LINKAGE SYSTEM

The mutants *m* and *h* (*minute* plaque and *host-range* modification, respectively) have been crossed with wild type, with the mutants called *r1*, *r7*, and *r13*, and with each other. The crosses with wild type yield only the parental types of virus, confirming that the mutants are unit modifications. The crosses with *r* mutants, and the intercross, extend the linkage system previously described (HERSHEY and ROTMAN 1948) as shown in fig. 4. The *h* locus is closely linked to the locus *r13*; the *m* locus belongs in a third linkage group C.

It should be understood that the diagram of fig. 4 is only a convenient representation of linkage relations whose structural basis remains to be elucidated (HERSHEY and ROTMAN 1948). The question of linear structure will be returned to in the discussion of this paper. At this point we insert an experiment which supports the general interpretation in terms of linkage.

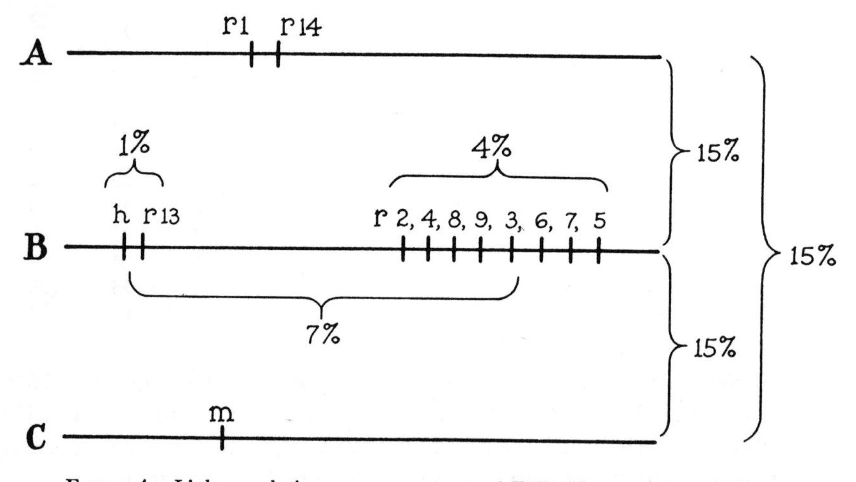

FIGURE 4.—Linkage relations among mutants of *T2H*. The percentages indicate yields of wild type in two factor crosses.

The double mutants *h r7* and *h r13* were isolated by making the respective crosses *h*×*r7* and *h*×*r13*. The three crosses *r7*×*r13*, *h r7*×*r13*, and *h r13*×*r7* were then compared with respect to the yield of r^+ virus, classified without respect to the host-range character. In each case the yield was the same within experimental error, seven percent of the total virus. This experiment shows that the small yield of recombinants (one percent of wild type) in the cross *h*×*r13* cannot be attributed to suppression of a hypothetical conjugation, which would affect the interaction of *h r7* with *r13* as well, but indicates some kind of linkage between the genetic factors concerned.

AVERAGE YIELDS OF VIRUS IN CROSSES BETWEEN HOST-RANGE AND *r* MUTANTS

Six crosses have been studied by the single burst technique; namely, *h*×*r1*, *h*×*r7*, *h*×*r13* and the corresponding reverse crosses, *h r*× wild type. Each cross was made three to five times for the collection of the single burst data, and each time the viral yield was examined also from a culture tube containing about 40,000 mixedly infected bacteria. The average yields from the culture tubes are summarized in table 2. They show that the *h* locus is very closely linked to *r13* (less than one percent of wild type), and that the linkage relations to *r1* and *r7* are approximately what would have been predicted from this fact, respectively 12 and 6 percent of wild type. According to arguments previously given (HERSHEY and ROTMAN 1948), the factors *h*, *r7*, and *r13* are

TABLE 2

Average Percent Distribution of Viral Types in Yields from about 40,000 Mixedly Infected Bacteria

The results shown are from the same experiments for which single burst data are also reported, except that one growth tube was lost among the crosses *h r7* by wild type. The total multiplicity of infection is about five of each type per bacterium; the adsorption period is five minutes; the total incubation period one hour. The distribution of viral types is computed from the results of mixed indicator platings. The column headed eop(h) gives the efficiency of plating of *h* virus on single indicator as compared with mixed indicator, and illustrates the mixed indicator effect mentioned in Methods. The column headed p(h) gives the percent of virus containing the *h* allele, and shows the effect of selection during growth.

CROSS	NO. OF EXPTS.		h^+r^+	$h\,r^+$	h^+r	$h\,r$	BURST SIZE	eop(h)	p(h)
h×*r1*	5	input	0	53	47	0		1.0	53
		yield	12	42	34	12	630	0.8	54
h r1×++	3	input	57	0	0	43		1.0	43
		yield	44	14	13	29	680	0.7	43
h×*r7*	4	input	0	49	51	0		1.1	49
		yield	5.9	56	32	6.4	650	0.8	62
h r7×++	2	input	49	0	0	51		1.0	51
		yield	42	7.8	7.1	43	690	0.8	51
h×*r13*	3	input	0	49	51	0		1.1	49
		yield	0.74	59	39	0.94	510	0.8	60
h r13×++	4	input	52	0	0	48		0.9	48
		yield	50	0.83	0.76	48	590	0.7	49

linked to each other, but *r1* is probably situated on an independently exchanging structure.

The results of table 2 show further that the two recombinants appear in equal numbers in any one cross, and that pairs of reverse crosses yield equal numbers of recombinants. It is these relations, which increase the resemblance to simple types of Mendelian segregation, that we wish to examine by the single burst technique. In the remainder of the experimental part of this paper we describe the results of this examination, but limit our comments chiefly to the technical problems encountered. The general implications of the data will be considered in the discussion.

VARIATIONS IN YIELDS OF PARENTAL TYPES OF VIRUS AMONG INDIVIDUAL BACTERIA

Yields of virus from single bacteria show large fluctuations in size (DELBRÜCK 1945b) and, in our experiments, variations in relative yields of the two infecting viruses. The variations in total yield are shown in fig. 5 which includes the complete data for six experiments in which the proportion of multiple bursts is small (100 bursts out of 484 tubes, or 11 probable multiples). The burst sizes range from 150 to several thousand, with a mean of 520, or 470 corrected for probable multiples. The distribution is the same for the mixed bursts, and for the bursts containing only one viral type. Owing to these variations, it is convenient to describe the individual bursts in terms of the fractional yield of the several viral types.

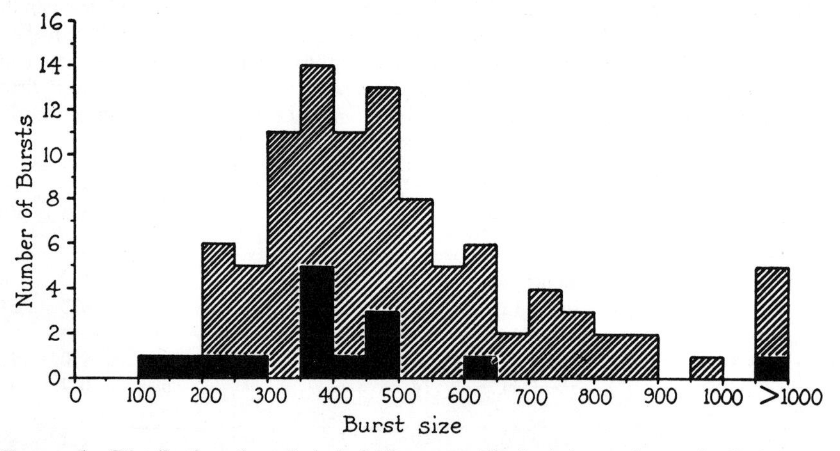

FIGURE 5.—Distribution of total viral yields among 100 single bursts from mixedly infected bacteria. The solidly shaded areas refer to unmixed yields.

Each cross yields four types of virus, wild type, the single mutants *h* and *r*, and the double mutant *h r*, of which two are parental and two are recombinant types. In order to examine the variations in relative yields of parental types independently of variations in yields of recombinants, it is convenient to express the former in terms of the proportion of virus containing a specified allele, viz:

$$p(h) = \frac{n(hr^{+})+n(hr)}{n\ (\text{total})} \tag{1}$$

$$p(r) = \frac{n(h^{+}r)+n(hr)}{n\ (\text{total})} \tag{2}$$

where n indicates the number of the specified viral types, $p(h)$ is the proportion of the yield containing the h allele, and $1-p(h)$, $p(r)$, and $1-p(r)$ are respectively the proportions containing the h^{+}, r, and r^{+} alleles. The fraction $p(h)$ is equal to $1-p(r)$ if the numbers of the two recombinant types are the same, or approximately equal if these numbers are small. A fair idea of the complete distribution of alleles is therefore given by the distribution of $p(h)$ alone. Two examples of this distribution, showing the proportions of the h allele in different single bursts for the crosses $h \times r1$ and $h \times r7$, are given in fig. 6.

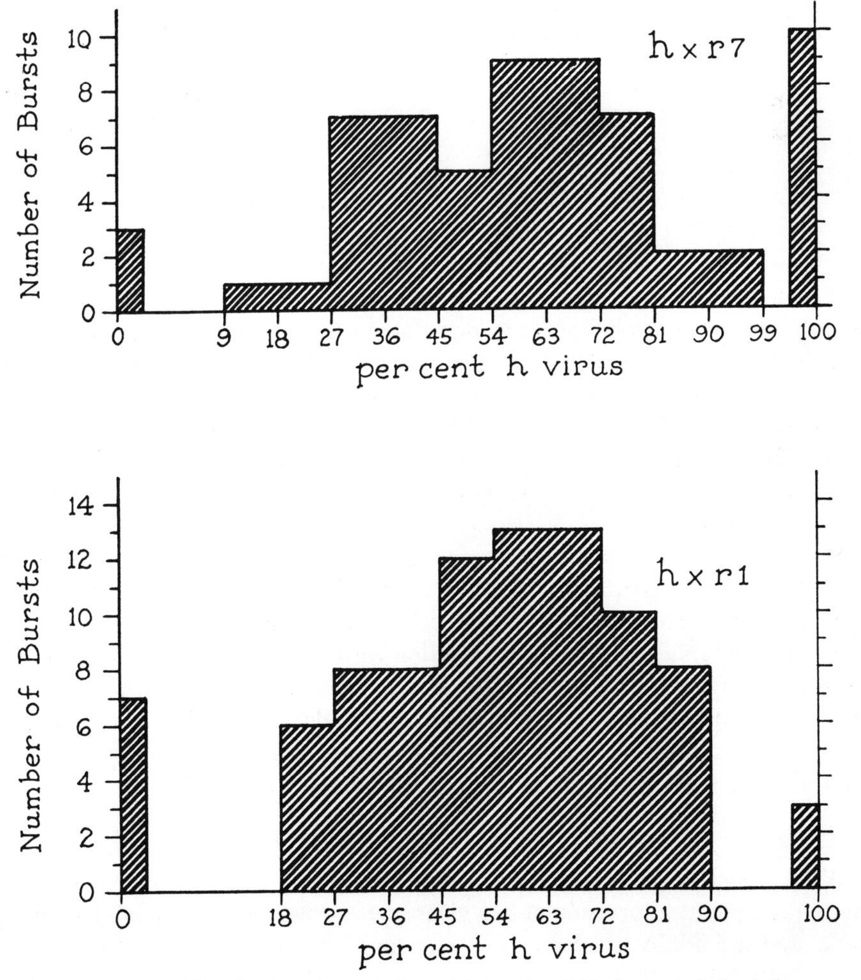

FIGURE 6.—Distribution of proportions of h virus in yields from single bacteria.

The variations shown in fig. 6 are evidently due in part to variations in relative numbers of the two kinds of virus adsorbed, and in part to variations in viral growth. For purposes of comparison, the variation in relative multiplicity has been computed on the assumption of a random distribution of two types of virus over a population of bacteria receiving on the average five particles of each kind. The distribution for this case is approximately that shown in table 3.

TABLE 3

Ideal Distribution of Multiplicities in Mixed Infection

The proportions of bacteria falling into the specified groups classified with respect to relative multiplicity of infection with two kinds of virus have been calculated for random adsorption with average multiplicity of five each of the two kinds.

NUMBERS OF FIRST KIND AS PERCENT OF TOTAL VIRUS ADSORBED	PERCENT OF BACTERIA
0 or 100	0.7 (exact)
1–9 or 91–99	0.2 (approximate)
10–18 or 82–90	2.0 "
19–27 or 73–81	5.1 "
28–36 or 64–72	10.8 "
37–45, 46–54, or 55–63	18.2 "
total	92.2

The distributions of yields actually found (fig. 6) differ from the theoretical distribution of multiplicities in showing a considerably broader spread, and a significant excess of yields containing only one kind of virus. These effects could be due in part to an inhomogeneity of the bacteria with respect to adsorbing power for virus; otherwise they suggest that a bacterium infected with two viruses is somewhat less likely to liberate a given one, than a bacterium infected with that one alone. DULBECCO (1949) has shown that the latter is, in fact, the case.

Another possible contribution to the variations described is connected with the relatively long period (five minutes) allowed for adsorption of virus, which permits some bacteria to be infected with one or more particles of one type of virus considerably in advance of infection by the second. Owing to the slow adsorption of the virus *T2H* and its mutants, the adsorption time cannot be much reduced without reducing the total multiplicity of infection, or introducing excessive amounts of virus. This contribution to the variation in composition of viral yields has not, therefore, been assessed.

COMPETITION BETWEEN VIRAL MUTANTS

The competition between viral mutants expresses itself in two ways; first, by the complete suppression of one virus or the other in mixedly infected bacteria, and second, by excessive growth of one of the two types in bacteria liberating both. These effects are slight among mutants of *T2H* so far examined, and probably do not influence appreciably the yields of recombinants in genetic crosses, as the following discussion will show.

The two distributions shown in fig. 6 illustrate the competitive relations encountered. In the cross *h*×*r7*, most of the unmixed yields contain the *h* rather than the *r* parental type. Corresponding to this, there is a tendency for the mixed yields to contain an excess of *h* virus. The combined effect is to cause a definite increase in yield of *h* virus at the expense of *r*, as compared with the input proportions. The cross *h*×*r13* also shows these characteristics, the effects being evident in table 2.

In the cross *h*×*r1*, on the other hand, the unmixed yields of each kind are approximately equal in number, and the mean proportion of *h* virus in the mixed bursts, in the total yield, and in the input mixture of viruses is the same. The crosses between wild type and *h r1*, *h r7*, and *h r13* are like *h*×*r1* in this respect, as shown in table 2.

It might be supposed that the suppression of one virus by a second is favored by an excess of the second. This is true only in a special sense, as DULBECCO (1949) has shown, and we have confirmed. An excess of one virus tends to suppress a minority type completely in some bacteria, but there is a compensating excess of this type among the mixed bursts, so that the average proportion of the minority virus in the yield averaged over many bacteria is the same as in the input mixture. This identity has been established with considerable precision for proportions of *r1* between 7 and 50 percent in mixed infection with wild type. The nature of this relationship, which is at first sight perplexing in the case of unequal multiplicity, has been explained by DULBECCO (1949) in terms of a limitation to the number of viral particles which can participate in growth in a single bacterium. If all those viral particles in excess of a certain number attached to the same bacterium fail to grow, and if the excluded ones are chosen at random, the result will be precisely the one described, provided there is no selection during the growth of the successful particles.

It is apparent that with certain viral pairs, the excluding mechanism does not operate at random, or there is continuing selection during growth. Thus *h* mutant slightly suppresses *r7* or *r13*, but not *r1* or wild type. Wild type suppresses *r13*, but not *r1* or *r7* (HERSHEY and ROTMAN 1948). There is no selection with respect to either *h* or *r* factors when wild type is crossed with *h r1*, *h r7*, or *h r13* (table 2).

The competitive relations discussed above are of immediate interest only in the negative sense that they probably do not influence the yields of recombinant virus in crosses. The evidence for the latter conclusion, drawn from data presented elsewhere in this paper, may be summarized as follows: (1) the linkage relations deduced from average yields of virus are the same as those deduced from single bursts selected for equality of yields of the two infecting viruses; (2) in the reverse crosses *h*×*r7* and *h r7* × wild type, one gets within experimental error equal numbers of all four recombinants in spite of the fact that in one case the infecting pair, and in the other the recombinant pair, have unequal excluding power; (3) in all crosses, the distribution of yields of recombinants among single bursts does not show one peak at zero and another above the mean, as is the case with the yields of a minority infecting type, but shows a single mode slightly less than the mean.

The last two lines of evidence cited seem to show that the principle of limited participation (DULBECCO 1949) referred to above, operates only during the initial stages of infection, or at any rate does not influence the yields of genetic recombinants arising within the mixedly infected bacteria. They suggest further that the *h* mutant is superior to *r7* or *r13* in excluding power only, not as a competititor during actual multiplication.

YIELDS OF GENETIC RECOMBINANTS FROM SINGLE MIXEDLY INFECTED BACTERIA

In order to study the variations in yields of recombinants intrinsic to the recombination process, one would like to exclude as many as possible of the accessory sources of variation. The most important of these are variations in burst size, and variations in the relative numbers of the two infecting viruses adsorbed to individual bacteria. It will be seen presently that effects of variations in burst size can be avoided by the simple expedient of computing proportionate yields of recombinants, these being independent of burst size. The effect of variations in relative multiplicity could be minimized either by going to very small or very large total multiplicities. Low multiplicities are uneconomical, because at multiplicities sufficiently small so that most of the mixedly infected bacteria receive only one viral particle of each type, very few of the test cultures will yield a mixed burst. High multiplicities also introduce difficulties (DULBECCO 1949). We have chosen to use total multiplicities between 10 and 20, within which range the yield of recombinants is constant.

As previously described, the elementary viral yields vary considerably in the relative numbers of the two parental types of virus and, as expected, these variations influence in turn the yields of recombinants. A correction for this source of variation was devised as follows. Assuming that the genetic interaction occurs between unlike viral pairs, and that the composition of the viral yield provides a direct measure of the composition of the intracellular viral population during growth, one computes an interaction coefficient

$$k = p(h)[1 - p(h)] \qquad (3)$$

in which p(h) is given by (1), and k expresses the influence of the composition of the population on the number of unlike viral pairs present in the cell, neglecting effects of genetic recombination.

The coefficient k has a maximum of 0.25 when half the viral yield contains the *h* allele. Dividing the proportions of recombinants by 4k serves therefore as a correction for inequality of yields of the parental viruses. This correction is ambiguous only for bursts in which the yields of the two recombinants are large and unequal, and bursts from which either recombinant is absent.

A summary of the single burst data is given in table 4, which includes the mixed bursts only. The bursts have been separated into the classes $k \geqq 0.21$ and $k \leqq 0.20$, to show the effect of the correction described above. It will be seen that the uncorrected mean proportion of recombinants is larger for the bursts with the larger k, and that the effect of dividing each proportion by 4k is to make the results homogenous. These facts justify the use of the correction. Its theoretical significance is clarified in the discussion.

TABLE 4

Single burst data for $h \times r$ crosses

k = a measure of disproportion between yields of parental types (Eq. 3).
$\bar{x}$ = average yield of the r^+ recombinant as percent of total virus.
$\bar{y}$ = average yield of the *r* recombinant as percent of total virus.
$\bar{n}$ = average burst size.
r(x, y) = coefficient of correlation between proportionate yields of the two recombinants.
r(n, x+y) = coefficient of correlation between burst size and sum of proportions of the two recombinants.
The variations of x, y and n/100 shown are standard deviations within the sample. The standard errors of the means are obtained by dividing these by the square root of the number of bursts.
The correction referred to is described in the text.

CROSS	NO. OF BURSTS	k	$4\bar{k}$		$\bar{x}$	$\bar{y}$	$\bar{n}/100$	r(x, y)	r(n, x+y)
h×*r1*	25	≦0.20	0.65	uncorr.	8.9±3.8	12.1±6.2	5.5±2.4		−0.25
				corr.	13.9±5.3	19.0±9.2		0.09	
	52	≧0.21	0.94	uncorr.	15.5±6.9	17.1±7.1	5.8±3.2		0.15
				corr.	16.6±6.3	18.1±7.2		−0.01	
h r1×++	19	≦0.20	0.67	uncorr.	13.6±5.9	13.2±4.4	5.1±1.9		−0.26
				corr.	20.1±7.4	20.8±8.5		−0.27	
	36	≧0.21	0.94	uncorr.	16.5±5.8	17.1±5.6	5.4±3.0		−0.11
				corr.	17.5±6.2	18.2±6.0		0.16	
h×*r7*	13	≦0.20	0.64	uncorr.	5.7±3.5	6.6±4.6	6.2±1.9		−0.43
				corr.	8.8±4.8	9.9±5.9		0.65	
	35	≧0.21	0.93	uncorr.	6.8±4.2	9.2±4.5	5.9±3.2		0.16
				corr.	7.2±4.3	9.8±4.8		0.53	
h r7×++	17	≦0.20	0.63	uncorr.	6.4±3.1	4.8±2.9	6.4±7.8		−0.45
				corr.	10.0±4.3	8.0±5.0		0.12	
	26	≧0.21	0.95	uncorr.	6.7±3.2	8.9±5.4	5.8±3.7		0.02
				corr.	7.1±3.6	9.3±5.6		0.47	
h×*r13*	29	≦0.20	0.61	uncorr.	0.5±0.5	0.8±0.8	5.2±2.1	0.07	0.35
	29	≧0.21	0.94	uncorr.	0.9±0.9	1.1±0.9	5.1±2.3	−0.05	−0.30
h r13×++	21	≦0.20	0.69	uncorr.	0.6±0.7	0.6±0.9	4.6±1.4	0.15	0.22
	46	≧0.21	0.94	uncorr.	0.8±0.7	0.7±0.6	4.9±2.3	0.21	0.04

The data of table 4 for mixed single bursts confirm fairly well the average data of table 2, except that the yields of recombinants are somewhat greater owing to the exclusion of the unmixed bursts, and that the yields corrected for unequal growth of parental viruses are higher still.

The chief point of interest is the question of the correlation between yields of the two recombinants in single bursts. This has been measured in terms of the correlation coefficient r (RIDER 1939). This measure varies between −1 and +1, a value near 0 indicating independence of variates, and values near unity indicating negative or positive correlation, respectively. The data of table 4 show clearly that there is no significant correlation between the proportions of the two recombinants in single bursts except for the crosses *h*×*r7* and *h r7*× wild type. Even for these crosses the correlation is weak and not entirely convincing, especially since the data are not completely unselected (see below).

The correlation between the uncorrected proportions of the two recombinants is shown in the form of scatter diagrams in fig. 7. These data might be expected to show some degree of spurious correlation owing to the fact that bursts with disproportionate yields of the two parental types tend to contain diminished numbers of both recombinants. This tendency can be seen in the

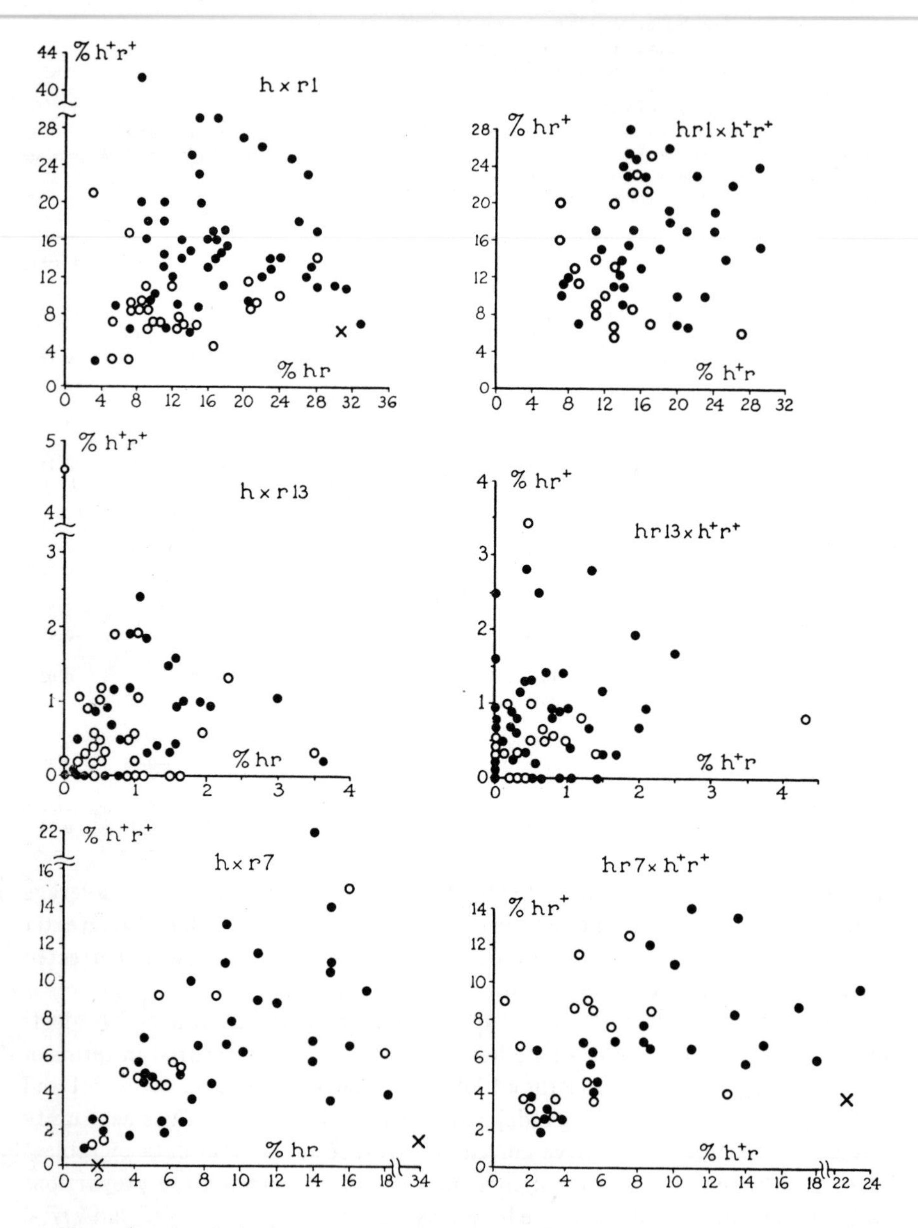

FIGURE 7.—Correlation between proportionate yields of the two recombinants in single bursts. The open circles indicate bursts with disproportionate yields of the two parental viruses. Crosses indicate yields omitted from the data of table 4.

diagrams in which the disproportionate yields ($k \leqq 0.20$) are indicated by open circles. Actually this effect is of minor importance, since the variations due to unknown causes are so much greater than those due to variations in k. Consequently, the uncorrected data lead to the same conclusions as the corrected data; namely, that the proportionate yields of the recombinants are uncorrelated in the crosses *h*×*r1*, *h*×*r13*, and the corresponding reverse crosses, but that there is a weak positive correlation for the crosses *h*×*r7* and *h r7*× wild type.

As mentioned earlier, the correlation data in table 4 are not unselected. The diagrams of fig. 7, however, show all the mixed bursts for the respective experiments, those omitted from the table being indicated by crosses in the diagram. It is plausible that some of the discrepant bursts came from bacteria infected with a spontaneous mutant present in one of the parental stocks of virus. In fact, two bursts from the cross *h*×*r7* were found to contain a large proportion of mutants, *m* in one case and weak inhibitor (HERSHEY 1946b) in the other, which almost certainly arose in this way. The *h* stock used in these crosses contained about 0.1 percent of *h r* virus, so that in crosses with *r* at least one bacterium in 200 was infected with three types of virus, and would be likely to yield an excess of one of the recombinant phenotypes. Unfortunately the recombinant progeny in the exceptional bursts were not checked by crossing with the parental stocks, which should be done in any further experiments of this type. For the present these bursts throw some doubt on the significance of the positive correlation between proportions of recombinants in the crosses *h*×*r7* and *h r7*× wild type.

The results of the cross *h*×*r13* are of special interest because of the small yield of recombinants. The distribution of the bursts with respect to absence of recombinants is shown in table 5. Nine of the 125 mixed bursts fail to show either recombinant, and 31 more lack one recombinant or the other. One can test the hypothesis that the two sister recombinants arise independently as follows. About 20 percent of the bursts fail to show a specified one of the two possible recombinants. If the absence of the one were independent of the absence of the other, about $(0.2)^2$ or four percent of the bursts should show neither recombinant. The number found, 9/125, is larger than this, but not significantly so. Moreover, bursts lacking one recombinant do not show less than the average proportion of the other (table 5). The data evidently fail to exclude the hypothesis of independent origin of the two recombinants, but do not, of course, rule out the hypothesis of reciprocal exchange.

Another question that arises in connection with the data is concerned with the number of genetic exchanges per bacterium. For explicitness, we consider separately the hypotheses of reciprocal and non-reciprocal exchange. If exchanges are reciprocal, the bursts lacking a single recombinant are the result of failure to recognize the few plaques of either type, of losses in the ten percent of each culture not examined, and of unspecified biological accidents. As previously computed, four percent or 5 of the 125 bursts fail to show either recombinant for one or another of these reasons, leaving only 4 without recombinants possibly owing to failure of exchange. This number is too small if some of the single absences result from erroneous recognition of one recombinant, but is otherwise subject only to its sampling errors. Taken as a measure of failure of reciprocal exchange, the fraction 4/125 implies an average of 3.4 exchanges per bacterium. If, on the other hand, exchanges are not reciprocal, the fraction (20 percent) of the bursts lacking any given recombinant corresponds to 1.7 genetic transfers per bacterium.

These estimates may be too low if conditions vary from bacterium to bacterium in such a way that genetic exchange is suppressed in some bacteria.

TABLE 5

Distribution of Bursts with Respect to Absence of Recombinants

See legend table 4. The proportions of recombinants have not been corrected for disproportionate yields of parental types of virus.

CROSS	CLASS	NO. OF BURSTS	$\bar{x}$	$\bar{y}$	$\bar{n}$	$\bar{k}$
$h \times r13$	both absent	2	0.0	0.0	390	0.20
	h^+r^+ absent	10	0.0	0.81	460	0.19
	$h\ r$ absent	2	2.4	0.0	390	0.19
	total	58	0.72	0.97	520	0.20
$h\,r13 \times ++$	both absent	7	0.0	0.0	340	0.21
	$h\,r^+$ absent	8	0.0	0.66	360	0.21
	h^+r absent	11	0.75	0.0	380	0.22
	total	67	0.73	0.64	480	0.22

Yields with small k and small burst size must have this effect, but are evidently not very important in the data of table 5, since the different classes are very similar with respect to k and burst size. In short, it is necessary to conclude that there are at least two or three genetic exchanges per bacterium, independently of the mechanism by which recombinants arise.

A different kind of estimate of the number of exchanges per bacterium is obtained from the number of recombinants actually found. The data are summarized in table 6 in the form of distributions of numbers of the several recombinant types. One finds on the average 3.4 recombinants of any one kind per bacterium. This evidently furnishes an upper limit to the number of exchanges per bacterium, insofar as exchanges yield viable and countable progeny. This result, taken in conjunction with the preceding estimates, leads to several remarkable conclusions.

First, since the two methods of estimation, one minimal and one maximal, yield about the same result, there must be in fact only two or three exchanges per bacterium in the crosses between closely linked factors.

Second, the recombinants must undergo little multiplication after they arise in the cell.

Third, the conditions of viral growth in different bacterial cells must be equally favorable to genetic recombination; otherwise a larger proportion of bursts would fail to show recombinants.

These conclusions are substantially confirmed by the distributions of numbers of recombinants shown in table 6, which are essentially of the Poisson type, with variance only moderately greater than the mean. In other words, the individual particles of any one recombinant must often arise independently of each other in the same bacterial cell, and with equal probability in different bacterial cells. The deviations from the Poisson distribution are nevertheless significant, and can be attributed to a moderate amount of growth of recombinants.

TABLE 6

Distributions of Numbers of Recombinants in Single Bursts from the Crosses $h \times r13$ *and* $h\ r13 \times$ *wild type*

The Poisson distributions show the numbers of tubes in the various classes expected if there were no growth of recombinants. The distribution with mean 3.4 is appropriate to the hypothesis of reciprocal exchange, and the distribution with mean 1.7 to the hypothesis of non-reciprocal genetic interaction.

NO. OF RE-COMBINANTS PER TUBE	NO. OF TUBES FOUND				POISSON DISTRIBUTIONS	
	h^+r^+	$h\ r$	$h\ r^+$	h^+r		
0	12	4	15	18	2.1	11.5
1	11	11	11	14	7.2	19.6
2	9	8	8	6	12.2	16.7
3	6	9	11	9	13.8	9.5
4	3	7	6	4	11.7	4.0
5	7	3	4	2	8.0	1.4
6	1	2	3	6	4.5	0.4
7	3	6	0	2	2.2	0.1
8	2	2	3	3	0.9	0.0
9	1	2	2	1	0.3	0.0
10–18	3	2	3	2	0.1	0.0
19–27	0	1	1	0	0.0	0.0
28–36	0	1	0	0	0.0	0.0
No. of tubes	58	58	67	67	63	63
Mean per tube	3.1	4.5	3.3	2.8	3.4	1.7
Variance	9.2	27	16	10	3.4	1.7

The conclusion that genetic recombination is not suppressed in some of the bacteria is also supported by the results of the other crosses, in which no bursts yielding both parental viruses and lacking both recombinants were found. Only one burst, from the cross $h \times r7$, failed to show one of the recombinants; it contained 95 percent of the h parent.

INDEPENDENCE BETWEEN PROPORTION OF RECOMBINANTS AND BURST SIZE

The data of table 4 do not show any significant correlation between burst size and proportion of recombinants, which means that the number of recombinants must be very nearly proportional to the total yield of virus in single bursts.

This conclusion must be qualified in view of the following considerations.

Some of the tubes contain one or more mixed bursts plus one or more unmixed bursts. Such tubes would tend to show less than average values of k and less than average yields of recombinants together with greater than average burst size. The number of such tubes is about five percent of the total in our experiments and these tend to be concentrated in the class $k \leqq 0.2$. This probably explains the negative correlation between proportions of recombinants and burst size among tubes selected for small k.

A larger proportion of the tubes, between 10 and 20 percent in our experiments, contain two or more mixed bursts. These tubes would tend to have greater than average k and greater than average burst size, but will not show exceptional proportions of recombinants. These tubes have the effect of weakening any correlation that may exist between burst size and proportion of recombinants, especially among the class $k \geqq 0.21$. The data previously considered do not, therefore, exclude the possibility of a weak positive correlation between proportion of recombinants and size of bursts.

Advantage was taken of the finding that high pH reduces size of bursts, to examine the relation between burst size and yield of recombinants in another

TABLE 7

Small Bursts from the Cross h×r7 in Broth of pH 9.0

See legend table 4. The proportions of recombinants have not been corrected for disproportionate yields of parental types of virus. The individual cultures contain an average of about 1.4 mixed bursts.

NO. OF BURSTS	k	$4\bar{k}$	$\bar{x}$	$\bar{y}$	$\bar{n}$	r(x, y)	r(n, x+y)
20	≦0.20	0.61	6.3±3.8	10.7±6.2	99±50	0.53	−0.34
34	≧0.21	0.93	7.4±3.5	10.5±4.6	123±73	0.61	0.35
54	all	0.81	7.0±3.7	10.6±5.2	114±66	0.56	0.12

way. Since increased pH was found also to cause some of the bacteria to fail to liberate virus, the single burst technique was chosen.

Bacteria were infected in the usual way with mutants *h* and *r7* in broth of pH 6.8. At the end of the five minute adsorption period, and without treatment with antiserum, single burst cultures were prepared after diluting in broth of pH 9.0. Preliminary experiments showed that the yield of virus was complete under these conditions within one hour, and than no inactivation occurred during two additional hours at 37°C, or overnight in the refrigerator. Entire samples were plated on single mixed indicator plates. One successful experiment yielded 66 bursts, of which 54 were mixed, among 104 tubes receiving on the average 1.4 bacteria per tube. Evidently most of the bacteria liberated some virus. The average burst size, after subtracting the virus carried over from the input (totalling 36 particles per tube), was only 114 per tube, or about 70 per bacterium corrected for the probable multiples. The average proportion of recombinants was nevertheless of normal size (table 7).

It will be noticed also that the correlation between the numbers of the two recombinants in these bursts is exceptionally good. The correlation is, however, slightly exaggerated owing to the fact that the 54 tubes contain on the average mixed yields of virus from about 1.4 bacteria per tube.

THE EFFECT OF A SHORT PERIOD OF ADSORPTION AND LOW MULTIPLICITY OF INFECTION ON THE DISTRIBUTION OF RECOMBINANTS

The following experiment shows that when the multiplicity of infection in the cross *h*×*r7* is reduced from five to about one of each viral type per bacterium, the distribution of recombinants among single mixed bursts is little if any altered.

Six crosses were made in the usual way, except that the period allowed for adsorption was reduced to one minute, without reducing the total input of virus. The amount of virus adsorbed was too small to be measured, but the multiplicity of infection can be estimated from the data given below.

The single burst cultures collected from the six crosses are sufficiently similar to be considered together. The mean number of bacteria per tube for the six sets, determined by colony counts from the growth tubes immediately before adding virus, is 0.23. The mean number of infected bacteria per tube determined by plaque counts of samples taken before lysis is 0.20. The mean number of bursts per tube calculated from the proportion, 141 out of 720, of tubes containing virus is 0.22. The 141 tubes therefore contained about 157 infected bacteria.

From the distribution of viral types among the tubes, namely, 69 containing *h* only, 22 containing *r* only, 50 containing both, and 579 containing neither, one finds the probable distribution with respect to bacteria to be 80 infected with *h* only, 28 with *r* only, 49 both, and 46 neither. The multiplicity of infection is therefore about 1.0 with respect to *h*, and 0.48 with respect to *r*. One can estimate further that about seven of the tubes contained one or more mixed bursts plus one or more unmixed; and that about three contained both *h* and *r* bursts without any mixed bursts. Also, among the mixedly infected bacteria, 45 percent were infected with one particle only of each viral type.

In making the above computations we have neglected the probability that the *h* mutant suppresses the growth of *r* in some bacteria adsorbing both types of virus. The apparent inequality of infection is probably due in some part to this effect. However, in other experiments with low multiplicity of infection with *h* and *r7* designed to check this point, the split into *h*, *r*, and mixed yielders was nearly equal. It seems likely, therefore, that in the experiments reported here the two viral types were unequally adsorbed for unknown reasons.

The tubes containing only one viral type may be dismissed by saying that their average content of virus did not differ significantly from that of the mixed yields, and that the *h* and *r* yields per bacterium were the same. There was one exceptional burst containing only $h\,r^{+}$ and $h\,r$ phenotypes. The characteristics of the remaining 49 cultures containing *h* and *r* virus are summarized in table 8. The data show no unusual features excepting the small burst size, which is a direct effect of the low multiplicity of infection, and the somewhat small proportion of recombinants, probably due to the appreciable number of superimposed unmixed bursts.

TABLE 8

Single Bursts from the Cross $h \times r7$ with Low Multiplicity of Infection

See legend table 4. The proportion of recombinants have not been corrected for disproportionate yields of parental types of virus. Adsorption time one minute. Multiplicity 1.0 *h* and 0.5 *r* per bacterium.

NO. OF BURSTS	k	$4\bar{k}$	$\bar{x}$	$\bar{y}$	$\bar{n}/100$	r(x, y)	r(n, x+y)
17	≦0.20	0.59	5.3±4.0	4.5±3.7	2.9±1.6	0.38	−0.17
32	≧0.21	0.95	4.4±3.1	6.1±5.4	3.5±2.0	0.20	−0.33
49	all	0.84	4.7±3.5	5.7±4.9	3.2±1.9	0.24	−0.30

The principal point to be made here is that the variation in yields of recombinants from tube to tube is not exceptional. In this connection it must be mentioned that 5 of the 49 tubes contained *h* and *r* virus without any recombinants. Of these, one was exceptional in containing only 24 viral particles, and another for the extreme disproportion of parental types (88 percent *h*). The remaining three, each containing from 450 to 570 particles, are probably superimposed unmixed *h* and *r* bursts.

It should be noted also that the correlation between the yields of the two recombinants in this set is not significant, since the observed correlation is exaggerated by the tubes containing unmixed *h* and *r* bursts without recombinants. Whether the poor correlation is accidental, or an effect of the low multiplicity of infection, remains to be determined. The negative correlation between burst size and proportion of recombinants can, however, be ascribed to the superimposed mixed and unmixed bursts, as well as to the unmixed *h* and *r* bursts, in some of the tubes.

IDENTITY OF RECOMBINANTS WITH THE CORRESPONDING ANCESTRAL TYPES

According to any simple hypothesis of factorial recombination, one expects the recombinant virus arising in crosses not to differ genetically from the corresponding ancestral type. Two kinds of test indicate that this is so. In the first kind of test (HERSHEY and ROTMAN 1948) stocks of the phenotypic wild type arising from the cross between two different *r* mutants were backcrossed to authentic wild type. No *r* mutants appeared in such crosses, and it was concluded that the stocks were genetically identical.

The second kind of test is the following. The double mutant *h r7*, itself obtained by crossing the two single mutants, was crossed with wild type and the recombinants *h* and *r* were re-isolated. These were then tested by making the homologous (parental *h* by recombinant *h* and parental *r* by recombinant *r*) and heterologous (parental *h* by recombinant *r* and parental *r* by recombinant *h*) back crosses. In both cases, the homologous cross yielded only one type of virus, and the heterologous cross yielded recombinants in the same proportion as found with the parental stocks. These tests show not only that the recombinants contain the same genetic markers as the corresponding progenitive types, but also that the region between the markers is unchanged.

MIXED YIELDS CONTAINING ONLY ONE PARENTAL TYPE OF VIRUS

Only four mixed bursts lacking one of the parental types of virus were found among the experiments reported in this paper. One, from the cross $h \times r1$, contained 86 percent $h^{+}r$ and 14 percent $h\ r$. A second, from the cross $h \times r7$ contained 99.6 percent $h\ r^{+}$ and 0.4 per cent $h\ r$. A third, from the same cross with low multiplicity of infection, contained 83 percent $h\ r^{+}$, and 17 percent $h\ r$. The fourth, from the cross $h\ r7 \times$ wild type, contained 23 percent $h\ r^{+}$ and 77 percent $h\ r$. In this case the yield of $h\ r^{+}$, which appeared to be homogenous, formed atypical plaques and proved on isolation to differ from any known mutant of *T2H*. It seems reasonable to suppose that these exceptional bursts contained progeny stemming from mutants contaminating the parental stocks of virus. On the other hand, the one exceptional burst following low multiplicity of infection, together with the failure to find similar bursts among the crosses involving *h* and *r13*, suggest that a different interpretation should be looked for. Genetic tests which might have clarified this point are lacking. For the present we conclude, as a first approximation, that recombinants arise only in those bacteria in which both parental types of virus succeed in multiplying.

It may be added here, because the question arises in connection with these exceptional bursts, that no correlation can be seen between the proportion in mixed bursts of the total virus containing the *h* allele, and the proportion of the recombinant virus containing the *h* allele. We have therefore omitted this datum from the tables.

DISCUSSION

In collecting and analyzing the data just described, we have had in mind the following questions. Does genetic exchange occur in the course of matings between viral particles, or is it the expression of a mechanism of growth such as that visualized by LURIA (1947), according to which the multiplying units in the cell are not phage particles, but simpler structures derived from them? Can the linkage relations represented in fig. 1 be interpreted in terms of linear chromosome-like structures? Are the genetic exchanges reciprocal, as one expects for simple cases of crossing over, or must one look for an alternative mechanism more intimately connected with the mode of reproduction of the virus?

It was soon apparent that the data for crosses between linked and unlinked factors tended to give different answers to these questions, and we were led to consider a model based on two distinct mechanisms of exchange. The necessity for this arises from the following facts.

First, the linkage data indicate a limitation at about seven percent to the proportion of wild type found in crosses between linked factors, which is difficult to reconcile, in terms of a single mechanism, with the existence of a second class of crosses yielding about 15 percent of wild type.

Second, the correlation between proportions of the two recombinants in the cross $h \times r7$, and the lack of a corresponding correlation in the cross $h \times r1$, is incompatible with a single mechanism for the two crosses. It must be recalled, however, that the correlations found are too weak to be wholly convincing.

Third, LURIA's (1947) evidence for a mechanism of independent multiplication and transfer of subunits of the virus, and ours for a system of linkage, require dissimilar types of interpretation.

The model to which these considerations seem to lead is described below, but we do not consider that we have decisive answers to any of the questions originally posed. The remainder of this discussion is of value only insofar as it clarifies the questions, and systematizes the experimental results so far obtained.

The two linkage structures bearing the markers *r1* and *h*, respectively, are assumed to be examples of the class of independently multiplying subunits of the virus whose minimal number LURIA and DULBECCO (1949) estimate at about 25. The reconstitution of virus from these units must be regulated in such a way that each particle receives one representative of each kind of unit. In the cross $h \times r1$ the choice between h and h^+, and between r and r^+, is decided nearly at random to yield on the average 37 percent of recombinants and 63 percent of the parental types in bacteria yielding equal numbers of the two parents. The deficit of recombinants below 50 per cent is unexplained, but may be thought of as an effect of incomplete mixing between neighboring clones of multiplying virus in the cell.

According to this hypothesis one expects from the cross $h \times r1$ proportionate yields of the two recombinants in a single burst to be:

$$p(h^+r^+) = m\left(\frac{n(h^+)}{n(h^+) + n(h)}\right)\left(\frac{n(r^+)}{n(r^+) + n(r)}\right) \tag{4}$$

$$p(hr) = m\left(\frac{n(h)}{n(h^+) + n(h)}\right)\left(\frac{n(r)}{n(r^+) + n(r)}\right) \tag{5}$$

where the expressions on the left refer to proportions of recombinant virus, the corresponding expressions on the right refer to the intra cellular yields of the respective unit linkage structures, and the coefficient m expresses the fraction of the intracellular virus which may be regarded as a random mixture of the two parental types, the remainder being considered unmixed. If the structures carrying the markers h, h^+, r, and r^+ grow independently in the cell, their yields will fluctuate independently, and no correlation will be expected between the numbers of the two recombinants in sufficiently small yields of virus. This expectation is borne out by the data for viral yields from single bacteria. The average yields of the two recombinants are equal, however, showing that the several unit structures grow at equal rates. According to equations (4) and (5), the proportionate yield of recombinants should not be influenced by burst size unless the latter has an effect on the fraction m. According to the data it does not, and m is a parameter having the average value 37/50. This interpretation requires that 26 percent of either kind of parental virus in the cell should multiply in effective isolation from the other parent.

It will be noticed that the expressions (4) and (5) reduce to mk if one makes the approximations mentioned in connection with equation (3). This provides a theoretical basis for the correction we have applied to yields of recombinants in crosses between unlinked factors. An analogous justification for its use in crosses between linked factors will appear in the discussion to follow.

The predictions for the cross *h*×*r7* are different from the preceding case, because here the markers are situated on homologous linkage structures, so that recombination requires something like crossing over, which in turn requires something like synapsis. The expected fractional yields of recombinants are

$$\mathrm{p}(h^{+}r^{+}) = \mathrm{p}(hr) = \tfrac{1}{2}\,\mathrm{msc}, \qquad (6)$$

in which m has been defined previously, s is a fraction independent of m expressing frequency of pairing, and c is a crossover frequency. In order to make c independent of m and s it is evidently sufficient to define the product ms as the fraction of the viral yield made up of particles in which the marked unit has descended from an unlike synapsed pair. The application of (6) leads to ambiguity if exchanges can occur between descendants of unlike synapsed pairs (HERSHEY and ROTMAN 1948). In what follows this difficulty does not appear to be very serious, but no rigorous analysis has yet been attempted.

For the cross *h*×*r7*, if exchanges are reciprocal, one expects the correlation between proportions of the two recombinants to be disturbed only by fluctuations in relative growth of the two exchange products, in contrast to the cross *h*×*r1*, where the correlation is subject to fluctuations in the growth of four independent units. That these fluctuations are individually considerable is shown by the variations in relative and total viral yields in mixedly infected bacteria. A weak but probably significant correlation between proportions of the two recombinants is nevertheless visible in the cross *h*×*r7*. No such correlation can be seen in the cross *h*×*r1*. If the mechanism of exchange for these two crosses were the same, the greater correlation would be expected in the cross *h*×*r1*, which gives the larger yield of recombinants.

The predictions for the cross *h*×*r13* are the same as for *h*×*r7* except as modified by the much smaller yield of recombinants, presumably owing to a smaller frequency of crossing over. We have shown that in this cross the recombinants come from two or three individual exchanges per bacterium, and that there is little growth of recombinants subsequent to exchange. These circumstances ought to be favorable for testing the hypothesis of reciprocal exchange. The data are nevertheless inconclusive of this point.

The experiments provide information about the sequence of events in the cell. A mechanism of exchange limited to an initial phase of multiplication is ruled out by the following consideration. If exchange occurred at a time when there were few replicas in the cell, any cross yielding a small average number of recombinants would show some individual bursts containing no recombinants and others containing a very large proportion, especially at low multiplicity of infection. Instead one finds a comparatively uniform yield of recombinants, and the distribution of their proportions is not affected by the multiplicity of infection.

Also if exchanges occurred freely throughout the period of multiplication of the virus, one would expect considerably greater variations in yields of recombinants than we have found. For instance, in the cross *h*×*r13*, in which there are only two or three exchanges per bacterium, the variations in yields of recombinants are not much greater than those expected to result from a random variation in the number of exchanges alone. Moreover, most of the bacteria yield only a few recombinants, so that little growth can have occurred subsequent to exchange. The conclusion is unavoidable that the exchanges are limited to the terminal phase of multiplication, or at any rate that recombinants are prevented from multiplying appreciably in most of the bacteria.

It is remarkable that the variations in proportions of recombinants are so little dependent on the degree of linkage (as between *h*×*r7* and *h*×*r13*), or on the postulated mechanism of exchange (as between the above and *h*×*r1*). The coefficients of variation in proportions of individual recombinants among single bursts are, for *h*×*r1*, about 40 percent; for *h*×*r7*, about 60 percent; and for *h*×*r13*, about 100 percent. This circumstance also supports the inference that the exchanges are limited to a late phase of multiplication.

The hypothesis stated permits one to examine further the structure of the linkage units. Since crosses between *r13* and any of the mutants belonging to the group closely linked to *r7* yield about the same proportion, seven percent, of wild type (HERSHEY and ROTMAN 1948), it might be supposed that one crossover between the distant markers is always accompanied by several others, so that 50 percent of the progeny of synapsed pairs of the units *r7* and *r13*, for example, would be recombinant types. If this supposition is correct the terms of equation (6) can be evaluated by setting $c = 0.5$ and $p(h^+r^+) = 0.07$. This gives 0.28 for the average fraction ms of virus descending from unlike synapsed pairs. If this fraction is assumed to be the same in other crosses involving the same linkage structure (the cross *h r7*×*r13* reported in this paper suggests that it is), one can write for them

$$p\ (\text{wild type}) = 0.14\ c, \qquad (7)$$

where c is the appropriate crossover frequency and the proportion of wild type is experimentally measured. The data for the three point crosses involving *r2*, *r3*, and *r6* (HERSHEY and ROTMAN 1948) are examined from this point of view in table 9. The proportions of wild type have been calculated for random crossing over between unit linear structures, using the crossover frequencies given by (7). It will be seen that the data are entirely compatible with the hypothesis tested. Additional tests of this kind are needed, however.

It will have been noticed that the average yield of recombinants in crosses between distant linked factors is very nearly half that found for unlinked factors. DR. M. DELBRÜCK has pointed out to us that this relationship can be understood in terms of random pairing between homologous structures. In the simplest case one visualizes unrepeated pairing, that is, pairing limited to a phase in which there is no multiplication, and during which no structure finds more than one partner. For this case, the frequency of synapsis in equation (6) is simply the ratio of the number of unlike homologous pairs to the total number of homologous pairs. This ratio can be written

$$s = \frac{2ab}{(a + b)(a + b - 1)} \tag{8}$$

where a and b are the respective numbers of the two unlike homologous structures. Inspection of (8) shows that this ratio is essentially 2k as given by equation (3) when a+b is large compared to unity. Instead of equation (6) we have, therefore,

$$p \text{ (wild type)} = mkc, \tag{9}$$

from which the proportion of either recombinant expected in crosses between distant linked factors can be computed as follows.

The parameter m, taken to be the average fraction of virus randomly mixed in the cells at the time of reconstitution of virus from subunits, was found to

TABLE 9

Three Point Linkage Tests of Linear Structure

The symbol *r2,3* refers to the double mutant containing *r* alleles at the loci *r2* and *r3*, etc.
c_1 is the crossover frequency for the region between *r2* and *r3*.
c_2 is the crossover frequency for the region between *r3* and *r6*.
The locus *r3* is assumed to lie between *r2* and *r6*.
The factor 0.14 is explained in the discussion.

CROSS	FRACTIONAL YIELD OF WILD TYPE		COMPUTATION
	EXPECTED	FOUND	
r2×r3	—	0.020	$c_1=0.020/0.14=0.14$
r3×r6	—	0.014	$c_2=0.014/0.14=0.10$
r2×r6	0.030	0.024	$0.14[c_1(1-c_2)+c_2(1-c_1)]$
r2,3×r6	0.012	0.008	$0.14\ c_2(1-c_1)$
r3,6×r2	0.018	0.014	$0.14\ c_1(1-c_2)$
r2,6×r3	0.002	0.003	$0.14\ c_1c_2$

be 37/50 in crosses between unlinked factors. In (9) we require the corresponding fraction at the time of pairing, and assume this to be the same. The average of k for bacteria giving mixed viral yields (table 4) is 0.21, or 0.19 if one includes the ten percent of bacteria yielding only one type of virus. If k and m vary independently, their mean product is the same as the product of means, or 0.14 averaged over all bacteria. The average yield of either recombinant from equation (9), for factors sufficiently far apart so that c=0.5, is accordingly seven percent, computed solely from the data for crosses between unlinked factors. This is the maximum actually found in crosses between linked factors (HERSHEY and ROTMAN 1948). Equation (9) also predicts, in agreement with the data for single bursts, proportionality between yields of recombinants and k.

The agreement supports the inferences previously drawn that the markers *r7* and *r13* are attached to the same linkage unit, and that the frequency of crossing over between them is 0.5. It suggests that the pairing itself is complete without appreciable repetition, and occurs at random except that about 26 percent of the units of each kind are effectively segregated from their opposite numbers. The measure of this segregation, m, is on this view the same for crosses between linked and unlinked factors. On the other hand, this interpretation cannot be rigorously correct, because one can show by multiple factor crosses (HERSHEY and ROTMAN 1948) that repeated exchanges, or exchanges among three viral particles, occur. An estimate of the amount of repeated pairing has not yet been attempted, except that the considerations just offered suggest either that it is small, or that random pairing is limited to a small proportion of the population.

It follows from equation (9) that the interpretation in terms of orderly pairing accords with the fact, otherwise very puzzling, that the proportion of recombinants is not affected by size of burst even in crosses between linked factors.

It has been seen that the linkage data support fairly well the idea of linear structure, but independent evidence for crossing over is meagre. According to any simple model of reciprocal exchange, a correlation between proportions of sister recombinants in individual bursts would be expected. This expectation has been only partially realized, and the question arises whether the linkage data themselves require the crossover hypothesis. The following model, suggested by DR. A. H. STURTEVANT, shows that they do not, and also shows that the question of reciprocity is closely connected with the question whether the exchanges are material transfers.

Suppose that the replication of linear structures occurs zipperwise along the pattern from one end to the other, but that the partners separate prematurely to yield fragmentary replicas. Additions to the fragments are subsequently possible only after pairing with the same or another homologous structure, which in mixedly infected bacteria could belong either to the same or a different parental line. Genetic recombination in a two factor cross will depend, then, on the contingency that the two marked regions of a given replica be laid down one after the other on homologous structures from the two unlike parents. With simple assumptions, all the consequences of the crossover hypothesis (equation (6)) follow from this model, except that the independent origin of the two recombinants provides an additional source of independent variation in their numbers.

The complications peculiar to this model have to do principally with the evidence that exchanges occur only during the terminal phase of growth. These complications are not very serious if one assumes that during early stages of growth the probability is great that a fragment will be started and completed on patterns belonging to the same parental line; that is, that the mixing of the cell contents is relatively incomplete, and the distance between unlike clones relatively great, for small total populations. It has to be stipulated further that the terminal mixing is independent of the final concentration of virus in the cell, to account for the lack of dependence of proportion of recombinants on burst size. Some hypothesis of this sort may prove useful if further experiments fail to strengthen the present evidence for reciprocal exchange.

It is notable that two very different lines of evidence, ours and that of LURIA (1947), have led to the idea of independently multiplying subunits of the virus. Our results differ from LURIA's only in calling for a system of linkage superimposed on the set of independent units. It remains to be seen whether a combination of genetic and radiological techniques bears out the present conclusions, and perhaps leads to an identification of the radiation-sensitive units with the linkage structures.

SUMMARY

Genetic recombination between two viruses differing by two mutational steps has been studied by infecting bacteria with the pair, and counting the numbers of the four types of virus found in yields from single bacteria. The crosses so examined include $h \times r1$ (unlinked), $h \times r7$ (linked), and $h \times r13$ (closely linked), where h refers to a mutant of altered host range, and $r1$, $r7$, and $r13$ are different mutations producing the same alteration in type of plaque. The reverse crosses, $h\,r \times$ wild type, were also studied. The results may be summarized as follows.

Nearly all mixedly infected bacteria yield both parental types of virus and two recombinants, according to the scheme $h + r = h\,r +$ wild type. The ten percent or so of bacteria yielding only one of the parental types seldom or never yield any recombinants. The rest of the bacteria always yield two recombinants, except for the occasional absence of one or both in the crosses between closely linked factors.

The average yields of the two recombinants in any one cross are the same, and are independent of the direction of exchange, so that reverse crosses involving the same pair of mutant factors yield the same number of recombinants. The proportionate yields of recombinants from individual bacteria are independent of burst size, and of the total multiplicity of infection, but depend on the relative yields of the two parental types. The effect of the latter is not marked, however, and the variations from bacterium to bacterium must be chiefly the result of variations in the number of genetic exchanges and in the growth of recombinants subsequent to exchange. These variations may be described by saying that one finds a moderately skewed distribution, with mode less than the mean, and with mean and standard deviation dependent on the linkage relations as follows: for $h \times r1$, 15 ± 6, for $h \times r7$, 7 ± 4, for $h \times r13$, 1 ± 1, expressed in round numbers as percent of either recombinant in the total yield of virus.

A weak but moderately convincing correlation between the proportionate yields of the two recombinants in individual bacteria is discernible in the cross *h*×*r7* and its reverse, but not in the other crosses.

In the cross *h*×*r13* only two or three genetic exchanges occur during the multiplication of the virus in a single bacterial cell. These exchanges take place near the end of the period of multiplication of the virus.

A hypothesis is outlined which is compatible with the genetic data and with the results of LURIA concerning reactivation of irradiated virus in bacteria receiving two or more individually noninfective particles. The hypothesis is an extension of that of LURIA, according to which one visualizes genetic interaction not between two viral particles, but between two sets of independently multiplying chromosome-like structures. Genetic exchange occurs either by reassortment of these structures, or by something like crossing over between homologous pairs, depending on the structural relation between the genetic factors concerned. The interpretation made brings the linkage relations into superficial agreement with the requirements of linear structure, but there is little evidence that the genetic exchanges are reciprocal, and accordingly little evidence that they are material exchanges.

LITERATURE CITED

DELBRÜCK, M., 1945a Interference between bacterial viruses III. The mutual exclusion effect and the depressor effect. J. Bact. **50:** 151–170.

1945b The burst size distribution in the growth of bacterial viruses. J. Bact. **50:** 131–135.

1945c Effects of specific antisera on the growth of bacterial viruses. J. Bact. **50:** 137–150.

DELBRÜCK, M., and W. T. BAILEY, Jr., 1946 Induced mutations in bacterial viruses. Cold Spring Harbor Symp. Quant. Biol. **11:** 33–37.

DELBRÜCK, M., and S. E. LURIA, 1942 Interference between bacterial viruses I. Interference between two bacterial viruses acting upon the same host, and the mechanism of virus growth. Arch. Biochem. **1:** 111–141.

DULBECCO, R., 1949 The number of particles of bacteriophage *T2* that can participate in intracellular growth. Genetics **34:** (In press).

HERSHEY, A. D., 1946a Mutation of bacteriophage with respect to type of plaque. Genetics **31:** 620–640.

1946b Spontaneous mutations in bacterial viruses. Cold Spring Harbor Symp. Quant. Biol. **11:** 67–77.

HERSHEY, A. D., and R. ROTMAN, 1948 Linkage among genes controlling inhibition of lysis in a bacterial virus. Proc. nat. Acad. Sci. **34:** 89–96.

LURIA, S. E., 1947 Reactivation of irradiated bacteriophage by transfer of self-reproducing units. Proc. nat. Acad. Sci. **33:** 253–264.

LURIA, S. E., and R. DULBECCO, 1949 Genetic recombinations leading to production of active bacteriophage from ultraviolet inactivated bacteriophage particles. Genetics **34:** (In press).

RIDER, PAUL R., 1939 An introduction to modern statistical methods. ix+220 pp. New York: Wiley & Sons.

GENETIC RECOMBINATION AND HETEROZYGOSIS IN BACTERIOPHAGE

A. D. Hershey and Martha Chase

Department of Genetics, Carnegie Institution of Washington, Cold Spring Harbor, New York

In this paper we summarize the principal features of inheritance in the bacteriophage T2H, and describe some new experiments.

The genetic structure of this virus has been analyzed in terms of mutational patterns (Hershey, 1946) and by recombination tests (Hershey and Rotman, 1949). These two types of evidence agree in showing that mutational changes occur in localized regions of a complex genetic system. Mutations producing different effects usually occur at different loci, but one example of multiple allelism has been found (Hershey and Davidson, 1951). In this instance, the locus of the alternative mutations could be analyzed rather completely because most of the host-range mutations selected in a particular way proved to belong to a single allelic series. It was found that one pair of distinct mutants satisfied all three criteria of allelism listed below, and that another pair satisfied none of them. The criteria used were the following:

(1) If the second of two successive mutations from wild type occur at the locus of the first, reversion to wild-type in a single step is possible.

(2) No genetic recombination can be observed between allelic mutant pairs.

(3) The map position of the locus is independent of its allelic state.

Biparental Recombination

The production of new genetic types of phage by intracellular interaction between different bacteriophages was first observed by Delbrück and Bailey (1946), who mentioned genetic recombination as one of two possible interpretations of their result. The principle of genetic recombination was established by experiments with genetically defined stocks of the bacteriophage T2H (Hershey and Rotman, 1948, 1949).

The main facts of genetic recombination in this bacterial virus can be illustrated by examples of the interaction between two classes of mutant. Rapidly lysing (*r*) mutants are easily recognized by inspection of the plaques they produce on an agar plate seeded with sensitive bacteria. The plaques are larger, and have a sharper margin, than those of the wild-type. Host range (*h*) mutants are able to infect a suitable bacterial "indicator" strain that is resistant to the wild-type

Reprinted by permission of the authors and the Long Island Biological Association from Cold Spring Harbor Symposia on Quantitative Biology, **16**, 471-479 (1951).

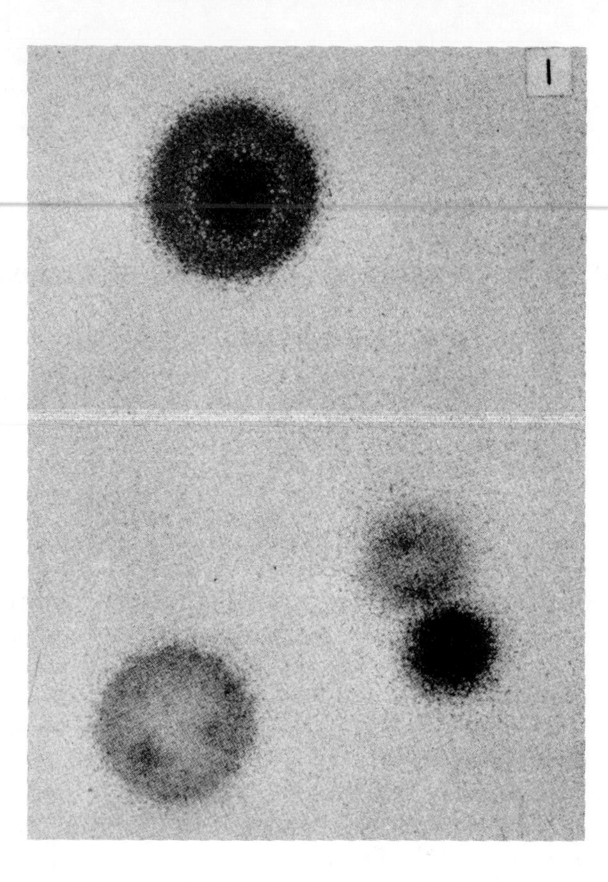

FIG. 1. Progeny of the cross $h \times r1$ plated on mixed indicator. The large clear plaque is *hr*; small clear, *h*; large turbid, *r*; small turbid, wild-type. The eccentric clearings in the *r* plaque result from secondary *h* mutations.

virus (Luria, 1945). The *h* mutants are normal with respect to type of plaque. By successive mutations, double (*hr*) mutants are readily obtained. The four kinds of virus, *wild*, *h*, *r*, and *hr*, can be recognized by plating on agar plates seeded with a mixture of sensitive (B) and indicator (B/2) strains of bacteria. Independently of the *r* character, *h* virus lyses both B and B/2 to produce clear plaques, and h^+ virus lyses only B to produce turbid plaques. Independently of the *h* character, *r* virus produces large plaques, and r^+ virus produces small ones.

Genetic recombination is observed in a "cross" in which sensitive bacteria are infected with a few particles of *h* and a few particles of *r* per cell. The viral progeny coming from the mixedly infected bacteria contains both parental types, together with a certain proportion of the two recombinants (Fig. 1). Analogous recombinants are found when two different *r* mutants are crossed. For example, the cross $r1 \times r2$ gives rise to the double mutant *r1r2* and wild-type (Hershey and Rotman, 1948).

In both types of cross, the yield of recombinants is characteristic for the

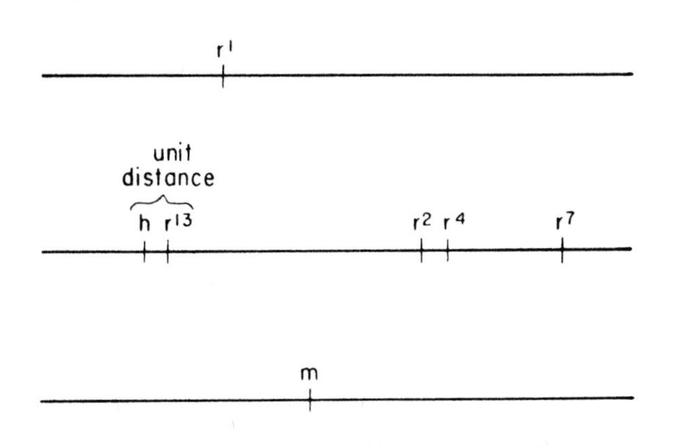

FIG. 2. Linkage relations among several genetic markers.

mutant pair, and the numerical results can be summarized in the form of a genetic map, as shown in Figure 2. On this map we have shown only a few markers that we wish to refer to in this paper. The letter *m* (*minute*) stands for a small plaque mutant. It is well established that the three loci, *r1*, *h*, and *m* assort independently of each other, and that the loci linked to *h* are arranged in linear order. Dr. N. Visconti (personal communication) has recently confirmed the earlier results on these points by a new method of three-point testing.

Triparental Recombination

Important information about genetic recombination comes from experiments in which the frequency of triparental recombination is measured. If bacteria are infected with the three mutants *h*, *m*, and *r1*, the recombinant *hmr* can arise only by interactions involving all three. The results for this triple infection and its reverse, *hr* × *hm* × *mr*, are shown in Table 1. About three per cent of the viral yield consists of the triparental recombinant in these crosses. This shows that interactions among three particles of virus occur with high frequency. A measure of this frequency can be expressed in terms of some artificial assumptions. If we suppose that multiplication precedes recombination, and that recombinants are formed during random successive pairings between phage particles, each particle would have to pair with three other particles to explain the results shown in Table 1. The genetic factors used in these experiments are unlinked. The data for triparental recombination in experiments with linked markers (Hershey and Rotman, 1948) lead to the same quantitative conclusion.

This conclusion is a stumbling block to the further understanding of the mechanism of genetic recombination, since it is extremely difficult to distinguish between successive interactions by pairs, and other types of interaction that might involve larger groups. The available information is insufficient, therefore, to decide between alternative hypotheses of viral interaction so far considered.

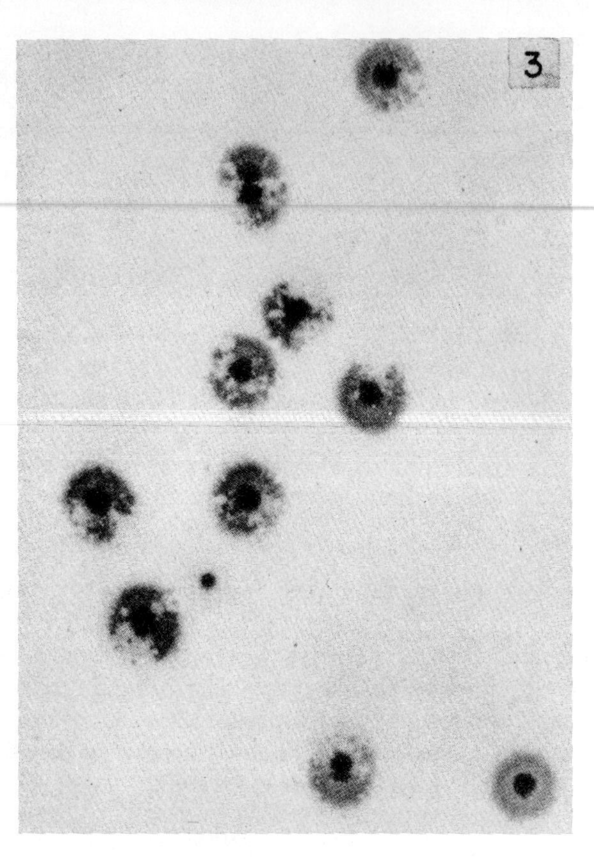

FIG. 3. Mottled plaques from bacteria infected with r and r^+ virus.

Experiments with Clumped Phage

The following observations are pertinent to the proper interpretation of experiments to be described in a later part of this paper. Since they are also of general interest, we record them separately.

The r mutants are unique among the known mutants of phage in that mixed colonies of r and r^+ phage are easily recognizable as mottled plaques. Mottled plaques are conveniently prepared by infecting bacteria with r and r^+ phage, and plating before lysis so that the plaques originate not from single phage particles, but from the mixed population liberated locally when the bacterium lyses (Fig. 3). We have made use of this characteristic mottling as a test for the aggregation of phage particles.

Platings of mixtures of r and r^+ phage do not show mottled plaques (except rarely by the overlapping of plaques), even after the mixture has been packed in a centrifuge to allow every opportunity for the particles to stick together. Mottling clumps can be produced, however, by agglutinating the mixture with antiserum.

To prepare mottling clumps of phage, one adds to a mixture containing half r and half r^+ phage, at a concentration of about 10^{11} particles per ml, an amount of

TABLE 1. TRIPARENTAL RECOMBINATION TESTS WITH THREE INDEPENDENTLY ASSORTING GENETIC FACTORS

Cross		Per cent distribution in yield							
		wild	*h*	*r*	*m*	*hr*	*hm*	*mr*	*hmr*
h × *m* × *r1*	(1)	25	17	22	12	9	5	7	2
	(2)	25	18	15	20	4	10	5	3
hm × *mr1* × *hr1*	(1)	3	6	5	10	17	19	14	26
	(2)	3	9	4	9	14	26	15	20

Results are shown for two independent experiments of each kind.

antiphage serum just sufficient to reduce the titer of the mixture by a factor 2 to 4 after equilibrium has been reached. This requires several hours at room temperature. The mixture now yields, on plating, about two per cent of mottled plaques.

Mottled plaques coming from clumps containing the doubly marked phages *hr1* and wild-type are found, on sampling, to contain the two parental types of phage, together with the expected recombinants. The same is true of mottled plaques originating from bacteria infected with *hr1* and wild-type. This shows that there is no strong selection among the several genetic types of phage during plaque formation. It shows, incidentally, that the genetic result of a mixed infection is of the same kind whether the parental phage particles attach to the bacterium at the same point, as with mottling clumps, or at different points, as in the usual mixed infection.

The mottling clumps are identifiable as clumps by their abnormal sensitivity to antiserum. When 90 per cent of a population containing two per cent of mottling clumps is inactivated by exposure (at low concentration, to avoid further aggregation) to antiserum, the proportion of mottling clumps among the survivors is less than 0.2 per cent.

When a population of phage containing two per cent of mottling clumps (*hr1* + wild-type) is adsorbed to B so as to infect one bacterium in ten, and the infected bacteria are plated on B after inactivating the unadsorbed phage with antiserum, two per cent of the plaques from infected bacteria are mottled. The resistance of the adsorbed clumps to antiserum shows that both members of a mottling clump infect the same bacterium. When the same population is adsorbed to B/2, and the infected cells are treated with antiserum or merely washed to remove unadsorbed phage, only *hr* plaques are formed on plates seeded with B. Evidently both members of a mottling clump have to make specific attachments to the bacterium in order to produce a mixed yield. This result probably explains why we are unable to prepare populations containing more than a small fraction of mottling clumps by agglutination with antiserum. Only those clumps in which the two kinds of virus are oriented in a manner favorable to the attachment of both to the same bacterium can produce mottled plaques.

Heterozygosis

Mixed yields of T2H from bacteria infected with r and r^+ phage always contain about two per cent of particles that give rise to mottled plaques. Samples of phage from these mottled plaques consist of approximately equal numbers of typical r and r^+ particles, with only traces of mottling phage particles. This distinguishes mottling phage particles from phage particles containing an unstable genetic factor affecting the r character (Hershey, 1946). These produce sectored rather than mottled plaques, and the sectored plaques contain sectoring particles and r particles, but no r^+.

The mottling phage particles do not consist of clumps. This is shown both by the genetic data to be described presently, and more generally by the following consideration of inactivation data.

Suppose, for example, that a mottling phage particle really consists of a small clump of j normal r^+ and k normal r particles. If the population containing this clump is heated sufficiently to reduce the titer by a factor 100, the chance that the mottling property of the specified clump will survive is at most $(1 - 0.99^j)(1 - 0.99^k)$, which is very much less than the chance (0.01) that a given phage particle will survive. The proportion of mottled plaques originating from clumps in a small surviving fraction of the population will, therefore, be very much less than the proportion of mottling clumps in the original population. Mottling particles do not behave in this way. In experiments in which populations containing mottling phage were inactivated by heating, by antiserum, by ultraviolet light, or by beta rays from P^{32}, no appreciable decrease in the proportion of mottling phage among survivors was seen. (The populations were examined at ten per cent and one per cent levels of survival.) The mottling particles are inactivated as a unit by the agencies mentioned, and possess the same resistance to inactivation as the non-mottling phage particles in the population.

We conclude that mottling phage coming from bacteria infected with r and r^+ virus contains both parental markers in a particle of otherwise normal properties. Since there is adequate reason to call these markers allelic genes, the mottling particles are appropriately termed heterozygotes. We use this word without intending to imply any specific structural basis for the observed properties of the particles.

There is no evidence that the heterozygotes can multiply in the heterozygous condition. The small proportion (roughly two per cent) of mottling phage particles that is found in the mottled plaques originating from heterozygotes is also found in mottled plaques coming from bacteria infected with mixtures of r and r^+ phage. The similarity of the two proportions suggests that the mottling particles have been formed in both instances during the development of the plaque.

The proportion of $r - r^+$ heterozygotes produced in bacteria infected with mixtures of r and r^+ virus does not vary significantly from two per cent for five different r markers (Table 4, left half), and is also about the same in crosses between h and r mutants, to which we now turn.

Information about the structure of the heterozygotes can be sought by analyzing them in terms of the segregants they yield. For this purpose, the viruses giving rise to the heterozygotes must differ by at least two genetic factors. Our experiments have been limited to differently linked pairs of *h* and *r* markers. The experimental method is simple. One samples mottled plaques containing the segregants from heterozygotes and replates the phage progeny on mixed indicator. The types of virus recognized in this way form the basis for classifying the original heterozygote.

By selecting mottled plaques, we limit the examination to heterozygotes segregating for *r* and r^+. The analysis yields information only about the pattern of segregation of the additional marker within this class. For any cross *hr* × wild-type, only three results are found.

TABLE 2. PER CENT DISTRIBUTION OF r-r^+ HETEROZYGOTES WITH RESPECT TO SEGREGATION PATTERN: CROSSES WITH EQUAL MULTIPLICITY OF INFECTION

Segregants found	*hr1* × *wild* (40)	*hr7* × *wild* (20)	*h* × *r7* (20)	*hr13* × *wild* (2)
hr-wild	6	6	0	74
h-hr	49	44	55	15
r-wild	45	50	40	11
h-r	..	0	5	0
No. tested	253	150	129	494

Per cent yields of recombinants in each cross are shown in parentheses.

(1) Segregants *h* and *hr*, corresponding to one parent and one recombinant of the original cross. Heterozygotes of this class lack the h^+ marker, or lose it during segregation.

(2) Segregants *r* and wild-type, corresponding to the second parent and second recombinant of the original cross. Heterozygotes of this class lack the *h* marker.

(3) Segregants *hr* and wild-type, corresponding to the two parents of the original cross, coming from doubly heterozygous phage particles. These segregants are necessarily accompanied by their recombinants.

Two qualitative results are evident. First, the heterozygotes segregate into pairs. This shows that segregation precedes multiplication, or that daughter heterozygotes segregate in only one way. Second, the double heterozygotes do not segregate into the two recombinants, *h* and *r*, but only into the two parents, *hr* and wild-type. It should be noted, however, that these two alternatives could not be distinguished in the cross *hr1* × wild-type, because of the large yields of recombinants in either case.

The quantitative results are summarized in Table 2. The doubly heterozygous class is a small minority in the crosses involving unlinked or distant markers, and forms a surprisingly small majority even for the closely linked factors *h* and *r13*.

The inferences that can be drawn from Table 2 are supported also by tests on a smaller scale of heterozygotes from the crosses *h* × *r1* and *h* × *r13*.

In view of the small proportion of doubly heterozygous particles produced in the crosses *hr1* × wild-type, and *hr7* × wild-type, there was some question whether we were really measuring this proportion. Two possible sources of error, namely, accidental overlaps of two plaques, and clumps containing two or more phage particles, were excluded by the following experiment. Plates showing not more than 50 plaques (as opposed to about 100 in other experiments) were prepared from a population of phage from the cross *hr1* × wild-type, of which 90 per cent had first been neutralized by antiserum. The antiserum treatment should have eliminated any clumps of phage, and the small number of plaques per plate should have eliminated overlaps. Eighty-three mottled plaques were sampled from these plates, of which five proved to contain both parental types of phage. This is the same proportion found in 170 plaques examined in other experiments. The estimate of six per cent shown in Table 2 is therefore correct.

The data of Table 2, together with the estimated total frequency (2%) of r-r^+ heterozygotes, measure the frequencies of three classes of heterozygotes among the progeny of crosses between h and r markers. These frequencies are, for the cross *hr7* × wild-type, 0.12 per cent *hr-wild;* 0.94 per cent *h-hr;* and 0.94 per cent *r-wild;* expressed in round numbers. The corresponding frequencies for the cross *hr13* × wild-type are 1.48, 0.26, and 0.26 per cent, respectively. What other heterozygotes might we expect to find among these progeny?

Two possible classes remain to be looked for; namely, the classes segregating into the pairs *hr, r;* and *h, wild;* coming from particles heterozygous for h but not for r. If the distribution of heterozygotes is symmetrical, that is, if the total frequency of heterozygosis for h is two per cent, and if the two undetected classes are of equal size, their individual frequencies would be 0.94 per cent for the cross *hr7* × wild-type, and 0.26 per cent for the cross *hr13* × wild-type.

One of the undetected classes can be efficiently measured by sampling clear r^+ plaques from platings of the progeny of the cross on mixed indicator, and retest-

TABLE 3. THE FREQUENCY OF *h-wild* HETEROZYGOTES PRODUCED IN CROSSES BETWEEN *hr* AND WILD-TYPE

	hr7 × *wild*	*hr13* × *wild*
Per cent clear r^+ plaques	13	1.3
No. mixed/no. tested	14/110	33/112
Per cent *h-wild* heterozygotes among progeny		
Expected	0.94	0.26
Found	1.7	0.38

ing to determine how many of the samples contain mixtures of h and wild-type phage, and how many contain h only. The proportion of clear r^+ plaques that yield mixtures, multiplied by the proportion of clear r^+ plaque-formers among the progeny of the cross, gives the frequency of *h-wild* heterozygotes in the population.

The results of this measurement for two crosses are compared with the expectation for symmetrical distributions of heterozygotes in Table 3. The findings are similar to those already described for r heterozygotes, namely:

In the cross *hr7* × *wild* (distantly linked markers) the great majority of particles heterozygous for *h* are not heterozygous for *r*.

In the cross *hr13* × *wild* (closely linked markers) the singly heterozygous class is smaller, but the proportion of heterozygotes yielding recombinants is large compared to the proportion of recombinants among the progeny as a whole.

In both crosses the total frequency of h-h^+ heterozygotes is roughly two per cent.

We conclude that the formation of particles heterozygous for *h* and for *r* obeys identical rules.

A method of somewhat similar principle is applicable to crosses between pairs of *r* mutants. This is important in that effects of linkage can be tested in different regions of the genetic map; unfortunately, not with very great precision. The principle of the test can be illustrated by the example *r2* × *r4*. Heterozygotes resulting from this cross should segregate to yield the following pairs: *r2* + *r2r4*, *r4* + *r2r4*, *r2* + *r4*, *r2* + *wild*, *r4* + *wild*. This list includes all possible pairs excepting the recombinant pair, which is assumed to be absent. The first two and the last two classes will all be of the same size for reasons of symmetry, and the sum of the frequencies of the last three classes will amount to two per cent of the population. If the two factors are not linked, heterozygotes belonging to the last three classes, and only these, will yield mottled plaques. If the factors are linked, only the last two classes will yield mottled plaques, and the difference between the proportion found and two per cent will measure the size of the doubly heterozygous class yielding *r2* + *r4*. The assumption that particles doubly heterozygous for linked factors do not produce mottled

TABLE 4. YIELDS OF r^+ AND MOTTLING PHAGE IN *r* CROSSES

Cross	Per cent r^+	Per cent mottled	Cross	Per cent r^+	Per cent mottled
r2 × *wild**	41	1.64 ± .24	*r2* × *r4*	0.85 ± .17	0.88 ± .17
	37	1.69 ± .18		0.80 ± .13	0.70 ± .14
r4 × *wild*	41	1.98 ± .10	*r2* × *r7*	3.8 ± .33	1.40 ± .18
				3.1 ± .37	1.19 ± .17
r7 × *wild*	46	1.63 ± .19			
	40	1.59 ± .21	*r4* × *r7**	3.7 ± .32	1.25 ± .19
				3.5 ± .29	1.90 ± .29
r13 × *wild**	50	1.88 ± .25			
	54	1.65 ± .33	*r13* × *r7**	8.1 ± .50	1.43 ± .17
				7.3 ± .52	1.27 ± .17
r1 × *wild**	45	2.17 ± .26			
	47	2.43 ± .21	*r1* × *r7*	17.9 ± 1.2	2.04 ± .26
			r1 × *r13*	16.7 ± .66	2.00 ± .27

The results shown are means and their standard deviations computed from counts of about 4000 plaques on 20 plates. The duplicate counts of the crosses marked with an asterisk were made from the same population on different days; the other duplicate counts represent independent experiments. The per cent r^+ in the left half of the table measures the equality of infection with the two parental viruses; in the right half it measures the linkage between *r* loci.

plaques is tested by examining plaques originating from bacteria mixedly infected with *r* mutant pairs, which shows that for map distances up to and including 10 units (*r7* × *r13*) the mottling is negligible.

The results of tests of this kind with six pairs of *r* mutants are shown in Table 4. Three facts emerge. The frequency of heterozygosis with respect to five different *r* loci is at least approximately the same. The effect of close linkage between the loci *r2* and *r4* is to produce a sufficiently large class of doubly heterozygous phage particles to cause a sharp decrease in the yield of mottling phage. No significant effect is seen for crosses between markers separated by a distance of three or four units or more. The method is evidently valid in principle, but too inaccurate to yield detailed information.

We return once more to crosses between phages carrying *h* and *r* markers to test the effect of unequal multiplicity on the pattern of segregation of the resulting heterozygotes (Table 5). The effect seen is to increase markedly the frequency of

TABLE 5. PER CENT DISTRIBUTIONS OF r-r^+ HETEROZYGOTES WITH RESPECT TO SEGREGATION PATTERN: CROSSES WITH 5-FOLD EXCESS OF *hr* OVER WILD-TYPE

Segregants found	*hr1* × *wild* (40)	*hr7* × *wild* (20)	*hr13* × *wild* (2)
hr-wild	2	4	71
h-hr	78	71	17
r-wild	20	25	12
h-r	. .	0	0
No. tested	117	55	161

Per cent yields of recombinants for each cross are shown in parentheses.

the parent-recombinant class containing the parental virus available in excess. This effect is not visible when the markers involved are closely linked.

Another experiment yields information about the sequence of events in the cell. It is based on the work of Doermann (1948a), who has shown that infected bacteria artificially lysed at various times during the latent period of viral growth do not yield any virus during the first half of the latent period, and that the yields rise linearly from zero to a maximum during the second half of the latent period. The current interpretation of this result is that the first half of the latent period is devoted to the multiplication of non-infective virus, and the second half to the conversion of non-infective into infective virus (Doermann and Dissosway, 1949; Luria, 1950; Hershey, 1951). During the second half of the latent period, the partial yields of virus can be obtained simply by adding cyanide to the cultures. Doermann (1948b) has also shown that very large yields of virus can be obtained when lysis is delayed for several hours, as happens in cultures containing high concentrations of bacteria infected with r^+ virus.

We have compared viral yields obtained from samples of the same bacterial suspension, infected with *hr7* and wild-type, by adding cyanide ten minutes after infection, by spontaneous lysis at the end of the normal latent period (21 to 40 minutes), and by spontaneous lysis delayed for five to six hours. The yields of virus per cell were respectively 10, 250, and 1710. The yields of recombinants were respectively 17, 29, and 42 per cent of the total virus. The yields of r-r^+ heterozygotes, however, did not differ significantly from two per cent in any of the three populations. The proportions of the different segregating classes were also the same among the heterozygotes in small samples from the first two yields. This experiment shows that the interactions between phage particles giving rise to recombinants (Doermann and Dissosway, 1949) and heterozygotes, are well under way by the time infective virus begins to form in the cell. The rise in proportion of recombinants during the latter half of the latent period, while the proportion of heterozygotes remains constant, suggests that the formation and segregation of heterozygotes may be continuing during this time.

Summary of New Facts

(1) When bacteria are infected with three kinds of phage carrying unlinked genetic markers, about three per cent of the progeny carry markers derived from all three parents.

(2) When bacteria are infected with two phages carrying allelic markers, about two per cent of the progeny particles segregate during further growth to yield both kinds of phage. This is true for five different *r* markers, and an *h* marker. The particles segregating to yield *r* and r^+ phage are conveniently studied because they produce mottled plaques.

(3) The mottle producers are not clumps of particles because they are inactivated as single units of normal sensitivity by antiserum, heat, β-rays, and ultraviolet light. Artificially prepared clumps are inactivated as multiple units.

(4) There is no indication that the mottling particles can multiply before segregating. In view of facts (3) and (4), the segregating particles are called heterozygotes for the specified marker.

(5) When the parental phage particles are marked at both *h* and *r* loci, the pattern of segregation shows the following characteristics:

(a) About two per cent of the progeny are heterozygous for *h*, and about two per cent for *r*.

b) The particles heterozygous for a single marker form four classes of approximately equal size, segregating into *h, hr; h, wild; r, hr;* and *r, wild;* respectively. respectively. Thus single heterozygotes yield one parent and one recombinant with respect to the original cross.

(c) When the two markers are linked, the double heterozygotes segregate to yield the two parents of the original cross, never the two recombinants, and never more than two kinds of phage. When the two markers are unlinked, these alternatives cannot be distinguished.

(d) When the two markers are unlinked or distant, heterozygosis for one marker is almost independent of heterozygosis for the second, and the doubly heterozygous class amounts to only three per cent of the total number of heterozygotes. Thus in the crosses *hr7* × wild-type and *hr1* × wild-type, which yield respectively 20 and 40 per cent of recombinants, the pooled heterozygotes segregate to yield about 48 per cent of recombinants.

(e) In the cross *hr13* × wild-type (closely linked markers) the doubly heterozygous class makes up about 59 per cent of the total number of heterozygotes. This cross yields about two per cent of recombinants, but the pooled heterozygotes segregate to yield about 20 per cent of recombinants.

(f) If the crosses involving unlinked or distant factors are varied by introducing a 5-fold excess of one parent, the effect is to increase the frequency of the single heterozygotes segregating to yield that parent. This effect is not visible if the markers are closely linked.

(6) The frequency of heterozygosis is independent of the yield of virus per bacterium when this is decreased by premature lysis with cyanide, or increased under conditions of lysis-inhibition.

Discussion

Information about inheritance in bacteriophage T2H comes from the analysis of mutations and from recombination tests. These two techniques agree in showing that mutations occur in localized genes. Recombination tests reveal that the genes are organized into linkage groups. For one of these groups, it appears that the arrangement of genes is linear. Inheritance in bacteriophage is therefore amenable to the same kind of genetic analysis that has served to elucidate nuclear organization in other organisms. The limitations peculiar to viral genetics should not be overlooked. It is not possible to recover the immediate products of recombination, unless the heterozygotes prove to be such; the mechanism of recombination is unknown; and cytogenetic techniques are inapplicable.

The analysis of heterozygotes raises new questions about the mechanism of genetic recombination. The surprising result is that the great majority of the heterozygotes recovered from a two-factor cross segregate as if they were homozygous or hemizygous for one of the marked genes, unless these are very closely linked. This means that the heterozygotes found, which should perhaps be called residual heterozygotes, may not be representative of the heterozygotes formed in the cell.

One feature of the residual heterozygotes is reassuring in this respect. The total frequency of heterozygosis is the same for five different *r* markers and one *h* marker. This makes it unlikely that the formation of residual heterozygotes is contingent on structural differences between different mutants.

The questions raised by the peculiar segregation pattern of heterozygotes are clarified somewhat in terms of the following alternatives.

(1) Residual heterozygotes may not be diploid particles, but particles containing one or more small extra pieces of genetic material. Double heterozygotes for distant markers contain two or more pieces. These pieces are substituted for the homologous pieces in one of the very early progeny of the segregating heterozygote. The residual heterozygotes need not differ from intracellular heterozygotes, and their production need not involve zygote formation.

2) Residual heterozygotes may be formed preferentially from zygotes in which recombination has occurred, and receive one parental and one recombinant

set of genes. In this case the residual heterozygotes are diploid, but are not representative of the zygotes from which they come.

(3) Residual heterozygotes may be representative zygotes that are doubly heterozygous in structure, but which undergo segregations accompanied by frequent losses to yield parental and recombinant pairs.

The third alternative can be excluded. In crosses involving the markers *h* and *r13*, one finds only two per cent of recombinants among the whole progeny, and about 20 per cent of recombinants among the segregants of heterozygous progeny. To explain this in terms of alternative (3), one would have to assume a low frequency of intracellular zygote formation. This assumption is incompatible with the high frequency of triparental recombination observed.

The questions about structure of heterozygotes can be generalized in the following way. We find that about two per cent of the progeny of crosses are heterozygous for each marker, and that the particles heterozygous for one are mostly not the particles heterozygous for the other, excepting close linkage. Since the frequencies are not specific for individual mutants, they are presumably independent of local structure, and every phage particle must carry doublings at one or more unmarked loci if total map distances are large. The alternatives (1) and (2) are to this extent applicable to all the progeny, and take the simple form: are phage particles diploid or not?

It is reasonable to assume that the formation of heterozygotes and the formation of recombinants are related processes, but there is no evidence that recombinants have their primary origin in structures resembling the residual heterozygotes. Instead, recombinants and residual heterozygotes may be alternative products of other structures about which we have no direct information. The residual heterozygotes have one characteristic that is suggestive in this connection: they segregate to yield one recombinant per heterozygote. The recombinants that are produced in crosses also have to be assumed to come from structures yielding one recombinant, to explain the independent or nearly independent distributions of sister recombinants among single cell yields of virus (Hershey and Rotman, 1949).

The frequency of double heterozygotes provides a measure of linkage that is independent of the results of recombination tests. Both measures show that *h* is linked to *r13* and that *r2* is linked to *r4*. The new measure is insensitive for large map distances since the crosses involving *h* and *r7*, and *h* and *r1*, which yield respectively 20 and 40 per cent of recombinants, produce the same number of double heterozygotes.

Conclusion

A preliminary analysis of heterozygous particles of the bacteriophage T2H raises new questions about the mechanism of genetic recombination, and suggests that new ideas are needed to explain this phenomenon.

The work reported in this paper was aided by a grant from the Division of Research Grants and Fellowships, U. S. Public Health Service.

REFERENCES

DELBRÜCK, M., and BAILEY, W. T., JR., 1946, Induced mutations in bacterial viruses. Cold Spr. Harb. Symposium Quant. Biol. *11*: 33–37.

DOERMANN, A. H., 1948a, Intracellular growth of bacteriophage. Yearb. Carneg. Instn. *47*: 176–182.

1948b, Lysis and lysis inhibition with *Escherichia coli* bacteriophage. J. Bact. *55*: 257–276.

DOERMANN, A. H., and DISSOSWAY, C. F.-R., 1949, Intracellular growth and genetics of bacteriophage. Yearb. Carneg. Instn. *48*: 170–176.

HERSHEY, A. D., 1946, Spontaneous mutations in bacterial viruses. Cold Spr. Harb. Symposium Quant. Biol. *11*: 67–77.

1951, Reproduction of bacteriophage. VIIth International Congress for Cell Biology, in press.

HERSHEY, A. D., and DAVIDSON, H., 1951, Allelic and non-allelic genes controlling host specificity in a bacteriophage. Genetics *36*: 667–675.

HERSHEY, A. D., and ROTMAN, R., 1948, Linkage among genes controlling inhibition of lysis in a bacterial virus. Proc. Nat. Acad. Sci., Wash. *34*: 253–264.

1949. Genetic recombination between host range and plaque type mutants of bacteriophage in single bacterial cells. Genetics *34*: 44–71.

LURIA, S. E., 1945, Mutations of bacterial viruses affecting their host range. Genetics *30*: 84–99.

1950, Bacteriophage: an essay on virus reproduction. Science *111*: 507–511.

DISCUSSION

VISCONTI (in reply to a comment by Horowitz): The excess of parental types in Dr. Hershey's experiments can be eliminated by selecting a class of recombinants and scoring inside this class for a third character. Making use of the three markers, *r1*, *h* and *m*, the following cross was made: $r1\ h\ m^+ \times r1^+\ h^+\ m$. The yield was plated on B, so that no difference could be detected between *h* and h^+. Of 1003 plaques observed, 177 were $r^+\ m^+$, thus giving a recombination value of 18 per cent. 128 of such plaques were "fished" and tested by a streaking method on B/2. Of the 128 tested, 63 were *h* and 65 h^+. In another experiment, 92 plaques were "fished" and tested by plating a sample on double indicator. 43 were *h;* 47 were h^+; and two were mixed. The two mixed plaques account for the 2 per cent of heterozygotes for the locus *h*.

THE STRUCTURE OF DNA

J. D. Watson[1] and F. H. C. Crick

Cavendish Laboratory, Cambridge, England

(Contribution to the Discussion of Provirus.)

It would be superfluous at a Symposium on Viruses to introduce a paper on the structure of DNA with a discussion on its importance to the problem of virus reproduction. Instead we shall not only assume that DNA is important, but in addition that it is the carrier of the genetic specificity of the virus (for argument, see Hershey, this volume) and thus must possess in some sense the capacity for exact self-duplication. In this paper we shall describe a structure for DNA which suggests a mechanism for its self-duplication and allows us to propose, for the first time, a detailed hypothesis on the atomic level for the self-reproduction of genetic material.

We first discuss the chemical and physical-chemical data which show that DNA is a long fibrous molecule. Next we explain why crystallographic evidence suggests that the structural unit of DNA consists not of one but of two polynucleotide chains. We then discuss a stereochemical model which we believe satisfactorily accounts for both the chemical and crystallographic data. In conclusion we suggest some obvious genetical implications of the proposed structure. A preliminary account of some of these data has already appeared in Nature (Watson and Crick, 1953a, 1953b).

I. Evidence for the Fibrous Nature of DNA

The basic chemical formula of DNA is now well established. As shown in Figure 1 it consists of a very long chain, the backbone of which is made up of alternate sugar and phosphate groups, joined together in regular 3′ 5′ phosphate di-ester linkages. To each sugar is attached a nitrogenous base, only four different kinds of which are commonly found in DNA. Two of these — adenine and guanine — are purines, and the other two — thymine and cytosine — are pyrimidines. A fifth base, 5-methyl cytosine, occurs in smaller amounts in certain organisms, and a sixth, 5-hydroxy-methyl-cytosine, is found instead of cytosine in the T even phages (Wyatt and Cohen, 1952).

---

[1]Aided by a Fellowship from the National Foundation for Infantile Paralysis.

Reprinted by permission of the authors and the Long Island Biological Association from Cold Spring Harbor Symposia on Quantitative Biology, **18**, 123-131 (1953).

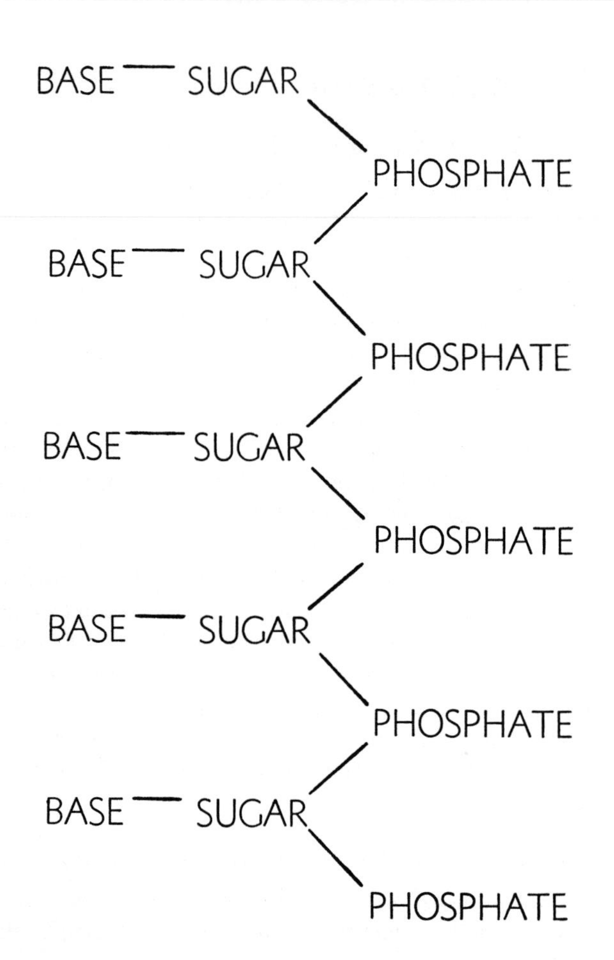

FIGURE 1. Chemical formula (diagrammatic) of a single chain of desoxyribonucleic acid.

It should be noted that the chain is unbranched, a consequence of the regular internucleotide linkage. On the other hand the sequence of the different nucleotides is, as far as can be ascertained, completely irregular. Thus, DNA has some features which are regular, and some which are irregular.

A similar conception of the DNA molecule as a long thin fiber is obtained from physico-chemical analysis involving sedimentation, diffusion, light scattering, and viscosity measurements. These techniques indicate that DNA is a very asymmetrical structure approximately 20 A wide and many thousands of angstroms long. Estimates of its molecular weight currently center between 5×10^6 and 10^7 (approximately 3×10^4 nucleotides). Surprisingly each of these measurements tend to suggest that the DNA is relatively rigid, a puzzling finding in view of the large number of single bonds (5 per nucleotide) in the phosphate-sugar backbone. Recently these indirect inferences have been confirmed by electron microscopy. Employing high resolution techniques both Williams (1952) and Kahler *et al.* (1953) have observed, in preparations of DNA, very long thin fibers with a uniform width of approximately 15-20 A.

II. Evidence for the Existence of Two Chemical Chains in the Fiber

This evidence comes mainly from X-ray studies. The material used is the sodium salt of DNA (usually from calf thymus) which has been extracted, purified, and drawn into fibers. These fibers are highly birefringent, show marked ultraviolet and infrared dichroism (Wilkins *et al.*, 1951; Fraser and Fraser, 1951), and give good X-ray fiber diagrams. From a preliminary study of these, Wilkins, Franklin and their co-workers at King's College, London (Wilkins *et al.*, 1953; Franklin and Gosling 1953a, b and c) have been able to draw certain general conclusions about the structure of DNA. Two important facts emerge from their work. They are:

(1) *Two distinct forms of DNA exist.* Firstly a crystalline form, Structure A, (Figure 2) which occurs at about 75 per cent relative humidity and contains approximately 30 per cent water. At higher humidities the fibers take up more water, increase in length by about 30 per cent and assume Structure B (Figure 3). This is a less ordered form than Structure A, and appears to be paracrystalline; that is, the individual molecules are all packed parallel to one another, but are not otherwise regularly arranged in space. In Table 1, we have tabulated some of the characteristic features which distinguish the two forms. The transition from A to B is reversible and therefore the two structures are likely to be related in a simple manner.

Table 1.
(From Franklin and Gosling, 1953a, b and c)

	Degree of orientation	Repeat distance along fiber axis	Location of first equatorial spacing	Water content	Number of nucleotides within unit cell
Structure A	Crystalline	28 A	18 A	30%	22-24
Structure B	Paracrystalline	34 A	22-24 A	> 30%	20 (?)

(2) *The crystallographic unit contains two polynucleotide chains.* The argument is crystallographic and so will only be given in outline. Structure B has a very strong 3.4 A reflexion on the meridian. As first pointed out by Astbury (1947), this can only mean that the nucleotides in it occur in groups spaced 3.4 A apart in

the fiber direction. On going from Structure B to Structure A the fiber shortens by about 30 per cent. Thus in Structure A the groups must be about 2.5 per cent A apart axially. The measured density of Structure A, (Franklin and Gosling,

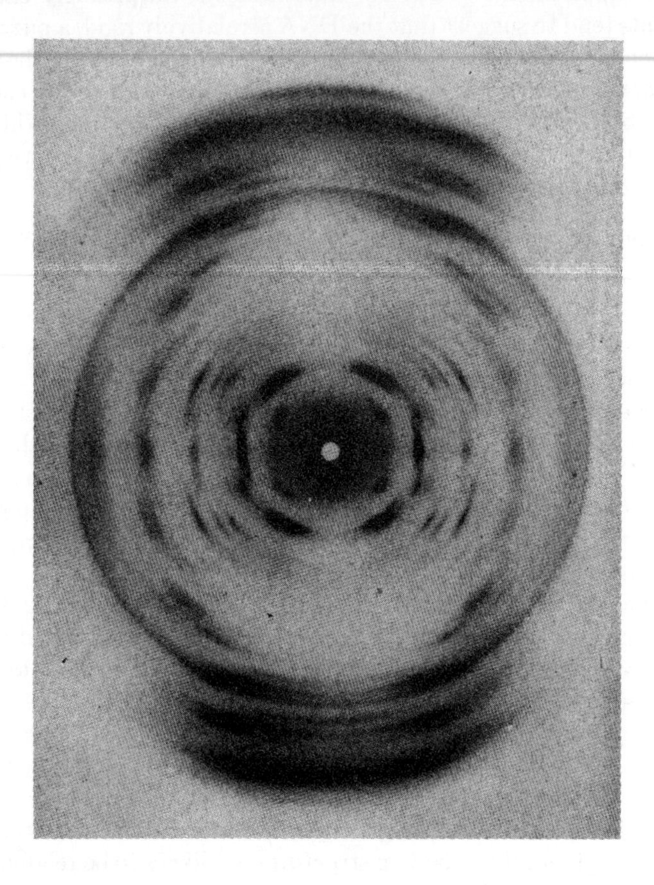

FIGURE 2. X-ray fiber diagram of structure A of desoxyribonucleic acid. (H. M. F. Wilkins and H. R. Wilson, unpub.)

1953c) together with the cell dimensions, shows that there must be *two* nucleotides in each such group. Thus it is very probable that the crystallographic unit consists of two distinct polynucleotide chains. Final proof of this can only come from a complete solution of the structure.

Structure A has a pseudo-hexagonal lattice, in which the lattice points are 22 A apart. This distance roughly corresponds with the diameter of fibers seen in the electron microscope, bearing in mind that the latter are quite dry. Thus it is probable that the crystallographic unit and the fiber are the one and the same.

III. DESCRIPTION OF THE PROPOSED STRUCTURE

Two conclusions might profitably be drawn from the above data. Firstly, the structure of DNA is regular enough to form a three dimensional crystal. This is in spite of the fact that its component chains may have an irregular sequence of purine and pyrimidine nucleotides. Secondly, as the structure contains two

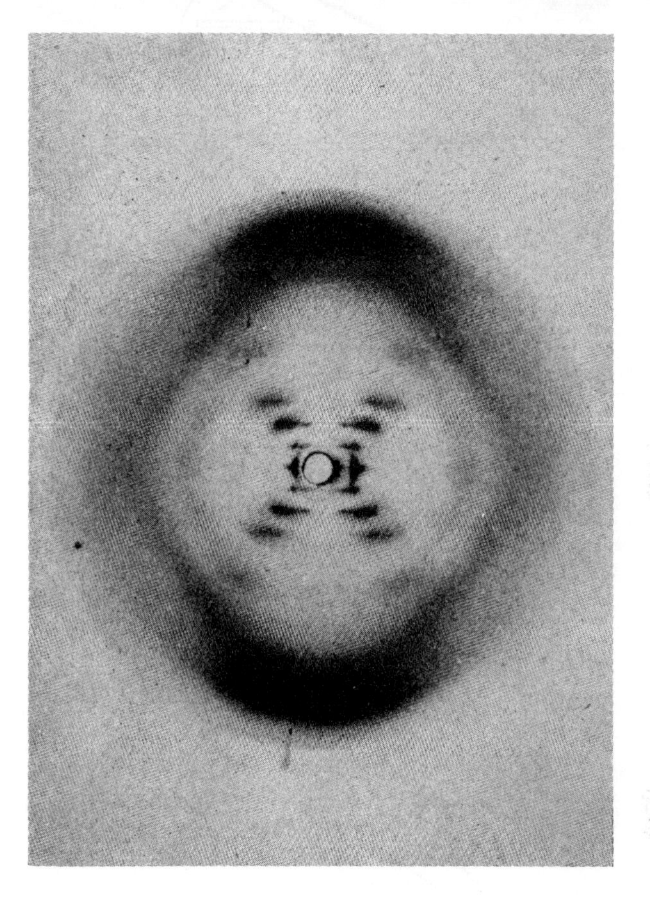

FIGURE 3. X-ray fiber diagram of Structure B of desoxyribonucleic acid. (R. E. Franklin and R. Gosling, 1953a.)

chains, these chains must be regularly arranged in relation to each other.

To account for these findings, we have proposed (Watson and Crick, 1953a) a structure in which the two chains are coiled round a common axis and joined together by hydrogen bonds between the nucleotide bases (see Figure 4). Both chains follow right handed helices, but the sequences of the atoms in the phosphate-sugar backbones run in opposite directions and so are related by a dyad perpendicular to the helix axis. The phosphates and sugar groups are on the outside of the helix whilst the bases are on the inside. The distance of a phosphorus atom from the fiber axis is 10 A. We have built our model to correspond to Structure B, which the X-ray data show to have a repeat distance of 34 A in the fiber direction and a very strong reflexion of spacing 3.4 A on the meridian of the X-ray

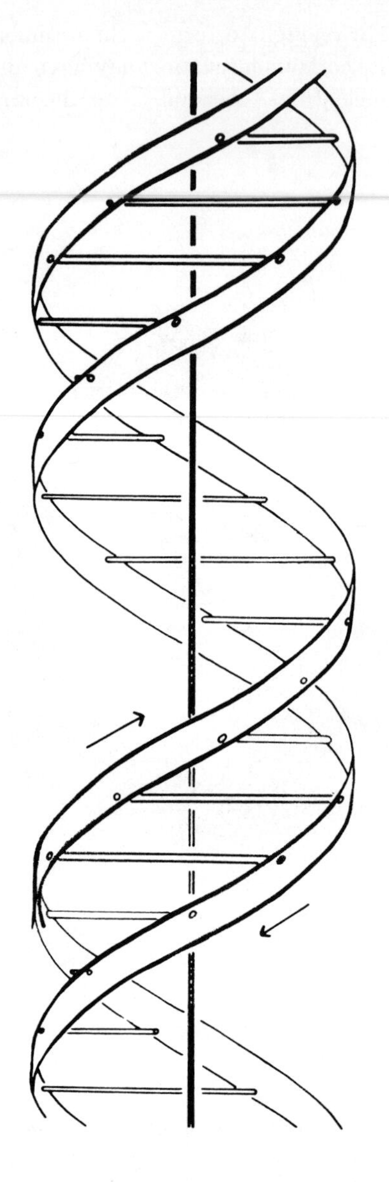

FIGURE 4. This figure is diagrammatic. The two ribbons symbolize the two phosphate-sugar chains and the horizontal rods the pairs of bases holding the chain together. The vertical line marks the fiber axis.

pattern. To fit these observations our structure has a nucleotide on each chain every 3.4 A in the fiber direction, and makes one complete turn after 10 such intervals, i.e., after 34 A. Our structure is a well-defined one and all bond distances and angles, including van der Waal distances, are stereochemically acceptable.

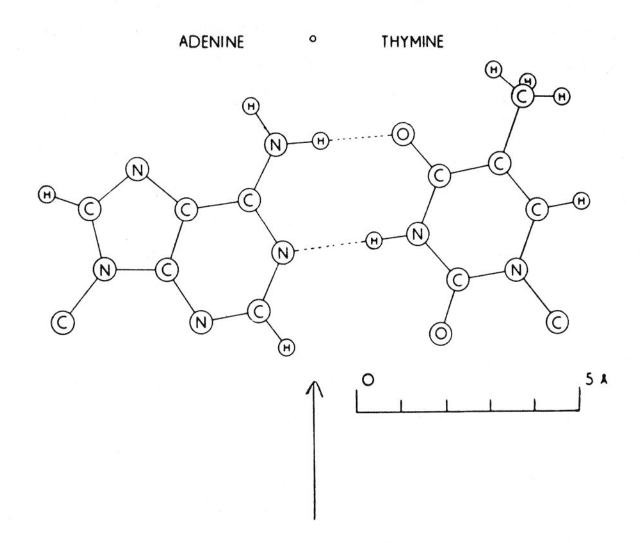

FIGURE 5. Pairing of adenine and thymine. Hydrogen bonds are shown dotted. One carbon atom of each sugar is shown.

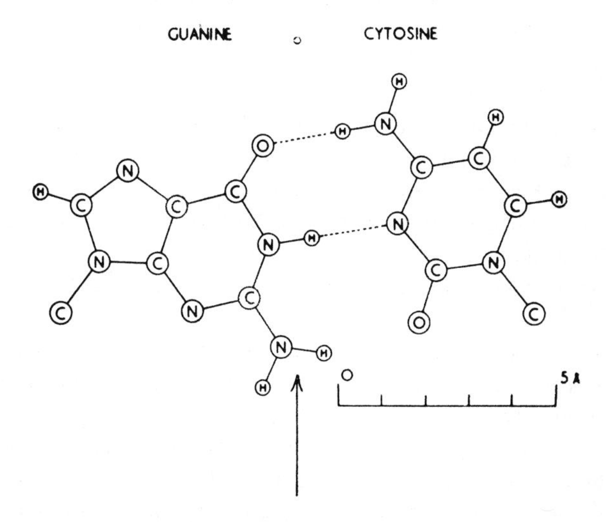

FIGURE 6. Pairing of guanine and cytosine. Hydrogen bonds are shown dotted. One carbon atom of each sugar is shown.

The essential element of the structure is the manner in which the two chains are held together by hydrogen bonds between the bases. The bases are perpendicular to the fiber axis and joined together in pairs. The pairing arrangement is very specific, and only certain pairs of bases will fit into the structure. The basic reason for this is that we have assumed that the backbone of each polynucleotide chain is in the form of a regular helix. Thus, irrespective of which bases are present, the glucosidic bonds (which join sugar and base) are arranged in a regular manner in space. In particular, any two glucosidic bonds (one from each chain) which are attached to a bonded pair of bases, must always occur at a fixed distance apart due to the regularity of the two backbones to which they are joined. The result is that one member of a pair of bases must always be a purine, and the other a pyrimidine, in order to bridge between the two chains. If a pair consisted of two purines, for example, there would not be room for it; if of two pyrimidines they would be too far apart to form hydrogen bonds.

In theory a base can exist in a number of tautomeric forms, differing in the exact positions at which its hydrogen atoms are attached. However, under physiological conditions one particular form of each base is much more probable than any of the others. If we make the assumption that the favored forms always occur, then the pairing requirements are even more restrictive. Adenine can only pair with thymine, and guanine only with cytosine (or 5-methyl-cytosine, or 5-hydroxy-methyl-cytosine). This pairing is shown in detail in Figures 5 and 6. If adenine tried to pair with cytosine it could not form hydrogen bonds, since there would be two hydrogens near one of the bonding positions, and none at the other, instead of one in each.

A given pair can be either way round. Adenine, for example, can occur on either chain, but when it does its partner on the other chain must always be thymine. This is possible because the two glucoside bonds of a pair (see Figures 5 and 6) are symmetrically related to each other, and thus occur in the same positions if the pair is turned over.

It should be emphasized that since each base can form hydrogen bonds at a number of points one can pair up *isolated* nucleotides in a large variety of ways. *Specific* pairing of bases can only be obtained by imposing some restriction, and in our case it is in a direct consequence of the postulated regularity of the phosphate-sugar backbone.

It should further be emphasized that whatever pair of bases occurs at one particular point in the DNA structure, no restriction is imposed on the neighboring pairs, and any *sequence* of pairs can occur. This is because all the bases are flat, and since they are stacked roughly one above another like a pile of pennies, it makes no difference which pair is neighbor to which.

Though any sequence of bases can fit into our structure, the necessity for specific pairing demands a definite relationship between the sequences on the two chains. That is, if we knew the actual order of the bases on one chain, we could automatically write down the order on the other. *Our structure therefore consists of two chains, each of which is the complement of the other.*

IV. Evidence in Favor of the Complementary Model

The experimental evidence available to us now offers strong support to our model though we should emphasize that, as yet, it has not been proved correct. The evidence in its favor is of three types:

(1) The general appearance of the X-ray picture strongly suggests that the

basic structure is helical (Wilkins *et al.*, 1953; Franklin and Gosling, 1953a). If we postulate that a helix is present, we immediately are able to deduce from the X-ray pattern of Structure B (Figure 3), that its pitch is 34 A and its diameter approximately 20A. Moreover, the pattern suggests a high concentration of atoms on the circumference of the helix, in accord with our model which places the phosphate sugar backbone on the outside. The photograph also indicates that the two polynucleotide chains are not spaced equally along the fiber axis, but are probably displaced from each other by about three-eighths of the fiber axis period, an inference again in qualitative agreement with our model.

The interpretation of the X-ray pattern of Structure A (the crystalline form) is less obvious. This form does not give a meridional reflexion at 3.4 A, but instead (Figure 2) gives a series of reflexions around 25° off the meridian at spacings between 3 A and 4 A. This suggests to us that in this form the bases are no longer perpendicular to the fiber axis, but are tilted about 25° from the perpendicular position in a way that allows the fiber to contract 30 per cent and reduces the longitudinal translation of each nucleotide to about 2.5 A. It should be noted that the X-ray pattern of Structure A is much more detailed than that of Structure B and so if correctly interpreted, can yield more precise information about DNA. Any proposed model for DNA must be capable of forming either Structure A or Structure B and so it remains imperative for our very tentative interpretation of Structure A to be confirmed.

(2) The anomolous titration curves of undegraded DNA with acids and bases strongly suggests that hydrogen bond formation is a characteristic aspect of DNA structure. When a solution of DNA is initially treated with acids or bases, no groups are titratable at first between pH 5 and pH 11.0, but outside these limits a rapid ionization occurs (Gulland and Jordan, 1947; Jordan, 1951). On back titration, however, either with acid from pH 12 or with alkali from pH $2\frac{1}{2}$, a different titration curve is obtained indicating that the titratable groups are more accessible to acids and bases than is the untreated solution. Accompanying the initial release of groups at pH 11.5 and in the range pH 3.5 to pH 4.5 is a marked fall in the viscosity and the disappearance of strong flow birefringence. While this decrease was originally thought to be caused by a reversible depolymerization (Vilbrandt and Tennent, 1943), it has been shown by Gulland, Jordan and Taylor (1947) that this is unlikely as no increase was observed in the amount of secondary phosphoryl groups. Instead these authors suggested that some of the groups of the bases formed hydrogen bonds between different bases. They were unable to decide whether the hydrogen bonds linked bases in the same or in adjacent structural units. The fact that most of the ionizable groups are originally inaccessible to acids and bases is more easily explained if the hydrogen bonds are between bases within the same structural unit. This point would definitely be established if it were shown that the shape of the initial titration curve was the same at very low DNA concentrations, when the interaction between neighboring structural units is small.

(3) The analytical data on the relative proportion of the various bases show that the amount of adenine is close to that of thymine, and the amount of guanine

close to the amount of cytosine + 5-methyl cytosine, although the ratio of adenine to guanine can vary from one source to another (Chargaff, 1951; Wyatt, 1952). In fact as the techniques for estimation of the bases improve, the ratios of adenine to thymine, and guanine to cytosine + 5-methyl cytosine appear to grow very close to unity. This is a most striking result, especially as the sequence of bases on a given chain is likely to be irregular, and suggests a structure involving paired bases. In fact, we believe the analytical data offer the most important evidence so far available in support of our model, since they specifically support the biologically interesting feature, the presence of complementary chains.

We thus believe that the present experimental evidence justifies the working hypothesis that the essential features of our model are correct and allows us to consider its genetic possibilities.

V. Genetical Implications of the Complementary Model

As a preliminary we should state that the DNA fibers from which the X-ray diffraction patterns were obtained are not artifacts arising in the method of preparation. In the first place, Wilkins and his co-workers (see Wilkins *et al.*, 1953) have shown that X-ray patterns similar to those from the isolated fibers can be obtained from certain intact biological materials such as sperm head and bacteriophage particles. Secondly, our postulated model is so extremely specific that we find it impossible to believe that it could be formed during the isolation from living cells.

A genetic material must in some way fulfil two functions. It must duplicate itself, and it must exert a highly specific influence on the cell. Our model for DNA suggests a simple mechanism for the first process, but at the moment we cannot see how it carries out the second one. We believe, however, that its specificity is expressed by the precise sequence of the pairs of bases. The backbone of our model is highly regular, and the sequence is the only feature which can carry the genetical information. It should not be thought that because in our structure the bases are on the "inside," they would be unable to come into contact with other molecules. Owing to the open nature of our structure they are in fact fairly accessible.

A Mechanism for DNA Replication

The complementary nature of our structure suggests how it duplicates itself. It is difficult to imagine how like attracts like, and it has been suggested (see Pauling and Delbrück, 1940; Friedrich-Freksa, 1940; and Muller, 1947) that self duplication may involve the union of each part with an opposite or complementary part. In these discussions it has generally been suggested that protein and nucleic acid are complementary to each other and that self replication involves the alternate syntheses of these two components. We should like to propose instead that the specificity of DNA self replication is accomplished without recourse to specific protein synthesis and that each of our complementary DNA chains serves as a template or mould for the formation onto itself of a new companion chain.

For this to occur the hydrogen bonds linking the complementary chains must break and the two chains unwind and separate. It seems likely that the single chain (or the relevant part of it) might itself assume the helical form and serve as a mould onto which free nucleotides (strictly polynucleotide precursors) can attach themselves by forming hydrogen bonds. We propose that polymerization of the precursors to form a new chain only occurs if the resulting chain forms the proposed structure. This is plausible because steric reasons would not allow monomers "crystallized" onto the first chain to approach one another in such a way that they could be joined together in a new chain, unless they were those monomers which could fit into our structure. It is not obvious to us whether a special enzyme would be required to carry out the polymerization or whether the existing single helical chain could act effectively as an enzyme.

Difficulties in the Replication Scheme

While this scheme appears intriguing, it nevertheless raises a number of difficulties, none of which, however, do we regard as insuperable. The first difficulty is that our structure does not differentiate between cytosine and 5-methyl cytosine, and therefore during replication the specificity in sequence involving these bases would not be perpetuated. The amount of 5-methyl cytosine varies considerably from one species to another, though it is usually rather small or absent. The present experimental results (Wyatt, 1952) suggest that each species has a characteristic amount. They also show that the sum of the two cytosines is more nearly equal to the amount of guanine than is the amount of cytosine by itself. It may well be that the difference between the two cytosines is not functionally significant. This interpretation would be considerably strengthened if it proved possible to change the amount of 5-methyl cytosine in the DNA of an organism without altering its genetical make-up.

The occurrence of 5-hydroxy-methyl-cytosine in the T even phages (Wyatt and Cohen, 1952) presents no such difficulty, since it completely replaces cytosine, and its amount in the DNA is close to that of guanine.

The second main objection to our scheme is that it completely ignores the role of the basic protamines and histones, proteins known to be combined with DNA in most living organisms. This was done for two reasons. Firstly, we can formulate a scheme of DNA reproduction involving it alone and so from the viewpoint of simplicity it seems better to believe (at least at present) that the genetic specificity is never passed through a protein intermediary. Secondly, we know almost nothing about the structural features of protamines and histones. Our only clue is the finding of Astbury (1947) and of Wilkins and Randall (1953) that the X-ray pattern of nucleoprotamine is very similar to that of DNA alone. This suggests that the protein component, or at least some of it, also assumes a helical form and in view of the very open nature of our model, we suspect that protein forms a third helical chain between the pair of polynucleotide chains (see Figure 4). As yet nothing is known about the function of the protein; perhaps it controls the coiling and uncoiling and perhaps it assists in holding the single polynucleotide chains in a helical configuration.

The third difficulty involves the necessity for the two complementary chains to unwind in order to serve as a template for a new chain. This is a very fundamental difficulty when the two chains are interlaced as in our model. The two main ways in which a pair of helices can be coiled together have been called plectonemic coiling and paranemic coiling. These terms have been used by cytologists to describe the coiling of chromosomes (Huskins, 1941; for a review see Manton, 1950). The type of coiling found in our model (see Figure 4) is called plectonemic. Paranemic coiling is found when two separate helices are brought to lie side by side and then pushed together so that their axes roughly coincide. Though one may start with two regular helices the process of pushing them together necessarily distorts them. It is impossible to have paranemic coiling with two regular simple helices going round the same axis. This point can only be clearly grasped by studying models.

There is of course no difficulty in "unwinding" a *single* chain of DNA coiled into a helix, since a polynucleotide chain has so many single bonds about which rotation is possible. The difficulty occurs when one has a pair of simple helices with a common axis. The difficulty is a topological one and cannot be surmounted by simple manipulation. Apart from breaking the chains there are only two sorts of ways to separate two chains coiled plectonemically. In the first, one takes hold of one end of one chain, and the other end of the other, and simply pulls in the axial direction. The two chains slip over each other, and finish up separate and end to end. It seems to us highly unlikely that this occurs in this case, and we shall not consider it further. In the second way the two chains must be directly untwisted. When this has been done they are separate and side by side. The number of turns necessary to untwist them completely is equal to the number of turns of one of the chains round the common axis. For our structure this comes to one turn every 34 A, and thus about 150 turns per million molecular weight of DNA, that is per 5000 A of our structure. The problem of uncoiling falls into two parts:

(1) How many turns must be made, and how is tangling avoided?

(2) What are the physical or chemical forces which produce it?

For the moment we shall be mainly discussing the first of these. It is not easy to decide what is the uninterrupted length of functionally active DNA. As a lower limit we may take the molecular weight of the DNA after isolation, say fifty thousand A in length and having about 1000 turns. This is only a lower limit as there is evidence suggesting a breakage of the DNA fiber during the process of extraction. The upper limit might be the total amount of DNA in a virus or in the case of a higher organism, the total amount of DNA in a chromosome. For T2 this upper limit is approximately 800,000 A which corresponds to 20,000 turns, while in the higher organisms this upper limit may sometimes be 1000 fold higher.

The difficulty might be more simple to resolve if successive parts of a chromosome coiled in opposite directions. The most obvious way would be to have both right and left handed DNA helices in sequence but this seems unlikely as we have only been able to build our model in the right handed sense. Another possibility might be that the long strands of right handed DNA are joined together by compensating strands of left handed polypeptide helices. The merits of this proposition are difficult to assess, but the fact that the phage DNA does not seem to be linked to protein makes it rather unattractive.

The untwisting process would be less complicated if replication started at the ends as soon as the chains began to separate. This mechanism would produce a new two-strand structure without requiring at any time a free single-strand stage. In this way the danger of tangling would be considerably decreased as the two-strand structure is much more rigid than a single strand and would resist attempts to coil around its neighbors. Once the replicating process is started the presence, at the growing end of the pair, of double-stranded structures might facilitate the breaking of hydrogen bonds in the original unduplicated section and allow replication to proceed in a zipper-like fashion.

It is also possible that one chain of a pair occasionally breaks under the strain of twisting. The polynucleotide chain remaining intact could then release the accumulated twist by rotation about single bonds and following this, the broken ends, being still in close proximity, might rejoin.

It is clear that, in spite of the tentative suggestions we have just made, the difficulty of untwisting is a formidable one, and it is therefore worthwhile re-examining why we postulate plectonemic coiling, and not paranemic coiling in which the two helical threads are not intertwined, but merely in close apposition to each other. Our answer is that with paranemic coiling, the specific pairing of bases would not allow the successive residues of each helix to be in equivalent orientation with regard to the helical axis. This is a possibility we strongly oppose as it implies that a large number of stereochemical alternatives for the sugar-phosphate backbone are possible, an inference at variance to our finding, with stereochemical models (Crick and Watson, 1953) that the position of the sugar-phosphate group is rather restrictive and cannot be subject to the large variability necessary for paranemic coiling. Moreover, such a model would not lead to specific pairing of the bases, since this only follows if the glucosidic links are arranged regularly in space. We therefore believe that if a helical structure is present, the relationship between the helices will be plectonemic.

We should ask, however, whether there might not be another complementary structure which maintains the necessary regularity but which is not helical. One such structure can, in fact, be imagined. It would consist of a ribbon-like arrangement in which again the two chains are joined together by specific pairs of bases, located 3.4 A above each other, but in which the sugar-phosphate backbone instead of forming a helix, runs in a straight line at an angle approximately 30° off the line formed by the pair of bases. While this ribbon-like structure would give many of the features of the X-ray diagram of Structure B, we are unable to define precisely how it should pack in a macroscopic fiber, and why in particular it should give a strong equatorial reflexion at 20-24 A. We are thus not enthusiastic about this model though we should emphasize that it has not yet been disproved.

Independent of the details of our model, there are two geometrical problems

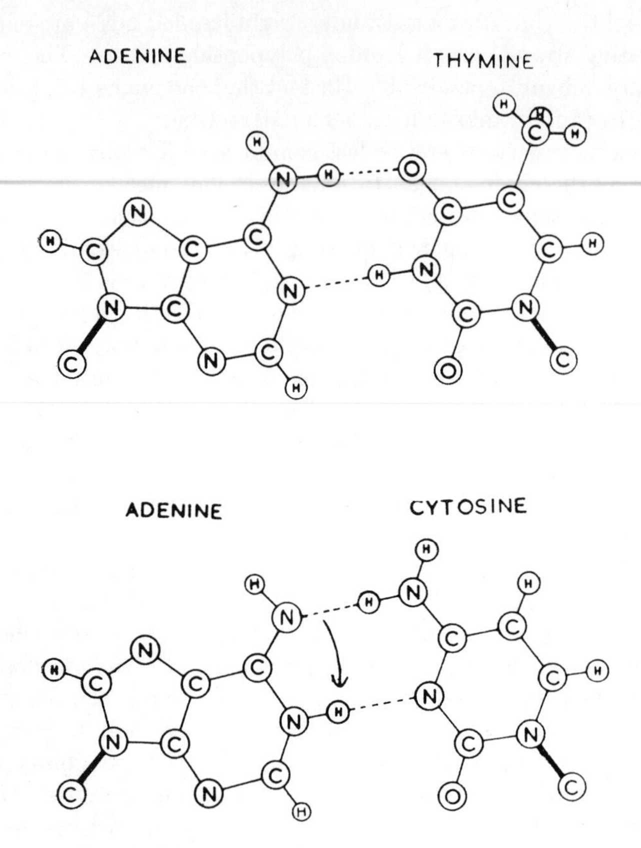

FIGURE 7. Pairing arrangements of adenine before (above) and after (below) it has undergone a tautomeric shift.

which *any* model for DNA must face. Both involve the necessity for some form of super folding process and can be illustrated with bacteriophage. Firstly, the total length of the DNA within T2 is about 8×10^5A. As its DNA is thought (Siegal and Singer, 1953) to have the same very large M. W. as that from other sources, it must bend back and forth many times in order to fit into the phage head of diameter 800 A. Secondly, the DNA must replicate itself without getting tangled. Approximately 500 phage particles can be synthesized within a single bacterium of average dimensions $10^4 \times 10^4 \times 2 \times 10^4$ A. The total length of the newly produced DNA is some 4×10^8 A, all of which we believe was at some interval in contact with its parental template. Whatever the precise mechanism of replication we suspect the most reasonable way to avoid tangling is to have the DNA fold up into a compact bundle as it is formed.

A Possible Mechanism for Natural Mutation

In our duplication scheme, the specificity of replication is achieved by means of specific pairing between purine and pyrimidine bases; adenine with thymine, and guanine with one of the cytosines. This specificity results from our assumption that each of the bases possesses one tautomeric form which is very much more stable than any of the other possibilities. The fact that a compound is tautomeric, however, means that the hydrogen atoms can occasionally change their locations. It seems plausible to us that a spontaneous mutation, which as implied earlier we imagine to be a change in the sequence of bases, is due to a base occurring very occasionally in one of the less likely tautomeric forms, at the moment when the complementary chain is being formed. For example, while adenine will normally pair with thymine, if there is a tautomeric shift of one of its hydrogen atoms it can pair with cytosine (Figure 7). The next time pairing occurs, the adenine (having resumed its more usual tautomeric form) will pair with thymine, but the cytosine will pair with guanine, and so a change in the sequence of bases will have occurred. It would be of interest to know the precise difference in free energy between the various tautomeric forms under physiological conditions.

General Conclusion

The proof or disproof of our structure will have to come from further crystallographic analysis, a task we hope will be accomplished soon. It would be surprising to us, however, if the idea of complementary chains turns out to be wrong. This feature was initially postulated by us to account for the crystallographic regularity and it seems to us unlikely that its obvious connection with self replication is a matter of chance. On the other hand the plectonemic coiling is, superficially at least, biologically unattractive and so demands precise crystallographic proof. In any case the evidence for both the model and the suggested replication scheme will be strengthened if it can be shown unambiguously that the genetic specificity is carried by DNA alone, and, on the molecular side, how the structure could exert a specific influence on the cell.

References

Astbury, W. T., 1947, X-Ray Studies of nucleic acids in tissues. Sym. Soc. Exp. Biol. *1*: 66-76.

Chargaff, E., 1951, Structure and function of nucleic acids as cell constituents. Fed. Proc. *10*: 654-659.

Crick, F. H. C., and Watson, J. D., 1953, Manuscript in preparation.

Franklin, R. E., and Gosling, R., 1953a, Molecular configuration in sodium thymonucleate. Nature, Lond. *171*: 740-741.

1953b, Fiber diagrams of sodium thymonucleate. I. The influence of water content. Acta Cryst., Camb. (in press).

1953c, The structure of sodium thymonucleate fibers. II. The cylindrically symmetrical Patterson Function. Acta Cryst., Camb. (in press).

Fraser, M. S., and Fraser, R. D. B., 1951, Evidence on the structure of desoxyribonucleic acid from measurements with polarized infra-red radiation. Nature, Lond. *167*: 760-761.

Friedrich-Freksa, H., 1940, Bei der Chromosomen Konjugation wirksame Krafte und ihre Bedeutung für die identische Verdoppling von Nucleoproteinen. Naturwissenshaften *28*: 376-379.

GULLAND, J. M., and JORDAN, D. O., 1946, The macromolecular behavior of nucleic acids. Sym. Soc. Exp. Biol. *1*: 56-65.

GULLAND, J. M., JORDAN, D. O., and TAYLOR, H. F. W., 1947, Electrometric titration of the acidic and basic groups of the desoxypentose nucleic acid of calf thymus. J. Chem. Soc. 1131-1141.

HUSKINS, C. L., 1941, The coiling of chromonemata. Cold Spr. Harb. Symp. Quant. Biol. *9*: 13-18.

JORDAN, D. O., 1951, Physiochemical properties of the nucleic acids. Prog. Biophys. *2*: 51-89.

KAHLER, H., and LLOYD, B. J., 1953, The electron microscopy of sodium desoxyribonucleate. Biochim. Biophys. Acta *10*: 355-359.

MANTON, I., 1950, The spiral structure of chromosomes. Biol. Rev. *25*: 486-508.

MULLER, H. J., 1947, The Gene. Proc. Roy. Soc. Lond. Ser. B. *134*: 1-37.

PAULING, L., and DELBRÜCK, M., 1940, The nature of the intermolecular forces operative in biological processes. Science *92*: 77-79

SIEGAL, A., and SINGER, S. J., 1953, The preparation and properties of desoxypentosenucleic acid. Biochim. Biophys. Acta *10*: 311-319.

VILBRANDT, C. F., and TENNENT, H. G., 1943, The effect of pH changes upon some properties of sodium thymonucleate solutions. J. Amer. Chem. Soc. *63*: 1806-1809.

WATSON, J. D., and CRICK, F. H. C., 1953a, A structure for desoxyribose nucleic acids. Nature, Lond. *171*: 737-738.

1953b, Genetical implications of the structure of desoxyribose nucleic acid. Nature, Lond. (in press).

WILKINS, M. H. F., GOSLING, R. G., and SEEDS, W. E., 1951, Physical studies of nucleic acids — nucleic acid: an extensible molecule. Nature, Lond. *167*: 759-760.

WILKINS, M. H. F., and RANDALL, J. T., 1953, Crystallinity in sperm-heads: molecular structure of nucleoprotein in vivo. Biochim. Biophys. Acta *10*: 192 (1953).

WILKINS, M. H. F., STOKES, A. R., and WILSON, H. R., 1953, Molecular structure of desoxypentose nucleic acids. Nature, Lond. *171*: 738-740.

WILLIAMS, R. C., 1952, Electron microscopy of sodium desoxyribonucleate by use of a new freeze-drying method. Biochim. Biophys. Acta *9*: 237-239.

WYATT, G. R., 1952, Specificity in the composition of nucleic acids. In "The Chemistry and Physiology of the Nucleus," pp. 201-213, N. Y. Academic Press.

WYATT, G. R., and COHEN, S. S., 1952, A new pyrimidine base from bacteriophage nucleic acid. Nature, Lond. *170*: 1072.

FINE STRUCTURE OF A GENETIC REGION IN BACTERIOPHAGE

By Seymour Benzer

BIOPHYSICAL LABORATORY, DEPARTMENTS OF BIOLOGICAL SCIENCES AND PHYSICS, PURDUE UNIVERSITY, LAFAYETTE, INDIANA

Communicated by M. Delbrück, April 6, 1955

This paper describes a functionally related region in the genetic material of a bacteriophage that is finely subdivisible by mutation and by genetic recombination. The group of mutants resembles similar cases which have been observed in many organisms, usually designated as "pseudo-alleles." (See reviews by Lewis[1] and

Reprinted by permission of the author and the National Academy of Sciences from the Proceedings of the National Academy of Sciences, **41** (6), 344-354, June, 1955.

Pontecorvo.[2]) Such cases are of special interest for their bearing on the structure and function of genetic determinants.

The phenomenon of genetic recombination provides a powerful tool for separating mutations and discerning their positions along a chromosome. When it comes to very closely neighboring mutations, a difficulty arises, since the closer two mutations lie to one another, the smaller is the probability that recombination between them will occur. Therefore, failure to observe recombinant types among a finite number of progeny ordinarily does not justify the conclusion that the two mutations are inseparable but can only place an upper limit on the linkage distance between them. A high degree of resolution requires the examination of very many progeny. This can best be achieved if there is available a selective feature for the detection of small proportions of recombinants.

Such a feature is offered by the case of the rII mutants of T4 bacteriophage described in this paper. The wild-type phage produces plaques on either of two bacterial hosts, B or K, while a mutant of the rII group produces plaques only on B. Therefore, if a cross is made between two different rII mutants, any wild-type recombinants which arise, even in proportions as low as 10^{-8}, can be detected by plating on K.

This great sensitivity prompts the question of how closely the attainable resolution approaches the molecular limits of the genetic material. From the experiments of Hershey and Chase,[3] it appears practically certain that the genetic information of phage is carried in its DNA. The amount of DNA in a particle of phage T2 has been determined by Hershey, Dixon, and Chase[4] to be 4×10^5 nucleotides. The amount for T4 is similar.[5] If we accept the model of DNA structure proposed by Watson and Crick,[6] consisting of two paired nucleotide chains, this corresponds to a total length of DNA per T4 particle of 2×10^5 nucleotide pairs. We wish to translate linkage distances, as derived from genetic recombination experiments, into molecular units. This cannot be done very precisely at present. It is not known whether all the DNA in a phage particle is indispensable genetic material. Nor is it known whether a phage "chromosome" (i.e., the physical counterpart of a linkage group identified by genetic means) is composed of a single (duplex) DNA fiber or whether genetic recombination is equally probable in all chromosomal regions. For the purpose of a rough calculation, however, these notions will be assumed to be true. Thus we place the total linkage map of T4 in correspondence with 2×10^5 nucleotide pairs of DNA. The total known length of the three linkage groups[7] in phage T4 amounts to some 100 units (one unit = 1 per cent recombination in a standard cross). In addition, there is evidence[8] for roughly another 100 units of length connecting two of the groups. Therefore, if we assume 200 recombination units to correspond to 2×10^5 nucleotide pairs, the recombination per nucleotide pair is 10^{-3} per cent. That is to say, given two phage mutants whose mutations are localized in their chromosomes at sites only one nucleotide pair apart, a cross between these mutants should give rise to a progeny population in which one particle in 10^5 results from recombination *between* the mutations (provided, of course, that recombination is possible between adjacent nucleotide pairs). This computation is an exceedingly rough one and is only intended to indicate the order of magnitude of the scale factor. Some preliminary results are here presented of a program designed to extend genetic studies to the molecular (nucleotide) level.

r Mutants.—The wild-type phages T2, T4, and T6 produce small plaques with rough edges when plated on strain B of *Escherichia coli.* From sectors of clearing in these plaques, mutants can be readily isolated which produce large, sharp-edged plaques (Hershey[9]). These mutants have been designated "r" for rapid lysis; they differ from the wild type by a failure to cause "lysis inhibition" on strain B (Doermann[10]). The wild type has a selective advantage over *r* mutants when the two types grow together on B. The genetics of r mutants was studied by Hershey and Rotman,[11] who found three regions in the linkage map of T2 in which various mutations causing the r phenotype were located, including one large "cluster" of mutants which were shown to be genetically distinct from one another. The genetic study of T4 by Doermann and Hill[7] showed r regions corresponding to two of those in T2. T6 also has at least two such r regions.

The rII Group.—For all three phages, T2, T4, and T6, the r mutants can be separated into groups on the basis of their behavior on strains other than B. This paper will be concerned only with one group, which will be called the "rII group." Mutants of the rII group are distinguished from those of other groups, and from wild type, by a failure to produce plaques on certain lysogenic strains[12] of *E. coli* which carry phage λ. As shown in Table 1, a mutant of the rII group produces

TABLE 1

PHENOTYPES (PLAQUE MORPHOLOGY) OF T4 WILD AND rII MUTANT PLATED ON VARIOUS HOSTS

	Host Strain		
	E. coli B	*E. coli* K12S	*E. coli* K12S (λ)
T4 wild type	Wild	Wild	Wild
T4 rII mutant	r Type	Wild	..

r-type plaques on strain B, wild-type plaques on strain K12S (nonlysogenic strain sensitive to λ), and no plaques on K12S (λ) (derived from K12S by lysogenization with λ). The wild-type phage produces similar plaques on all three strains. In the case of T4, with which we shall be concerned in this paper, the efficiencies of plating are approximately equal on the three strains, except, of course, for rII on K12S (λ). The three bacterial strains will be here designated as "B," "S," and "K."

Approximately two-thirds of the independently arising r mutants isolated on B are of the rII type. This group includes the "cluster" of r mutants of T2 described by Hershey and Rotman and the r47 and r51 mutants described by Doermann and Hill in the corresponding map region of T4 but does not include r mutants located outside that region. Similarly, all newly isolated mutants showing the rII character have turned out to fall within the same region, as indicated in Figure 1.

The properties of the rII group are especially favorable for detailed genetic study. An rII mutant has three different phenotypes on the three host strains (Table 1): (1) altered plaque morphology on B, (2) indistinguishable from wild type on S, and (3) unable to produce plaques on K. These properties are all useful. By virtue of their altered plaque type on B, r mutants are readily isolated, and those of the rII group are identified by testing on K. Where it is desired to avoid a selective disadvantage compared with wild type, e.g., in measuring mutation rates, S can be used as a nondiscriminating host. The failure of rII mutants to plate on K enables one to detect very small proportions of wild-type particles due to reversion or due to recombination between different rII mutants.

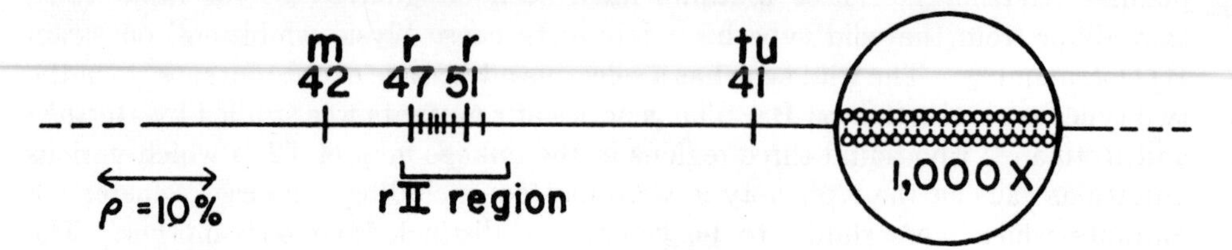

Fig. 1.—Partial linkage map of T4 (Doermann), indicating the location of the rII region. *m* and *tu* designate "minute plaque" and "turbid plaque" mutations. The circular inset shows, diagrammatically, the corresponding dimensions of the DNA chain magnified 1,000 diameters.

Fate of rII Mutants in K.—Wild-type and rII mutants adsorb equally well to strains S and K. Whereas the wild type provokes lysis and liberation of a burst of progeny on both strains, the rII mutant grows normally only on S. Infection of K with an rII mutant provokes very little (and/or very late) lysis, although all infected cells are killed. The block in growth of rII mutant is associated with the presence of the carried phage λ. The reason for this association is unknown.

Quantitative Differences in Phenotype.—While all rII mutants show the same phenotypic effect of poor multiplication on K, they differ in the degree of this effect. A certain proportion of K infected with rII actually liberates some progeny, which can be detected by plating the infected cells on B. The fraction of infected cells yielding progeny defines a "transmission coefficient" characteristic of the mutant. The transmission coefficient is insensitive to the multiplicity of infection but depends strongly upon the physiological state of the bacteria (K) and upon temperature. Under given conditions, however, the coefficient can be used as a comparative index of degree of phenotypic effect, a "leaky" mutant having a high coefficient. As can be seen in Table 2, a wide range of values is found.

TABLE 2

Properties of T4 Mutants of the rII Group*

Mutant Number	Map Position	Transmission Coefficient	Reversion Index (units of 10^{-6})
r47	0	0.03	<0.01
r104	1.3	.91	<1
r101	2.3	.03	4.5
r103	2.9	.02	<0.2
r105	3.4	.02	1.8
r106	4.9	.55	<1
r51	6.7	.02	170
r102	8.3	.02	<0.01

* Three parameters are given for each mutant. The map position is computed from the sum of the nearest intervals shown in Figure 2 and is given in percentage recombination units, taking the position of r47 as zero. The "transmission coefficient" is a measure of phenotypic effect determined by infecting bacteria K with the mutant in question and is given as the fraction of such infected cells yielding plaques on strain B. The "reversion index" is the average fraction of wild-type particles arising in lysates of the mutant grown from a small inoculum on a nonselective host.

Plaques on K.—Some rII mutants produce no plaques on K, even when as many as 10^8 particles (as measured by plaque count on B) of a stock are plated. Other rII mutants, however, produce various proportions of plaques on K. When the plaques appearing on K are picked and retested, they fall into three categories: (1) a type which, like the original mutant, produces very few plaques on K and r-type plaques on B; (2) a type which produces plaques (often smaller than wild type) on K with good efficiency but r-type plaques on B; and (3) a type indistinguishable from the original wild. These three types are understood to be due to the following: (1) "leaking" effects, i.e., ability of the mutant to grow slightly on K, so that there is a chance for a few visible plaques to form; (2) a mutation which partially undoes the effect of the rII mutation, so that multiplication in K is possible, but the full wild phenotype is not achieved; and (3) apparent reverse mutation, which may or may not be genuine, to the original wild type.

The proportion of each type occurring in a stock is characteristic and reproducible for a particular rII mutant but differs enormously from one rII mutant to another. There is no evident correlation in the rates of occurrence of the three types.

Reversion Rates of rII Mutants.—Reversion of r mutants to a form indistinguishable from wild type was demonstrated by Hershey,[9] who made use of the selective advantage of wild type on B to enrich its proportion in serial transfers. Given the inability of rII mutants to produce plaques on K, such reversions are easily detected, even in very small proportion. An index to the frequency of reversion of a particular rII mutant can be obtained by preparing a lysate from a small inoculum (about 100 particles, say, so that there is very little chance of introducing a wild-type particle present in the stock). If S is used as the host, both rII mutant and any reversions which arise can multiply with little selection, as shown by control mixtures. The average fraction of wild-type particles present in several lysates is an index which can be shown to be roughly proportional to the probability of reversion per duplication of the rII mutant. Under the conditions of measurement the index is of the order of 10–20 times the probability of reversion per duplication. The plaques appearing on K must be tested by picking and replating on B. This eliminates the "spurious" plaques produced by partial reversions and by leaky mutants, which show up as r type on B. As may be seen in Table 2, the reversion indices for rII mutants vary over a very wide range. One mutant has been found which reverts 10 times more frequently than r51, so that the reversion rates cover a known range of over 10^5-fold.

It has not been proved that these apparent reversions constitute a genuine return to the original wild type. However, the possibility of suppressor mutations distant from the site of the rII mutation has been ruled out by backcrosses to the original wild type. Krieg[13] found very few, if any, r-type recombinants in backcrosses of several reversions, localizing the reverse changes to within a few tenths of a per cent linkage distance from the original rII mutations. One case of "partial reversion" has also been tested by backcrossing, and failure to observe rII-type recombinants localized the "partial reverse mutation" to within the rII region.

Mapping of the rII Region.—A cross between two rII mutants is made by infecting a culture of B with equal multiplicities (three per bacterium) of each type. The yield after lysis contains the two parental types and, if the parents are genetically distinct, two recombinant types, the double mutant and wild type. In the average yield from many cells, the recombinant types occur in equal numbers.[11] In all cases thus far tested, double rII mutants, like single mutants, do not produce plaques on K. On the assumption that this is generally true, the proportion of recombinants in the yield can be measured simply by doubling the ratio of the plaque count on K (which registers only the wild recombinant) to the count on B (which registers all types). The percentage of wild type thus measured agrees well with a direct count of plaque types on B.

In this way, a series of six rII mutants of T4 (the first six isolated—not selected in any way) have been crossed with each other and with r47 and r51 (kindly supplied by A. H. Doermann) in 23 of the 28 possible pairs. The results of these crosses are given in Figure 2 and are compatible with the indicated seriation of the mutants. The distances are only roughly additive; there is some systematic deviation in the sense that a long distance tends to be smaller than the sum of its component shorter ones. Part of this discrepancy is accounted for by the Visconti-Delbrück correction for multiple rounds of mating.[14] Reversion rates were small enough to be negligible in these crosses. Thus, while all rII mutants in this set fall into a small portion of the phage linkage map, it is possible to seriate them unambiguously, and their positions *within* the region are well scattered.

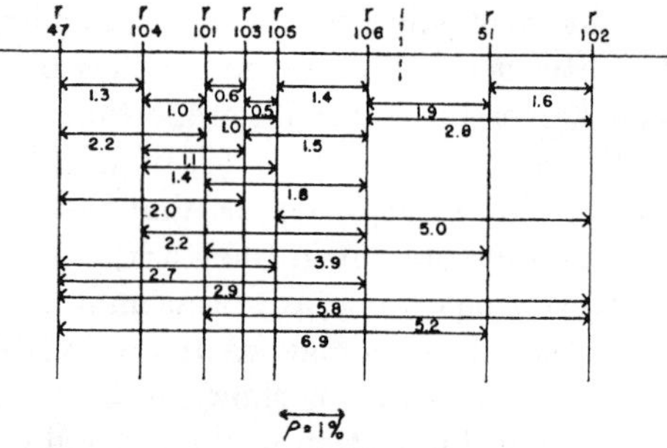

FIG. 2.—Larger-scale map of eight rII mutants, including Doermann's r47 and r51. Newly isolated mutants are numbered starting with *101*. The recombination value (in per cent) for each cross is obtained by plating the progeny on K and on B and doubling the ratio of plaque count on K to count on B.

Tests for Pseudo-allelism.—The functional relatedness of two closely linked mutations causing similar defects may be tested by constructing diploid heterozygotes containing the two mutations in different configurations.[1, 2] The *cis* form, with both mutations in one chromosome, usually behaves as wild type, since the second chromosome supplies an intact functional unit (or units). However, the *trans* form, containing one of the mutations in each chromosome, may or may not produce the wild phenotype. If it does, it is concluded that the two mutations in question are located in separate functional units.

In applying this test to the rII mutants, the diploid heterozygote can be simulated by a mixed infection with two kinds of phage. The rII phenotype is a failure to lyse K, whereas the wild phenotype is to cause lysis. If K is mixedly infected with wild type and rII mutant, the cells lyse, liberating both types of phage. Thus the presence of wild type in the cell supplies the function which is defective in rII type, and the rII mutation can be considered "recessive." Although it has not yet been tested, the *cis* configuration of double rII mutant plus wild type is also presumed to produce lysis in all cases. The *trans* configuration is obtained by infecting K with the pair of rII mutants in question. This is found to give lysis or not, dedepending upon which rII mutants compose the pair. The results are summarized by the dotted line in Figure 2, indicating a division of the rII region into two segments. If both mutants belong to the same segment, mixed infection of K gives the mutant phenotype (very few cells lyse). If the two mutants belong to different segments, extensive lysis occurs with liberation of both infecting types (and recombinants). These results are summarized in Figure 3. Thus, on the basis of this test, the two segments of the rII region correspond to independent functional units.

Actually, for mixed infection of K with two (nonleaky) mutants of the *same* segment, a very small proportion of the cells do lyse and liberate wild recombinants, that proportion increasing with the linkage distance between the mutations. For two rII mutants separated by 1 per cent linkage distance (measured by a standard cross on B) the proportion of mixedly infected K yielding any wild particles is about 0.2 per cent.

This value has bearing upon the effect upon K/B values of the heterozygous phage particles which arise in a cross between two rII mutants on B. In such a cross between closely linked rII mutants, the progeny should include about 2 per cent of particles containing a *trans* configuration heterozygous piece.[15] When one of these is plated on K, there is a certain chance that a wild recombinant may form in the first cycle of infection, leading to production of a plaque. If it is assumed that these are no more likely to do so than a mixed infection of K with two complete mutant particles, it can be concluded that the effect of these heterozygous particles upon the count on K is negligible, provided that both rII mutants belong to the same segment. For mutants in different segments, however, the "efficiency" of the heterozygous particles should be much greater, and recombination values measured by the K/B method should run considerably higher than the true values. The recombination values in Figure 2 for crosses which transgress the segmental divide are probably subject to some correction for this reason.

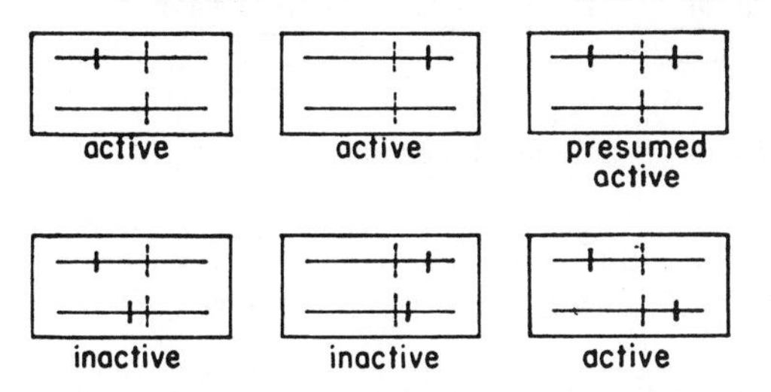

FIG. 3.—Summary of tests for "position-effect pseudo-allelism" of rII mutants. Each diagram represents a diploid heterozygote as simulated by mixed infection of a bacterium (K) with two types of phage containing the indicated mutations. *Active* means extensive lysis of the mixedly infected cells; *inactive* means very little lysis. The dotted line represents a dividing point in the rII region, the position of which is defined by these results.

Rough Mapping by Spot Test.—If a stock of either of two rII mutants is plated on K, no plaques arise; but if both are plated together, some bacteria become infected by both mutants and, if this leads to the occurrence of wild-type recombinants, plaques are produced. If the two mutants are such that wild recombinants cannot arise between them (e.g., if they contain identical mutations), no plaques appear. A given rII mutant may thus be tested against several others on a single plate by first seeding the plate with K plus the mutant in question (in the usual soft agar top layer) and then spotting with drops containing the other rII mutants.

Inspection of such a plate immediately places the unknown mutant in the proper segment, since spotting any mutant of segment A against any mutant of segment B gives a very clear spot, due to the extensive lysis of mixedly infected bacteria. However, for a pair of mutations belonging to the same segment, plaques are produced only by the relatively few mixedly infected bacteria which give rise to wild recombinants. The greater the linkage distance between the mutations, the larger the number of plaques that appear in the spot. A group of mutants of the same segment may thus be seriated by seeding one plate with each and spotting with all the others. Given a previously seriated group, a new mutant can thus be quickly located within the group. This method works best for mutants which are stable (i.e., low reversion rate) and nonleaky, so that large numbers of phage particles can be plated. Reversions or pronounced leaking effects obviously cause an obscuring background.

This test has been applied to a large group of stable, nonleaky rII mutants. Their approximate locations as deduced from these tests are shown in Figure 4. Some of the mutants showed anomalies which made it impossible to locate them as members of a series. They gave very little recombination with any of the mutants located within a certain span, while behaving normally with respect to mutants located outside that span. They are indicated in Figure 4 by horizontal lines extending over the span.

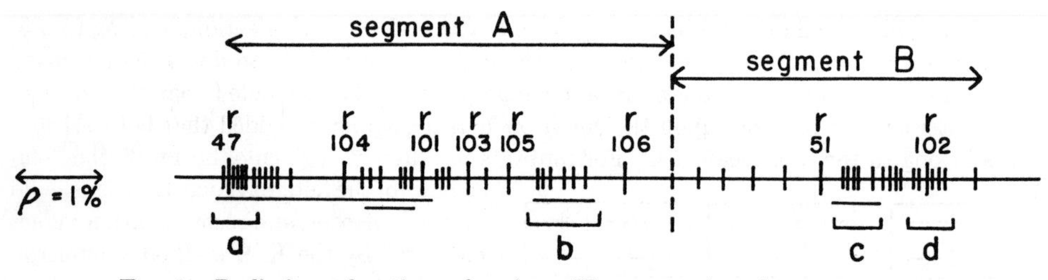

Fig. 4.—Preliminary locations of various rII mutants, based upon spot tests

Spot tests on numerous other mutants have shown that mutants of varied reversion rates, transmission coefficients, and rates of "partial reversion" occur at scattered positions in both segments.

Mapping of "Microclusters."—The spot test enables us to pick out "microclusters," i.e., groups of very closely neighboring mutations. Four such groups selected for further study are indicated in Figure 4, and the results of mapping them are given in Figure 5. While some intervals show reasonably good additivity properties, there are some mutants which give violently anomalous results. Thus in microcluster *a*, r47 gives no wild recombinants (i.e., less than 1 in 10^6) with any of the other three mutants, but two pairs of the three do show recombination. These results can be understood if it is assumed that each mutation extends over a certain length of the chromosome, and production of wild type requires recombination within the space *between* those lengths. According to this interpretation, the mutations would cover the lengths indicated by the bars in Figure 5. These anomalies resemble those observed in the spot tests, only they are more limited in span.

This observation raises the question of whether there exist true "point" mutations (i.e., involving an alteration of only one nucleotide pair) or whether all mutations involve more or less long pieces of the chromosome. It must be remembered that the mutants used in these experiments were selected for extreme stability against reversion. This procedure would be expected to enrich the proportion of mutants containing gross chromosomal alterations. So far as is known, the anomalous cases observed could equally well be imagined to be due to double (i.e., two near-by "point") mutations, inversions, or deletions of the wild-type chromosome. In continuing these experiments, it would seem well advised to employ only mutants for which some reversion is observed.

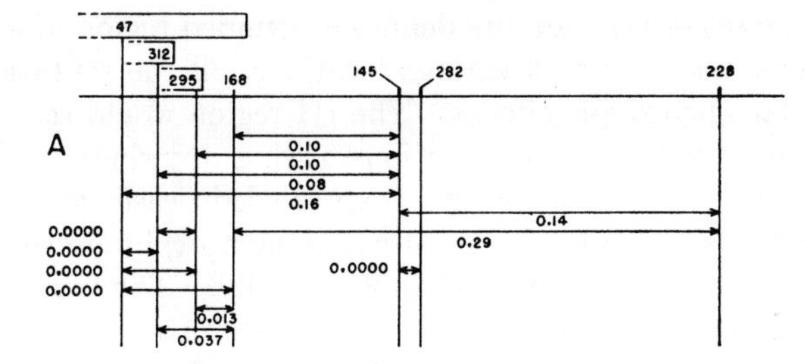

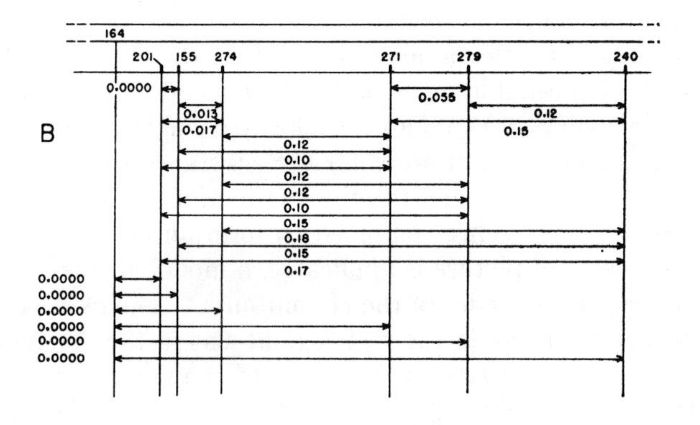

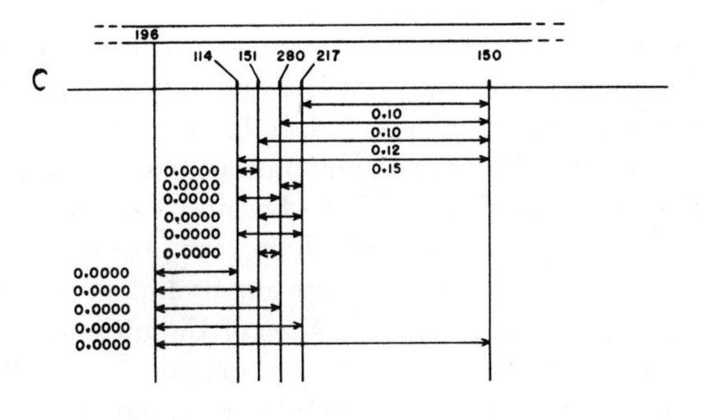

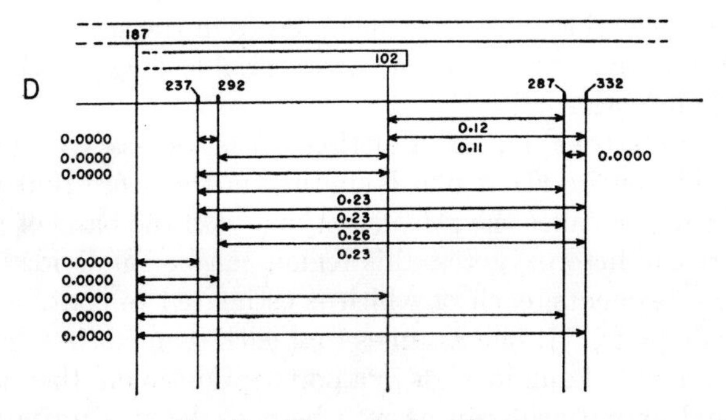

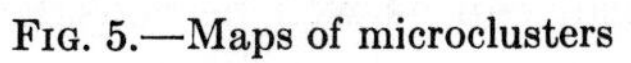
FIG. 5.—Maps of microclusters

Discussion.—The set of rII mutants defines a bounded region of a linkage group in which mutations may occur at various locations, all the mutations leading to qualitatively similar phenotypic effects. The rII region would seem, therefore, to be functionally connected, so that mutations arising anywhere within the region affect the same phenotype. This effect is expressed, in case strain B is the host, by failure to produce lysis inhibition; in case S is the host, by no consequence; and in case K is the host, by inability to multiply normally. The failure of an rII mutant to mature in K can be overcome by the presence of a wild-type phage in the same cell. This could be understood if the function of the region in the wild-type "chromosome" were to control the production of a substance or substances needed for reproduction of this phage in K cells.

The phenotypic test for "pseudo-allelism" leads to the division of the region into two functionally distinguishable segments. These could be imagined to affect two necessary sequential events or could go to make up a single substance the two parts of which must be unblemished in order for the substance to be fully active. For example, each segment might control the production of a specific polypeptide chain, the two chains later being combined to form an enzyme. While it is not known whether this sort of picture is applicable, a model of this kind is capable of describing the observed properties of the rII mutants. The map position of a mutation would localize a change in the region (and also in the "enzyme" molecule), the reversion rate would characterize the type of change involved in the genetic material, and the degree of phenotypic effect would be an expression of the degree of resultant change in the activity of the enzyme. A "leaky" mutant would be one where this latter effect was small. While no obvious correlation has yet been observed among these three parameters of rII mutants, one may well show up upon more exhaustive study.

"Clustering" of similar mutants separable by crossing-over has been observed for several characters in phage by Doermann and Hill and appears to represent the rule. This may well be the rule in all organisms, simply because functional genetic units are composed of smaller recombinational and mutational elements. One would expect to see this effect more readily in phage because the probability of recombination per unit of hereditary material is much greater than for higher organisms.

By extension of these experiments to still more closely linked mutations, one may hope to characterize, in molecular terms, the sizes of the ultimate units of genetic recombination, mutation, and "function." Our preliminary results suggest that the chromosomal elements separable by recombination are not larger than the order of a dozen nucleotide pairs (as calculated from the smallest non-zero recombination value) and that mutations involve variable lengths which may extend over hundreds of nucleotide pairs.

In order to characterize a unit of "function," it is necessary to define what function is meant. The entire rII region is unitary in the sense that mutations anywhere within the region cause the rII phenotype. On the basis of phenotype tests of *trans* configuration heterozygotes, this region can be subdivided into two functionally separable segments, each of which is estimated to contain of the order of 4×10^3 nucleotide pairs. If one assumes that each segment has the "function" of specifying the sequence of amino acids in a polypeptide chain, then the specification of each individual amino acid can as well be considered a unitary function. It would seem feasible, with this system, to extend genetic studies even to the level of the latter functional elements.

Summary.—It has been discovered that the mutations in the rII region of phage T4 have a characteristic in common which sets them apart from the mutations in all other parts of the map. This characteristic is a host-range reduction, namely, a failure to produce plaques on a host (K) lysogenic for phage λ. The mutant phage particles adsorb to and kill K, but normal lysis and phage release do not occur.

All mutants with this property are located within a sharply defined portion of the phage linkage map. Within that region, however, their locations are widely scattered. An unambiguous seriation of the mutants, with roughly additive distances, can be accomplished, except for certain anomalous cases.

The simultaneous presence of a wild-type phage particle in K enables the multiplication of rII mutants to proceed, apparently by supplying a function in which the mutant is deficient. A heterozygous diploid in the *trans* configuration is simulated by a mixed infection of K with two mutant types. The application of the phenotype test to pairs of rII mutants leads to the division of the region into two functionally separable segments.

Spontaneous reversion to wild-type had been observed for most of these mutants. It remains to be seen whether these are genuine reversions. Each mutant reverts at a characteristic rate, but the rates for different mutants differ enormously. Partial reversions to intermediate types are also observed.

The mutants differ greatly in degree of residual ability to grow on K. There is no evident correlation between map position, reversion rate, and degree of residual activity of the various mutants.

The selective feature of K for wild-type recombinants offers the possibility of extending the recombination studies to an analysis of the fine details of the region. Preliminary studies of this type indicate that the units of recombination are not larger than the order of one dozen nucleotide pairs and that mutations may involve various lengths of "chromosome."

I am much indebted to A. D. Hershey and A. H. Doermann for stocks of their genetically mapped mutants, to Sydney Brenner and David Krieg for stimulating discussion, and to Max Delbrück for his invaluable moderating influence.

* Supported by a grant-in-aid from the American Cancer Society upon recommendation of the Committee on Growth of the National Research Council.

[1] E. B. Lewis, *Cold Spring Harbor Symposia Quant. Biol.*, **16**, 159–174, 1951.

[2] G. Pontecorvo, *Advances in Enzymol.*, **13**, 121–149, 1952.

[3] A. D. Hershey and M. Chase, *J. Gen. Physiol.*, **36**, 39–56, 1952.

[4] A. D. Hershey, J. Dixon, and M. Chase, *J. Gen. Physiol.*, **36**, 777–789, 1953.

[5] E. K. Volkin, personal communication.

[6] J. D. Watson and F. H. C. Crick, *Cold Spring Harbor Symposia Quant. Biol.*, **18**, 123–131, 1953.

[7] A. H. Doermann and M. B. Hill, *Genetics*, **38**, 79–90, 1953.

[8] G. Streisinger and V. Bruce, personal communication.

[9] A. D. Hershey, *Genetics*, **31**, 620–640, 1946.

[10] A. H. Doermann, *J. Bacteriol.*, **55**, 257–276, 1948.

[11] A. D. Hershey and R. Rotman, *Genetics*, **34**, 44–71, 1949.

[12] E. M. Lederberg and J. Lederberg, *Genetics*, **38**, 51–64, 1953.

[13] D. Krieg, personal communication.

[14] N. Visconti and M. Delbrück, *Genetics*, **38**, 5–33, 1953.

[15] A. D. Hershey and M. Chase, *Cold Spring Harbor Symposia Quant. Biol.*, **16**, 471–479, 1951; C. Levinthal, *Genetics*, **39**, 169–184, 1954.

*INDUCTION OF SPECIFIC MUTATIONS WITH 5-BROMOURACIL**

By Seymour Benzer† and Ernst Freese‡

BIOPHYSICAL LABORATORY, PURDUE UNIVERSITY, LAFAYETTE, INDIANA

Communicated by M. Delbrück, December 6, 1957

Introduction

The hereditary characteristics of an organism occasionally undergo abrupt changes (mutations), and genetic techniques have traced these to alterations at definite locations in the genetic structure. Recently, the fineness of this genetic mapping has been extended to the level where the finite molecular units (nucleotides) of the hereditary material limit further subdivision. At this level, local details of the hereditary material should exert their influence; the frequency of mutation at a particular point should depend upon the local molecular configuration. It is therefore feasible to try to correlate genetic observations with precise molecular models, such as the one proposed by Watson and Crick[1] for the structure of DNA.

In a fine-structure study of spontaneous mutations in phage T4, the mutability at different points in the genetic structure was, in fact, found to be strikingly varied.[2] To relate mutability to actual chemical structure, it would seem promising to employ mutagenic agents of specific types, to act selectively on particular configurations. Since the initial discovery by Muller[3] and Stadler[4] on induct on of mutations with X-rays and the discovery of chemical mutagenesis by Auerbach and Robson[5] and by Oehlkers,[6] many physical agents and chemical substances have been found to be mutagenic in many organisms. Some mutagens act selectively; in particular the induced reversion from biochemically dependent to independent strains has been shown to depend upon the mutant and the mutagen used. (For chemical mutagens in bacteria see Demerec.[7]) A recent comprehensive review of this subject has been published by Westergaard.[8] Mutagens in some cases produce gross chromosomal aberrations; in others the alterations are so small as to

Reprinted by permission of the authors and the National Academy of Sciences from the Proceedings of the National Academy of Sciences, **44** (2), 112-119, February, 1958.

be beyond the limited resolving power of genetic techniques for the organism used.

The absence of this limitation makes phage a suitable organism for our purposes. There have been reports of induction of mutations in phage by ultraviolet light,[9,10] nitrogen mustard,[11] streptomycin,[12] and proflavine.[13] A very provocative discovery is that analogues of the normal bases may be built into DNA in place of the usual ones and also raise the mutation rate. In particular, one such analogue, 5-bromouracil, has been proven by Dunn and Smith[14] to be incorporated into the DNA of phage (in place of thymine), and Litman and Pardee[15] have shown that it greatly increases the frequency with which phage mutants of various types arise.

In the present work, this possibility of directly affecting the DNA structure is combined with a genetic analysis of high resolving power, to make a fine-structure study of mutagenesis. Our attention will be restricted to the *r*II region of the genome of phage T4. The mutational alterations arising by 5-bromouracil induction are compared to, and shown to differ from, those which occur spontaneously.

METHODS AND MATERIALS

Strains: *phage* T4B; *bacterium* B (*E. coli* B) for the isolation of mutants and as plating bacterium for the determination of phage titers; S (*E. coli* K12S) for the preparation of phage stocks; K (*E. coli* K12S lysogenic for prophage lambda) as the selective strain for genetic tests.

Media: *broth* 1 per cent bacto-tryptone (Difco) plus 0.5 per cent NaCl; *glucose-salts* medium;[16] *sulfanilamide medium* same as used by Litman and Pardee,[15] except for higher sulfanilamide concentration (2 mg/ml) and addition of 1 μg/ml calcium pantothenate, 1 μg/ml pyridoxine, 1 μg/ml thiamine, 1 μg/ml uracil, and 20 μg/ml L-tryptophane (tryptophane required for adsorption of phage T4B to B in synthetic medium). Plates contain *broth* plus 1.3 per cent agar (Difco) with a top layer of broth plus 0.7 per cent agar.

A sample of *5-bromouracil* purified by ion-exchange column, was kindly supplied by Dr. Rose Litman.

Isolation of the Mutants.—Spontaneous mutants: Details on the isolation of spontaneously arising *r* mutants of phage T4, their properties, and the methods used in mapping them genetically are given in earlier publications.[2, 17] In brief, a stock of standard ("wild") type phage T4 (derived from a single T4 particle) is plated on B. Each phage particle produces a plaque containing around 10^7 progeny. The progeny include occasional *r* mutants, which can be found by picking the plaque and replating its contents. In order to assure that each mutant arises by an independent mutational event, no more than one *r* mutant is isolated from any one plaque of the standard type. Each *r* mutant is replated (to free it from any contaminating particles of standard type), an isolated *r*-type plaque is picked, and a stock of the mutant grown on bacteriums in broth.

Induced mutants: These were isolated from the yield of bacteria infected and allowed to burst in the presence of sulfanilamide and 5-bromouracil. A culture of B was prepared by inoculation of 0.4 ml. of overnight culture (grown in glucose-salts medium) into 20 ml. of sulfanilamide medium and aeration for 3.5 hours to reach a cell concentration of 7×10^8 per ml. At this time, 1 mg. of 5-bromouracil and 4×10^4 particles of T4 standard-type phage[18] were introduced simultaneously. Drops of the mixture were rapidly distributed—one drop into each of 200 tubes. After incubation at 37° C. (for 30 minutes) to allow the infected cells to burst, the content of each tube was plated on B. As is typical in this sulfanilamide medium, the average yield per cell was very small, of the order of one viable progeny particle per infected cell. Each plate contained (after incubation) from 30 to 100 plaques, in most cases including one or more *r*-type plaques. The over-all proportion of *r*-type particles among the progeny was about 2 per cent. To assure the independent origin of each mutant, no more than one *r* plaque was picked from a plate. Each such mutant was purified by replating, and a stock prepared on S in broth.

Genetic Mapping of the Mutants.—Different *r* mutants of T4, although producing similar plaques on B, fall into groups distinguished by their behavior on a second host, K. Those mutants with which we are here concerned, of the *r*II group, do not produce plaques on K. This property is the key to the high resolution with which they can be mapped genetically. When two *r*II mutants are crossed, the appearance of any standard-type recombinants among the progeny is readily detected by plating on K. If standard-type progeny *are* produced in a cross (above the background rate due to spontaneous reversion of the mutants), it is concluded that the two mutants contain alterations at different locations in their genetic structures.

Our objective is to compare these locations for spontaneously arising and for 5-bromouracil-induced mutants. The task of crossing a large number of mutants, two by two, to see which pairs yield recombinants is enormous. However, this process can be shortened by making use of a set of mutants having large alterations, as shown in Figure 1. Each new isolated *r*II mutant is crossed with each mutant of this set (by means of simple spot tests). By noting with which mutants of the set it does or does not produce standard-type recombinants, the mutation can be assigned to a particular *segment* of the map. Thereafter, only mutants belonging to the *same* segment need be crossed with each other. Thus the number of crosses required for analyzing a batch of mutants is greatly reduced.

The genetic procedure has therefore been to (1) isolate many independently arising *r*-type mutants; (2) choose those of the *r*II group; (3) test each *r*II mutant against the mutants of Figure 1, thereby locating its mutational alteration in a particular segment of the map; and (4) cross the mutants belonging to the same segment with each other to determine which mutations share common locations. For the present purposes, no attempt was made to determine the *order* of these locations *within* a map segment.

Reversion Rates of Mutants.—The different *r*II are characterized not only by the positions of their mutational alterations in the map but also by differences in their frequency of reversion to particles that resemble the standard type in their plating behavior on K and B. These revertants arise spontaneously during the growth of a given *r*-type phage, and their typical frequency, in a stock grown up from an inoculum of 100 *r* phages, is called the "reversion index."

RESULTS

Over-all Mutation Frequencies.—The ratio of the induced to the spontaneous rate of mutation cannot be given accurately, since different procedures of isolation were used. A rough estimate may be made as follows: In a broth lysate of T4B grown (on S) from an inoculum of a few particles up to a population of 10^{10}, the proportion of spontaneously appearing *r* particles is typically 2×10^{-4}. Under the conditions used for induction, on the other hand, *r* mutants appeared in a proportion of around 2 per cent in the progeny from a single growth cycle. To obtain the probability of mutation *per phage replication*, these values must in each case be adjusted to account for the accumulation of mutants during the growth of the population. This effect, which is roughly proportional to the logarithm of the ratio of final to initial phage titer, should be several fold (perhaps four times) larger for a lysate than for one cycle of growth. Therefore, the rate of induced over-all *r* mutations can be estimated as several hundred times the spontaneous rate.

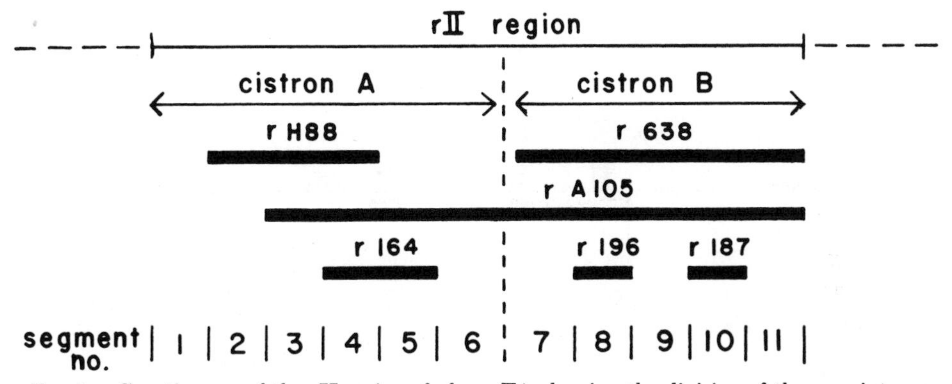

FIG. 1.—Genetic map of the *r*II region of phage T4, showing the division of the map into segments by a set of *r*II mutants having large alterations. Each of the two "cistrons" is a functional unit defined by the cis-trans test.

The relative positions of the alterations have been established by their overlapping relationships with a much larger set of mutants. To locate the defect of a new mutant, it is crossed with each member of the set, and standard-type recombinants are tested for. From the results of these crosses the defect can be assigned to one of the segments. For example, if a mutant gives standard-type recombinants with all except *r* H88, *r* A105, and *r* 164, its defect must be located in segment 4. One which gives recombinants with all must have its defect in segment 1. Segments 7, 9, and 11 are not distinguished by this set of mutants.

Genetic Analysis of the Mutants.—Spontaneous mutants: A series of 238 spontaneously arising mutants was isolated, numbered *r* 101 through *r* 338, and analyzed as described above. Of the mutants, 132 belonged to the *r*II group. Of these, 6 were not readily mappable because of high reversion rates or leakiness (ability to grow feebly on K). The results of mapping the remaining 126 mutants are shown in Figure 2.

The relative positions of the sites indicated *within* a map segment have no significance. Any two mutants that yield standard type progeny when crossed are sketched as horizontally separated, while those groups for which recombination could not be detected (at a level of about 0.01 per cent recombinant progeny or more) are assigned to the same or adjacent horizontal sites. Some mutants fail to give recombinants with (any of two or more) other mutants known to give recombinants with each other; the alterations of such mutants are represented as horizontal bars. A striking feature of the map is the existence of certain "hot spots," where mutations recur with high probability.

Induced mutants: A series of 170 *r* mutants, arising under the action of 5-bromouracil in sulfanilamide medium, was numbered N 1 through N 170. Of these, 89 were of the *r*II type. Twelve of the latter were not readily mappable because

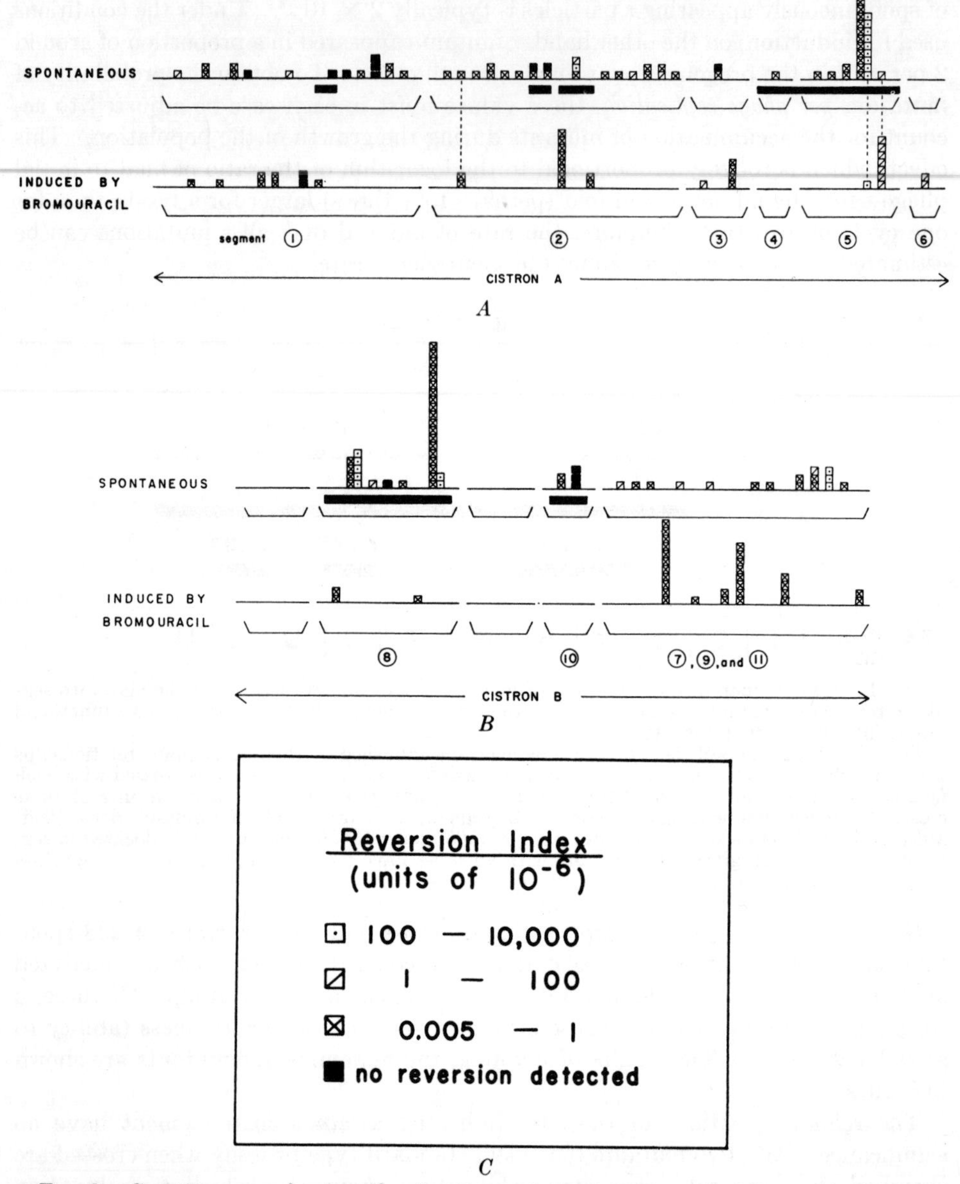

FIG. 2.—Genetic maps showing the locations of spontaneous and 5-bromouracil-induced mutational alterations in the *r*II region of phage T4 divided into cistron A and B. Each mutant is represented by a box, placed in the proper segment of the map and shaded to indicate its reversion index. The relative order (but not the lengths) of segments 1, 2, 3, 4, 5, 6, 8, and 10 have been established. Segments 7, 9, and 11, are lumped together and considered as one segment. The order and position of different mutations within one segment have not been determined.

they were leaky. The results of mapping the remaining 67 mutants are shown in Figure 2. This set of mutants reveals "5-bromouracil hot spots" that are located at different positions from the spontaneous ones.

It must be emphasized that the vertical scales in Figure 2 are very different for the two sets of mutants. The over-all induced mutation rate was several hundredfold higher, and only half as many induced mutants are mapped; therefore, the occurrence of an induced mutant once represented in the induced set corresponds to roughly 10^3 times higher mutability than the occurrence of a spontaneous mutant once represented in the spontaneous set. Hence, for those "hot spots" in the induced set for which no spontaneous mutation has been observed, the mutability with bromouracil is at least 10^4 times larger than is the spontaneous mutability.

Reverse Mutations.—Among the spontaneous *r*II mutants, not only are forward mutation frequencies different for different sites, but the reversion indexes as well cover an enormous range. Among the 132 spontaneous *r*II mutants, reversion indexes range as high as 5×10^{-2} down to less than 10^{-8}. For 19 of them, reversion has not been detected.

The induced mutants, on the other hand, are more homogeneous with respect to reversion index. There is only one mutant of very high reversion index (N 76) and two non-reverting mutants (N 101, N 32). Most of the remainder have reversion indexes of the order of 10^{-8}. Notably rare are mutants containing larger aberrations (i.e., ones that fail to give standard-type recombinants with two or more other mutants that do themselves show recombination).

Some preliminary experiments have been performed on the induction of reversion of various mutants with 5-bromouracil. For some mutants, in particular, chosen from some of the "5-bromouracil hot spots," increases over the spontaneous rate of reversion by factors as high as 10^4 have been observed. Some spontaneous mutants show no or only much smaller effects. These experiments are still in progress.

DISCUSSION

Clearly, the mutagenic effect of 5-bromouracil is not merely a general enhancement of spontaneously occurring mutations. Rather, it is a *specific* effect. In denoting the action of a mutagen as specific, one might be comparing the effects on different phenotypic characteristics in the whole organism, different cistrons, or different locations within a single cistron. Were it not for the high resolution of our genetic techniques, it might have been erroneously concluded that 5-bromouracil acts aspecifically, since, among all the induced mutants of the *r* phenotype, the proportion of *r*II mutants and even the ratio of A cistron to B cistron mutants are quite comparable to the spontaneous values. It is only at finer resolution that the different effects are revealed, and it is seen that mutations are, for the most part, induced at specific places in the genetic structure.

Since the proportion of large aberrations and non-reverting mutants is notably smaller among the 5-bromouracil-induced mutations, the induced changes in the genetic structure appear to involve small molecular substitutions rather than large changes of the genome. Further, the more homogeneous properties of the induced mutants with respect to reversion rates indicate that a certain class of molecular transitions may be involved here.

Under the conditions used, the *total* frequency of occurrence of all *r*II mutants in 5-bromouracil was raised several hundred fold above the spontaneous rate. The increase in rate at specific locations in the genetic structure was much larger. For example, 11 occurrences of mutation at one site were observed out of 67 induced *r*II mutants, while none occurred at that site among twice as many spontaneous *r*II mutants. Thus the probability of mutation at that point, per replication of the phage, was raised by a factor greater than twice eleven times several hundred, or of the order of 10^4.

Conversely, note the site at which there were 19 occurrences among 132 spontaneous *r*II mutants, while among the 67 induced mutants none were observed. Therefore, 5-bromouracil had little, if any, positive mutagenic effect at that point. The disappearance of the spontaneous "hot spot" does not, of course, mean that spontaneous mutations at that point were suppressed but simply that they were not increased in proportion to other mutations.

Only three sites (indicated by dotted lines in the figure) are represented in both sets of mutants. In each of those cases, there was only a single occurrence in one of the sets, so that the ratio of induced to spontaneous frequencies cannot be reliably computed. The mutation rate seems to have been truly increased by 5-bromouracil in 2 of the cases (2 and 7 occurrences in the induced set) because one occurrence among the induced series represents a thousandfold greater probability of mutation. In the third case, there is, in the induced set, a single occurrence of a highly revertable mutant that appearaed nine times in the spontaneous set. This single event probably belongs to the small background of spontaneous mutations among the induced ones (*ca* 1 or 2 in 100).

The methods used in the isolation of the two sets of mutants were quite different, and one cannot be sure whether factors other than the addition of 5-bromouracil could have affected the results. Although sulfanilamide alone does not appreciably increase the total mutation rate, the possibility that the distribution of mutations might change has not been excluded. Sulfanilamide, as an analogue of *p*-amino benzoic acid, inhibits the formation of folic acid, thereby inhibiting nearly all the methylation and hydroxymethylation steps (Cohen and Barner).[19] In our sulfanilamide medium, nearly all the major chemicals containing the methyl or hydroxymethyl group are added except the deoxyribonucleotides of thymine and 5-hydroxymethylcytosine, which thus are expected to be deficient. The deficiency in thymine facilitates the incorporation of 5-bromouracil into DNA. Whether the deficiency in 5-hydroxymethylcytosine enhances the probability of the false incorporation of 5-bromouracil into a hydroxymethylcytosine site of the phage DNA remains to be seen.

One is not in a position, from these experiments alone, to reach a clear conclusion as to the molecular mechanism of mutagenesis; thus, at this stage, it cannot be decided whether or not the tautomeric shift of the DNA bases from the *keto*- to the *enol*- form is mainly responsible for the production of point mutations, as suggested by Watson and Crick.[1] If it is assumed that only two kinds of nucleotide pairs are present in DNA (i.e., adenine—thymine, and guanine—5-hydroxymethylcytosine), the existance of hot spots of spontaneous mutation and the appearance of different hot spots with 5-bromouracil would suggest that not every nucleotide pair of a given type mutates with the same probability. Rather, the mutability of a nucleotide pair would have to depend upon its position.

In any case, the striking results of this preliminary investigation indicate that it would be fruitful to pursue this line of investigation, using a range of mutagenic substances in systems where the chemical events are under proper control.

SUMMARY

A set of spontaneously arising *r*II mutants of phage T4 is compared with a set of mutants induced by the action of 5-bromouracil. When analyzed by genetic mapping techniques of high resolution, the two sets of mutants are found to be quite different. The mutagen does not merely enhance the over-all mutation rate but acts at specific locations in the hereditary structure.

The induced mutants are mostly of the nature of small, revertible alterations rather than gross defects. The reversion rates of induced mutants are less varied than those of spontaneous mutants, indicating that a certain class of molecular transition is involved.

These preliminary results encourage the hope that this sort of genetic analysis can lead toward an understanding of the mechanism of mutation and the identification of the specific chemical configurations composing the genetic structure.

Note: The occurrence at a given location of one mutation in the induced set corresponds to *roughly 10^3 times higher mutability* of this spot in 5-bromouracil than is indicated by the occurrence of one mutation in the spontaneous set.

* Aided by grants from the National Science Foundation and the American Cancer Society

† Present address: Medical Research Council for Molecular Biology, Cavendish Laboratory, Cambridge University, England.

‡ Research Fellow of the Damon Runyon Memorial Fund for Cancer Research. Present address: Biological Laboratories, Harvard University, Cambridge, Massachusetts.

[1] J. D. Watson, and F. H. C. Crick, *Cold Spring Harbor Symposia Quant. Biol.*, **18**, 123, 1953.

[2] S. Benzer, in *The Chemical Basis of Heredity*, ed. McElroy and Glass (Baltimore: Johns Hopkins Press, 1957).

[3] H. J. Muller, *Science*, **66**, 84, 1927.

[4] L. Stadler, *Science*, **68**, 1928.

[5] C. Auerbach and J. M. Robson, *Nature*, **157**, 302, 1946.

[6] F. Oehlkers, *Z. Ind. Abst. u. Vererbungsl.*, **81**, 313, 1943.

[7] M. Demerec, *Caryologia*, Vol. suppl. **201**, 1954.

[8] M. Westergaard, *Experientia*, **13**, 224, 1957.

[9] R. Latarjet, *Compt. rend.*, **228**, 1345, 1948.

[10] J. J. Weigle, these Proceedings, **39**, 628, 1953.

[11] L. Silvestri, *Bull. I.S.M.*, **28**, 193, 1949.

[12] B. Fernandez, F. L. Haas, and O. Wyss, these Proceddings, **39**, 1052, 1953.

[13] R. de Mars, *Nature*, **172**, 964, 1953.

[14] D. B. Dunn and J. D. Smith, *Nature*, **174**, 304, 1954.

[15] R. M. Litman, and A. B. Pardee, *Nature*, **178**, 529, 1956.

[16] R. M. Herriott, and J. L. Barlow, *J. Gen. Physiol.*, **36**, 17, 1952.

[17] S. Benzer, these Proceedings, **41**, 344, 1955.

[18] In order to minimize the background of *r* mutants present in the stock of standard type, which is usually around 2×10^{-4}, several stocks of T4 were grown, and one with a small proportion of *r* mutants was selected. In the stock used, this proportion was less than 10^{-4}.

[19] S. S. Cohen and H. D. Barner, *J. Bacteriol.*, **71**, 588, 1956.

EXPERIMENTS ON PHOTOREACTIVATION OF BACTERIOPHAGES INACTIVATED WITH ULTRAVIOLET RADIATION[1]

R. DULBECCO

Department of Bacteriology, Indiana University, Bloomington, Indiana[2]

Received for publication October 24, 1949

Kelner (1949), working with conidia of *Streptomyces griseus*, discovered that light belonging to the visible range is capable of reactivating biological material that has been rendered inactive by ultraviolet radiation (UV). Shortly after Kelner's discovery was known, a similar phenomenon in bacteriophages (bacterial viruses) was observed by accident. Plates of nutrient agar containing UV-inactivated phage and sensitive bacteria had been left for several hours on a table illuminated by a fluorescent lamp. After incubation it was noticed that the number of plaques was higher on these plates than on similar plates incubated in darkness. A short report of this phenomenon of "photoreactivation" (PHTR) has already been published (Dulbecco, 1949). The present paper contains the results of a first group of experiments concerning PHTR of seven bacteriophages of the T group active on *Escherichia coli*, strain B.

MATERIALS AND METHODS

Stocks of each phage were prepared by inoculating material from a single plaque into a culture of *E. coli* B in a synthetic medium M9,[3] except for phage T5, of which a stock in Difco nutrient broth was used. In some experiments the phage was purified by two or three steps of differential centrifugation; the phage was resuspended in M/15 phosphate buffer pH 7, with $MgSO_4$ added to a concentration 10^{-3} M. Unless otherwise specified, the experiments described in this paper were performed with phage T2. *Escherichia coli*, strain B, was used throughout. In some experiments bacteria were grown in nutrient broth with aeration and the culture was infected with phage when it was in the logarithmic phase of growth (about 10^8 cells per ml); these bacteria will be referred to as "bacteria in broth." In other experiments bacteria were grown in broth up to a concentration of about 2×10^8 cells per ml, then washed with saline (0.85 per cent NaCl) and resuspended in saline, kept at 37 C for 30 minutes, and then infected; these bacteria will be referred to as "resting bacteria."

[1] This work was done under an American Cancer Society grant, recommended by the Committee on Growth of the National Research Council, under the direction of Dr. S. E. Luria. The author wishes to express his appreciation to Dr. Luria for facilitating this work materially and for numerous discussions during its progress. The manuscript was completed at the California Institute of Technology. The author also wishes to acknowledge his indebtedness to Dr. M. Delbrück for helpful discussions on the interpretation of the data.

[2] Present address: Kerckhoff Laboratories of Biology, California Institute of Technology, Pasadena 4, California.

[3] NH_4Cl, 1.0 g; KH_2PO_4, 3.0 g; Na_2HPO_4, 6.0 g; NaCl, 0.5 g; $MgSO_4$, 0.1 g; distilled water, 1,000 ml; 4 g per liter glucose added after separate sterilization.

Reprinted by permission of the author and the Williams and Wilkins Co., from the JOURNAL OF BACTERIOLOGY, **59** (3), 329-347, March, 1950.

Inactivation of the phages was accomplished with a low-pressure mercury discharge lamp (General Electric "germicidal" lamp, 15 watts), giving most of the UV energy in the line 2,537 A. The output of the lamp was kept constant by alimenting it through a "sola" stabilizer and by using it only after it had been burning for at least 20 minutes.

The stocks to be irradiated were diluted in phosphate buffer plus $MgSO_4$ and exposed to the lamp at a 20-inch distance either in an open petri dish with continuous shaking (3 ml of phage in a 10-cm petri dish) or in a quartz cell 2 mm thick with parallel faces. Relative measurements of the incident UV doses were made in some experiments by timing the exposure; in other experiments rela-

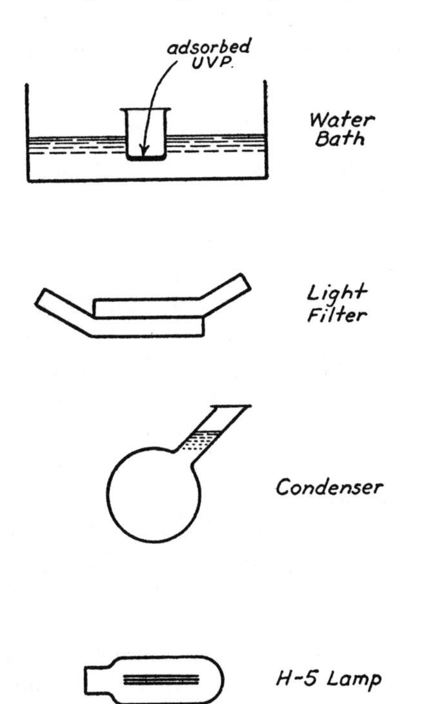

Figure 1. Diagram of the apparatus employed for illumination in liquid.

tive and absolute measurements were conducted with a calibrated Westinghouse SM-200 meter with tantalum photocell WL-775. A dose of UV will be expressed as seconds of exposure to the germicidal lamp. The reactivating light was used in two different ways:

Illumination on the plate. The plates, prepared by the agar layer method (Gratia, 1936; Hershey *et al.*, 1943), were exposed right side up to the light of two parallel fluorescent discharge lamps, 40 watts each, at a distance of 12 inches at room temperature.

Illumination in liquid. The apparatus used is illustrated in figure 1. A mercury discharge lamp, medium pressure (General Electric H-5 lamp, 250 watts) was used as the light source. The light was condensed through a spherical pyrex flask filled with distilled water and passed through suitable filters (see later section); for white light experiments infrared rays were absorbed by a filter of $CuSO_4 \cdot 5H_2O$ (5 per cent in water, 1 inch thick) and ultraviolet rays shorter than 330 mμ by a Corning glass filter no. 738. A mixture of phage and bacteria was exposed to light in a small beaker (5 ml of mixture in a beaker 4 cm in diameter) kept in a thermostatically regulated water bath and shaken by a reciprocating motion in a horizontal plane to ensure uniform distribution of the material and uniform illumination. Some experiments were done with a 100-watt General Electric H-4 lamp without a condenser.

In the experiments with illumination in liquid the ratio "phage particles: bacteria" was kept very low (about 10^{-3}) to decrease the probability of multiple infection of bacteria and the occurrence of reactivation by multiplicity (Luria, 1947).

EXPERIMENTAL RESULTS

Role of the Bacteria in the PHTR of Inactive Phage

Phage particles inactivated by UV (UVP) can be reactivated by light only if the particles are mixed with sensitive bacteria during illumination. Illumination of UVP alone is without effect, as is shown by the following experiment: Phage T2 was irradiated with the germicidal lamp for 30 seconds (dark survival = 2×10^{-5}) and divided into two equal samples. The first sample was immediately plated and incubated in darkness; the second one was exposed to the light of a fluorescent lamp (80 watts at a 12-inch distance) for 1 hour at room temperature and then divided into two parts, one of which was plated and incubated in darkness, the other under the same light. The sum of plaque counts of two plates for each sample are given in table 1 (I).

In another similar experiment the UVP was first spread on the surface of a nutrient agar plate and then exposed to the light; after illumination sensitive bacteria were spread on the same plate in darkness. In this condition also PHTR was not produced.

These experiments clearly indicate that illumination of UVP in the absence of bacteria has no reactivating effect; they do not show, however, whether PHTR occurs only for adsorbed phage or also for nonadsorbed phage in the presence of bacteria. This point was investigated by mixing UVP with bacteria in nutrient broth without added NaCl (under these conditions the adsorption is slight), illuminating the mixture, and testing for reactivation of the nonadsorbed phage particles. A sample of phage irradiated with the germicidal lamp for 30 seconds was mixed with a culture of bacteria in broth without added NaCl, containing 10^9 cells per ml. The mixture was exposed to the light of an H-4 lamp at a 6-inch distance for 10 minutes at 28 C, then centrifuged; samples from the supernatant were plated and incubated both in darkness and in the light. The plaque counts (two plates for each sample) are given in table 1 (II), together with an assay of the irradiated phage diluted in broth by a factor equal to the one used in the experiment. The result of this experiment clearly indicates that the unadsorbed phage particles are not reactivated by light.

Illumination of bacteria alone followed by the addition of UVP does not produce any PHTR. Bacteria spread on the surface of several nutrient-agar plates were exposed to the light of a fluorescent lamp (80 watts, 12-inch distance) for 4 hours at room temperature; then UVP were spread on the same plates in darkness, and the plates were incubated in darkness. Control plates, spread with bacteria at the same time, were kept in darkness and received UVP at the same time as the illuminated plates. Equal numbers of plaques were found in all plates whether the bacteria had been preilluminated or not, showing that preillumination of bacteria does not cause PHTR of UVP added later. In another experiment a suspension of resting bacteria was illuminated with a light of 365-mμ wave length at 37 C for a period long enough to give a very high PHTR in adsorbed UVP, and the UVP was added at the very moment at which the light was turned off; no measurable PHTR was observed.

TABLE 1

Effect of light on inactivated phage T2 alone and on unadsorbed inactivated phage T2r mixed with sensitive bacteria

EXPERIMENT	TREATMENT	PLAQUE COUNT 0.1 ML
I. Illumination of UVP alone	1. UVP not illuminated and plated with B. Plates incubated in darkness.	17
	2. UVP illuminated alone and plated with B. Plates incubated in darkness.	6
	3. UVP illuminated alone and plated with B. Plates incubated under light.	609
II. Effect of light on unadsorbed phage in presence of bacteria	1. UVP alone.	72
	2. UVP mixed with B in saltless broth; illuminated 10 minutes; centrifuged; supernatant plated with B; plates incubated in darkness.	86
	3. Same as II, 2, but with plates incubated under light.	>1,000

If bacteria killed by heating to 60 C for 20 minutes are substituted for living bacteria, no PHTR takes place. Actually the plaque count decreases, probably because of an irreversible adsorption of phage by the dead bacteria without the release of new phage.

Illumination of bacteria prior to infection does not diminish the photoreactivability of UVP added later, as shown by the following experiment: Bacteria were spread on the surface of nutrient agar plates and exposed to the light of a fluorescent lamp (80 watts, 12-inch distance) for 4 hours at room temperature; then UVP was spread on the plates, which were afterwards incubated under the same light. After incubation the plates showed the same number of plaques as control plates containing nonpreilluminated bacteria and UVP, incubated under the same light.

From these experiments with phage T2 one may conclude that PHTR occurs only for UVP adsorbed on sensitive bacteria and that illumination either of UVP or of bacteria before infection has no detectable effect.

To test how soon after phage adsorption PHTR can occur, UVP and bacteria were mixed on several plates, and the plates were immediately exposed to the light of an H-4 lamp at an 8-inch distance at 28 C. The exposure was continued for 10, 20, 30, or 50 seconds. The plaque count was found to increase even after 10 seconds, showing that no measurable delay exists between adsorption and the beginning of PHTR and that PHTR has no measurable latent period.

Action of Bacterial Extracts on PHTR

Some attempts were made to obtain PHTR by illuminating mixtures of UVP with cell-free bacterial extracts. Bacteria were grown in nutrient broth to a concentration of about 5×10^8 cells per ml and harvested in a Sharples centrifuge. Two extraction procedures were used: (a) the thick bacterial suspension was frozen at -30 C, the frozen paste was then ground with carborundum powder and extracted with phosphate buffer (pH 7.5) for about 10 minutes, and the extract was clarified by centrifugation; (b) the bacteria were broken in a sonic vibrator after the bacterial paste was diluted with an equal volume of phosphate buffer, and the extract was clarified in the centrifuge. In both cases the supernatant was a thick, yellowish liquid, which showed a high degree of enzymatic activity (methylene blue reduction, tryptophanase). Both extracts still contained a few living cells, which could be eliminated either by filtration or by repeated freezing at -30 C.

UVP was mixed into various dilutions of the extracts, and the mixtures were kept either in light or darkness and assayed for active phages at different times. Only extracts still containing living cells gave some PHTR. Removal of almost all living cells eliminated PHTR.

PHTR as a Function of the Dose of the Inactivating UV Light

For several phages of the T group (T2, T4, T5, T6) the curve obtained by plotting the logarithm of the active fraction against the UV dose approaches a straight line (Latarjet and Wahl, 1945), at least for high values of the dose, whereas an inflection with downward concavity, of dubious origin, may appear for low doses. Three other phages (T1, T3, T7) show, on the contrary, an inflection with upward concavity of unknown origin.

If the inactivated phages are adsorbed on bacteria and exposed to light of high intensity for a sufficient length of time, the active fraction increases and reaches a maximum (see later section). After this maximum is reached, the curve showing the logarithm of the active fraction against the UV dose has for each phage the same shape as the curve obtained in darkness, but for a given UV dose the slope of the curve obtained after PHTR is lower than the slope of the curve in darkness.

The fact that both curves in the light and in darkness tend to be straight lines with different slopes for high UV doses is an indication that absorption of

UV light in the phage has a probability, a, of producing a photoreactivable inactivation and a probability, b, of producing a nonphotoreactivable inactivation; $a + b$, the probability of producing any inactivating damage, is proportional to the cross section of the phage for UV. Assuming $a + b = 1$, a is the photoreactivable sector of the cross section, b the nonphotoreactivable sector; b is measured by the ratio of the slope of the curve after maximum PHTR to the slope of the curve in darkness, both measured in the straight parts.

The photoreactivable sector, a, varies between 1 (complete photoreactivability) and 0 (no photoreactivability) and can therefore be used as an index of the photoreactivability. Values of a for different phages are given in table 2.

Influence on PHTR of the Interval of Time between Infection and Exposure to Light

In the experiments reported in the present and following sections the influence of various experimental conditions on PHTR was analyzed. A quantitative determination of PHTR was made by measuring either the "active fraction" or the "amount of PHTR" in an UVP sample after a given exposure to light. The active fraction is the ratio of the number of active particles after PHTR to the total number of adsorbed particles and is equal to the sum of the fraction active

TABLE 2

Photoreactivability of the phages of the T group

PHAGE	T1	T2	T3	T4	T5	T6	T7
Photoreactivable sector of cross section (a)	0.68	0.56	0.39	0.20	0.20	0.44	0.35

in the darkness plus the fraction reactivated by light; the amount of PHTR is the reactivated fraction.

The influence on PHTR of the interval of time between infection and exposure to light was determined for UVP adsorbed on bacteria in broth and on resting bacteria (see "Material and Methods"). Bacteria and UVP were mixed in darkness; samples of the mixture were kept in darkness for various intervals of time and then exposed to light for a period long enough to produce maximum PHTR. After illumination, samples were plated and incubated in darkness, and the active fraction was determined. In this procedure the bacteria infected with irradiated phage particles had to be exposed to light much longer than the latent period between infection and liberation of phage adsorbed on bacteria in broth. When bacteria in broth were used, therefore, the mixtures were plated before the end of the latent period and illumination was continued by exposing the plates; when resting bacteria were used, illumination could be continued indefinitely in liquid, since no phage liberation takes place under these conditions.

Experiments with bacteria in broth. The experiments were performed with phage T2 at 28 C. The amount of PHTR decreased rapidly as the time interval between infection and the beginning of exposure to light increased; after about 20 minutes only a small amount of PHTR was produced, as is shown in table 3.

This decrease in PHTR might be caused by a gradual decrease in the amount of PHTR per time unit as the time interval between infection and illumination increases, by a limitation of the time interval after infection in which PHTR can occur, or by both. The amount of PHTR per time unit was determined in experiments in which exposure to light was started at various times after infection. The results, shown in figure 2, indicate that the amount of PHTR per time unit remained practically constant for about 15 minutes. The decline in maximum PHTR must be due, therefore, to a limitation of the time within which PHTR can occur after infection, the useful time interval ending between 20 and 30 minutes after infection under the experimental conditions; after this time very little or no PHTR can take place.

Experiments with resting bacteria. As is shown in table 4, the maximum amount of PHTR obtainable in phage T2r irradiated with the germicidal lamp for 18 seconds remains fairly constant for at least 70 minutes after infection at 37 C;

TABLE 3

The effect of the time interval between infection and exposure to light (*bacteria in broth*)

Phage T2r, irradiated for 20 seconds with the germicidal lamp, was mixed with bacteria and adsorption was allowed to continued for 2 minutes, after which it was interrupted by serum anti-T2. Exposure to light (H-4 lamp, 12-inch distance) was begun at various times and was continued for 100 minutes at 28 C. Amount of PHTR is lower than in experiment reported in table 4, because in the present experiment a lower light intensity was used, and the time in which the light could be utilized for reactivation was limited, since bacteria in broth were used.

TIME INTERVAL BETWEEN INFECTION AND EXPOSURE TO LIGHT	ACTIVE FRACTION
min	
0	5.3×10^{-3}
10	1.4×10^{-3}
20	3.5×10^{-4}
30	5.0×10^{-4}
Active fraction in darkness	3.0×10^{-4}

longer intervals have not been tested. The amount of PHTR per time unit is not influenced by the time interval between infection and illumination.

The differences between experiments with bacteria in broth and with resting bacteria indicate that under the experimental conditions the system "UVP-metabolizing bacteria" undergoes a gradual change that in its late phases prevents PHTR, a change absent in the system "UVP–resting bacteria."

Kinetics of PHTR

PHTR as a function of the time of exposure to the reactivating light. The following experiments employed inactive phage T2r and resting bacteria, with illumination in liquid. Inactive phage diluted in phosphate buffer was mixed with bacteria at time 0 at 37 C in darkness, and 10 minutes were allowed for complete adsorption. At the eleventh minute a sample was plated in darkness; at the twelfth minute the mixture was exposed to light, and samples were taken at

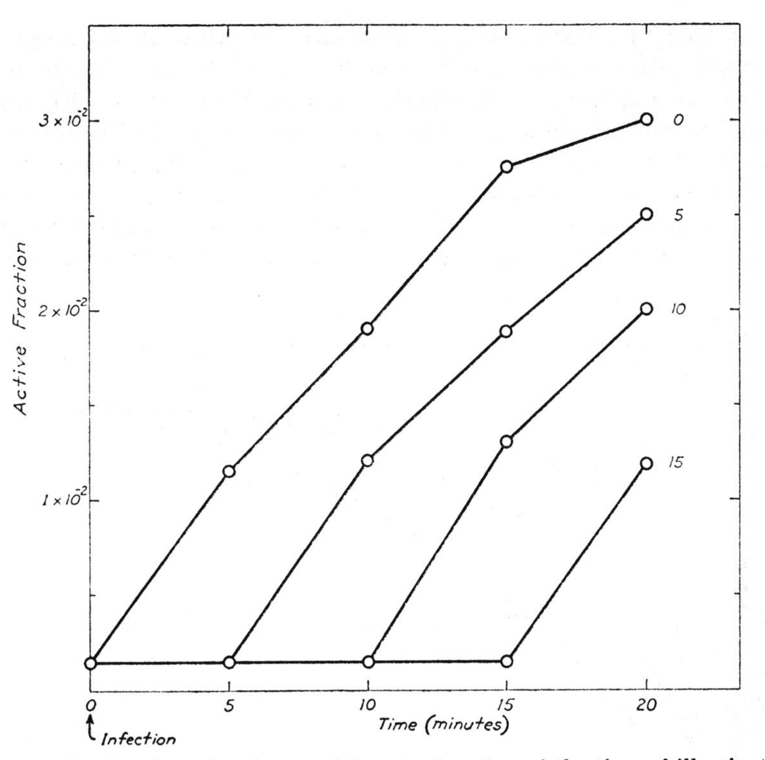

Figure 2. The fraction of active particles as a function of the time of illumination (in minutes) and of the interval between infection and exposure to light. Each curve gives the active fraction as a function of the time of illumination (in minutes) for a different interval between infection and exposure to light; the interval is indicated (in minutes) at the right end of each curve. Phage T2r was irradiated for 20 seconds with the germicidal lamp, adsorbed on bacteria in broth, and exposed to light in broth at 28 C.

TABLE 4

The effect of the time interval between infection and exposure to light (resting bacteria)

Phage T2r, irradiated for 18 seconds with the germicidal lamp, was adsorbed onto resting bacteria suspended in saline. Exposure to light (H-5 lamp with condenser, wave length 365 mμ) began at various times. Illumination was carried out in liquid.

TIME INTERVAL BETWEEN INFECTION AND EXPOSURE TO LIGHT	ACTIVE FRACTION
min	
0	5×10^{-2}
10	5×10^{-2}
30	6×10^{-2}
50	5.4×10^{-2}
70	6×10^{-2}
Active fraction in darkness	10^{-3}

various time intervals thereafter and plated in darkness; all plates were incubated in darkness. The experiments lasted 140 minutes at most; control experi ments showed that resting bacteria that have adsorbed active phage do not liberate any phage in this time interval. The active fraction always increased with the time of illumination, the increase becoming less and less with increasing time, so that a maximum was reached as is shown in figure 3. The time at which the maximum was reached depended on the light intensity, a longer time being required when the intensity was lower; when the light intensity was varied in such a way that the maximum was reached in a period between 20 and 140 minutes, approximately the same maximum was reached in all cases, as is shown in figure 3.

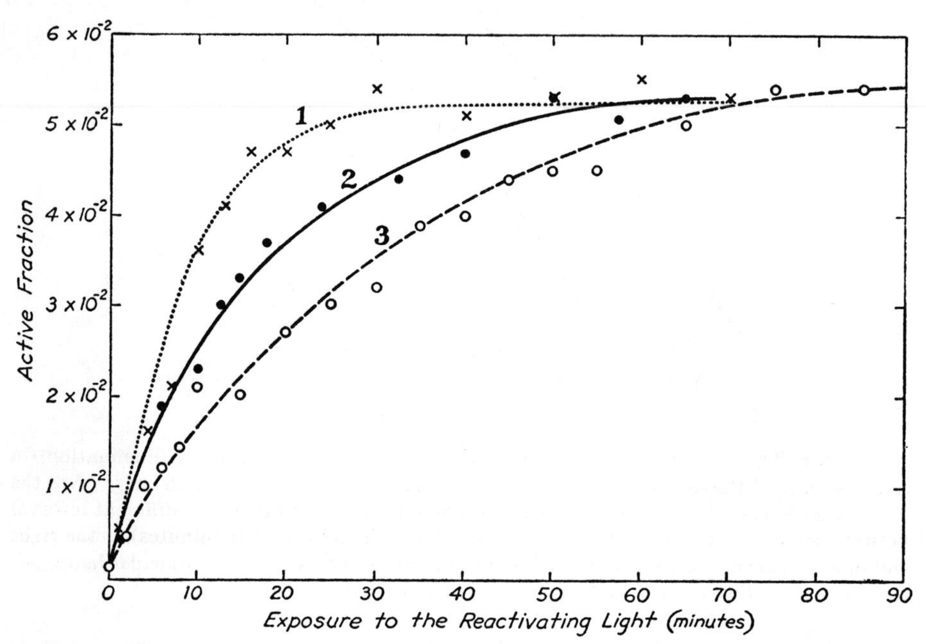

Figure 3. The fraction of active particles as a function of the time of illumination and of the light intensity. The active fraction is plotted against the time of illumination (in minutes). Phage T2r was irradiated for 20 seconds with the germicidal lamp, adsorbed on resting bacteria, and illuminated in liquid at 37 C. Curve 1 was obtained with a light of intensity 10 (in arbitrary units), curve 2 with a light of intensity 2.9, and curve 3 with a light of intensity 0.6.

The amount of PHTR (defined in previous section) observed in a sample of UVP after a given time of illumination ($p(t)$), divided by the amount of PHTR obtained in the same sample when PHTR has reached the maximum value ($p(\infty)$), will be indicated at the "relative amount of PHTR"; it can vary between zero and one.

By subtracting the relative amount of PHTR from unity, one obtains the fraction of photoreactivable particles that are still inactive after a time, t, of illumination $\left(= 1 - \frac{p\,(t)}{p\,(\infty)}\right)$. The logarithm of this quantity plotted against the time of illumination always gave a straight line for different intensities of the reactivating light and for different doses of the inactivating UV. A curve of this type is reproduced in figure 4. The linearity of the experimental curves was found to be statistically significant by comparing, with the χ^2 test, the experimental data for the active fractions with data calculated on this assumption, as is shown in table 5. This result shows that PHTR is a one-hit phenomenon; a

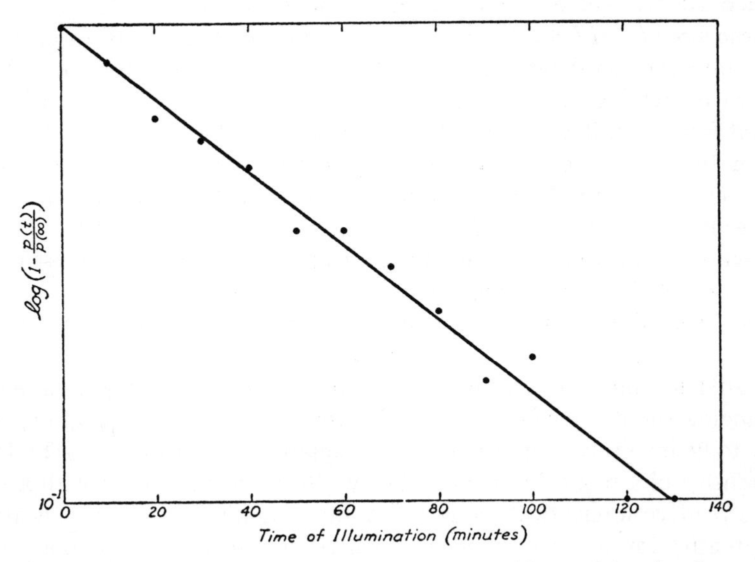

Figure 4. The logarithm of the fraction of photoreactivable particles that has not been reactivated after a given time of illumination $\left(1 - \frac{p(t)}{p(\infty)}\right)$ plotted against the time of illumination (in minutes). Phage T2r was irradiated for 20 seconds with the germicidal lamp, adsorbed on resting bacteria, and illuminated in liquid at 37 C.

TABLE 5

A comparison between observed and calculated active fractions after different times of illumination

EXPERIMENT NO.	UV DOSE IN SECONDS	DEGREES OF FREEDOM	χ^2	P
312	10	10	12.1	>0.20
313	30	11	10.6	>0.40
315	20	12	14.3	>0.20
319	20	11	19.8	0.05

photoreactivable particle is reactivated by one quantum only, independently of the UV dose.

The dependence of the amount of PHTR on the time of illumination is expressed by the equation

$$p(t) = (1 - e^{-ft})\, F(D)$$

in which t is the time of illumination, $F(D)$ the photoreactivable fraction, which is a function of the dose, D, of UV. Value f is the probability per time unit that a particle is photoreactivated and can be called the PHTR rate; it is proportional to the slope of the line giving $\log\left(1 - \frac{p(t)}{p(\infty)}\right)$ versus time of illumination. Value f may depend on several variables, such as dose of UV, intensity of the reactivating light, temperature, and metabolic condition of the bacteria during PHTR. This dependence will be examined in the next sections.

Dependence of PHTR rate on dose of UV and intensity of the reactivating light. PHTR rate (f) was determined for UVP inactivated with different UV doses, adsorbed on resting bacteria, and illuminated in liquid at 37 C with light of constant intensity; it was found to be approximately constant for doses of UV between 10 and 30 seconds. The results, however, are not yet definite on this point, and a decrease of f by a factor 1.2 when the UV dose increases from 10 to 30 seconds cannot be excluded. This result shows that the probability for an adsorbed quantum to reactivate a photoreactivable phage particle is practically independent of the inactivating UV dose.

Value f was also determined for different intensities of the reactivating light on UVP inactivated with the same UV dose, adsorbed on resting bacteria, and illuminated in liquid at constant temperature. The intensity was varied either by changing the distance of the sample from an H-4 lamp—assuming the intensity to be inversely proportional to the square of the distance—or by lowering the intensity of a monochromatic light by filters and measuring with a thermopile the relative intensities. Value f was found to increase almost linearly with light intensity for low intensities but for high intensities to tend to a maximum as is shown in figure 5. The highest value of the PHTR rate observed in these experiments was about 1.4×10^{-3} sec^{-1} and corresponds to a half-time of about 8 minutes.

For low light intensities, f being a linear function of the intensity, the probability of PHTR occurring in a bacterium-phage complex is a linear function of the dose of the reactivating light (equal to intensity × time), whereas for high intensities the same dose has less effect. For low intensities and relatively short exposures the dependence of amount of PHTR on light dose is also approximately linear.

Action Spectrum of PHTR

Seven wave lengths were tested for photoreactivating activity. The corresponding monochromatic lights were obtained in the following ways (see Bowen, 1946):

(1) Group of lines near 313 mμ of the mercury arc (with a small amount of 334 mμ). Light: mercury lamp H-4 without glass envelope. Filter: 3 cm $NiSO_4 \cdot 7H_2O$, 350 g + $CoSO_4 \cdot 7H_2O$, 10 g made up to a liter with water; 1 cm potassium hydrogen phthalate, 5 g in 1,000 ml water.

(2) Group of lines 365 mμ of the mercury arc. Mercury lamp H-5 (General Electric); Corning glass filter combination nos. 738, 5860.

(3) Group of lines 404 mμ of the mercury arc. Lamp H-5. Filter: 2 cm $Cu(NO_3)_2 \cdot 6H_2O$, 200 g in 100 ml water. Iodine 0.75 g in 100 ml carbon tetrachloride.

(4) Group of lines 434 mμ of the mercury arc. Lamp H-5. Filter: 2 cm $CuSO_4 \cdot 5H_2O$, 25 g + 300 ml ammonium hydroxide (d = 0.88), made up to 1 liter with water; 1 cm $NaNO_2$, 75 g in 100 ml water.

(5) Band around 500 mμ (between 480 and 520 mμ, center 500 mμ). Projection lamp with ribbon filament. Filter: Wratten no. 47, Wratten no. 58, 2 cm $CuSO_4$, 5 per cent.

(6) Line 546 mμ of the mercury arc. Mercury discharge lamp H-5. Corning glass filter combination, nos. 3484, 4303, 5120.

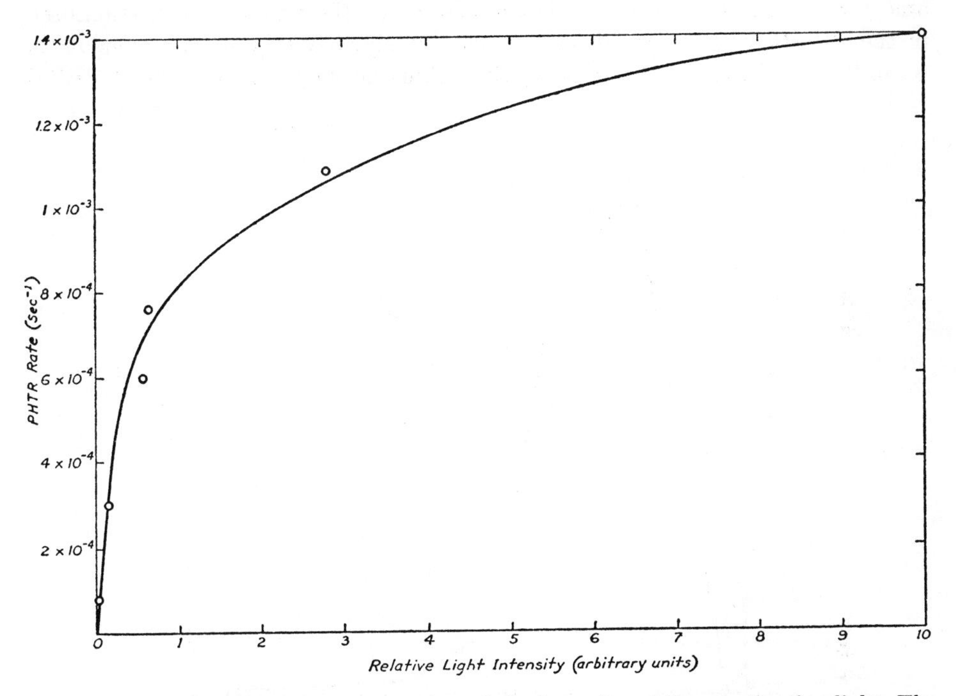

Figure 5. The PHTR rate as a function of the intensity of the reactivating light. The PHTR rate is expressed in sec^{-1} and the light intensity in arbitrary units. Phage T2r was irradiated for 20 seconds with the germicidal lamp, adsorbed on resting bacteria, and illuminated in liquid at 37 C.

(7) Group 576–579 mμ of the mercury arc. Lamp H-5. Filter: 1 cm mixture of $CuCl_2 \cdot 2H_2O$, 10 g in 10 ml water and $CaCl_2$, 3 M, 90 ml; 2 cm $K_2Cr_2O_7$, 15 g in 200 ml water.

The efficiency of the different lights was determined in the following way: For each light the range of intensity was first determined, in which the PHTR rate is approximately proportional to the light intensity; the intensity of the most effective wave lengths was reduced by filters until it fell into this range. The rate of PHTR was then determined for each wave length, and the relative intensities were measured with a thermopile. The time of illumination was short, so that the amount of PHTR was very nearly proportional to the dose of reactivating light (see previous section).

The dose of light of each wave length necessary to give a standard amount of

PHTR in a given time was calculated from these data, and the reciprocal of this dose (given in arbitrary units) was taken as a measure of the activity of that wave length. In figure 6 the activity of the wave lengths tested is plotted against the wave length.

The activity of a given light may be underestimated, since it is known that light of the wave lengths used in PHTR may damage the bacteria (Hollaender, 1943) or the phages (Wahl and Latarjet, 1947). The killing action of the seven wave lengths on active phage adsorbed on bacteria was therefore determined, and it was found that with the light intensity and the time of illumination used in the PHTR experiments an appreciable killing activity was only evident for wave length 313 mμ. To correct for this killing activity, the amount of PHTR

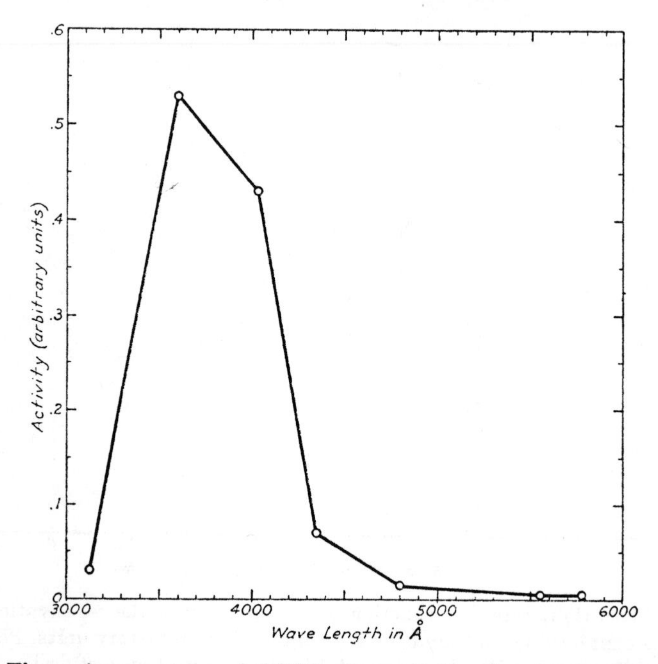

Figure 6. The action spectrum of PHTR. The activity of each wave length, given in arbitrary units, is plotted against the wave length. Phage T2r was irradiated for 20 seconds with the germicidal lamp, adsorbed on resting bacteria, and illuminated in liquid at 37 C.

obtained after a given exposure to this light was increased by a factor equal to the decrease in titer of active phage adsorbed on B exposed to the same light for the same length of time in equal experimental conditions. The curve of PHTR as a function of the time of exposure to 313 mμ light, obtained in this way, was almost linear and was used in calculating the activity of the light.

The activity of the seven wave lengths tested gives only the general shape of the action spectrum. It consists of a band covering the range from about 300 mμ on the side of the short wave lengths to about 500 mμ on the side of the long ones, with a maximum around 365 mμ. The greatest photoreactivating activity occurs therefore in the near ultraviolet.

The action spectrum of PHTR is related to the absorption spectrum of the pigment that absorbs the reactivating light (see Loofbourow, 1948, for discussion of this relation); we tried, therefore, to obtain on this basis some information about the photosensitive pigment. The action spectrum is not detailed enough to give a specific indication; it shows, however, that the pigment is not contained in the unmodified phage, since the absorption spectrum of purified

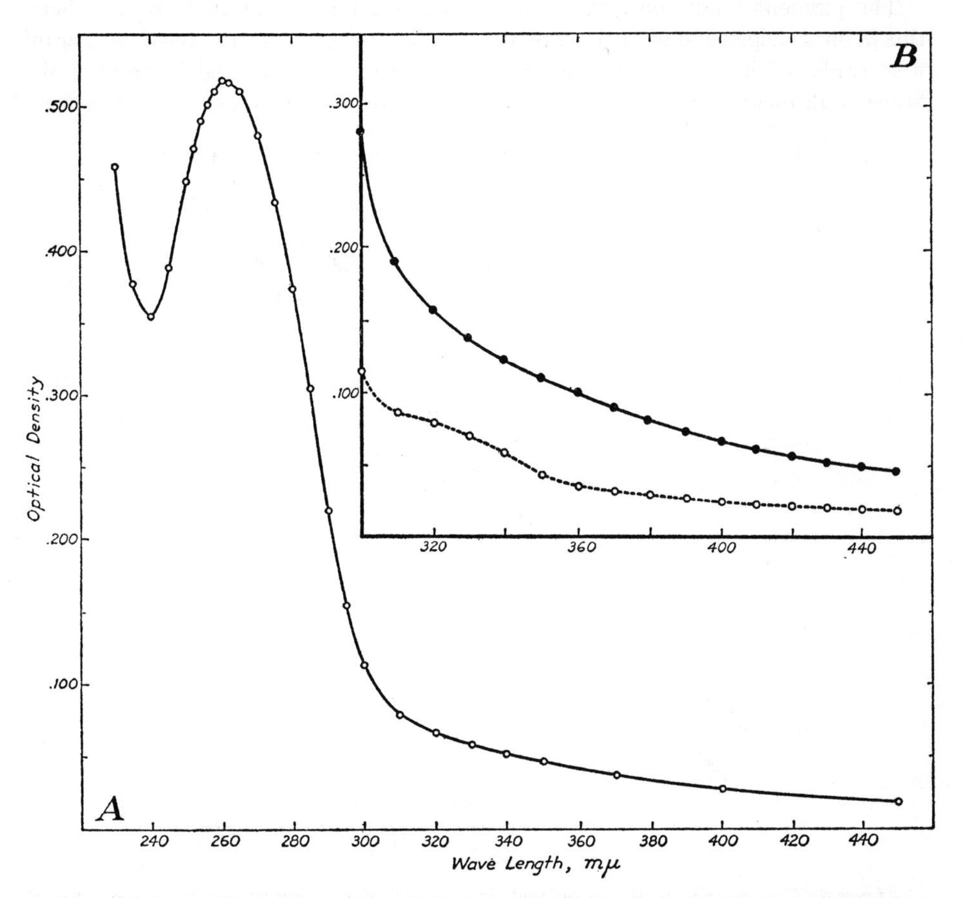

Figure 7. Absorption spectra of purified phage T2. The optical density is plotted against the wave length. The spectra were obtained with a Beckman quartz spectrophotometer. The phage was suspended in phosphate buffer (M/15, pH 7) plus $MgSO_4$ 10^{-3} M. *A*. Active phage, concentration 5.5×10^{10} infecting units per ml. *B*. Upper curve: absorption spectrum of active phage for wave lengths longer than 320 mμ, concentration 2.3×10^{11} infecting units per ml; lower curve: absorption spectrum of the same phage after 2 hours' irradiation with the germicidal lamp at a distance of 12 inches.

phage has no band comparable to the action spectrum of PHTR. This is shown by figure 7*A*, which reproduces the absorption spectrum of purified phage T2. For wave lengths longer than 320 mμ the absorption closely follows Rayleigh's law of scattering and is, therefore, due to scattering of the light. This is shown more convincingly by plotting the logarithm of the optical density at different wave lengths against the logarithm of the wave length; according to Rayleigh's law one should obtain a straight line with slope 4 (see Oster, 1948, 323, formula 6). As shown in figure 8*A*, the curve, obtained from the same data used for figure 7*A*, is a straight line in the range of wave lengths 320 to 450 mμ; the slope of the curve is 3.7, instead of 4, owing to the size of the phage particles, which is larger than required for the strict application of Rayleigh's law (La Mer, 1948).

The pigment might be formed in the phage after UV irradiation. To check this point a suspension of purified phage T2 containing 2.3×10^{11} particles per ml was irradiated in an open shallow container with the germicidal lamp at a distance of 12 inches for variable lengths of time up to 4 hours, and the absorption

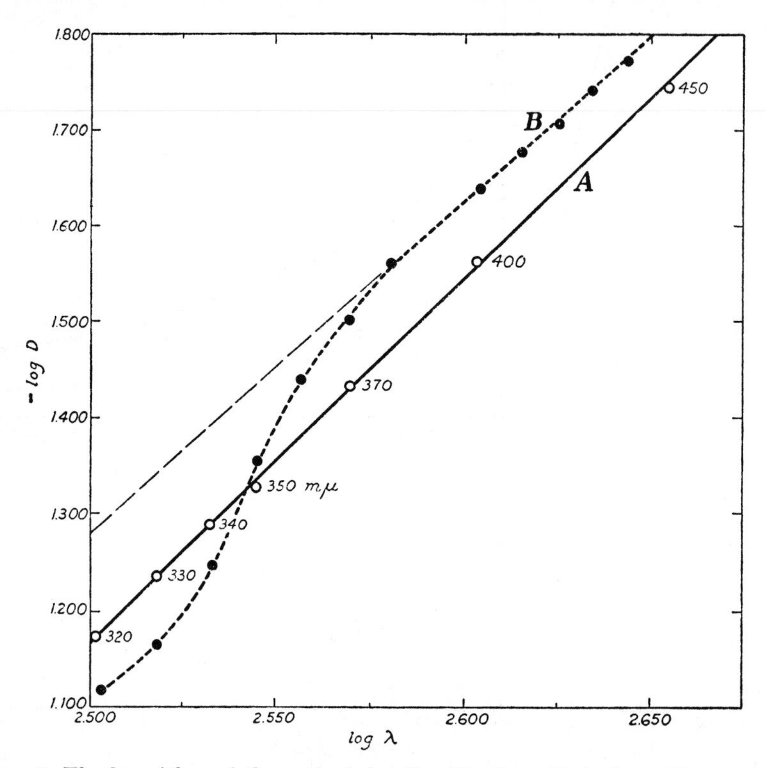

Figure 8. The logarithm of the optical density, *D*, of purified phage T2 versus the logarithm of the wave length for the range 320 to 450 mμ. *A*. Active phage (the same data as in figure 7*A*). *B*. Phage after long UV irradiation (same data as in figure 7*B*). Dashed line shows the curve expected for pure scattering.

spectrum was determined at regular intervals. The absorption spectrum was found to undergo complex changes as the irradiation proceeded; we shall limit our attention to the modifications occurring in the range of wave lengths longer than 320 mμ. A general decrease in absorption in this region was observed, and after about one hour of irradiation a faint band was noticed, which became more evident during the next hour (figure 7*B*). This band has maximum absorption around 330 mμ and extends to about 380 mμ on the side of longer wave lengths (figure 8*B*); its limit on the side of shorter wave lengths cannot be determined because of overlapping with the general phage absorption.

The maximum absorption of this band is located at a shorter wave length than the maximum of the action spectrum of PHTR; this difference, however, is not such as to exclude the band from belonging to the photosensitive pigment, because the location of the band may be shifted toward longer wave lengths if the pigment is bound with some bacterial constituent after adsorption of the inactive phage on bacteria.

Influence of the Metabolic Conditions of Bacteria in PHTR of Phages

PHTR is not appreciably different whether the phage is adsorbed by bacteria in broth or in a synthetic medium; the rate of PHTR is somewhat lower with resting bacteria than with bacteria suspended in nutrient media.

The influence of oxygen on PHTR was determined. Resting bacteria and UVP were placed in separate compartments of a Thunberg tube, nitrogen was bubbled for about 20 minutes through the bacterial suspension, the tube was then evacuated by a pump, and air was replaced with nitrogen, the operation being re-

TABLE 6

PHTR rate and Q_{10} at different temperatures

The Q_{10} was determined from the ratio of Q_d of the rates at two successive temperatures, using the formula: $Q_{10} = (Q_d)^{10/d}$, where d is the temperature interval between two observations. Phage T2r irradiated for 20 seconds with the germicidal lamp, illuminated in liquid.

TEMPERATURE (C)	PHTR RATE (SEC^{-1})	Q_{10}
3	1.25×10^{-5}	
11	6.2×10^{-5}	7.5
16	1.3×10^{-4}	4.2
24	2.3×10^{-4}	2.1
30	3.9×10^{-4}	2.4
37	5.6×10^{-4}	1.7

peated 4 times. Phage and bacteria were mixed and the tube was exposed to light. The control consisted of an open tube from which oxygen had not been removed. The same amount of PHTR was observed in both tubes. Oxygen is therefore not necessary for PHTR, at least not for the initial photochemical reaction. We also found that cyanide in 10^{-2} M concentration does not affect PHTR.

The Effect of Temperature on PHTR

PHTR can occur at temperatures too low to allow growth of active phage (+1 C). To obtain a measurable amount of PHTR at this temperature, one must mix UVP and bacteria in the dark at 37 C to allow enough adsorption, then chill the mixture to 1 C and expose it to light.

Determinations of PHTR rate with constant illumination were made at 3, 11, 16, 24, and 37 C, using phage T2 irradiated for 20 minutes with the germicidal lamp. The Q_{10} was determined for each interval, and the results are reproduced in table 6.

The behavior of the Q_{10} is similar to that found for complex bacterial activities and for enzymatic reactions (Rahn, 1932) and is an indication that the physiological state of the bacterium conditions the probability of the photoreactivating event.

PHTR of Phage Inactivated with X-Rays

It was previously reported (1949) that no PHTR had been detected for phage inactivated by X-rays. This statement is valid only if X-ray irradiation is performed on phage in synthetic medium. With phage T2 inactivated by X-rays in nutrient broth a slight amount of PHTR can be observed. This amount is probably reduced by the poor adsorption of phage inactivated by X-rays, as discovered by Watson (1948). After correction for the limited adsorption (data kindly supplied by Watson), the PHTR of X-ray-inactivated phage is still considerably less than that for phage inactivated to the same extent by UV.

SUMMARY AND DISCUSSION

In the following brief discussion we shall try to arrange the results of our experiments in an order that will bring out their theoretical implications, and we shall present a working hypothesis for the mechanism of PHTR.

(1) The damage caused by UV in bacteriophage consists of two kinds: photoreactivable and nonphotoreactivable damage. These two kinds of damage occur with comparable cross sections; they may reflect the presence of two kinds of UV-absorbing constituents in each phage particle. Further information should be obtainable by determining the action spectrum for the two types of inactivation.

(2) Only phage particles adsorbed on bacteria undergo PHTR; PHTR can occur within a few seconds after adsorption, indicating that PHTR is due to reactions occurring in the early phase of the interaction between inactive phage and bacterium; perhaps surface reactions are involved, and this may account for the failure to reproduce PHTR with bacterial extracts. PHTR does not require the presence of external metabolic substrates or of oxygen and is not inhibited by cyanide, but is influenced by the physiological condition of the bacteria after infection.

(3) The photosensitive pigment has an action spectrum with a maximum near 365 mμ. Normal phage does not have an absorption band corresponding to this action spectrum. UV-treated phage shows an absorption band with a maximum near 330 mμ. Perhaps this is the photosensitive pigment created by UV irradiation in the phage. The shift from 330 to 365 mμ could be due to the binding of the pigment with bacterial constituents upon adsorption of a phage particle on the bacterium. The alternative possibility is that the photosensitive pigment exists in the bacterium prior to infection. Further studies of the absorption band of UV-irradiated phage and of the action spectrum of PHTR are needed.

(4) At low intensities of illumination the probability of PHTR occurring in a bacterium-phage complex is proportional to the dose of light. From this we might conclude that the individual light quanta absorbed by the bacterium-

phage complex do not co-operate to produce PHTR but that each quantum individually has a chance to accomplish PHTR and that this chance is independent of any other quanta absorbed by the complex. We would thus be led to conjecture that PHTR is due to a primary photochemical reaction.

(5) The picture is complicated by the finding that at high intensities the rate of PHTR ceases to be proportional to the intensity of illumination, reaching a maximum value, and by the finding of a complex temperature dependence. These findings require the participation of dark reactions in the mechanism of PHTR.

(6) The probability of PHTR per time unit (PHTR rate) is practically independent of the dose of UV used for inactivation. This finding shows that photoreactivation is an all-or-none phenomenon, and it may indicate that photoreactivable inactivation is always due to one injury, elimination of which restitutes activity.

To explain all the known features of PHTR, we propose the following working hypothesis: The photoreactivable inactivation is due to formation of molecules of an inhibitor in the phage; although many of these molecules may be formed in one phage particle, just one molecule is the inactivating one in each case, for example, by blocking a reaction necessary for phage growth in a small area of the contact surface between phage and bacterium. Restoration of phage activity requires the permanent removal of the inactivating inhibitor molecule. Dissociation does not occur by thermal activation; but absorption of a light quantum of a given wave length produces a transient and reversible dissociation. During the time the inhibitor is dissociated it can be captured by a receptor and destroyed with dark reaction. This makes the removal permanent and constitutes reactivation.

PHTR therefore requires a system made by phage, inhibitor, pigment, and receptor. The inhibitor belongs to the phage, the receptor to the bacterium being perhaps of enzymatic nature; the pigment may belong to either one and may be identified either with the inhibitor or with the receptor. The system is completed after adsorption of the inactive phage on bacteria.

The probability of PHTR (PHTR rate) for low light intensity is proportional to the time integral in which the inhibitor is dissociated and therefore to the number of quanta absorbed (dose of the reactivating light). For high intensities the activation times due to absorption of different quanta overlap somewhat, so that equal doses become less efficient. When the light intensity is so high that the inhibitor is dissociated without interruption during illumination, the probability of PHTR reaches a maximum value. The probability of PHTR is also proportional to the probability that the dissociated inhibitor will be captured and destroyed by the receptor in the time unit and therefore depends on temperature, which influences the dark reactions, and on some physiological conditions of the bacteria, which may affect the efficiency or the amount of the receptor.

REFERENCES

BOWEN, E. J. 1946 The chemical aspects of light. Clarendon Press, Oxford.

DULBECCO, R. 1949 Reactivation of ultraviolet-inactivated bacteriophage by visible light. Nature, **163**, 949–950.

GRATIA, A. 1936 Des rélations numériques entre bactéries lysogènes et particules de bactériophage. Ann. inst. Pasteur, **57**, 652–676.

HERSHEY, A. D., KALMANSON, G., AND BRONFENBRENNER, J. 1943 Quantitative methods in the study of the phage-antiphage reaction. J. Immunol., **46**, 267–280.

HOLLAENDER, A. 1943 Effect of long ultraviolet and short visible radiation (3500 to 4900Å) on *Escherichia coli*. J. Bact., **46**, 531–541.

KELNER, A. 1949 Effect of visible light on the recovery of *Streptomyces griseus* conidia from ultra-violet irradiation injury. Proc. Natl. Acad. Sci. U. S., **35**, 73–79.

LA MER, V. K. 1948 Monodisperse colloids and higher-order Tyndall spectra. J. Phys. Colloid Chem., **52**, 65.

LATARJET, R., AND WAHL, R. 1945 Précisions sur l'inactivation des bactériophages par les rayons ultra-violets. Ann. inst. Pasteur, **71**, 336–339.

LOOFBOUROW, J. R. 1948 Effects of ultraviolet radiation on cells. Growth, **12**, Suppl., 75-149.

LURIA, S. E. 1947 Reactivation of irradiated bacteriophage by transfer of self-reproducing units. Proc. Natl. Acad. Sci. U. S., **33**, 253–264.

LURIA, S. E., AND DELBRÜCK, M. 1942 Interference between bacterial viruses. II. Interference between inactivated bacterial virus and active virus of the same strain and of different strain. Arch. Biochem., **1**, 207–218.

OSTER, G. 1948 The scattering of light and its applications to chemistry. Chem. Rev., **43**, 319–365.

RAHN, O. 1932 Physiology of bacteria. P. Blakiston's Son and Co., Philadelphia. *Refer to* p. 123, 221.

WAHL, R., AND LATARJET, R. 1947 Inactivation de bactériophages par des radiations de grande longeur d'onde (3400–6000 Å). Ann. inst. Pasteur, **73**, 957–971.

WATSON, J. D. 1948 Inactivating mutations produced by X-rays in bacteriophages. Genetics, **33**, 633.

GENETIC RECOMBINATIONS LEADING TO PRODUCTION OF ACTIVE BACTERIOPHAGE FROM ULTRAVIOLET INACTIVATED BACTERIOPHAGE PARTICLES[1]

S. E. LURIA AND R. DULBECCO

Department of Bacteriology, Indiana University, Bloomington, Indiana

WITH AN APPENDIX BY R. DULBECCO

Received June 28, 1948

THE potentialities of bacteriophage genetics have been revealed by the discovery of genetic recombinations among related phage particles infecting the same bacterial cell (DELBRÜCK and BAILEY 1946). The complexities of these genetic systems have been further illustrated by the work of HERSHEY and ROTMAN (1948) on a number of different genetic determinants involved in the determination of the alternative phenotypes r^+ and r in phage *T2H*. A different approach to the genetic mechanisms of bacteriophages originated from the chance observation by DELBRÜCK and BAILEY that, after exposure to ultraviolet light, some phages gave variable plaque counts, depending on the relative concentrations of phage lysates and host cells at the time of assay. In investigating this phenomenon, one of us (LURIA 1947) discovered a mechanism of phage reactivation by interaction among inactive particles in the course of intracellular growth. The detailed investigation of this phenomenon has indicated new possibilities for a quantitative analysis of the genetic structure of these viruses and has suggested a possible mechanism for their reproduction.

A preliminary discussion of some of the results reported in this paper has appeared (LURIA 1947); their implications for a number of problems have been discussed in a forthcoming publication (LURIA 1948). The present article is intended to present the results in detail, and, by describing techniques and methods of analysis, to serve as a background for future publications on this topic.

The analysis of the results presented in the following pages is based on the hypothesis that inactivation of bacteriophage particles by ultraviolet light is due to production of discrete alterations in individual portions of genetic material. Although the internal evidence in support of this hypothesis, as presented in this paper, is quite satisfactory, it must be said that satisfactory external evidence from other lines of attack is not yet available. The conclusions reached in this article must be considered for the time being as working hypotheses for further investigation.

MATERIAL AND GENERAL METHODS

The system of phages *T1-T7*, their *r* mutants, and their common host *Escherichia coli* strain B have repeatedly been described, as well as the use of

[1] This work was done under an AMERICAN CANCER SOCIETY grant recommended by the COMMITTEE ON GROWTH OF THE NATIONAL RESEARCH COUNCIL. We wish to acknowledge the able assistance of MRS. J. P. HEADDY.

Reprinted by permission of the authors and Genetics, Inc., from GENETICS, 34, 93-125, March, 1949.

bacterial mutants resistant to one or more phages as indicators for one phage in the presence of another (see DELBRÜCK 1946). Plate counts for viable bacteria, and plaque counts in agar layer for active phage were used throughout, employing 1.1 percent agar in "Difco" nutrient broth plus 0.5 percent NaCl. All plates were incubated at 37°C. Experimental bacterial cultures in the logarithmic phase of growth were grown with aeration at 37°C from standard inocula.

The phage stocks were lysates in glucose+ammonia (or lactate+ammonia) medium. These media give negligible absorption of the ultraviolet light used in this work. High titer phage lysates (over 1×10^{11} particles per ml) might give some ultraviolet screening effect because of bacterial debris and of phage itself. Whenever possible, therefore, phage was irradiated after a dilution 1:5 or higher in the same medium. The source of ultraviolet was a General Electric Company germicidal bulb, 15 watts, alimented through a stabilizer. At a distance of 50 cm from the center of this bulb, the flux—measured with a Westinghouse SM-200 meter with tantalum phototube WL-775—is about 7 $\text{erg} \times \text{mm}^{-2}\ \text{sec}^{-1}$. The beam contains mainly radiation of wavelength 2537 Å. Samples were irradiated in a thin layer (not over 0.4 mm) in open Petri dishes rocked during exposure.

The technique of "one-step growth" experiment in its various forms has been described in detail previously (DELBRÜCK and LURIA 1942).

EXPERIMENTAL

Inactivation and reactivation of bacteriophages

Plaque counts on phage suspensions exposed to ultraviolet for various lengths of time generally give survival ratios whose logarithms are proportional to the dose, that is, to the time of exposure (see LATARJET and WAHL 1945, and figure 1). The logarithmic rate indicates a one-hit mechanism of inactivation (LEA 1947), and we can assume that the hit consists of the successful absorption of one quantum. The probability that one quantum produces inactivation is, however, very small: for phage *T2*, for example, one inactivating hit is produced by a dose corresponding to almost 10^4 quanta absorbed per particle (M. ZELLE, personal communication). Only one absorption in 10^4 on the average is, therefore, effective, the others probably producing excitations that do not lead to the inactivating effect.

When the average number of effective hits per particle is r, the proportion of active to total phage will be e^{-r}. For $r=1$, $e^{-r}=0.37$; the corresponding dose is the "inactivation dose" in LEA's terminology (1947). If doses are expressed in multiples of the inactivation dose, their values give directly the average number of hits per particle.

Phage particles inactivated by ultraviolet light are adsorbed by bacteria (LURIA and DELBRÜCK 1942). This is detected because adsorption of one particle by a bacterium causes death of the latter. One can, therefore, measure the rate of adsorption of inactive particles from the survival of bacteria in mixtures containing bacteria and irradiated phage in known proportions. If, on the average, x particles are adsorbed per bacterium, a fraction e^{-x} of the

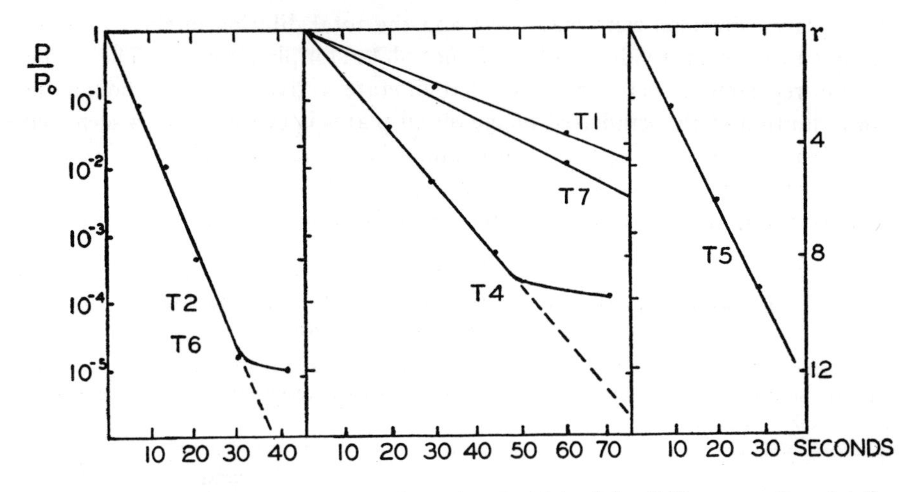

FIGURE 1.—Inactivation of various phages by ultraviolet light. P/P_0=proportion of active phage particles after irradiation. $r=\ln P_0/P$=average number of lethal hits per phage particle. The doses are expressed in seconds of exposure. The deviations for high doses in the curves for *T2*, *T4*, and *T6* are due to reactivation occurring on the assay plates (see text). The broken lines represent extrapolations from the logarithmic portions of the curves.

bacteria should receive no particle and survive. By this means, we could establish that for irradiated phages *T2*, *T4*, *T5*, and *T6*, even for high doses, the rate of adsorption is the same as for unirradiated phage. An experiment of this type is shown in table 1. Only for very high doses a slight reduction occurs in the ability of phage to kill bacteria. This reduction is never such as to require important corrections in the analysis presented in later sections.

With phages *T2*, *T4*, *T5*, and *T6* (the "large particle" phages) the plaque counts on irradiated samples are not independent of the mode of assay. They depend on the concentration of the samples when first mixed with bacteria, in a way illustrated in table 2. In these experiments, bacteria were mixed with various concentrations of irradiated phage. Before lysis and phage liberation

TABLE 1

Killing of bacteria by irradiated phage

0.9 ml of a bacterial culture was mixed with 0.1 ml of each of five suspensions of phage *T2r* that had received various doses of radiation. After 10 minutes, samples were diluted and plated for viable bacterial count.

EXPERIMENT NO.	PHAGE INPUT, PARTICLES PER ML	BACTERIAL INPUT, CELLS PER ML	DOSE OF RADIATION		SURVIVING BACTERIA PER ML	SURVIVAL / INPUT e^{-x}	PHAGE ADSORBED PER BACTERIUM x
			SECONDS	HITS PER PARTICLE			
			0	0	2.3×10^8	0.20	1.60
			60	18	2.4×10^8	0.21	1.56
129	2×10^9	1.15×10^9	70	21	2.2×10^8	0.19	1.66
			80	24	1.6×10^8	0.14	1.96
			100	30	2.7×10^8	0.23	1.47

took place, dilutions were made to bring the total dilution of the irradiated sample to a constant value, and an aliquot plated for plaque count. The plaque counts represent infected bacteria that liberate active phage. Although the total dilution of the irradiated phage on all plates is the same, it is seen that the plaque counts are higher when bacteria have first been placed in contact with a more concentrated phage lysate.

This means that bacteria may produce active phage if they pick up the irradiated particles from a concentrated phage suspension, but not from a dilute one. The immediate explanation is that from a concentrated lysate the bacteria receive some other "factor," which, inside the bacterium, somehow *reactivates* an "inactive" particle and which is not present in dilute lysates. An "inactive" particle can be defined as one that has lost the ability to initiate production of active phage unless adsorbed by a bacterium together with the unknown "factor."

TABLE 2

Dependence of plaque counts on irradiated phage T6r on the concentration of the phage sample that is mixed with bacteria

A sample of phage *T6r* containing 1.5×10^{10} particles/ml was irradiated for 20 seconds. The bacterial suspension (B) contained 2×10^9 cells/ml. Each plate received 0.05 ml of phage dilution and 0.2 ml of suspension (B).

EXPERIMENT NO.	MIXTURE NO.	PROCEDURE	DILUTION OF PHAGE WHEN FIRST MIXED WITH (B)	TOTAL DILUTION FROM THE ORIGINAL PHAGE TO THE SUSPENSION FROM WHICH SAMPLES ARE PLATED	PLAQUE COUNT (SUM OF TWO PLATES)
5	1	0.1 ml *T6r*→0.9 ml (B); kept 10 min. at 37°C; diluted $1:10^3$, 0.05 cc plated	1:10	$1:10^4$	1318
	2	0.1 ml (*T6r* 1:10)→0.9 ml (B); kept 10 min. at 37°C; diluted $1:10^2$, 0.05 ml plated	$1:10^2$	$1:10^4$	474
	3	0.1 ml (*T6r* $1:10^3$)→0.9 ml (B); kept 10 min. at 37°C; diluted 1:10, 0.05 ml plated	$1:10^4$	$1:10^4$	250
	4	0.05 ml (*T6r* $1:10^4$) plated	Less than $1:10^5$ (on plate)	$1:10^4$	57

Reactivation still occurs after storage of irradiated phage for weeks in an ice-box. Reactivation gives rise to fully active phage particles. This can be proved either by sampling phage from the plaques or by letting the bacteria, in which reactivation occurs, lyse in liquid and then testing the lysate for active particles.

The occurrence of reactivation for certain phages accounts for deviations from the logarithmic inactivation rate found for these same phages (see figure 1). As the dose of radiation increases beyond a certain point, the survival, as determined by plaque count, appears to diminish less rapidly. This is due to an unavoidable partial reactivation. In a phage titration, we mix approximately 5×10^7 bacteria with an amount of phage suspension such as to give approximately 100 plaques, and pour the mixture on an agar plate. On the one hand, if we are dealing with a fully active sample, the bacteria only come in contact with 100 active particles. On the other hand, in assaying an irradiated suspension containing, for example, one active particle in 10^6, we expose the bacteria to 10^8 inactive particles plus a correspondingly large amount of other lysate constituents, besides the residual 100 active particles. Conditions permitting reactivation, therefore, obtain in these plating mixtures, and reactivation disturbs and often completely obscures the count of the residual active phage. For this reason, the survival of fully active phage for high doses must be obtained by extrapolation from the logarithmic part of the curve, a necessarily inefficient procedure. If deviations in the survival rate for high doses occurred, this extrapolation would not be justified. One possible cause of error—screening of some phage particles from radiation by components of the lysate itself—was excluded by irradiating concentrated phage *T6* mixed with phage *T1*, and testing for the inactivation rate of the latter, which is not disturbed by reactivation phenomena. The inactivation rate of *T1* remains the same as in the absence of *T6* up to doses that correspond to 100 hits per particle of phage *T6*.

Identification of the reactivating factor

What is the "factor" present in irradiated stocks of phages *T2*, *T4*, *T5*, or *T6*, which, if acting on bacteria that have adsorbed inactive phage particles, allows production of active phage? Since phage stocks are lysates produced by lysis of the common host *E. coli* B, the factor might be either of phage or of bacterial origin.

The factor was identified as being phage itself, inactive or active, in that *reactivation occurs in bacteria that adsorb either more than one inactive particle of a given phage, or one inactive particle of one phage plus some active or inactive particles of a related phage.* The evidence for this conclusion, which is illustrated in part by the data in table 3, can be summarized as follows.

(a) Addition of an excess of supernatant from a heavy bacterial culture to a mixture of dilute irradiated phage plus bacteria gives no increase in plaque count. The factor in the lysates is not a normal bacterial secretion.

(b) Concentrated lysates of phages *T1*, *T5*, or *T7* added to a mixture of bacteria and dilute irradiated *T2* (or *T4*, or *T6*) do not cause reactivation. No heterologous lysate causes reactivation of *T5*. The test for cross-reactivation is done by plating the mixtures, before lysis, with bacterial indicator strains sensitive to the phage whose reactivation is tested, but not to the others. Since all phage stocks are lysates of common host cells, the factor is not an unspecific bacterial product liberated upon lysis.

TABLE 3

Reactivation of phage T2 under various conditions

Phage *T2*, containing 2×10^{10} particles per ml, was irradiated for 35 seconds. Phages *T6* and *T4*, containing 4×10^{10} particles per ml, were irradiated for 30 seconds. Phages *T1* and *T5* contained 3×10^{10} particles per ml. The bacterial suspensions (B) and (B/6) contained 10^9 cells per ml.

MIXTURE NO.	CONTENTS	AFTER 10 MINUTES	PLAQUE COUNT (SUM OF TWO PLATES)	REACTIVATION
1	0.1 ml Phage *T2* dil. 1:500+1.9 ml (B)	0.05 ml plated with B	22	−
2	0.1 ml Phage *T2* dil. 1:500+1.9 ml (B/6)	0.05 ml. plated with B/6	20	−
3	0.1 ml Phage *T2* pure +1.9 ml (B)	dil. 1:500, 0.05 ml plated with B	4000	+
4	0.1 ml Phage *T2* pure +1.9 ml (B/6)	dil. 1:500, 0.05 ml plated with B/6	3000	+
5	0.1 ml Phage *T2*. dil 1:500+0.1 ml irrad. *T6*+1.8 ml (B)	0.05 ml plated with B/6	670	+
6	0.1 ml Phage *T2* dil. 1:500+0.1 ml unirrad. *T6*+1.8 ml (B)	0.05 ml plated with B/6	190	+
7	0.1 ml Phage *T2* dil. 1:500+0.1 ml irrad. *T4*+1.8 ml (B)	0.05 ml plated with B/4	661	+
8	0.1 ml Phage *T2* dil. 1:500+0.1 ml irrad. *T6*+1.8 ml (B/6)	0.05 ml plated with B/6	10	−
9	0.1 ml Phage *T2* dil. 1:500+0.1 ml unirrad. *T6*+1.8 ml (B/6)	0.05 ml plated with B/6	12	−
10	0.1 ml Phage *T2* dil. 1:500+0.1 ml irrad. *T4*+1.8 ml (B/6)	0.05 ml plated with B/4	883	+
11	0.1 ml Phage *T2* dil. 1:500+0.1 ml unirrad. *T1*+1.8 ml (B)	0.05 ml plated with B/1, 5	18	−
12	0.1 ml Phage *T2* dil. 1:500+0.1 ml unirrad. *T5*+1.8 ml (B)	0.05 ml plated with B/1, 5	17	−

(c) Concentrated lysates of phages *T2* (or *T4*, or *T6*), whether fully active or irradiated, can reactivate irradiated particles of any other *T-even* phage. These phages are morphologically, serologically, and probably genetically related, whereas *T5* belongs to a fully separate group (DELBRÜCK 1946). The "factor" in the lysates appears to carry the same pattern of relatedness. It is not produced by irradiation, since its presence can be proved in unirradiated lysates by the technique of cross-reactivation.

(d) Reactivation is independent of contact between phages prior to infection of the host: a mixture of bacteria and phages gives the same amount of reactivation independently of how long the phages have been together before adding the bacteria.

(e) Phage *T4r* purified by fast centrifugation (kindly supplied by DR. T. F. ANDERSON) shows both self-reactivation as a function of concentration in the mixtures, and ability to reactivate phages *T2* or *T6*. The factor, therefore, is present in such a purified phage suspension.

(f) Reactivation of phage *T2* by lysates of *T6*, for example, only occurs in presence of bacteria capable of adsorbing both phages. Inactive phage *T2* in presence of bacteria *B/6*, by which it is adsorbed, is not reactivated by *T6*, which is not adsorbed, but is reactivated by *T4*, which is adsorbed. This proves that the "factor" has the same host specificity as the phage in whose lysate it is found.

The last point, particularly, was considered crucial in showing that production of active phage from an inactive particle was actually due to infection of the same bacterial cell with other particles, either of the same or of a different but genetically related phage, active or inactive. Further confirmation came from the experiments discussed below, which showed that in a mixture of inactive phage and bacteria the number of bacteria yielding active phage is never greater than the number of bacteria that adsorb two or more inactive particles, and in some cases actually equals it. The same holds true for reactivation of an inactive phage, for instance *T2*, by a related one, for instance *T4*; the number of bacteria liberating active *T2* is lower than—or equal to—the number of bacteria receiving at least one particle of each phage. The analysis of cross-reactivation between these different wild-type phages will not be discussed further in this paper, but will form the subject of a future publication.[2]

(g) All bacteria which, after infection with inactive particles, do not liberate active phage also fail to lyse. This was proved by mixing bacteria and inactive phage under conditions in which some reactivation occurs, plating a sample of the mixture for plaque count, and another sample for direct microscopic observation of lysis on agar. The results of such experiments proved that the fraction of bacteria that are lysed is the same as the fraction of bacteria that liberate active phage. The other infected bacteria fail to grow and divide, and can be seen still apparently unchanged 24 hours later.

Reactivation and genetic transfer

The limitation of cross-reactivation to the *T-even* phages immediately brought out a similarity between this phenomenon and that of genetic transfer described by DELBRÜCK and BAILEY (1946). In the latter case, bacteria simultaneously infected with the phages $T2r^+$ and $T4r$—the r character being the result of mutation from the wild-type, which can be designated as r^+—liberate a mixture of particles of the four types, $T2r^+$, $T2r$, $T4r^+$, and $T4r$, among which the second and third represent new types. These must owe their origin to some sort of recombination involving the genetic determinants for the alternative r^+ and r phenotypes. Evidence for the discrete nature of these determinants has since been reported by HERSHEY and ROTMAN (1948).

We assumed then, as a working hypothesis for the analysis of the reactivation phenomenon, that inactivation by ultraviolet light resulted from "lethal mutations" in a number of discrete genetic determinants among inactive particles in the same bacterium to reconstitute fully active particles. This hypothesis can be formulated quantitatively in terms of measurable

[2] Cross-reactivation between *T*-even phages has the limitation that the individual phages are distinguishable only by test of differential properties such as ability to grow on different hosts and rate of inactivation by different antisera. Cross-reactivation can only be defined as the production, upon mixed infection, of active particles having the distinctive properties of an inactive parent particle.

quantities by making a number of simple assumptions. We shall first develop this simple theory and then describe the experiments by means of which it was tested.

Theory

We shall assume that in each particle of a given phage there exist n "units" (or "loci") each capable of undergoing a lethal mutation when exposed to ultraviolet light. Since one effective hit is sufficient to inactivate a phage particle, a lethal mutation can be defined as an effective hit, that is, as an alteration of one unit which makes the phage particle unable to initiate by itself the production of active phage in a bacterium. A particle may undergo more than one lethal mutation, and mutations will be distributed at random and independently among the different units, the distribution depending only on the sensitivity of each unit.

We shall now make the assumption that the sensitivity of all units is the same, and show later that this assumption, if incorrect, only requires a numerical correction which does not invalidate the applicability of the theory.

Our next assumption is that *active phage cannot be produced in a bacterium unless the infecting particle or particles, taken as a group, contain at least one copy of each unit in non-lethal form.* This assumption is an essential feature of the theory, and corresponds to treating each unit as a *discrete, material, independent hereditary unit* endowed with genetic continuity and individuality. An inactive unit cannot be replaced by copies of different units. This assumption implies that production of active units cannot result from the cooperation of two or more lethal units, but only from actual reproduction of active units.

When a population consisting of M phage particles is irradiated with a given dose, there will be produced in each particle, on the average, r lethal mutations, or a total of $M \times r$ mutations in the whole population. Since M particles contain $M \times n$ units, each unit will receive on the average $Mr/Mn = r/n$ lethal mutations.

A given unit, taken at random, will have a probability $e^{-r/n}$ of not having a lethal mutation, and a probability $(1-e^{-r/n})$ of having at least one.

We ask next: what is the probability that each of the n units is present in at least one non-lethal copy in a group of k particles that enter a bacterium? According to our assumptions, this probability should represent an upper limit for the probability that a bacterium produces active phage.

If a bacterium is infected by k particles, the probability that a given unit is lethal in all of them is: $(1-e^{-r/n})^k$, and the probability that it is non-lethal in at least one of them is: $1-(1-e^{-r/n})^k$.

The probability that at least one non-lethal copy of each of the n units is present in the k particles is the product of the probabilities referred to the individual units. Since we have assumed equal sensitivity for all units—that is, r/n constant for all units for each value of r—the product will be

$$[1 - (1 - e^{-r/n})^k]^n. \tag{1}$$

The expression (1) represents the probability that a bacterium infected by k particles receives at least one full non-lethal complement of the n units.

In a mixture of phage with bacteria, however, there is a distribution of the number of phage particles infecting individual bacteria. With relatively good approximation—see Appendix—this distribution can be considered as a Poisson distribution. If x is the average number of particles adsorbed per bacterium, the fraction of bacteria with k particles is: $x^k e^{-x}/k!$

The fraction of bacteria receiving k particles which carry a full complement of non lethal units is then:

$$\frac{x^k e^{-x}}{k!}\,[1-(1-e^{-r/n})^k]^n. \qquad (2)$$

Finally, the fraction of the total bacterial population which receives all units in a non-lethal form is the sum of the expression (2) for all possible values of k:

$$Z=\sum_{k=0}^{\infty}\frac{x^k e^{-x}}{k!}\,[1-(1-e^{-r/n})^k]^n. \qquad (3)$$

This expression embodies the following consequences of our hypothesis:

(a) No full complement of active units can be present in uninfected bacteria ($k=0$).

(b) Of the bacteria with one phage particle ($k=1$), only those with an active particle fulfill the requirement for active phage production ($Z=xe^{-x}e^{-r}$).

(c) Any bacterium that receives at least one active particle fulfills the requirement for active phage production, whether it also receives inactive particles or not. For each unit of that particle, $1-e^{-r/n}=0$; hence, $(1-e^{-r/n})^k=0$, and $[1-(1-e^{-r/n})^k]^n=1$.

(d) For any given value of $r>0$, Z increases with increasing x, that is, the probability of having a full complement of active units increases as the number of particles adsorbed per bacterium increases.

(e) For any given value of x, Z diminishes with increasing r, that is, the probability of having all active units diminishes as the dose of radiation increases.

For the purpose of comparison with data from different experiments, it is more convenient to eliminate from the computation those bacteria that receive either zero or one phage particle, since they are not expected to contribute to reactivation. This is done by using instead of Z the expression

$$z=\sum_{k=2}^{\infty}\frac{x^k e^{-x}}{k!}\,[1-(1-e^{-r/n})^k]^n. \qquad (4)$$

z represents the fraction of bacteria in the total population that have two or more phage particles, which together contain a full complement of active units. Since the fraction m of bacteria with two or more phage particles ("multiple-infected bacteria") is

$$m=1-(x+1)e^{-x} \qquad (5)$$

the multiple-infected bacteria receiving a full complement of active units represent a fraction

$$y = z/m = \frac{\sum_{k=2}^{\infty} \frac{x^k e^{-x}}{k!} [1 - (1 - e^{-r/n})^k]^n}{1 - (x + 1)e^{-x}}. \qquad (6)$$

The expression y thus obtained is a function of x (average number of phage particles adsorbed per bacterium), of r (average number of lethal hits per particle), and of n (number of units per particle).

We shall call w the ratio between the number of bacteria that actually liberate active phage (plaque count) and the number of multiple-infected bacteria. For each mixture of bacteria and irradiated phage, we can determine experimentally r, x, and the plaque count, and obtain from these the values of m and w. We can then compare the experimental values of w with the calculated values of y for several different values of n.[3]

The function $y = F(r, x, n)$ was tabulated numerically for a range of values of r (between 3 and 50), of x (between 0.05 and 20), and of n (between 10 and 60). We used for k those ranges of values for which the contributions of the corresponding classes were relevant. The corresponding curves were drawn for $y = F(r)$ (x and n constant), and for $y = F(x)$ (r and n constant).

Before comparing the experimental results with the curves, it is useful to discuss briefly what we may expect from the comparison. If reactivation only occurs in bacteria with more than one inactive particle, w should never be greater than unity. If among the requirements for reactivation there are those stated in the assumptions of our theory, the ratio w/y should never be greater than unity. Finally, if the requirements stated in our assumptions are *necessary* and *sufficient* for reactivation, the ratio w/y should be unity, that is, active phage should be produced in all those bacteria that receive a full complement of the hypothetical units in non-lethal form. Should this obtain, it would then be possible to calculate the value of n for each phage from the experimental values of w.

It is important to keep in mind that the assumptions of our theory, up to this point, do not contain any implication as to the nature, properties, or mechanism of transfer of the postulated units. They only assert that each unit has genetic individuality and can be made lethal by radiation as a result of one photochemical reaction, which is of the "all or none" type and independent of other reactions of the same type in other units of either the same or other phage particles. Production of active phage is conditioned by the presence in one bacterium of one active copy of each unit, this copy not being replaceable by any number of inactive copies.

The theory does not imply that all phage particles receive the same number of lethal hits, but that the lethal hits are distributed at random among the units of all phage particles.

[3] In preliminary reports (LURIA 1947, 1948) we used the symbol y both for the theoretical and experimental probabilities of reactivation. We also gave values of $1/y$ instead of y(or w). The present notation, while consistent with the previous one, makes the presentation more logical.

Comparison of theory with experiment

Quantitative experiments consisted of testing mixtures of bacteria and irradiated bacteriophage for the number of bacteria that liberate active phage. Only phages *T2*, *T4*, and *T6* were studied in detail.

In a typical experiment, such as the one described in detail in table 4, a standard culture of bacteria, grown to a titer of either 10^8 cells per ml or 10^9 cells per ml, was chilled by immersion in a water bath at 5–6°C. This treatment interrupts multiplication without changing the ability to resume immediate multiplication and to support normal growth of phage upon return to 37°C. In experiments with bacteria grown to a titer of 10^9 (latest part of logarithmic growth phase), immersion in ice-water is not necessary, since multiplication stops almost immediately upon interruption of aeration and transfer to room temperature.

Ten minutes after interrupting multiplication, a sample of the culture is diluted and assayed for viable count. If several mixtures of bacteria and phage are to be prepared, the culture may have to be used for one or two hours, in which case at least one other similar assay is made at the end of the experiment to make sure that no proliferation has occurred. At intervals, undiluted samples of the culture are placed into test tubes, and a constant volume of irradiated (or control) phage variously diluted is added. In this way, we know for each mixture the input of bacteria and of phage per ml. For irradiated samples, the input of active phage is determined from one or more assays done at very high dilution. When this is impossible—for high doses of radiation—the amount of active phage is determined by extrapolation from the first part of the inactivation curve.

Adsorption is interrupted by heavy dilution after a short time (generally five or ten minutes). The amount of adsorption is determined either by determination of free phage in the supernatant of a centrifuged sample from a mixture containing active phage, assuming similar adsorption in all other mixtures (see table 1), or by determining the bacterial survival in samples from various mixtures. With the *T-even* phages, 80 to 95 percent of the phage is adsorbed in ten minutes. The value for the multiplicity of infection, x, for each mixture is used in calculating the fraction m of bacteria with two or more phage particles: $m = 1-(x+1)e^{-x}$.

Before lysis begins, a suitably diluted sample of the mixture is plated with an excess of sensitive bacteria for plaque count. The plaque count—corrected, when necessary, for the active phage by subtracting the value corresponding to the latter—is divided by m to obtain the experimental value w for that mixture (see table 4).

A large number of experiments, yielding a total of over 1000 values of w, for various doses of radiation and for different multiplicities, were done with the *T-even* phages. Phage *T5* was only partially investigated, because of difficulties in obtaining reproducible results in view of the low and irregular adsorption rate for this phage.

The data for phages *T-even* include those for several of their r mutants,

TABLE 4

Reactivation of phage T2r in a series of mixtures of irradiated phage with bacteria.
Sample experiment, being a part of Experiment No. 155

Culture of *E. coli B* chilled at 6°C = (B). Bacterial titer by plate count: 1.1×10^8 cells per ml.
Phage *T2r* (stock No. 18c diluted 1:4) irradiated for 20, 30, 40, and 50 seconds.
Control phage, diluted $1:10^7$; 0.1 ml gives 220 plaques. Titer $= 2.2 \times 10^{10}$
Phage irradiated 20 sec., dil. $1:10^4$; 0.1 ml gives 483 plaques. Titer $= 4.8 \times 10^7$. Survival $(e^{-r}) = 2.2 \times 10^{-3}$. $r = 6.1$.
Phage irradiated 30 sec. dil. $1:4 \times 10^3$; 0.1 ml gives 36 plaques. Titer $= 1.45 \times 10^6$. Survival $(e^{-r}) = 6.6 \times 10^{-5}$. $r = 9.6$.

MIXTURE NO.	CONTENTS	PLAQUES PER ML OF MIXTURE (SAMPLES PLATED AFTER 10 MINUTES AT 37°C WITH SUITABLE DILUTION)	PHAGE INPUT	ADSORBED* PHAGE	MULTIPLICITY OF INFECTION x	MULTIPLE-INFECTED BACTERIA m	PLAQUE COUNT**	$\frac{\text{PLAQUE COUNT}}{m} = w$
1	0.1 ml (Phage irrad. 20 sec. dil. 1:2.5)+0.9 ml (B)	9×10^7	8.8×10^8	8.2×10^8	8.2	1×10^8	9×10^7	0.9
2	0.1 ml (Phage irrad. 20 sec. dil. 1:10)+0.9 ml (B)	2×10^7	2.2×10^8	2.05×10^8	2.05	5.5×10^7	2×10^7	0.36
3	0.1 ml (Phage irrad. 30 sec. dil. 1:2.5)+0.9 ml (B)	7.5×10^7	8.8×10^8	8.2×10^8	8.2	1×10^8	7.5×10^7	0.75
4	0.1 ml (Phage irrad. 30 sec. dil. 1:10)+0.9 ml (B)	1×10^7	2.2×10^8	2.05×10^8	2.05	5.5×10^7	1×10^7	0.18
5	0.1 ml (Phage irrad. 30 sec. dil. 1:100)+0.9 ml (B)	2.2×10^5	2.2×10^7	2.05×10^7	0.20	1.6×10^6	2.2×10^5	0.14
6	0.1 ml (Phage irrad. 40 sec. pure)+0.9 ml (B)	8.8×10^7	2.2×10^9	2.05×10^9	20.5	1×10^8	8.8×10^7	0.88
7	0.1 ml (Phage irrad. 40 sec. dil. 1:2.5)+0.9 ml (B)	4.3×10^7	8.8×10^8	8.2×10^8	8.2	1×10^8	4.3×10^7	0.43
8	0.1 ml (Phage irrad. 40 sec. dil. 1:10)+0.9 ml (B)	4.7×10^6	2.2×10^8	2.05×10^8	2.05	5.5×10^7	4.7×10^6	0.085
9	0.1 ml (Phage irrad. 40 sec. dil. 1:100)+0.9 ml (B)	4×10^4	2.2×10^7	2.05×10^7	0.20	1.6×10^6	4×10^4	0.025
10	0.1 ml (Phage irrad. 50 sec. pure)+0.9 ml (B)	5.4×10^7	2.2×10^9	2.05×10^9	20.5	1×10^8	5.4×10^7	0.54
11	0.1 ml (Phage irrad. 50 sec. dil. 1:2.5)+0.9 ml (B)	2.3×10^7	8.8×10^8	8.2×10^8	8.2	1×10^8	2.3×10^7	0.23
12	0.1 ml (Phage irrad. 50 sec. dil. 1:100)+0.9 ml (B)	5.4×10^3	2.2×10^7	2.05×10^7	0.20	1.6×10^6	5.4×10^3	0.0034
13	0.1 ml (Phage Control dil. 1:100)+0.9 ml (B)	2.1×10^7						
	Free in supernatant	1.5×10^6						

* *Determination of adsorption.* Mixture No. 13:
Adsorbed phage $= 2.2 \times 10^7 - 1.5 \times 10^6 = 2.05 \times 10^7$
Fraction adsorbed = 0.93
Bacteria per tube $= 1 \times 10^8$
Multiplicity of infection = 0.205
Infected bacteria (calculated) $= 1.85 \times 10^7$
Infected bacteria + free phage $= 2.0 \times 10^7$
Plaque count (experimental) $= 2.1 \times 10^7$

** No correction is made for active phage in the input, since this correction would only affect the second (or higher) decimal figure.

TABLE 5

Probability of reactivation for various phages as a function of dose and of multiplicity of infection

Values of the ratio w between bacteria that yield active phage and multiple-infected bacteria.

EXPERIMENT NO.	PHAGE	MULTIPLICITY x	AVERAGE NUMBER OF HITS PER PARTICLE						
		r	2.6	4.8	6.0	9.5	10.0	12.5	15.8
		0.2				0.14		0.025	0.0034
		0.4						0.028	0.0055
		1						0.055	0.01
		2			0.36	0.18		0.085	
155	*T2r*	4						0.18	0.08
		8			1.0	0.83		0.48	0.26
		20						0.98	0.6
		0.1		0.56	0.42		0.1		
		0.2	(1.0)	(0.83)	0.40		0.1		
		1	(0.9)	(0.59)	0.44		0.17		
		2			0.5		0.23		
156	*T2r*	4			0.67		0.43		
		8			1.05		0.74		
		20			1.0		1.0		
		r	3.6	6.1	7.9	9.6	11.7	12.8	15.5
		0.2				0.065			
		0.4		0.15		0.075		0.03	
		0.8		0.21		0.1		0.035	
162	*T6r*	2		0.27		0.18		0.05	
		4		0.59		0.26		0.18	
		8		0.83		0.67		0.37	
		0.35	(1)		0.27		0.07		0.016
		0.7	(1)		0.37		0.08		0.016
70	*T6*	1.4			0.37		0.12		0.04
		2.8			0.37		0.14		0.06
		5.6			0.48		0.21		0.08
		r		5			10		
		0.35		0.4			0.027		
160	*T4*	0.7		0.29			0.042		
		1.4		0.28			0.06		
		2.8		0.42			0.13		
		7		0.8			0.38		
		14		1.0			0.77		

The values in parentheses are from separate experiments.

which were found to have the same probability of reactivation as the respective wild types. The results cover ranges of values of r from 2.5 to over 30, and of x from 0.02 to 20.

The individual values of w, and those of the variables, r and x, are obtained from the following actual measurements: 1) titer of phage; 2) total number of bacteria; 3) survival of phage; 4) survival of bacteria and/or assay of free phage; 5) plaque count from the mixture. Each of these measurements involves an error of estimation due to dilution and sampling errors. Several of these determinations, however, are the same within each experiment. The results from individual experiments are, therefore, more consistent than those from different experiments, as shown in table 5.

The only graphic representation that could show all values of w for each phage and allow of comparison with the calculated values of y would be a tri-dimensional plot of w as a function of r and of x. As second best choice, we plotted the values of w as a function of r for several values of x taken as constant, and as a function of x for several values of r taken as constant. Individual values of w fluctuate rather widely, but the data as a whole make it possible to draw curves, which represent averages and which can be considered as the curves for w as a function of r and of x. A number of such plots using all the experimental points for the corresponding values of the variables, are presented in figures 2, 3, and 4 (multiplicity of infection as variable) and figures 5, 6, and 7 (dose of radiation as variable).

The trend of these plots is similar to that of the theoretical curves for y, and it is possible to find for each phage a constant value of n (number of units) such that the corresponding values of y become very similar to those of w for low values of x and for any value of r. That is, it is possible for each phage to determine a constant number of units for which the experimental probability of reactivation equals the theoretical one for any dose of radiation provided the multiplicity of infection is low. The corresponding theoretical curves for y have been drawn in the plots of the values of w. For phage *T2*, the best fit is for $n=25$; for *T4*, $n=15$; for *T6*, $n=30$ (see especially figures 5, 6, and 7).

The main feature emerging from the curves in figures 2, 3, and 4 is that the values of w tend to unity for increasing multiplicity of infection. In several cases, the number of cells that liberate phage actually reaches the number of multiple-infected cells, but in no case does it go beyond it, proving that reactivation does not occur in single-infected cells.

The curves in figures 5, 6, 7, for w as a function of r, are of the multiple-hit type, indicating that suppression of phage production depends on damage in a number of elements. The values of w tend to unity for low doses, again showing that reactivation potentially can take place in every multiple-infected cell.

Comparison in figures 2–4 with the curves for y, chosen to fit the experimental curves for low values of x, shows that the general similarity is limited by a systematic deviation. As the multiplicity increases, both w and y tend asymptotically to unity, but w increases more slowly. This means that, as the number of phage particles per bacterium increases, the probability of reacti-

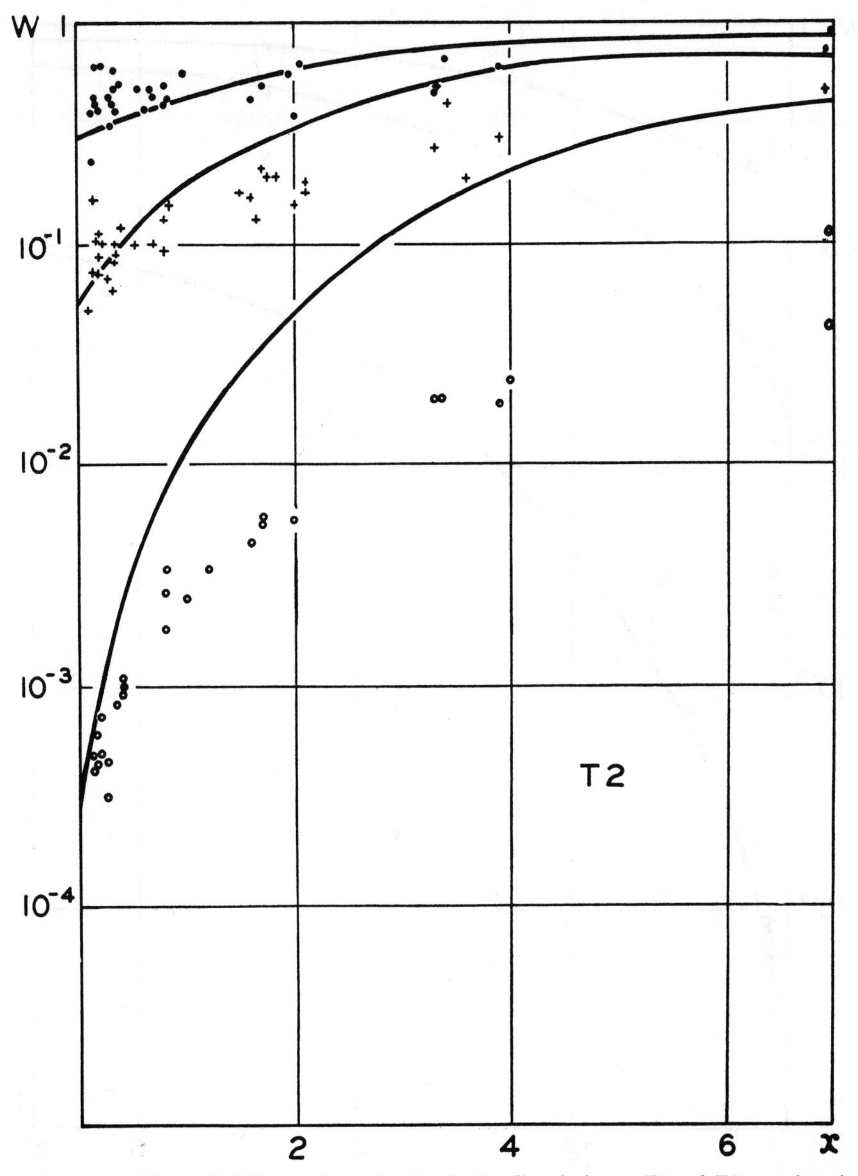

FIGURE 2.—The probability w of reactivation for irradiated phages *T2* and *T2r* as a function of the multiplicity of infection x, for several doses of radiation. Abscissae: values of x. Ordinates: values of w.

● values of w for $r = 6$ hits per particle.
+ values of w for $r = 10$ hits per particle.
○ values of w for $r = 20$ hits per particle.

Solid lines: theoretical curves for y as a function of x for $n = 25$, and for the values of r given above.

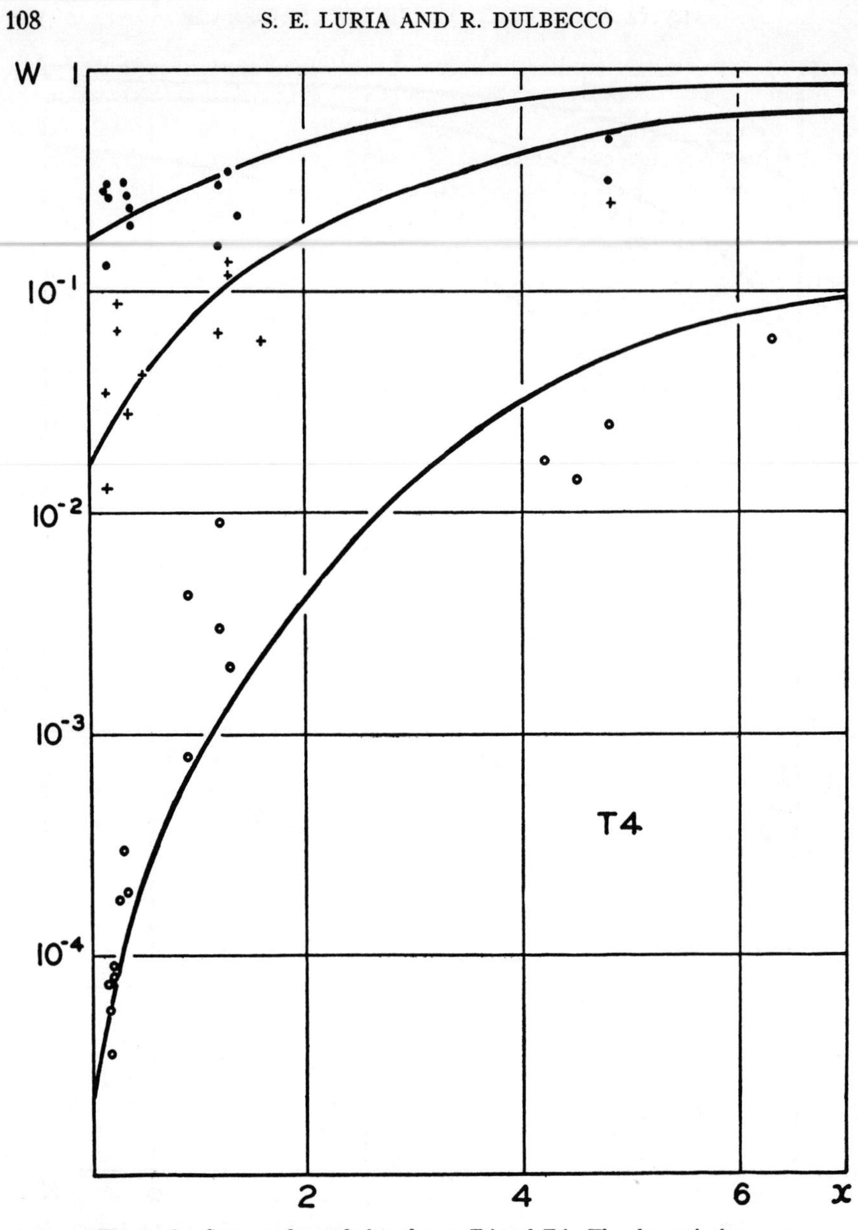

FIGURE 3.—Same as figure 2, for phages *T4* and *T4r*. The theoretical curves for y correspond to $n=15$.

vation, while steadily increasing, does not keep pace with the theoretical function y. The cooperation within groups consisting of more than two particles is not as successful in bringing about reactivation as required by the simple theory, whereas pairs of particles apparently collaborate with an efficiency of one hundred percent.

The deviation for higher multiplicities is reflected in the curves of figures 5–7. The curves for w as a function of the dose are very close to the theoretical curves for low multiplicities, up to $x=0.5$; for higher multiplicities they fall below the corresponding curves for y calculated for the same number of units. We can actually find, for each value of x, a curve for y—for the same n but corresponding to a lower x—which fits the experimental curve. The corresponding theoretical curves are drawn in figures 5–7. This indicates that groups of more than two particles collaborate in reactivation as if they consisted of a lower but definite number of particles.

It is interesting to notice that the systematic deviation from theory for

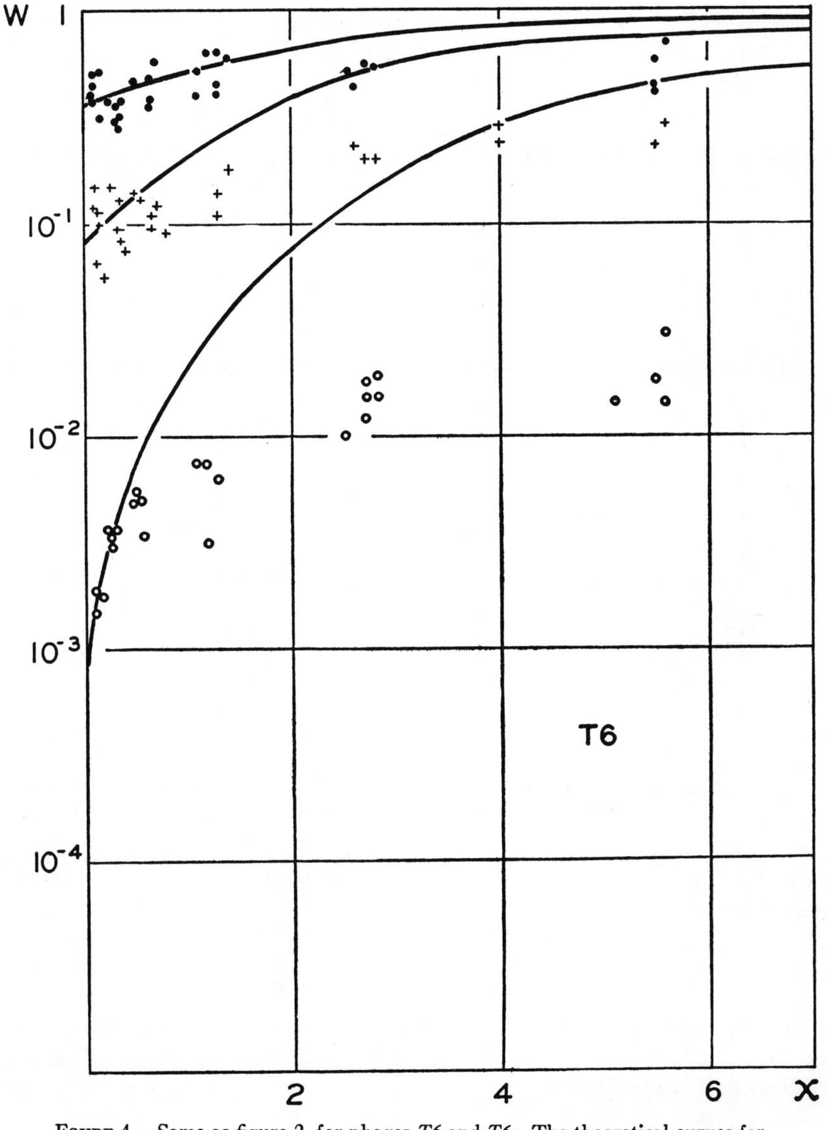

FGURE 4.—Same as figure 2, for phages *T6* and *T6r*. The theoretical curves for y correspond to $n=30$.

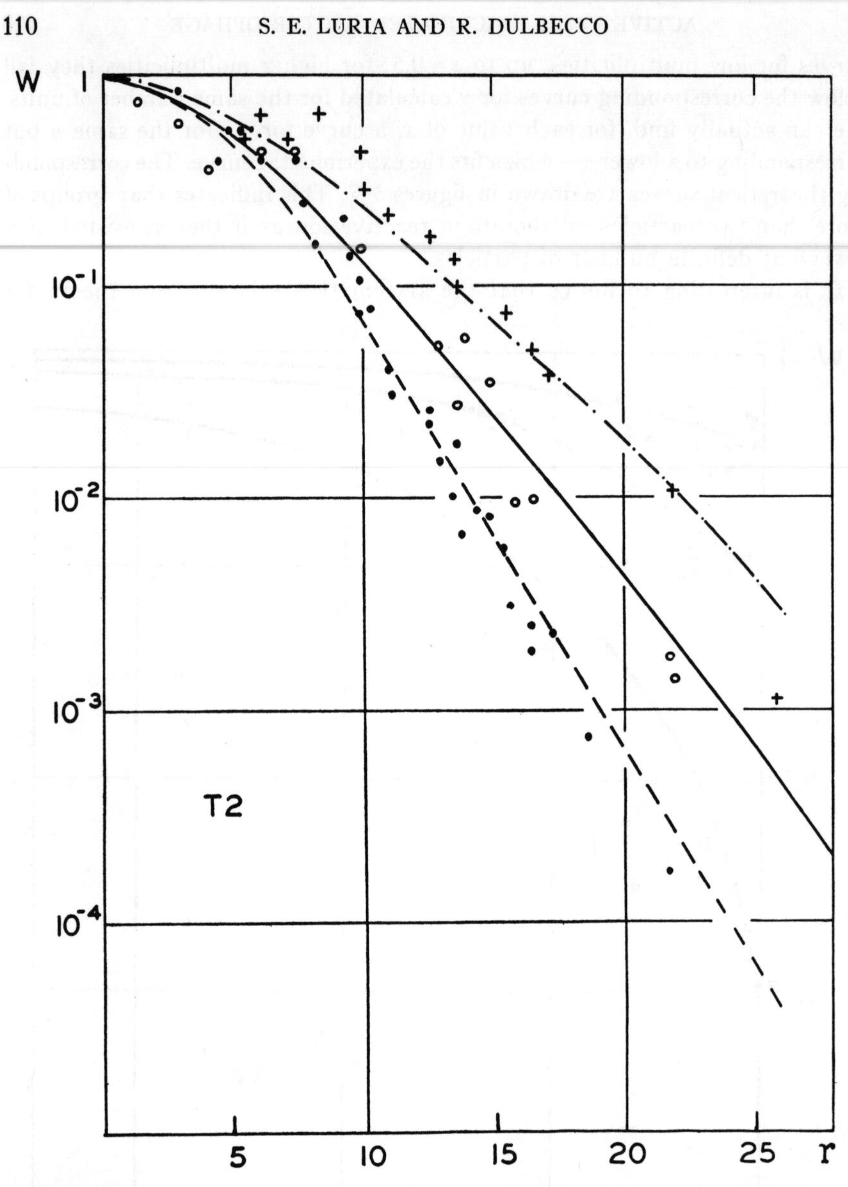

FIGURE 5.—The probability w of reactivation for phages *T2* and *T2r* as a function of the dose of irradiation r (in hits per particle) for several multiplicities. Abscissae: values of r. Ordinates: values of w.

● values of w for $x=0.1$–0.2.
○ values of w for $x=0.8$–1.5.
+ values of w for $x=2.5$–4.0.

Broken line: theoretical curve for y as a function of r for $n=25$, $x=0.15$. Solid line: theoretical curve for y as a function of r for $n=25$, $x=0.6$. Broken and dotted line: theoretical curve for y as a function of r for $n=25$, $x=1.3$.

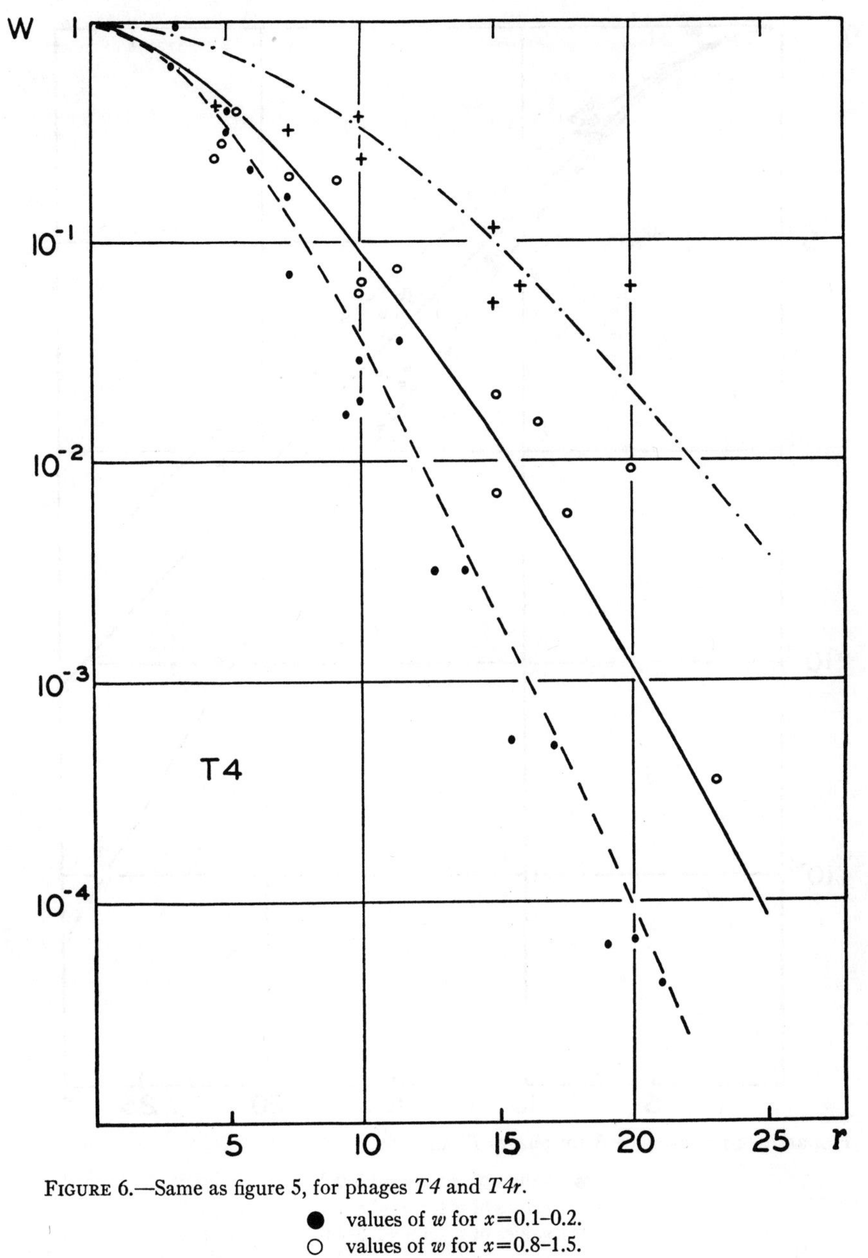

FIGURE 6.—Same as figure 5, for phages *T4* and *T4r*.

● values of w for x=0.1–0.2.
○ values of w for x=0.8–1.5.
+ values of w for x=4–7.

Broken line: curve of y for n=15, x=0.15. Solid line: curve of y for n=15, x=1.1. Broken and dotted line: curve of y for n=15, x=4.0.

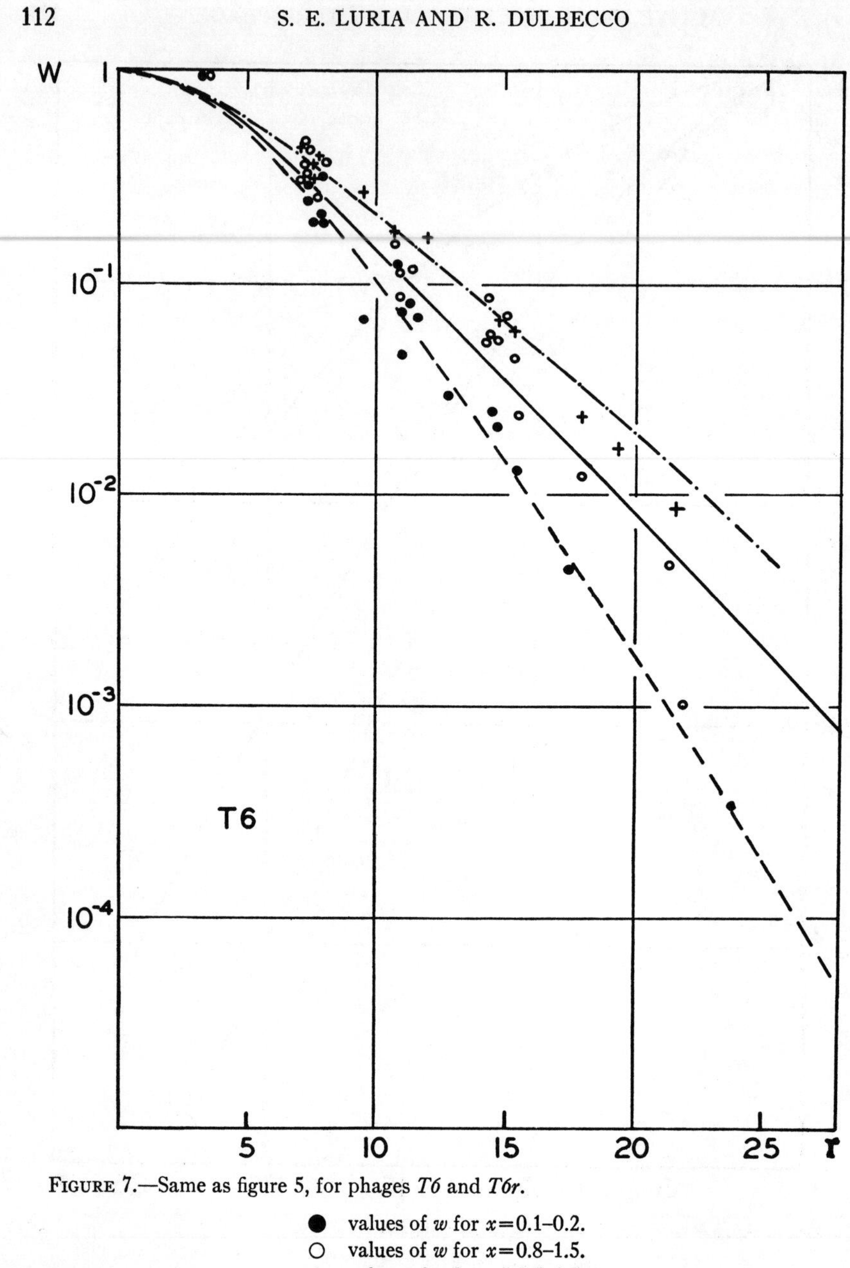

FIGURE 7.—Same as figure 5, for phages *T6* and *T6r*.

● values of w for x=0.1–0.2.
○ values of w for x=0.8–1.5.
+ values of w for x=2.5–4.0.

Broken line: curve of y for n=30, x=0.15. Solid line: curve of y for n=30, x=0.5. Broken and dotted line: curve of y for n=30, x=0.9.

increasing multiplicities is less evident for phages *T2* than for *T6*, and still less for *T4*, diminishing in the same order as the calculated number of units.

To summarize, the results show that the probability of production of active phage from inactive particles depends on the dose of radiation and on the multiplicity of infection in a way similar to the one predicted by the simple theory, which assumes lethal mutations in discrete transferable units of equal radiation sensitivity and a hundred percent efficient recombination of active units to reconstitute active particles. All deviations can be accounted for by a limitation in the efficiency of recombination when the active units derive from more than two inactive particles.

Several explanations may be offered for this limitation; some of them have been tested experimentally. Lysis from without—failure to liberate phage due to excessive multiplicity of infection (DELBRÜCK 1940)—was found not to take place for multiplicities of the order of those for which the deviations from theory occur. Limitations in the number of particles of a given phage that can participate in phage growth were looked for and found (see DULBECCO 1949a), but their magnitude cannot account for the differences between w and y.

The process of reactivation must involve complex mechanisms of transfer of genetic material among phage particles. Whatever these mechanisms, it is reasonable to expect that they will work less efficiently as the number of phage particles increases. Limitations may conceivably be caused by steric reasons—shape of the particles, position in the bacterium—or by physiological reasons—limited number of units of some catalyst, competition for substrates.

Estimation of the number of units

We have compared our results with the theoretical curves for y calculated for different values of n, the unknown number of transferable units per particle. The curves that best fit the results for phages *T2* and *T2r* are those for $n=25$; for *T6* and *T6r*, $n=30$; for *T4* and *T4r*, $n=15$. For phage *T5*, no accurate estimate of n was obtained, but n appears to be lower than for *T4*.

If the interpretation of the results based on the simple theory is justified, we must consider the values thus obtained for n as minimum estimates of the number of radiation-sensitive, transferable units per phage particle. The estimates are minima because of the assumption of equal sensitivity of all units. Should there be units more sensitive than others, they would be hit more often, and in order to obtain the correct probability of reactivation we should assume more units of the less sensitive type. For example, if one unit were twice as sensitive as the average of the others, one locus of the average sensitivity should be added to our estimate in order to distribute the probability of inactivation over all units in such a way that the reactivation probability remains the same.

In our preliminary report (LURIA 1947) we calculated n in a different manner, by assuming that for low multiplicities and low doses, where the probability of reactivation appeared to be approximately constant as a function of x, we could consider all multiple-infected bacteria as double-infected. This corresponded to putting $k=2$ in formula (6) and to comparing the experimental values of w with the values of y for $x=0$. Upon closer analysis, this method proved incorrect, because the contribution of higher multiple infection cannot be neglected, even for low multiplicities. Analysis of more data showed that the probability of reactivation is in fact not constant for low values of x, but appears to be so for low doses, because the differences are small and of the order of the experimental errors. The use of the wrong approximation made our previous estimates of n too high.

Yield of active phage from bacteria in which reactivation occurs

The yield of active phage following reactivation was studied systematically for phages *T2r* and *T4*. After infection, bacteria were diluted and allowed to lyse in liquid, as in a typical "one-step growth" experiment. The latent period before lysis is somewhat longer than for active phage (about 26 minutes instead of 21 for *T2*, 30 minutes instead of 25 for *T4*), and the rise in phage titer upon liberation somewhat slower. All yields were calculated from plaque counts after the titer had reached a steady level. The results, shown in table 6, indicate that the yields are generally somewhat lower than those from bacteria infected with active phage particles. No clear relation of yield to dose of radiation or to probability of reactivation was detected. For *T2r* irradiated with high doses, there is a certain tendency toward higher yields for higher multiplicities.

Mixed infection with active and inactive phage

Transfer of genetic material involved in reactivation must occur between active and inactive phage particles, since, as we saw before, an active particle of a *T-even* phage can reactivate an inactive particle of another *T-even* phage. If transfer occurred by reciprocal exchanges of genetic material, we should expect that upon mixed infection with active and inactive particles of the same phage some of the active particles would receive inactive units and, therefore, be inactivated. This possibility was tested for phages *T2* and *T4* by experiments of the following type.

Bacteria are added to mixtures containing various proportions of active phage and of phage of the same strain irradiated with different doses. For each mixture, the average numbers of active and of inactive particles adsorbed per bacterium are calculated and, hence, the number of bacteria receiving both active and inactive phage. A plaque count before lysis gives the number of bacteria that liberate phage, while a plaque count after lysis gives the yield of phage per bacterium. In this manner, we can determine whether inactive phage suppresses production of active phage from bacteria that also adsorb an active particle, or possibly affects the yield.

The results of these tests can be listed as follows:

(a) a bacterium receiving an active particle plus one inactive particle of the same phage—no matter how many hits the latter has received—never fails to liberate active phage;

(b) part of the bacteria that adsorb one active particle plus several inactive ones (the latter carrying enough lethal hits, so that reactivation does not occur among them) fail to liberate active phage. This suppression of active phage production is evident for multiplicities 5 or higher of inactive phage *T4*, and for multiplicities 8 or higher of inactive phage *T2*. The suppression is independent of the time allowed for adsorption of the phages. It may in part be

TABLE 6

The yield of active phage from bacteria in which reactivation takes place

PHAGE	MULTIPLICITY OF INFECTION	DOSE				
		HITS	0	6	12	18
T2r	0.2–0.25		114	51	122	
	0.5–0.6		50	42	22	
	2.9		89		100	29
	7.7		59			60
	9		100	70	94	
	10–11		73	120	59	130
		HITS	0	7.5	15	18
T4	0.65		260	120	87	200
	1.1		200	87	162	
	1.6		275		140	140
	2.7		212		197	
	7–8				135	200
	14–15				250	85

accounted for by the limitation phenomenon described by the junior author (DULBECCO 1949a);

(c) for those bacteria that liberate active phage, the yield per bacterium is not affected by the presence of inactive particles, but remains the same as in controls without the inactive phage;

(d) when bacteria are infected with several heavily irradiated particles that do not give reactivation, and a few minutes later with one active particle, suppression of phage production occurs in a proportion of bacteria that increases with the interval between infections. Suppression is evident with an interval of 2.5 to 4 minutes and practically complete after 10 minutes. These time intervals between infections are, of course, averages, since infection may occur earlier or later for individual bacteria in the same mixture. The yield from those bacteria that liberate phage still remains normal.

The suppression of active phage reproduction by inactive phage in excess indicates the existence of some type of "mutual exclusion" between particles of the same phage. Such exclusion is also indicated by the experiments of DULBECCO (1949a).

More detailed analysis of the interaction between active and inactive phage, using genetic markers, will be reported in future papers. Our results discussed above are in agreement with earlier observations (LURIA and DELBRÜCK 1942) on interference by a large excess of irradiated phage *T2* with the growth of active phage *T2* when the inactive phage was mixed with bacteria one minute and a half before the active one.

Cross-reactivation between phage particles differing by one character

Only one group of experiments will be discussed here, because of its bearing on the analysis of the data presented in this article. Bacteria were infected with

TABLE 7

Cross-reactivation between one inactive particle of phage T2 and one inactive particle of phage T2r

Compare column (3) with column (1)

EXPERIMENT NO.	DOSE OF RADIATION, HITS	MULTIPLICITY OF INFECTION FOR *T2*	MULTIPLICITY OF INFECTION FOR *T2r*	(1) FRACTION OF BACTERIA RECEIVING *one* INACTIVE PARTICLE *T2* AND *one* INACTIVE PARTICLE *T2r* AMONG THE BACTERIA THAT LIBERATE ACTIVE PHAGE, CALCULATED	(2)* OTHER BACTERIA THAT COULD GIVE MOTTLED PLAQUES (AS FRACTION OF THE BACTERIA THAT LIBERATE ACTIVE PHAGE), CALCULATED	(3) FRACTION OF MOTTLED PLAQUES, FOUND
1A	2.9	0.055	0.055	0.19	0.045	0.14
2A	4.6	0.055	0.049	0.335	0.053	0.16
3A	6.2	0.055	0.055	0.42	0.074	0.155
4A	3.4	0.053	0.053	0.24	0.046	0.14
5A	5.0	0.053	0.053	0.355	0.068	0.20
7A	3.9	0.05	0.05	0.28	0.046	0.14
8A	6.5	0.05	0.05	0.19	0.087	0.21

* The values in this column include all bacteria with two or more particles of one type and one or more of the other type, plus all bacteria with an active particle of one type and an inactive particle of the other. The values are upper limits, since only a fraction of these bacteria will actually give mottled plaques.

phages *T2* and *T2r*, both irradiated ($r = 5$ or 6). Low multiplicities were used, so that a large proportion of the infected bacteria only received one inactive particle, and, of those that received two, a great proportion received one particle of each type. The infected bacteria were plated before lysis, and the plaques examined for the proportion of "mottled plaques," that is, of plaques containing both *T2* and *T2r* active phages. Such plaques can only arise from bacteria infected with both phages. It is seen from the data shown in table 7 that more than half the bacteria infected with one inactive particle of each of the two phages actually liberate a mixture of active particles of both types.

This proves that recombination cannot result from reciprocal exchanges of units between the infecting particles bringing together into one particle all the active units before multiplication begins. Evidently, this particle should be either *T2* or *T2r*, and could not give rise to active particles of both types. This conclusion will be analyzed further in the discussion. Quantitative analysis of the number and contents of mixed yields from mixed infection with *T2* and *T2r* shall be the subject of future publications.

Phages inactivated by X-rays or nitrogen mustard

In a preliminary article (LURIA 1947) it was stated that no reactivation had been detected for *T-even* phages inactivated by hard X-rays, using the same technique employed for ultraviolet. The same was found in our laboratory by MISS M. E. WILLIS for phages *T2* and *T6* inactivated by a nitrogen mustard (methyl bis (β-chloroethyl) amine hydrochloride).

Experiments by MR. J. WATSON, still in progress in our laboratory, have recently shown, however, that phage *T2* inactivated by hard X-rays can take part in reactivation, but this reactivation occurs with such a low probability that special techniques are required for its detection. In part, the low probability of reactivation of X-ray inactivated phage is due to reduced rate of adsorption. This work will be reported by Mr. WATSON in a future publication.

It seems possible that phages *T1* and *T7*, for which no reactivation was detected after ultraviolet inactivation, may also be found by similar techniques to give some reactivation. It is clear that the probability of reactivation will be low if the number of transferable units is small, or if each lethal mutation involves several units. Its detection will be difficult whenever the number of bacteria in which reactivation occurs is small in comparison with the number of bacteria that receive residual active phage.[4]

DISCUSSION

The experiments described above have given results consistent with the hypothesis that inactivation of several and possibly all bacteriophages by ultraviolet light is to be attributed to lethal mutations in discrete units of genetic material. A genetic basis for inactivation of viruses and bacteria by radiation has often been postulated either on statistical grounds or by analogy (see RAHN 1929; LEA 1947). Our results bring new support to this view, and suggest that most, if not all, the inactivating effect of ultraviolet light (2537 Å) on certain phages is due to the production of localized lethal mutations.

The hypothesis of inactivation by lethal mutations and reactivation by transfer of genetic material following multiple infection, as developed in this paper, has been useful in suggesting a quantitative analysis of the reactivation phenomena and has led to fairly accurate predictions of the experimental results. The following discussion assumes the correctness of this working hypothesis.

[4] While this paper was in press, the senior author found that some reactivation by multiple infection takes place with phage *T1* inactivated by ultraviolet light. For equal multiplicity of infection and equal number of hits, the frequency of reactivation is much lower with *T1* than with any of the *T-even* phages and with *T5*. Assuming that the type of analysis presented in this paper applies to the results with *T1*, a value of n smaller than 5 would be obtained.

According to our analysis, active phage is reconstituted from inactive by reincorporation of active units derived, directly or indirectly, from the inactive particles in a kind of hybridization. As in hybridization, the possibility of recombinations between particles of different wild-type phages suggests the existence of common genetic determinants and the absence of complete incompatibility. It is possible that various interference phenomena among different phages may result from such an incompatibility.

Reassembly of material from inactive particles into active ones is a remarkably efficient process. Genetic material from several inactive particles may be brought together, although the relative efficiency of cooperation diminishes as the number of particles involved in this pluriparental reproduction increases.

We have given estimates for the minimum number of transferable units per particle for several phages. It is interesting to notice that phage *T4*, more resistant than the related phages *T2* and *T6* to ultraviolet light (figure 1), appears to have fewer units. This may indicate absence of a portion of genetic material present in the other *T-even* phages.

LEA and SALAMAN (1946), analyzing the dependence of the rate of inactivation of phages by X-rays as a function of the density of ionization, and assuming that the radiosensitive material consisted of spherical units, arrived at the conclusion that a large phage contained 14 such units, whereas a small phage contained one only. Although the hypotheses involved were probably oversimplifications, the conclusion receives qualitative support from our results.

We must consider next the possible mechanisms of genetic transfer. We may divide the mechanisms into two groups, those in which the reproducing element is supposed to be at all times the phage particle as a whole, and those in which the reproducing elements are assumed to be component parts of the particle.

The simplest hypothesis of the first group would be that reactivation results from pairing (or grouping) or the initial infecting particles, followed by reciprocal exchanges such as occur in chromosomal crossing-over; if these exchanges lead to formation of an active particle, the latter proceeds to multiply. This simple hypothesis can easily be disproved. The high efficiency of reactivation would require very large numbers of successive reciprocal exchanges to bring together all active genetic material before multiplication takes place. Mixed infection with one active and one inactive particle should also lead to the occasional loss of active phage, since we know that genetic recombinations occur between active and inactive particles. Finally, the fact that infection with one particle each of inactive *T2* and inactive *T2r* yields a mixture of active *T2* and active *T2r* disproves this hypothesis, since any number of reciprocal exchanges between the original particles *before multiplication* could never lead to formation of active particles of both types.

Another interpretation based on reciprocal exchanges would be that inactive particles reproduce, and that exchanges occur at various stages of the reproduction among the original particles or their inactive offspring. These exchanges should be numerous enough to make the probability of incorporation of all active units into an active particle close to unity, and an active particle, once formed, should be favored in multiplication. Without completely disproving it, our results make this explanation very unlikely. The fact that the probability of reactivation increases greatly by increasing (for example, from 8 to 20) the multiplicity of infection with heavily irradiated particles would require a very high number of exchanges. To obtain high yields of active phage in these cases we should assume, moreover, that the exchanges take place early, and that the active particles, once formed, multiply with little or no interference from the inactive particles in large excess. This seems contradicted by the fact already mentioned that active particles can actually undergo interchanges with inactive ones. Altogether, there is strong evidence that inactive units have less chance than active units of entering the final particles, even when the active units derive from inactive particles.

In search for a mechanism that could selectively bring together the active units, the senior author (LURIA 1947) suggested the hypothesis of independent reproduction of individual units to form a "gene pool," from which the new active particles could be derived. Inactive units were considered to be those that cannot reproduce and that have, therefore, little chance of incorporation into the final particles. The tendency to reduction in yield may be due to occasional incorporation of some of the original inactive units. No hypothesis is made as to how the units reproduce or reassemble. The last step is the most difficult to visualize, and we incline to the belief that the original particles may play a role in it, possibly by supplying a framework for reassembly. This is suggested by the limited efficiency of collaboration among large groups of particles, which indicates a certain tendency of the units to remain together with their original companions.

One may ask whether, inside bacteria in which reactivation does not take place, the active units present in the infecting particles reproduce or not. COHEN (1948) states that no desoxyribose nucleic acid is synthesized in bacteria infected with particles of *T2* exposed to doses of ultraviolet light much higher than those employed in our study. Preliminary cytological evidence, collected with the collaboration of DR. C. F. ROBINOW in our laboratory, indicates that in infected bacteria, in which reactivation does not take place, there is no accumulation of stainable material supposedly representing desoxyribose nucleotides. If this evidence is confirmed and found to apply to the conditions of our experiments, it might then suggest, either that there is no reproduction of active units when they are not all present (which might altogether invalidate the hypothesis of independent reproduction), or that at least part of the reproduction of the active units may take place without increase in desoxyribose nucleotides.

The hypothesis of a "gene pool," although by no means the only possible one,[5] fits all results of reactivation. Its validity may soon be amenable to

[5] Another possibility, suggested by DR. A. H. STURTEVANT, would be a process of zipperwise replication of the various units of a phage particle. When in this process an inactive unit was reached, replication could only continue if the partial replica came in contact with another phage particle in which that unit was active. The process would then continue by addition of replicas of the active units of the second phage particle. If repeated several times, such a mechanism would provide for selective recombination of all active units.

critical test. In postulating a phase in phage growth in which particles, as we know them in the extracellular phase, are not present, the hypothesis accounts for the repeated failures to obtain active phage by premature artificial disruption of infected bacteria. It agrees with the observation made by FOSTER (1948) in our laboratory that in the presence of proflavine the reactions leading to production of active phage proceed normally for a part of the latent period, but, upon lysis, no active particle is liberated. According to FOSTER (1948) active phage particles are present in the infected bacterium after the proflavine sensitive stage is passed—beginning 12 to 14 minutes after infection for phages *T2* or *T6*. A similar conclusion was reached by A. H. DOERMANN on the basis of experiments on the effect of other inhibitors on the growth of *T3* and *T4r* (DOERMANN 1948). That viruses multiplying inside the host cell may not have the same organization as in the extracellular form has been suggested before for certain animal viruses (see BLAND and ROBINOW 1939).

Our theory does not assume any degree of linkage among units, although linkage may be compatible with the theory. Each group of strongly linked units would behave as one unit, possibly as a particularly sensitive one. Weakly linked units would probably reduce the probability of reactivation for high doses, when lethal units present in one group would hinder the utilization of the linked active units for reactivation.

In their work on the *r* and *h* mutants of phage *T2 H*, HERSHEY and ROTMAN (1948, 1949) found evidence for a series of determinants exhibiting various degrees of linkage, from those apparently unlinked (high frequency of independent transfer, no correlation between the frequencies of complementary recombinant types in the yield) to others rather strongly linked. For the latter ones, the authors considered that their results suggested the possibility of reciprocal exchanges.

As a working hypothesis we may assume, together with HERSHEY and ROTMAN (1949) that unlinked determinants may be located in different reactivation units, possibly transferred by a gene pool mechanism, while linked determinants may be located in the same reactivation unit. If reciprocal exchanges were found to occur, then homologous units or groups of units should be supposed to pair or group together at some stage in the growth process. Techniques recently developed in our laboratory should soon permit a study of the inactivation of individual genetic determinants and a solution of some of these problems. It appears, therefore, advisable to refrain from further discussion at the present time.

The formation of active phage from inactive by transfer of discrete units requires some revision of the interpretation of experiments on irradiation of phage inside infected bacteria with ultraviolet light (LURIA and LATARJET 1947). In case of multiple infection, the survival curves for phage-producing ability immediately after infection indicated suppression by damage of a number of centers, with the sensitivity of individual centers lower than that of extracellular phage particles. It now seems clear that what was measured was the rate of inactivation of individual units rather than of whole particles. The curves for suppression of the phage-producing ability of multiple-infected bacteria immediately after infection are similar to the curves for the probability of reactivation for a comparable group of irradiated particles. For example, the suppression curve given by LURIA and LATARJET (1947) for bacteria infected by five particles of phage *T2* is very similar to the curve for the probability of reactivation w as a function of r for $x=5$. It is clear that in interpreting experiments on inactivation of intracellular phage it will be necessary to take into account the occurrence of genetic transfers.[6]

SUMMARY

Coli-bacteriophages *T2*, *T4*, *T5*, and *T6* inactivated by ultraviolet light are still adsorbed by sensitive bacteria. Bacteria infected by only one inactive phage particle are not lysed and do not yield active phage. Infection of bacteria with more than one inactive particle leads to lysis and production of active phage in a fraction of the bacteria. This fraction diminishes with increasing doses of radiation and increases with increasing numbers of particles adsorbed per bacterium. The assumption is made that inactivation is due to lethal mutations in a number of genetic "units" of the phage particle, and that production of active phage from inactive is due to recombination of non-lethal units to form active particles. The values of the probability of active phage production calculated from these assumptions agree with the experimental results with certain limitations. In order to explain the very high frequency of recombination, the hypothesis is proposed that phage growth occurs by independent reproduction of each unit followed by reassembly of the units into complete phage particles. The minimum number of units per particle is estimated for various phages.

LITERATURE CITED

BLAND, J. O. W., and C. F. ROBINOW, 1939 The inclusion bodies of vaccinia and their relationship to the elementary bodies studied in cultures of the rabbit's cornea. J. Path. Bact. **48:** 381–403.

COHEN, S. S., 1948 The synthesis of bacterial viruses. I. The synthesis of nucleic acid and protein in *Escherichia coli* B infected with $T2r^+$ bacteriophage. J. Biol. Chem. **174:** 281–293.

DELBRÜCK, M., 1940 The growth of bacteriophage and lysis of the host. J. Gen. Physiol. **23:** 643–660.

1946 Bacterial viruses or bacteriophages. Biol. Rev. Cambridge Phil. Soc. **21:** 30–40.

DELBRÜCK, M., and W. T. BAILEY, JR., 1946 Induced mutations in bacterial viruses. Cold Spring Harbor Symp. Quant. Biol. **11:** 33–37.

DELBRÜCK, M., and S. E. LURIA, 1942 Interference between bacterial viruses. I. Interference between two bacterial viruses acting upon the same host, and the mechanism of virus growth. Arch. Biochem. **1:** 111–141.

DOERMANN, A. H., 1948 Intracellular growth of bacteriophage. Carnegie Instn. Wash. Yearb. (in press).

[6] While this paper was in press, one of us (DULBECCO 1949b) discovered that ultraviolet irradiated phages can be reactivated by exposure to visible light of short wave length in presence of bacterial cells. This "photoreactivation" differs from reactivation by multiple infection in many of its features. Photoreactivation does not take place to any appreciable extent under the conditions in which the experiments reported in this paper were performed. A series of experiments of the type exemplified in table 4, but carried out in dim yellow light—under conditions that completely avoid photoreactivation—gave results undistinguishable from those of the earlier experiments, in which no precaution had been taken to control illumination.

DULBECCO, R., 1949a The number of particles of bacteriophage *T2* that can participate in intracellular growth. Genetics **34:** (in press).

——— 1949b Reactivation of ultraviolet inactivated bacteriophage by visible light. Nature (in press).

FOSTER, R. A. C., 1948 An analysis of the action of proflavine on bacteriophage growth. J. Bact. **56:** 795–809.

HERSHEY, A. D., and R. ROTMAN, 1948 Linkage among genes controlling inhibition of lysis in a bacterial virus. Proc. nat. Acad. Sci. **34:** 89–96.

1949 Genetic recombination between host-range and plaque-type mutants of bacteriophage in single bacterial cells. Genetics **34:** 44–71.

LATARJET, R., and R. WAHL, 1945 Précisions sur l'inactivation des bactériophages par les rayons ultraviolets. Ann. Inst. Pasteur **71:** 336–339.

LEA, D. E., 1947 Actions of radiations on living cells. xii+402 pp. Cambridge: University Press.

LEA, D. E., and M. H. SALAMAN, 1946 Experiments on the inactivation of bacteriophage by radiations, and their bearing on the nature of bacteriophage. Proc. roy. Soc., B, **133:** 434–444.

LURIA, S. E., 1947 Reactivation of irradiated bacteriophage by transfer of self-reproducing units. Proc. nat. Acad. Sci. **33:** 253–264.

1948 Bacteriophage mutations and genetic interactions among bacteriophage particles inside the host cell. A.A.A.S. Symposium on Genetics of Microorganisms (in press).

LURIA, S. E., and M. DELBRÜCK, 1942 Interference between bacterial viruses. II. Interference between inactivated bacterial virus and active virus of the same strain and of a different strain. Arch. Biochem. **1:** 207–218.

LURIA, S. E., and R. LATARJET, 1947 Ultraviolet irradiation of bacteriophage during intracellular growth. J. Bact. **53:** 149–163.

RAHN, O., 1929 The size of bacteria as the cause of the logarithmic order of death. J. gen. Physiol. **13:** 179–205.

APPENDIX

ON THE RELIABILITY OF THE POISSON DISTRIBUTION AS A DISTRIBUTION OF THE NUMBER OF PHAGE PARTICLES INFECTING INDIVIDUAL BACTERIA IN A POPULATION

R. DULBECCO

In calculating the average number x of phage particles adsorbed per bacterium (multiplicity of infection) from the number of uninfected bacteria, and, from x, the proportion of bacteria with any given number k of particles, the assumption is made that the distribution of particles per bacterium is a Poisson distribution. One limitation to this assumption may arise from differences in the surface area of individual bacteria. This limitation was analyzed as follows.

In a mixture of P particles and B bacteria, each phage particle has a probability $p=c(1/B)$ to be adsorbed by a given bacterial cell. In actual cases where P and B are large and c is between 0.4 and 0.9, we have : $x=cP/B$.

If c is constant for all bacteria, the distribution of k is a Poisson distribution; if not, the distribution of k will be different. We assume, in first approximation, that the adsorption capacity of a bacterium is proportional to its surface, and that the surface is proportional to the length—considering bacteria as cylinders with uniform diameter and negligible end surfaces.

The distribution of bacterial lengths was obtained experimentally on standard cultures of *E. coli* B containing 10^8 cells per ml. Negative stains with nigrosin were made without fixation, and, after the slides were dried, 764 cells were measured with an ocular micrometer (Filar). The distribution of lengths is given in figure 8, and will be referred to as the "B distribution." Measurements on five cultures gave similar distributions.

For the purpose of obtaining the distribution of phage particles adsorbed per bacterial cell, or "P distribution," we shall split the bacterial population in-

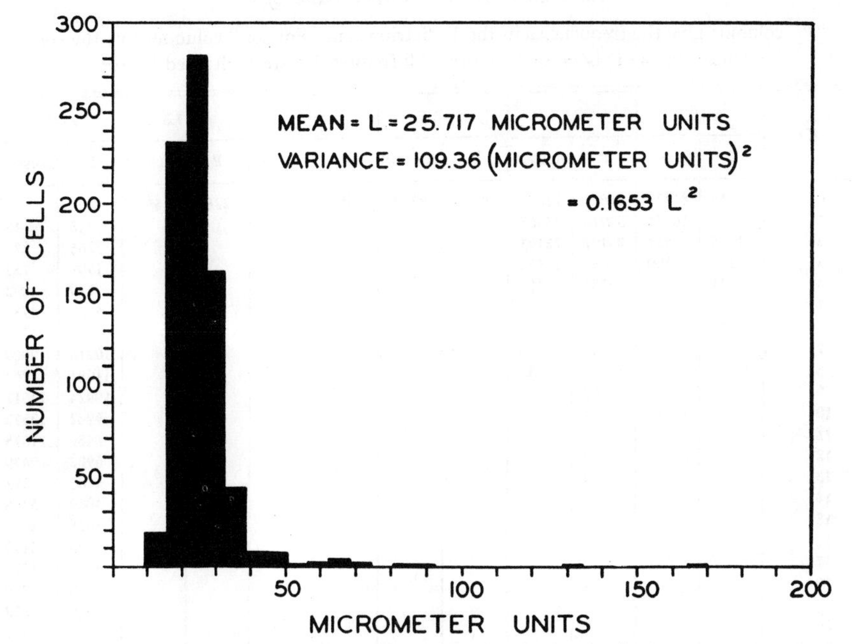

FIGURE 8.—The distribution of bacterial lengths in standard cultures of *Escherichia coli* strain B containing 10^8 cells per ml.

to a number of subpopulations, each comprehending one of the length classes in figure 8, and assume that the adsorption capacity of all cells within each subpopulation is constant.

By the calculation given at the end of this paper, the following properties of the P distribution are derived:

a) its arithmetic mean is equal to x, that is, to the multiplicity of infection, as for a Poisson distribution.

b) its variance is equal to the variance x of the Poisson distribution, plus a term equal to the variance of the B distribution: $\text{var}(P) = x + \text{var}(B)$.

If we express the variance in terms of the mean x taken as the unit of measure, we obtain for our experimental cultures: $\text{var}(P) = x + 0.1653x^2$. This equation expresses the relation between the variance of the P distribution for an ideal population with uniform capacity of adsorption and the variance for a real population with a capacity of adsorption distributed with a given variance.

The P distributions for several values of x, calculated from the actual B distribution, are given in table 8, together with the Poisson distributions for the same values of x. It is clear that for low multiplicities of infection there is little difference between actual and Poisson distributions. For higher multiplicities, the discrepancies increase; still, for $x=1.5$, they only affect relevantly the proportions of bacteria with 5 or more particles.

TABLE 8

The P distribution for various values of x

"P" columns give the frequencies in the P distribution, "Poisson" columns give the frequencies in the Poisson distribution. All frequencies are multiplied by 10^5.

K	x=0.2		x=1.5		x=2.5		x=5		x=7.5		x=10	
	P	POISSON	P	POISSON	P	POISSON	P	POISSON	P	POISSON	P	POISSON
0	82115	81873	24686	22313	10400	8208	1409	674	228	55	32	5
1	15977	16374	32918	33468							218	45
2	1735	1637	23197	25101							765	227
3	155	109	11658	12551							1908	757
4	14	6	4751	4707							3739	1892
5	2		1721	1412							6065	3784
6			611	353							8411	6303
7			238	76							10218	9009
8			109	14							11081	11261
9			62	2							10924	12512
10			38								9942	12512
11			29								8489	11375
12			19								6902	9479
13			12								5383	7292
14			8								4089	5208
15			5								3036	3472
16			3								2219	2170
17			1								1600	1276
18			1								1140	709
19											810	373
20											579	187
21–23											931	147
24–26											464	11
27–30											293	
31–33											172	
34–36											110	
37–39											67	
>39											305	

The calculation of x from the bacterial survival—assuming (B uninfected)$/B=e^{-x}$—only gives reliable results for values of x up to about 2. For higher multiplicities, it leads to an underestimation of x.

THEORY

The bacterial population is considered as a mixture of an infinite number of subpopulations homogeneous in adsorption capacity. Within each subpopulation there is a Poisson distribution of phage particles per bacterium, whose frequency function is:

$$f_j(k) = \frac{e^{-x_j} x_j^{\,k}}{k!} \qquad (1)$$

where x_j is the multiplicity of infection in the jth subpopulation. x_j is obtained from the B distribution of bacterial lengths: if we call l_j the length of the bacteria in the jth class, we have:

$$x_j = x \frac{l_j}{L} \tag{2}$$

where x = multiplicity of infection in the total population, L = arithmetic mean of the B distribution (average bacterial length).

The frequency function of the distribution of phage particles per bacterium in the *total* population (P distribution) is

$$f(k) = \sum_{j=0}^{\infty} n_j f_j(k) = \sum_{j=0}^{\infty} \frac{n_j e^{-x_j} x_j^k}{k!} \tag{3}$$

where n_j is the frequency of the jth subpopulation in the B distribution

$$\sum_{j=0}^{\infty} n_j = 1$$

The Poisson distribution of phage particles per bacterium within each homogeneous subpopulation of bacteria has the following first two moments:

First moment about the origin $= (\mu_1')_j = x_j$

Second moment about the mean $= (\mu_2)_j = x_j$

For the P distribution in the total population, remembering formula (3), we have a mean

$$(\mu_1')_P = \sum_{k=0}^{\infty} k \sum_{j=0}^{\infty} n_j f_j(k) = \sum_{j=0}^{\infty} n_j \sum_{k=0}^{\infty} k f_j(k) = \sum_{j=0}^{\infty} n_j (\mu_1')_j = \sum_{j=0}^{\infty} n_j x_j;$$

from formula (2) we obtain:

$$(\mu_1')_P = x. \tag{4}$$

To find the variance $(\mu_2)_P$ of the P distribution, let us remember that, in general,

$$\mu_2 = \mu_2' - (\mu_1')^2 \tag{5}$$

where μ_2' is the second moment about the origin. We have then:

$$(\mu_2')_P = \sum_{k=0}^{\infty} k^2 \sum_{j=0}^{\infty} n_j f_j(k) = \sum_{j=0}^{\infty} n_j \sum_{k=0}^{\infty} k^2 f_j(k) = \sum_{j=0}^{\infty} n_j (\mu_2')_j$$

where $(\mu_2')_j$ is the second moment about the origin of the distribution of phage particles per bacterium in the jth subpopulation. But $(\mu_2')_j = x_j + (x_j)^2$ (since, in general, $\mu_2' = \mu_2 + (\mu_1')^2$), and, for each homogeneous subpopulation, $(\mu_2)_j = (\mu_1')_j = x_j$. We obtain, therefore:

$$(\mu_2')_P = \sum_{j=0}^{\infty} n_j (\mu_2')_j = \sum_{j=0}^{\infty} n_j x_j + \sum_{j=0}^{\infty} n_j (x_j)^2. \tag{6}$$

Finally, introducing the values obtained from (4) and (6) in formula (5):

$$(\mu_2)_P = \sum_{j=0}^{\infty} n_j x_j + \sum_{j=0}^{\infty} n_j (x_j)^2 - x^2. \tag{7}$$

The first term on the right side of equation (7) equals x; the other two terms equal the variance of the B distribution, expressed as function of x. We obtain therefore,

$$(\mu_2)_P = x + \text{var (B)}.$$

INACTIVATION OF BACTERIOPHAGES BY DECAY OF INCORPORATED RADIOACTIVE PHOSPHORUS*

By GUNTHER S. STENT and CLARENCE R. FUERST‡

(*From the Virus Laboratory, University of California, Berkeley*)

(Received for publication, September 29, 1954)

It was observed by Hershey, Kamen, Kennedy, and Gest (1951) that bacteriophages are unstable if they contain radiophosphorus P^{32} of high specific activity. From day to day, progressively decreasing fractions of such populations of radioactive phage are still able to form plaques when plated on a sensitive bacterial strain, and the rate of loss of infective titer depends on the specific activity of the P^{32} assimilated. It is the purpose of this communication to present experiments in which these observations of Hershey *et al.* have been extended to the study of the lethal effects of P^{32} decay in various strains of bacteriophage at various temperatures and to the examination of some of the biological properties of the inactivated bacteriophage particles. Some of these experiments have already been reported in preliminary form (Stent, 1953 *a*).

Materials and Methods

Bacteriophages T1, T2, T3, T5, T7, and their host, *E. coli* B/r, and phage λ and its host, *E. coli* strain K12S, were used in this study. Strain B/r, a radiation-resistant mutant derived from strain B, was kindly supplied to us by Dr. Aaron Novick.

Glycerol–casamino acid medium refers to a medium devised by Fraser and Jerrel (1953). *H medium* is a glycerol-lactate medium of the following composition per liter of distilled water: 1.5 gm. KCl, 5 gm. NaCl, 1 gm. NH_4Cl, 0.25 gm. $MgSO_4 \cdot 7H_2O$, 10^{-4} N $CaCl_2$, 0.07 M sodium lactate, 2 gm. glycerol, 0.5 gm. bacto-peptone Difco and 0.5 gm. bacto-casamino acids Difco. H medium contains 6 mg./liter total phosphorus, of which 5 mg./liter are supplied by the casamino acids and 1 mg./liter by the peptone. Control experiments show that this phosphorus is assimilated by cultures of *E. coli* neither more nor less readily than inorganic phosphate.

The techniques described by Adams (1950) were employed for the general procedures of bacteriophagy.

Radiophosphorus was obtained as carrier-free $H_3P^{32}O_4$ from the Isotope Division of the Atomic Energy Research Establishment, Harwell, England. Measurements

* This investigation was supported by grants from the National Cancer Institute of the National Institutes of Health, Public Health Service and The Rockefeller Foundation.

‡ Holder of a National Research Council of Canada Special Scholarship.

Reprinted by permission of The Rockefeller Institute from THE JOURNAL OF GENERAL PHYSIOLOGY, **38** (4), 441-458, March 20, 1955.

of radioactivity were made on dry samples by means of an end-window GM tube, whose counting efficiency for P^{32} had been established by reference to a standard solution of radiophosphorus supplied by the National Bureau of Standards, United States Department of Commerce. The specific radioactivity of the growth media was determined by radioactive counting and chemical analysis of total phosphorus in the case of a number of T2 lysates in order to establish the specific inactivation rate αN for that phage and to confirm the value obtained by Hershey *et al.* To conserve the supply of isotope, the specific activity of the growth medium in the case of the other phages was usually estimated only by reference to the rate of inactivation of a stock of T2 grown in an aliquot of the same medium.

Bacteriophages of high specific activity were grown in the following way: A volume of the radioactive stock solution containing the desired amount of P^{32} was evaporated to dryness in a boiling water bath and resuspended in 0.1 ml. of H medium. The radioactive growth medium was then adjusted to neutral pH and inoculated with 0.01 ml. of a culture of 2×10^7 cells/ml. of B/r already in its exponential phase of growth in non-radioactive H medium. The growth of the radioactive culture at 37°C. was followed by microscopic counts in a Petroff-Hausser bacterial counting chamber. When the bacterial density reached 5×10^7 cells/ml., the culture was infected with 0.01 ml. of a stock containing 10^7 phages/ml. and incubated until microscopic counts indicated satisfactory lysis. At this point, the remainder of the 0.1 ml. culture was diluted into cold glycerol–casamino acid medium and assayed for its titer of infective phage particles.

Experimental Results

Rate of Inactivation.—

Hershey *et al.* observed that if a stock of T2 or T4 containing P^{32} at high specific activity was assayed daily, the logarithm of the number of surviving phages fell linearly with the number of P^{32} atoms that had decayed up to the time of assay. The slope of this survival curve was found to be proportional to the specific activity of the medium in which the phages had been grown, provided that the stock was stored in sufficiently great dilution under conditions in which control lysates containing an equal amount of non-incorporated P^{32} were stable. This indicated that the inactivation of one phage particle was not due to the radiation emitted by the radioactivity contained in other phages but was the consequence of the disintegration of one of its own atoms of P^{32}. The rate of change in the fraction s of surviving phage particles with the time t in days may, therefore, be expressed as

$$ds/dt = -\alpha N^* \lambda s \tag{1}$$

in which α is the fraction of the P^{32} disintegrations which are lethal (hereafter referred to as the "efficiency of killing"), N^* the number of radioactive phosphorus atoms per phage particle, and λ the fractional decay of P^{32} per day. Integration of (1) and substitution of more practical parameters lead to

$$\log_{10} s = -1.48 \times 10^{-6} \alpha A_0 N (1 - e^{-\lambda t}) \tag{2}$$

in which A_0 is the specific radioactivity (in millicuries per milligram of phosphorus) of the growth medium and N the total number of phosphorus atoms per phage particle. Hence, a plot of $\log_{10} s$ *vs.* $(1 - e^{-\lambda t})$, the fraction of all P^{32} atoms decayed by the tth day, should be a straight line with slope proportional to A_0, the relation actually observed experimentally.

We have studied the inactivation by P^{32} decay of five virulent coliphages T1, T2, T3, T5, T7, and of the temperate coliphage λ. All these strains, except the pair T3–T7, are serologically unrelated, differ in their chemical constitution, morphology, genetic structure, and manner of interaction with bacterial host cells. Radioactive stocks of each strain were grown by the procedure indicated above in media ranging in specific radioactivity from 100 to 300 mc./mg. At these specific activities, approximately 0.03 to 0.1 per cent of all phosphorus atoms are present as the P^{32} isotope. The lysates, whose titer usually represented at least a thousandfold increase over the inoculum, were stored at 4°C. in casamino acid–glycerol medium and the number of infective centers assayed from day to day. The results are presented in Fig. 1 in which the logarithm of the fraction of the survivors in the different phage stocks is plotted against $(1 - e^{-\lambda t})$. It is seen that in agreement with equation (2) a straight line survival curve is obtained in every case. The specific death rates αN, having the dimension *lethal atoms per phage* and obtained by dividing the observed slopes of the lines of Fig. 1 by $-1.48 \times 10^{-6} A_0$, are listed in Table I. Control experiments, not shown in Fig. 1, indicated that non-radioactive stocks of all six strains were stable in casamino acid–glycerol medium at 4°C. and that the radioactive lysates had been diluted sufficiently far to avoid inactivation by any external P^{32}. The six phages evidently fall into two classes of sensitivity to P^{32} inactivation. One class, composed of T2 and T5, is characterized by 4.5×10^4 lethal atoms per phage, the value already observed by Hershey *et al.* for T2 and T4. The sensitivity of the other group, comprising T1, T3, T7, and λ, corresponds to 1.5×10^4 lethal atoms per phage. Hence the strains of the second group are only one-third as sensitive to inactivation by decay of P^{32} as those of the first.

Phosphorus Content and Efficiency of Killing.—

The efficiency of killing per disintegration, α, may be calculated from the specific death rate, αN, if the number of phosphorus atoms per infective unit is known. The phosphorus content of each phage strain was, therefore, determined by means of the following procedure, the results of which are listed in Table I.

A stock of each phage was grown in H medium containing P^{32} at a low but accurately determined specific activity. The lysate was clarified and freed of bacterial debris by two low speed centrifugations (10 minutes at 5,000 *g*) and the phage sedimented and washed three times in nutrient broth by high speed centrifugations (60 minutes at 10,000 R.P.M. for T2, T5; 90 minutes at 15,500 R.P.M. for T1, T3, T7). The number of plaque-forming units and the P^{32} content of the purified suspension

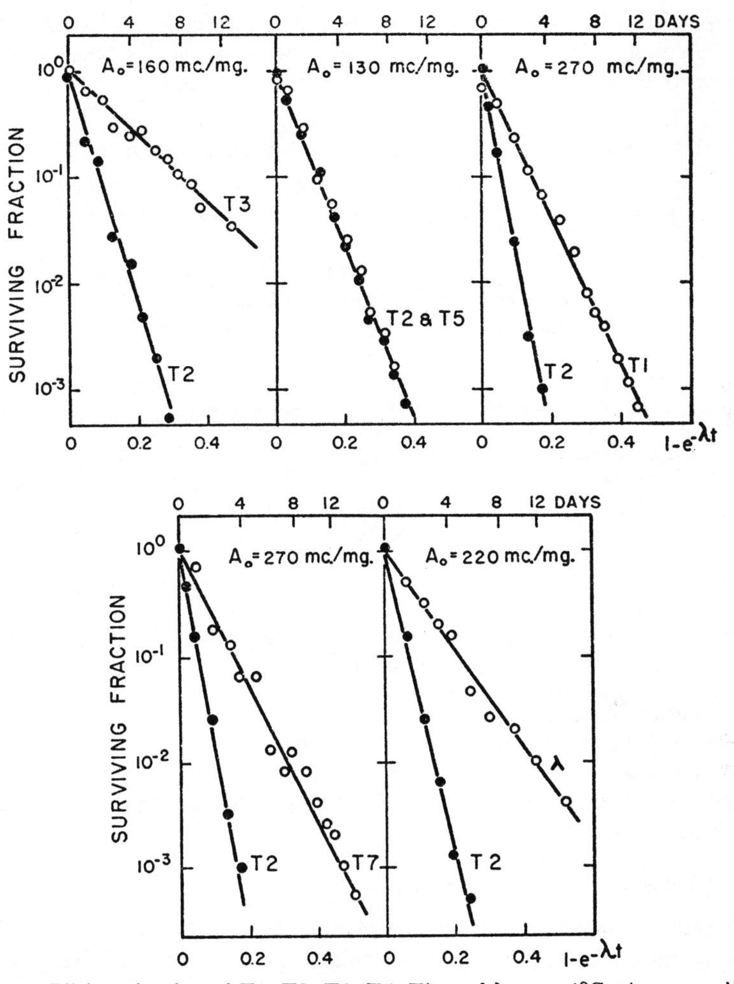

FIG. 1. P^{32} inactivation of T1, T2, T3, T5, T7, and λ at +4°C. A_0 = specific activity of growth medium.

were then assayed and the phosphorus content per infective unit calculated on the basis of the specific activity of the growth medium. In each case, more than 90 per cent of the P^{32} of the purified suspension could be adsorbed specifically to sensitive bacterial cells, indicating that practically all the radioactivity resided in morphologically intact bacteriophage particles. The results of this analysis agree well with the phosphorus content of T2 determined by Hershey, Kamen, Kennedy, and Gest

(1951) and by Hershey and Chase (1952). The agreement is poor, however, with the estimations of the phosphorus contents of T1, T2, T3, T5, and T7 by Labaw (1951) whose values are about twice as great as those found here. No values are listed in Table I for the phosphorus content of λ, since it was not possible to prepare a purified suspension of P^{32}-labelled λ in which the bulk of the radioactivity could be adsorbed specifically to sensitive bacteria. Neither the reason for this behavior of λ nor the nature of the non-adsorbed material has yet been discovered.

The last column of Table I lists the efficiency of killing, α, of P^{32} decay in each of the five strains of T phage. It is seen that in all the strains studied here, α is near the value 0.09 originally observed by Hershey *et al.*; *i.e.*, on the

TABLE I

Evaluation of the Parameters of the Equation

$$\log_{10} s = -1.48 \times 10^{-6} A_0 \alpha N (1 - e^{-\lambda t})$$

at 4°C.

Phage strain	A_0	Slope of death curve	αN Lethal atoms per phage	P per infective unit	N Atoms of P per phage	α
	mc./mg.			*mg.*		
T2	160*	−10.5	4.5 × 10⁴	2.3 × 10⁻¹⁴	4.5 × 10⁵	0.10
T5	130‡	−8.1	4.2 × 10⁴	1.8 × 10⁻¹⁴	3.5 × 10⁵	0.12
T1	270‡	−7.0	1.7 × 10⁴	0.7 × 10⁻¹⁴	1.4 × 10⁵	0.12
T3	160*	−3.1	1.3 × 10⁴	0.9 × 10⁻¹⁴	2 × 10⁵	0.07
T7	270‡	−6.4	1.6 × 10⁴	0.9 × 10⁻¹⁴	2 × 10⁵	0.08
λ	220‡	−4.8	1.5 × 10⁴	?	?	?

* Determined radiochemically.

‡ Determined by comparison with control T2 stock.

average one of about every ten P^{32} disintegrations inactivates any phage particle in which it occurs.

Effect of Temperature on the Efficiency α.—

The rate of inactivation by decay of P^{32} was also measured at two lower temperatures in the frozen state. For this purpose, aliquots of diluted radioactive lysates of all six phage strains were stored either at +4°C., or in the frozen state at −20°C. or −196°C. (the temperature of boiling liquid nitrogen). Samples were then thawed from day to day and assayed for the fraction of surviving infective centers. Frozen controls with corresponding non-radioactive lysates showed that, depending on the strain, from 45 to 90 per cent of the infective centers survive freezing and thawing and that, except in the case of storage of T2 at −20°C., the fraction recovered is independent of the length of time of storage (Sanderson, 1925; Rivers, 1927). It was found that at these lower temperatures the rate of inactivation by P^{32} decay of all five strains was significantly reduced. Since the rate of radioactive decay is independent of temperature, it follows that a reduction in α by the altered environmental conditions must be responsible for the reduced rate of bacteriophage inactivation. Table II lists the observed values of the slope of the inactivation curves at +4, −20, and −196°C. and the fractional reduction of α compared to its magnitude at +4°C. It is seen that radioactive decay proceeding at −20°C. inactivates the phages with an efficiency of only 70 per cent of decay proceeding at +4°C. Lowering the temperature to −196°C.

TABLE II

The Relative Efficiency of P^{32} Inactivation at Low Temperatures

Phage strain	A_0	Storage at +4°	Storage at −20°		Storage at −196°	
		Slope*	Slope*	$\frac{\alpha(-20°)}{\alpha(+4°)}$	Slope*	$\frac{\alpha(-196°)}{\alpha(+4°)}$
	mc./mg.					
T2	160	−10.5			−6.8	0.65
	130	−8.6			−5.6	0.65
	125	−8.3			−5.7	0.69
T5	130	−8.5	−5.8	0.68	−4.5	0.53
	125	−8.1	−5.6	0.69	−4.6	0.57
T1	270	−7.0	−4.8	0.69	−3.9	0.56
T3	160	−3.1			−1.6	0.52
T7	270	−6.4	−4.6	0.72	−3.6	0.56
λ	220	−4.8	−3.4	0.71	−3.3	0.54

* Refers to the value of $-1.48 \times 10^{-6} A_0 \alpha N$.

reduces the fraction of lethal disintegrations even further. At this temperature the efficiency of killing in T1, T3, T5, T7, and λ is only 55 per cent and in T2 only 65 per cent of its value at +4°C.

Since low temperatures appear to reduce the efficiency α, it seemed possible that radioactive decay occurring at temperatures higher than +4°C. might inactivate bacteriophages with greater efficiency. At elevated temperatures, however, bacteriophages are subject to thermal inactivation, and it is only possible to study the combined effects of heat inactivation and radioactive decay. To examine, therefore, the efficiency α at reasonably high temperatures, a heat-stable mutant, $T5_{st}$, was first selected from our strain of T5 by the procedure of Adams (1953). When stored in glycerol–casamino acid medium at

65°C. a stock of $T5_{st}$ loses 90 per cent of its titer in 5 hours. $T5_{st}$ is inactivated by P^{32} decay at 4°C. with the same specific death rate as the wild type T5. One stock of $T5_{st}$ was grown in H medium containing radioactive phos-

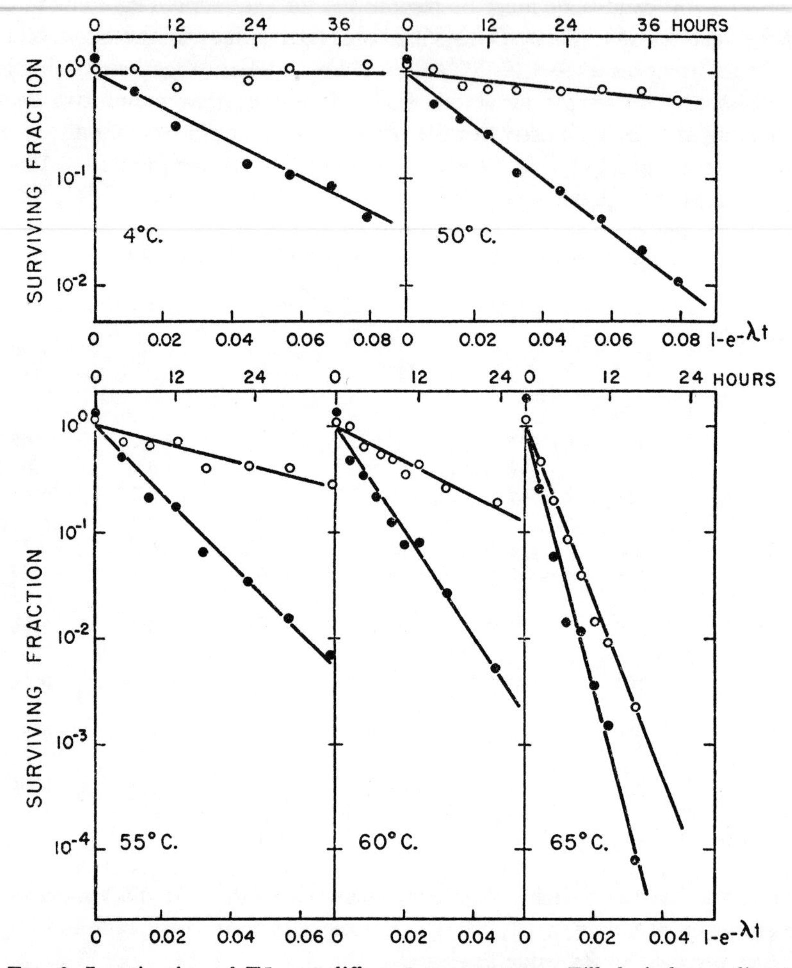

FIG. 2. Inactivation of $T5_{st}$ at different temperatures. Filled circles, radioactive lysate, A_0 = 300 mc./mg. Open circles, non-radioactive control lysate.

phorus at specific activity of 300 mc./mg. (at which level 0.1 per cent of all phosphorus is P^{32}) and one in non-radioactive H medium. After dilution into glycerol–casamino acid medium, aliquots of both lysates were stored at 4, 50, 55, 60, and 65°C. and assays of the number of infective centers made from time to time. The result of this experiment is presented in Fig. 2. It is seen that the rate of inactivation of the radioactive lysate is almost the same at 4,

50, and 55°C., at which temperatures the non-radioactive control lysates exhibited little or no heat inactivation. At 60 and 65°C., however, considerable increases in the rate of inactivation of the radioactive $T5_{st}$ lysate are observed, at which temperatures the non-radioactive control lysate now also exhibits an increasing instability. Since the rate of loss of titer of the radioactive lysate may be presumed to be the sum of the rate of death due to heat and to radioactive decay, the rate of P^{32} inactivation can be estimated at any temperature by subtraction of the slope of the survival curve of the non-radioactive con-

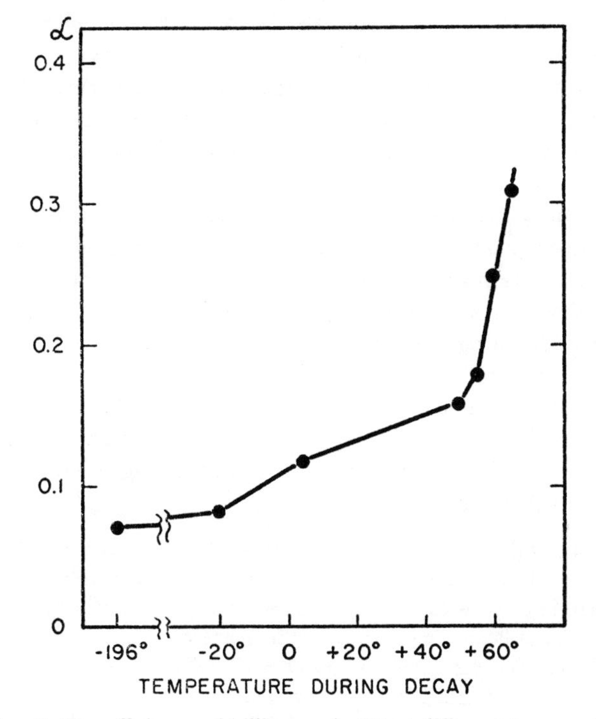

FIG. 3. The efficiency of killing, α, in T5 at different temperatures.

trol from that of the radioactive lysate. (This subtraction of slopes is justified only in experiments of short duration, while $(1 - e^{-\lambda t})$ is still approximated by λt.) The efficiency of killing α at that temperature can then be computed from this difference of rates by means of equation (2). The result of such calculations based on the slopes of Fig. 2 is presented graphically in Fig. 3, in which α has been plotted against the temperature of decay. It is evident that α increases slowly between 4 and 55°C. and begins to rise sharply after that point. At 65°C., α has reached the value 0.31, which means that now almost one in every three P^{32} disintegrations is lethal to $T5_{st}$. Also included in Fig. 3 are the results of the estimations of α in T5 at low temperatures.

Evidently, it is possible to effect at least a fourfold variation in α by varying the temperature of storage from the lowest to the highest practicable range. It is to be noted that the increase in α per degree is greater between -20 and $+4°C$. than between $+4$ and $+50°C$. This, no doubt, implies that α is affected not only by the ambient thermal energy, but also by the change of phase from liquid to solid state.

P^{32} Decay after Infection.—

Hershey and Chase (1952) have shown that when T2 infects a sensitive bacterium, the phosphorus, and hence the DNA, of the bacteriophage particle enters the host cell, whereas the bulk of the phage protein remains outside. It may then be asked whether P^{32} decay can still prevent the reproduction of the parental phage and the ultimate emergence of infective progeny if such decay occurs only after the introduction of the DNA of a radioactive T2 particle into the interior of the bacterial cell.

In order to study the effect of P^{32} decay after infection, it is necessary to arrest intracellular phage development reversibly for days or weeks so that the slow radioactive decay may proceed at an early stage of the brief 20 minute latent period. This can be achieved by quick-freezing the bacterial cells shortly after infection and storing them at $-196°C$. in liquid nitrogen. As in the case of free phages, non-radioactive controls show that more than half of the infected centers survive freezing and thawing, and that the fraction recovered is independent of the length of storage at $-196°C$. In those infected bacteria which survive, phage development resumes upon thawing where it had left off at the moment of freezing.

A culture of strain B/r was grown in nutrient broth to a density of 10^8/ml., centrifuged, and resuspended in fresh broth at one-fourth of its original volume. The suspension was then infected with 3×10^7/ml. radioactive T2 particles, containing P^{32} at a specific activity of 88 mc./mg. Phage development was again arrested 2.5 minutes after infection by chilling the culture in ice. The infected bacteria were separated from the small fraction of unadsorbed free phage by centrifugation and resuspended in cold glycerol–casamino acid medium. Aliquots of 0.1 ml. of this final suspension were frozen and stored in liquid nitrogen. From day to day, one of the aliquots was thawed by addition of 1.9 ml. of warm medium and plated at once for the number of surviving infective centers. A control culture infected with non-radioactive T2 under otherwise identical conditions was similarly frozen, stored, and assayed. Aliquots of the initial radioactive stock of free T2 and a non-radioactive control stock were also stored in liquid nitrogen and assayed for their survival from day to day.

The results of this experiment are presented in Fig. 4. It is seen that in the population of bacteria infected for 2.5 minutes with a multiplicity of 0.075 radioactive T2, per cell, the logarithm of the fraction of individuals capable of giving rise to a plaque when plated after thawing decreases linearly with $(1 - e^{-\lambda t})$. The slope of the survival curve is about three-fourth that of the rate of inactivation of the free radioactive T2 stored at the same temperature. (Neither the control culture infected with non-radioactive T2 nor the

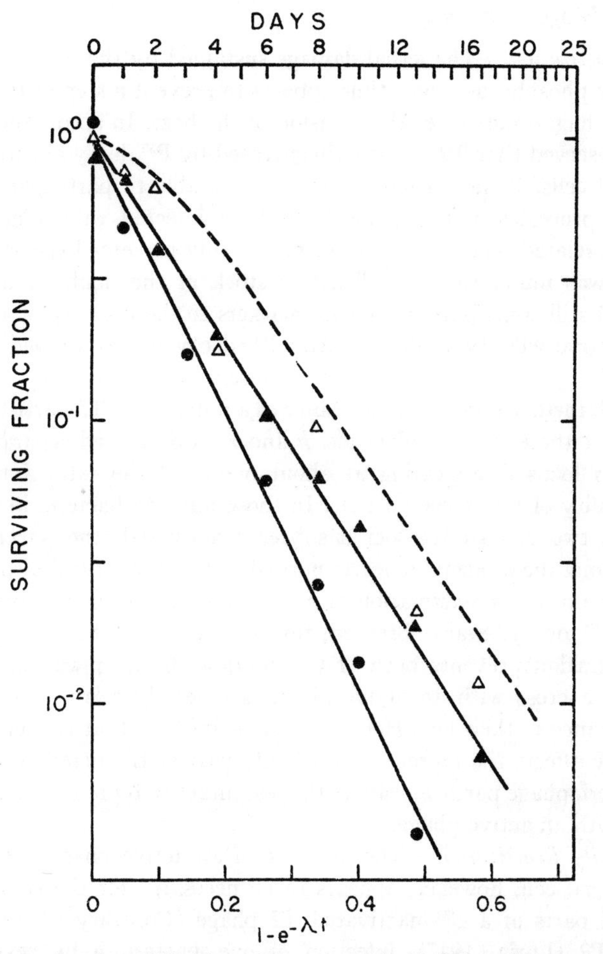

FIG. 4. P^{32} inactivation of T2 (A_0 = 88 mc./mg.) inside infected bacteria at −196°C. Filled triangles, multiplicity of infection: 0.075 (monocomplexes). Open triangles, multiplicity of infection: 2.2 (multicomplexes). Filled circles, free T2. The dashed curve indicates the expected survival of infective centers at a multiplicity of 2.2 in the absence of multiplicity reactivation.

corresponding free phage showed any significant loss of titer.) Hence P^{32} decay occurring in the DNA after it has been separated from the protein "coat" and exchanged its place in the phage head for the protoplasm of the host cell is still capable of destroying the reproductive capacity of the parent phage, although this inactivation now proceeds with a slightly reduced efficiency. Results similar to those presented in Fig. 4 have also been obtained after infection of bacteria with radioactive T3 and λ phages.

State of the Phage after Decay.—

Cross-Reactivation.—The lethal damage sustained by the phage upon decay of one of its phosphorus atoms thus appears to prevent a step of the reproductive cycle which occurs after the invasion of the host. In accordance with this view, we observed that T2 particles inactivated by P^{32} decay are still adsorbed to bacterial cells. In fact, such phages are still able to participate in the reproductive processes occurring inside bacteria infected with a normal, non-inactivated related phage. In experiments already presented elsewhere (Stent, 1953 *b*) it was found that a radioactive stock of the double mutant strain T2hr_1 could still contribute its genetic markers to the progeny of a cross with non-radioactive wild type T2++ after P^{32} decay had destroyed the ability of the T2hr_1 particles to reproduce themselves *in solo* (*cross-reactivation*). It appeared, furthermore, that the ability of a radioactive T2 particle to donate either one of these two unlinked loci h and r_1 is destroyed separately by P^{32} decay, each locus disappearing at about one-third the rate of the plaque-forming ability of the whole particle. In those infected bacteria in which only one of the two radioactive loci has been inactivated, the surviving locus appears among the progeny in nearly normal yield. Stahl (1954) also discovered the existence of cross-reactivation of genetic markers after inactivation of T4 phage by P^{32} decay. Stahl observed, furthermore, that the likelihood that a P^{32} disintegration prevents both of two markers from appearing among the progeny of a cross with an active phage is inversely related to the genetic linkage distance of their loci. Hence it may be inferred that the lethal damage of P^{32} decay affects the reproduction of only part of the hereditary substance of the bacteriophage particle, leaving the rest intact to reproduce itself in mixed infection with an active phage.

Multiplicity Reactivation.—The presence of an active phage particle in the same bacterial cell, however, appears to be necessary for the survival of the undamaged parts of a P^{32}-inactivated T2 phage. Contrary to ultraviolet-inactivated T2 (Luria, 1947), infection of one bacterium by several P^{32}-inactivated particles does not lead to the production of active phage (*multiplicity reactivation*).

In order to test for multiplicity reactivation following P^{32} decay, the stock of radioactive T2 employed in the experiment presented in Fig. 4 was used to infect B/r bacteria at a multiplicity of 2.2 phage particles per cell. As in the low multiplicity experiment of Fig. 4, the mixture of bacteria and radioactive phage was incubated at 37°C. for 2.5 minutes before being frozen, stored at −196°C., and assayed for surviving infective centers from day to day. At a multiplicity of infection of 2.2, the fraction of all infected bacteria to which two or more phages are adsorbed (multicomplexes) is 0.73. Hence if two or more T2 particles were able to cooperate in the production of active progeny after each individual had already sustained a "lethal" P^{32} disintegration, then the rate of inactivation of 0.73 of the plaque formers in this experiment should have been significantly reduced over the rate of inactivation of singly infected cells. If, on the other hand, the plaque-forming ability of a multiply infected cell is destroyed as soon as each of the infecting particles has been inactivated by P^{32} decay, then the infective centers in this experiment should have disappeared with the "multiple hit" kinetics indicated in Fig. 4 by a dashed curve. The result of this experiment is also shown in Fig. 4. It is seen that inactivation of multicomplexes proceeds at roughly the same rate as inactivation of singly infected bacteria, indicating the absence of any appreciable multiplicity reactivation. Experiments in which P^{32} decay was first allowed to take place in free T2 and in which bacteria were then multiply infected with the inactivated phages likewise failed to reveal any multiplicity reactivation.

Latent Period of Survivors.—Since the efficiency of killing, α, is less than 0.1 at low temperatures, it is apparent that after an amount of decay which

TABLE III

Photoreactivation of T2

Treatment of T2	Assayed in dark	Assayed in light
	Titer	Titer
Before P^{32} decay	1.7×10^8	1.7×10^8
After P^{32} decay	1.7×10^4	1.3×10^4
Before ultraviolet irradiation	2.5×10^9	2.5×10^9
After ultraviolet irradiation	1.4×10^5	1.3×10^7

leaves only a small fraction of the initial phage population still active has taken place under these conditions there have occurred many non-lethal P^{32} disintegrations in the survivors. In the case of T2, these survivors, however, exhibit no evident effects of this non-lethal decay and reproduce with normal latent period and burst size. This is in contrast to the survivors of ultraviolet light irradiation whose multiplication is significantly retarded (Luria, 1944).

Photoreactivation.—T2 bacteriophages inactivated by ultraviolet light can be "photoreactivated" by exposure of bacteria infected with such phages to visible light (Dulbecco, 1949). To examine whether phage inactivated by decay of incorporated P^{32} could be similarly reactivated by light, assays were made of a radioactive T2 stock before and after decay to 0.0001 of the initial titer, incubating the assay plates either in the dark or under a strong fluorescent light. A non-radioactive control stock of T2 was inactivated with ultraviolet light to a survival of 0.000056 and similarly assayed in dark and light. The result of this experiment is presented in Table III, in which it may be seen that no photoreactivation of the P^{32}-inactivated T2 took place, although the titer of the ultraviolet-inactivated control was raised by nearly a factor of 100 by exposure to visible light.

DISCUSSION

Cause of Death.—

An atom of P^{32} decays into the stable isotope of sulfur, S^{32}, upon ejection of a beta electron–neutrino pair of total kinetic energy 1.7 mev. The beta particle produces ionizations along its path, which are capable of damaging biological materials in a way similar to x-rays. Hershey, Kamen, Kennedy, and Gest, however, showed by means of calculations based on the volume of the T2 particle, the density of ionizations along the beta track and the known efficiency of killing per x-ray ionization, or by reconstruction experiments in which non-radioactive phage particles were irradiated with beta particles emitted by external, non-incorporated P^{32} atoms, that beta particle ionizations could not be the principal cause of the inactivation of radioactive bacteriophage particles. Hershey *et al.* concluded, rather, that a short range consequence of the nuclear reaction, *e.g.* the recoil sustained by the disintegrating nucleus upon ejection of beta electron and neutrino, or the transmutation of phosphorus into sulfur, was responsible for death. The present finding that the sensitivity of radioactive phages to P^{32} decay is reduced only slightly after infection supports this view. For, it appears likely that the state of aggregation of the phage DNA is more compact in the phage head than in the protoplasm of the host cell (Watanabe, Stent, and Schachman, 1954). Hence the chance of irradiation of one part of the phage DNA by distant P^{32} atoms of another would have been seriously reduced once infection was under way.

Efficiency of Killing.—

Hershey *et al.* suggested that the fact that only one P^{32} disintegration in about ten was lethal to T2 or T4 might reflect a division of the phage DNA into 10 per cent "essential" and 90 per cent "non-essential" structures. Under this view, any P^{32} disintegration in the former would be surely lethal and any in the latter generally harmless. The present finding that α is nearly the same in various phage strains of greatly different size, morphology, and biological properties makes this hypothesis less likely. The dependence of α on temperature, furthermore, excludes the possibility that the anatomy of the phage is the sole factor responsible for the efficiency of killing. It seems, rather, that α must at least in part reflect some structural aspect of the DNA molecule, the substance whose function is presumably destroyed by the decay of its radioactive P^{32} atoms.

The lethal effects of P^{32} decay can perhaps be best understood in terms of the macromolecular structure of DNA, recently uncovered by Watson and

Crick (1953), of which a schematic diagram is presented in Fig. 5. This structure reveals DNA as a double helix composed of two intertwined polynucleotide chains of opposite polarity held together laterally by specific hydrogen bonds between purine and pyrimidine bases of opposite strands. The radioactive P^{32} atoms are located in the diester bonds responsible for the continuity of

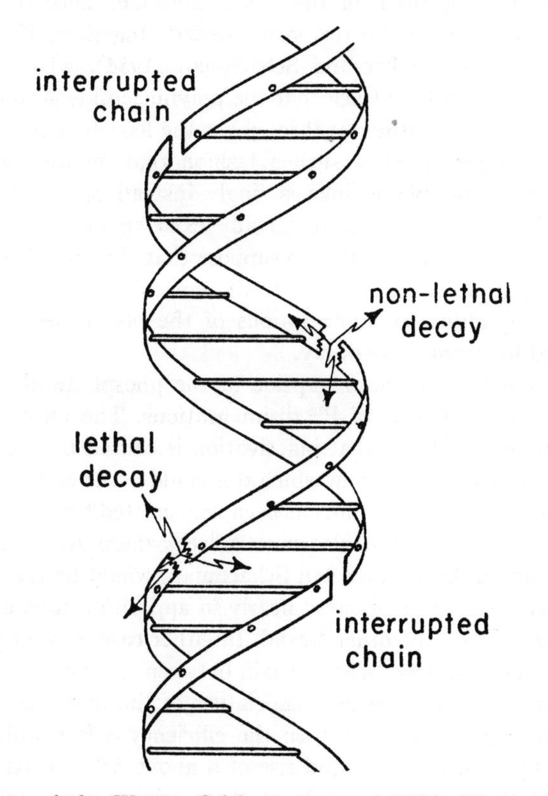

FIG. 5. Schema of the Watson-Crick structure of DNA. The two ribbons symbolize the two phosphate-sugar chains, and the horizontal rods represent the pairs of bases holding the chains together through a pair of hydrogen bonds. The breaks in the ribbons indicate the spontaneous interruptions of the polynucleotide chains proposed by Dekker and Schachman.

the polynucleotide chains. It appears almost inevitable that every ester linkage is destroyed upon decay of its radioactive phosphorus atom. First of all, the maximum recoil sustained by the phosphorus nucleus is of the order of 80 ev. (the average value being somewhat lower owing to the random orientation of neutrino and beta electron), whereas the energy of the P-O bond holding the atom in place is less than 5 ev. The ester bond is, therefore, probably broken by the Szilard-Chalmers reaction (*cf.* Libby, 1947). Secondly, even if the recoil does not rupture the phosphate ester linkage, *i.e.* if the phosphorus nucleus remained in place after all, then the two deoxyribose residues are forthwith linked by a *sulfate* diester, which should undergo spontaneous hydrolysis in aqueous medium (Kremann, 1907). Inspection of the structure shown in Fig. 5 indicates, however, that breakage of one ester link would not necessarily lead to the disruption of the DNA molecule, since the multitude of hydrogen bonds still hold the two sister strands together. This has recently been pointed out by Dekker and Schachman (1954), who propose on the basis of physicochemical evidence that the polynucleotide strands of "native" DNA are not actually continuous throughout the length of the macromolecule but are already interrupted in such a fashion that on the average one out of twenty to fifty phosphate links is singly instead of doubly esterified, as indicated in Fig. 5. Thus, if there already exist spontaneous breaks within intact DNA, it is not unreasonable to suppose that the low efficiency of killing per P^{32} disintegration means that the DNA molecule can continue to function even after a few additional interruptions of the polynucleotide chains have been generated by radioactive decay.

An event secondary to the disruption of the phosphate diester must then attend the lethal fraction α of P^{32} disintegrations. The most reasonable hypothesis would appear to be that inactivation is caused by a complete cut of the DNA *double* helix. One way in which this could occur is that enough energy liberated by the decaying P^{32} atom has been transmitted by a sequence of elastic collisions to the other strand to also cause a break there. Another possibility, in view of the proposal by Dekker and Schachman, would be that the lethal decay takes place in an atom situated nearly in apposition to one of the few incomplete ester links on the other strand. In either case, a complete cut results because few or no hydrogen bonds remain between the spots where both sister strands are broken to oppose the dissociation of the macromolecule into two smaller pieces. The effect of heat on the efficiency α is readily explained in terms of this hypothesis. The rapid rise of α above 55°C. must be due to the dissociation of the hydrogen bonds at these temperatures (*cf.* Dekker and Schachman), thus causing less and less resistance to separation of the two strands by the energy of the radioactive disintegration. A greater and greater fraction of the P^{32} decays can, therefore, result in a complete cut of the double helix. The effect of freezing and of low temperatures on reducing α might be explained by the increase of viscosity of the medium in which the two pieces involved in the break have to move; *i.e.*, that when the DNA is embedded in ice there exists a greater chance that the energy of the P^{32} transmutation has already been dissipated before the cut has actually taken place.

Action of Ionizing Radiations.—

It would be possible, though technically rather difficult, to ascertain whether, in agreement with the hypothesis just proposed, decay of incorporated P^{32}

actually depolymerizes highly radioactive DNA molecules with an efficiency similar to α. It is known, however, that x-rays and other ionizing radiations do break down DNA to random fragments of progressively smaller molecular weight at doses comparable to those necessary for the "direct" inactivation of bacteriophages (Taylor, Greenstein, and Hollaender, 1948; Conway, Gilbert, and Butler, 1950). Hence it is not unlikely that the lethal effect of x-ray ionizations inside the phage particle is also one of cutting DNA molecules, similar to that postulated above for P^{32} decay. Two sets of facts would appear to make this comparison useful:

(*a*) The efficiency of killing per x-ray ionization inside the volume of the phage particle is only of the order of 0.05 in the bacteriophage strains studied here (Watson, 1950); *i.e.*, similar in magnitude to α. The energy released by each x-ray ionization is thought to be 32 ev., *i.e.* similar in magnitude to that of the P^{32} recoil, and to be confined to a radius of a few Angstrom units (Lea, 1947). (The average energy available locally may actually be either more or less than 32 ev. because, on one hand, the ionizations tend to occur in clusters but, on the other hand, their energy has been determined only in air and not in a condensed phase.) Since the two polynucleotide chains of the DNA macromolecules are separated by at least 10 A (Watson and Crick, 1953), it would appear possible that many of the ionizations, like many of the P^{32} disintegrations, damage only one of the strands without causing a complete rupture of the double helix.

(*b*) The x-ray sensitivity of T1 depends on temperature very much like α. At temperatures below freezing, the rate of inactivation by x-rays is only 65 per cent of that just above freezing (Bachofer *et al.*, 1953). At higher temperatures, the sensitivity first remains relatively constant and then increases sharply above 50°C., reaching a sixfold greater value at 60°C. (Adams and Pollard, 1952). These observations had already suggested to Adams and Pollard that the weakening of secondary, interchain bonds by heat at the moment of the x-ray ionization might be responsible for increasing the chance of causing lethal damage at higher temperatures. As in the case of P^{32} decay, it is apparent that the greater the extent to which the hydrogen bonds of the DNA macromolecule are dissociated, the more likely will a cut of the double helix result from an energetic rupture of a single polynucleotide strand.

SUMMARY

The inactivation of the phages T1, T2, T3, T5, T7, and λ by decay of incorporated P^{32} has been studied. It was found that these phages fall into two classes of sensitivity to P^{32} decay: at the same specific activity of P^{32} in their deoxyribonucleic acid (DNA), T2 and T5 are inactivated three times as rapidly as T1, T3, T7, and λ. Since the strains of the first class were found to contain about three times as much total phosphorus per phage particle as those of the second, it appears that the fraction of all P^{32} disintegrations which are lethal is very nearly the same in all the strains. This fraction α depends on the temperature at which decay is allowed to proceed, being 0.05 at −196°C., 0.1 at +4°C., and 0.3 at 65°C.

Decay of P^{32} taking place only after the penetration of the DNA of a radioactive phage particle into the interior of the bacterial cell can still prevent the reproduction of the parental phage, albeit inactivation now proceeds at a slightly reduced rate. T2 phages inactivated by decay of P^{32} can be cross-reactivated; *i.e.*, donate some of their genetic characters to the progeny of a mixed infection with a non-radioactive phage. They do not, however, exhibit any multiplicity reactivation or photoreactivation.

The fact that at low temperatures less than one-tenth of the P^{32} disintegrations are lethal to the phage particle and the dependence of the fraction of lethal disintegrations on temperature can be accounted for by the double stranded structure of the DNA macromolecule.

REFERENCES

Adams, M. H., Methods of Medical Research, (I.H. Comroe, editor), Chicago, The Year Book Publishers, 1950, **2,** 1.

Adams, M. H., *Ann. Inst. Pasteur*, 1953, **84,** 1.

Adams, W. R., and Pollard, E. C., *Arch. Biochem. and Biophysic.*, 1952, **36,** 311.

Bachofer, C. S., Ehret, C. F., Mayer, S., and Powers, E. L., *Proc. Nat. Acad. Sc.*, 1953, **39,** 744.

Conway, B. E., Gilbert, L., and Butler, J. A. V., *J. Chem. Soc.*, 1950, 3421.

Dekker, C. A., and Schachman, H. K., *Proc. Nat. Acad. Sc.*, 1954, **40,** 894.

Dulbecco, R., *J. Bact.*, 1949, **59,** 329.

Fraser, D., and Jerrel, E. A., *J. Biol. Chem.*, 1953, **205,** 291.

Hershey, A. D., and Chase, M., *J. Gen. Physiol.*, 1952, **36,** 39.

Hershey, A. D., Kamen, M. D., Kennedy, J. W., and Gest, H., *J. Gen. Physiol.*, 1951, **34,** 305.

Kremann, R., *Monatsh. Chem.*, 1907, **28,** 13.

Labaw, L. W., *J. Bact.*, 1951, **62,** 169.

Lea, D. E., Action of Radiations on Living Cells, Cambridge, University Press, 1947.

Libby, W. F., *J. Am. Chem. Soc.*, 1947, **69,** 2523.

Luria, S. E., *Proc. Nat. Acad. Sc.*, 1944, **30,** 393.

Luria, S. E., *Proc. Nat. Acad. Sc.*, 1947, **33,** 253.

Rivers, T. M., *J. Exp. Med.*, 1927, **45,** 11.

Sanderson, E. S., *Science*, 1925, **62,** 377.

Stahl, F. W., in a discussion of a paper by Doermann, Chase, and Stahl, *J. Cell. and Comp. Physiol.*, 1954, in press.

Stent, G. S., *Cold Spring Harbor Symp. Quant. Biol.*, 1953 *a*, **18,** 255.

Stent, G. S., *Proc. Nat. Acad. Sc.*, 1953 *b*, **39,** 1234.

Taylor, B., Greenstein, J. P., and Hollaender, A., *Arch. Biochem.*, 1948, **16,** 19.

Watanabe, I., Stent, G. S., and Schachman, H. K., *Biochim. et Biophysic. Acta*, 1954, **15,** 38.

Watson, J. D., *J. Bact.*, 1950, **60,** 697.

Watson, J. D., and Crick, F. H. C., *Nature*, 1953, **171,** 737; *Cold Spring Harbor Symp. Quant. Biol.*, 1953, **18,** 123.

RESISTANCE TO ULTRAVIOLET LIGHT AS AN INDEX TO THE REPRODUCTION OF BACTERIOPHAGE

S. BENZER[1]

California Institute of Technology, Pasadena, California

Received for publication July 18, 1951

Infection of a susceptible bacterium by a single phage particle initiates a series of events climaxed, after a time called the latent period, by bursting of the cell and the release of a number (burst size) of replicas of the initial phage. We are here concerned primarily with the intervening process of phage replication which takes place behind the cloak of the cell wall. By prematurely disrupting infected cells, Doermann (1948) found that infective phage replicas are already present well before the time at which the bacterium bursts, i.e., about two-thirds of the way through the latent period. At earlier times, however, no plaque-forming particles are recovered, not even the initial phage. Our attention is, therefore, focused upon this "dark" period, during which the infecting phage must undergo some modification, and the key processes of phage reproduction come to pass.

Luria and Latarjet (1947) conceived the following experiment in an attempt to use target theory for an analysis of the intracellular developments. It had been shown by Anderson (1948) that a bacterium (*Escherichia coli*, strain B) could be subjected to rather heavy doses of ultraviolet light and still survive in its ability to support the growth of phage T2. Thus, if one were to infect cells of strain B with single particles of T2 and irradiate the phage-bacterium complexes, the survival of infectivity (the ability to release at least one phage particle, thereby forming a plaque) of the complex should be determined by the survival of the phage part. If the irradiation is done immediately after infection, one should obtain the same survival curve for complexes as for the free phage irradiated before addition to bacteria, i.e., an approximately exponential or "one-hit" curve. If complexes are allowed to develop to the point where several intracellular phage particles are present, the inactivation of the complex requires at least one "hit" in each phage, and a multiple-target survival curve should be obtained. The set of curves for samples irradiated at different stages in the latent period would be expected to resemble the theoretical curves of figure 1. These multiple-target curves, plotted on a semilogarithmic graph, are characterized by asymptotes of constant slope equal to that for the single phage particle. The intercept of the asymptote, extrapolated to zero dose, corresponds to the logarithm of the number of targets.

[1] On leave of absence from the Department of Physics, Purdue University. This investigation was conducted in part at Oak Ridge National Laboratory and continued while the author was at the California Institute of Technology as a Postdoctoral Fellow of the Atomic Energy Commission, and a Fellow in Cancer Research of the American Cancer Society, recommended by the Committee on Growth.

Present Address: Institut Pasteur, Paris 15, France.

Reprinted by permission of the author and the Williams and Wilkins Co., from the JOURNAL OF BACTERIOLOGY, **63** (1), 59-72, January, 1952.

In experiments with *E. coli*, strain B, and phage T2, Luria and Latarjet found that immediately after infection the survival curve agreed with that of free phage. However, at later times, instead of showing a progressive increase in multiplicity with constant slope, the curves during the first half of the latent period showed a progressive decrease in slope (i.e., a decrease in sensitivity to ultraviolet) while remaining essentially exponential in character. At mid-latent period the curves became multiple-target in character, and thereafter the sensitivity increased again. Since the results did not resemble the family of curves

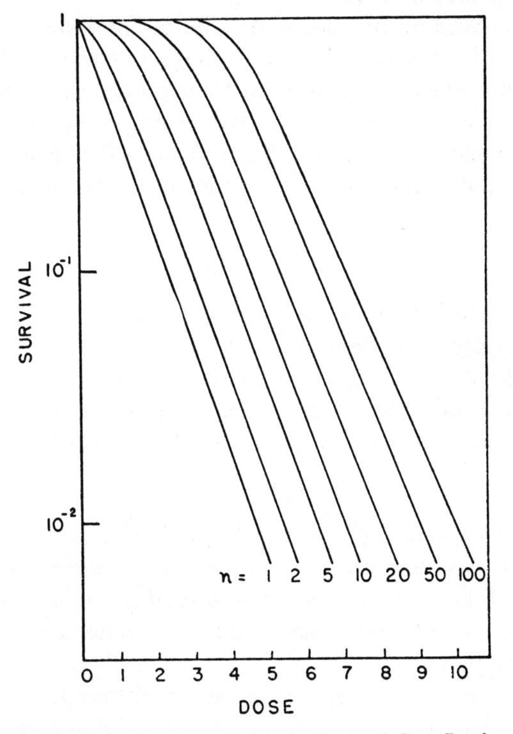

Figure 1. Theoretical survival curves for complexes (after Luria and Latarjet, 1947).

For an individual target the survival y is given by e^{-D}, where D is the dose in arbitrary units.

For a complex containing n identical, independent targets, the survival of any one of which is sufficient for survival of the complex, $y = 1 - (1 - e^{-D})^n$.

in figure 1, it was not possible to perform a target-theory determination of the number of intracellular phage particles. Latarjet (1948) repeated these studies, using X-rays, and observed changes which were similar in character although differing in degree.

Further investigation of this problem was suggested by the discovery of "multiplicity reactivation" (Luria, 1947; Luria and Dulbecco, 1949). In this phenomenon, two ultraviolet inactivated phage particles, when infecting the same cell, can combine their resources, leading to the production of active phage.

This result may also be stated in the following way: complexes formed by infection of a cell with two phage particles do not have a survival curve corresponding to the two-target curve of figure 1; at any given dose of ultraviolet the probability of the complex being infective is greater than given by that curve. This effect occurs to a marked degree with phage T2 and would be expected to cause anomalous results in an experiment of the Luria-Latarjet type, where intracellular multiplication is going on. However, there are other phages, T7 for instance, with which multiplicity reactivation does not occur, and it seemed of interest to extend the experiments to such a phage.

Another possible cause of anomalous results is "photoreactivation" of phage (Dulbecco, 1950). Ultraviolet inactivated phage particles may be reactivated, after adsorption to a sensitive bacterium, by exposure to white light. Thus, we may expect the infectivity of a phage-bacterium complex to have a higher resistance to ultraviolet if exposed to light (after ultraviolet irradiation) than if kept in the dark. Precautions are therefore necessary in order to avoid this effect.

MATERIALS

Phages: T7, T2, and T2r, prepared from lysates in broth, purified by centrifugation, and resuspended in buffer.

Bacterium: *Escherichia coli*, strain B, grown in broth.

Growth medium (broth): bacto-tryptone, 1 per cent plus 0.1 M NaCl.

Buffer: 1/15 M phosphate buffer, pH 7, plus 0.1 M NaCl, plus 10^{-3} M $MgSO_4$.

METHODS

A Luria-Latarjet experiment involves the following steps:

1. Phage particles are added to a suspension of bacteria and time is allowed for infection of the cells to occur, then unadsorbed phage is eliminated.

2. The complexes are allowed to develop and samples are removed at various stages of the latent period.

3. Each sample is exposed to several doses of ultraviolet.

4. Aliquots are plated to determine the fraction of infective centers surviving each dose. These operations must be completed before the end of the latent period. Furthermore, since the radiation resistance of the infective centers changes rapidly with time, it is essential for accurate results that growth start almost simultaneously in all cells and that it be halted during irradiation.

In an attempt to best satisfy these requirements, the following procedure is used:

1. *Adsorption of phage without growth.* The bacteria are prepared from an aerated broth culture in the logarithmic phase (1×10^8 cells per ml). The cells are centrifuged, resuspended in buffer, centrifuged again, resuspended in buffer at a concentration of 1×10^9 per ml, and aerated by bubbling at 37 C for one hour in order to exhaust intracellular nutrients and bring the bacteria to a starved condition. A purified suspension of phage particles in buffer is then added. Under these conditions adsorption takes place, but no lysis or phage liberation

(Dulbecco, 1950). However, the absence of phage liberation is not sufficient to exclude the possibility that intracellular growth progresses to a fairly advanced intermediate stage without reaching completion.

We can test for this by making use of the large change in resistance to ultraviolet of T2r complexes. If intracellular development proceeds, the resistance should increase with time. In figure 2, it can be seen that so long as the infected cells are kept in buffer and no nutrient is added, the resistance remains constant. The value of the resistance is only slightly higher than that of the free phage

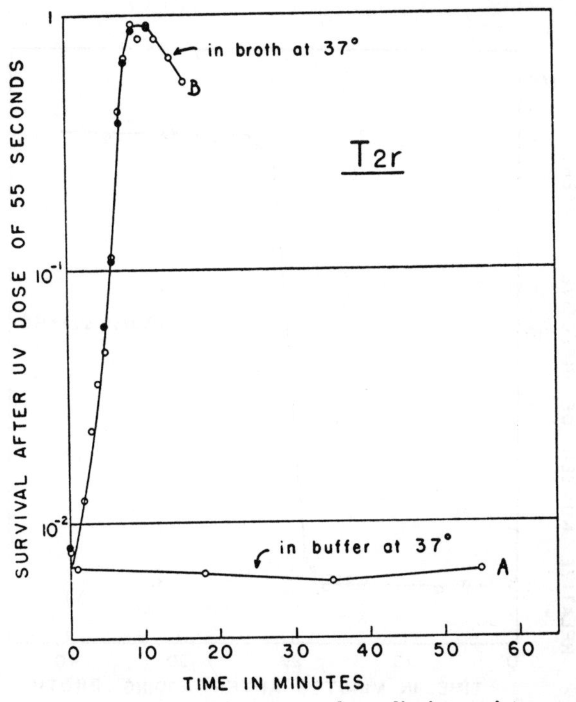

Figure 2. Effect of addition of nutrient upon the radiation resistance of T2r complexes formed in buffer. The ordinate is obtained by exposing a sample of complexes to ultraviolet for 55 seconds and determining the fraction which survives. (A) No nutrient added; (B) broth added at time zero.

(see later). Thus, the intracellular development does not progress beyond a very early stage. Even if the adsorption period extends over many minutes, each complex is arrested in its development, and adsorption is effectively simultaneous.

In experiments with bacteria grown in synthetic medium (instead of broth) there was a slow increase of resistance, even in buffer, as if considerable intracellular nutrient reserves remained even after starving for an hour. This resistance reached a maximum value corresponding to that attained after several minutes of growth in the presence of ample extracellular nutrient.

T2r is adsorbed to the extent of over 90 per cent in 10 minutes in buffer. At the same buffer concentration, T7 adsorption is extremely slow, but the rate is greatly increased by using buffer diluted 10 times with distilled water (Watson, personal communication). Therefore, throughout the experiments with T7 diluted buffer was used. The number of infective centers obtained (with either phage) was usually found to be less, by one-third to one-half, than the number of phages adsorbed. The cause of this "abortive adsorption" is not understood. To eliminate unadsorbed phage, the cells are washed by centrifugation and resuspended in fresh buffer.

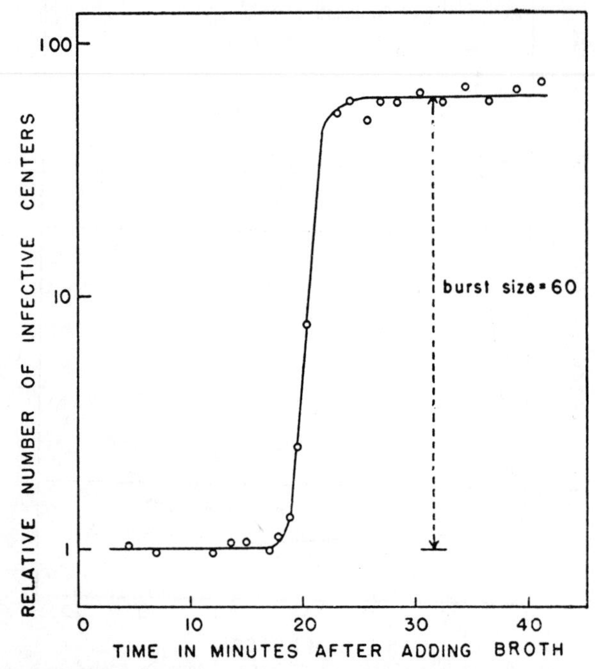

Figure 3. One-step growth curve at 37 C for T2r complexes formed in buffer. Broth added at time zero. "Infective center" signifies a plaque-forming unit, either an infected cell or a free phage particle.

2. *Growth.* To the suspension of infected cells in buffer at 37 C, an equal volume of broth at the same temperature is added, and time is reckoned from this moment. In the case of phage T2r the radiation resistance promptly begins to rise (figure 2). From the one step growth curve in figure 3, it may be seen that the (minimum) latent period for T2r is 19 minutes, and the average burst size is 60. For T7, the latent period is 12 minutes, and the burst size is 150. To stop development at any chosen time during the latent period, a sample is removed and diluted rapidly (by blowing out of a pipette) into buffer chilled in an ice bath. The chilling brings the change in radiation resistance to an immediate

halt; the resistance remains constant for hours provided the sample is kept chilled. The pipettes used for addition of broth and removal of samples are previously equilibrated at 37 C in an incubator.

In this manner, growth may be started and stopped in all cells simultaneously, and the timing controlled to within a few seconds. Furthermore, many samples may be taken at close intervals within the same growth experiment and the irradiation conducted afterwards at leisure.

For samples chilled very close to the end of the latent period (after 16 minutes for T2r or 9 minutes for T7) lysis is not prevented by chilling. After a delay, there appears a gradual increase in plaque count, presumably due to slow lysis of cells containing completed phage particles.

3. *Irradiation.* One or two ml of the suspension to be irradiated are placed in a shallow watch glass. The suspension is transparent to ultraviolet by virtue of the large dilution (100×) of the broth. Ice in a small dish is used to chill the suspension from below (figure 4). This prevents growth during the irradiation. Chilling also serves to reduce greatly the rate of photoreactivation (Dulbecco, 1950) which might otherwise be caused by the visible light emitted by the ultraviolet lamp.

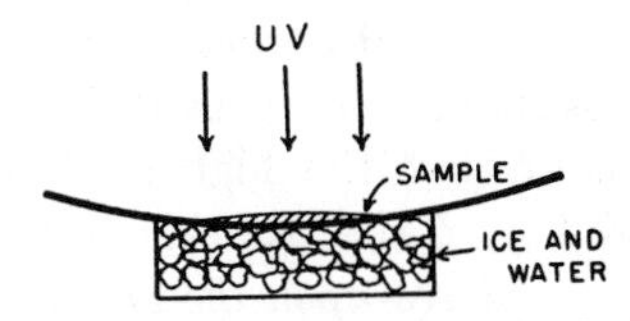

Figure 4. Arrangement for chilling sample during irradiation.

Ultraviolet is supplied by a 15 watt "germicidal lamp" (General Electric Company). The energy emitted in the 2537 A line accounts for almost all the antiphage activity. The intensity of ultraviolet is such that T2r survives to the extent of 10^{-2} after an exposure of 40 seconds. This same intensity is used throughout the experiments, and the doses are, therefore, given in units of seconds. All manipulations after irradiation are conducted in dim yellow light to minimize the possibility of photoreactivation.

4. *Plating.* Aliquots of samples subjected to various doses of ultraviolet are plated in a top layer of soft agar, seeded with unirradiated B, on broth agar plates. The resultant plaques are counted to determine the fraction of complexes whose infectivity has survived the irradiation.

Note on multiplicity of infection. It is essential that the proportion of phage particles to bacteria be kept quite small in order that very few multicomplexes (i.e., bacteria infected with more than one phage particle) be formed. This is particularly important in the case of T2, where the phage exhibits multiplicity reactivation and the multicomplexes are much more resistant to ultraviolet than monocomplexes. Thus, if one assumes a Poisson distribution of phages per bacterium, and a survival value of 10^{-2} is to be accurate within 10 per cent, the average multiplicity of infection must be 2×10^{-3} or less. In order to have such a low multiplicity of infection and still have a measurable concentration of survivors after growth, dilution, and irradiation, it is necessary to start with a high concentration of bacteria (1×10^9 per ml). Concentrations either half or twice this value were found to give the same results.

PRELIMINARY CONSIDERATIONS

1. *Ability of irradiated bacteria to support phage growth.* It is necessary to know the validity, under the conditions used, of the basic assumption that the irradiation of the bacteria does not affect their ability to support phage growth. For this reason Anderson's experiments were repeated, using phage T2r. Starved bacteria, prepared as previously described, were irradiated in buffer before addition of phage. The number of infective centers produced per adsorbed phage was determined by plating and compared to the result with unirradiated bacteria. At the intensity of ultraviolet here used, 4,000 seconds of irradiation are required to reduce to one-half the number of bacteria capable of liberating phage after infection with T2r. Since the largest doses used in irradiating infected cells were 1,000 seconds, inactivation of the bacterial part of the complex should have had a negligible effect upon the survival curve. It is conceivable, however, that the sensitivity of the bacterial part of the complex does not remain unchanged throughout the latent period. Indeed, it becomes difficult to separate the complex into phage and bacterial components once growth has started.

For T7, it is likewise found that the highest dose used (350 seconds) has negligible effect upon the ability of the bacteria to yield phage after infection.

2. *Effect of irradiation of complexes upon the latent period and burst size of the survivors.* It is found that a progressive lengthening of the latent period and decrease in burst size are produced by increasing doses of ultraviolet. For T2 monocomplexes irradiated at mid-latent period with a dose such that 5 per cent survive to form visible plaques, the latent period of the survivors is doubled and the burst size is reduced to 10 per cent of normal. This effect results in a smaller and more variable size of the plaques formed by surviving monocomplexes. The degree of the effect appears to be determined primarily by the dose of ultraviolet rather than the percentage inactivation of the complexes. Therefore, it is most apparent at times during the latent period when the largest doses are required for obtaining survival curves. In plotting survival curves and attempting to analyze them by target theory, we are assuming that inactivation of a complex is an all-or-none phenomenon. It must be realized that the delay in lysis and reduction in burst size of the surviving infective centers could also lead to failure of some of them to produce visible plaques. However, for the doses used in this paper, the plaques observed with T2r and T7 do not taper gradually down to zero in diameter; probably few infective centers fail to be counted for this reason.

RESULTS

Experiments with T2r. T2 (used by Luria and Latarjet) and its mutant T2r, which has the same sensitivity to ultraviolet as T2, gave similar results. It is preferable to work with T2r because it produces larger plaques, thereby obviating in some measure the difficulty created by the decrease in plaque size at large doses.

In figure 5 a complete set of curves for T2r (latent period 19 minutes) is given. These qualitatively confirm the observations of Luria and Latarjet with T2. The free phage does not have a strictly exponential survival curve, but the changes in resistance during the latent period are so large that this may be ignored for our purposes. At $t = 0$ (i.e., for a sample irradiated before the addition of nutrient) the resistance of monocomplexes is slightly higher (by 20 per cent) than that of free phage. This may be partially due to a small amount of development of the phage which can take place in buffer.

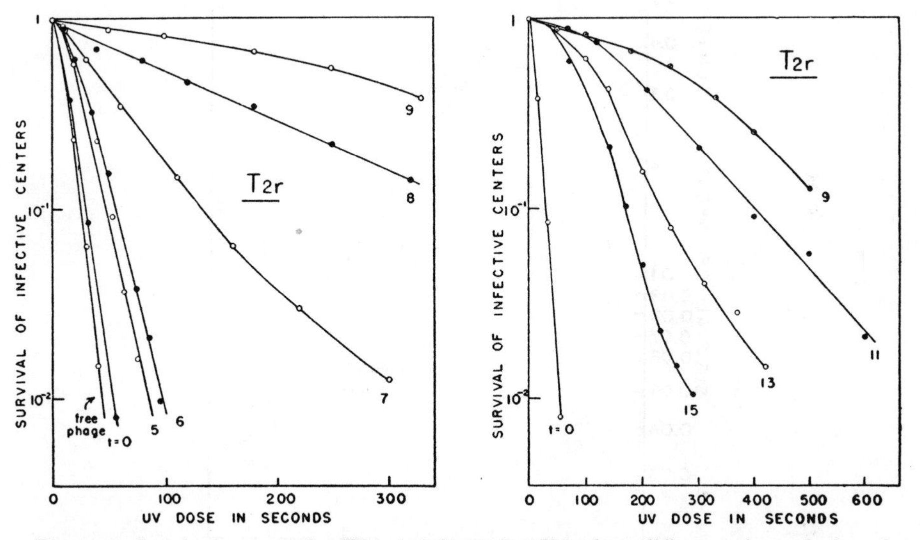

Figure 5. Survival curves for T2r complexes irradiated at different times during the latent period. Each curve is marked with the time in minutes after adding broth to the complexes formed in buffer. All data are from the same growth experiment at 37 C (latent period = 19 minutes). Average multiplicity of infection = 2×10^{-3}.

As development proceeds, the resistance of all complexes increases. An especially rapid rise occurs between 6 and 8 minutes, the curves still remaining essentially exponential. The smallness of the bend (at large doses) in the survival curve taken at 7 minutes is very significant, since it implies that, at least up to this point (one-third of the way into the latent period), development has progressed rather uniformly in all infected cells. If, at 7 minutes, 10 per cent of the infective centers had progressed to a stage corresponding to 8 minutes (by virtue of 15 per cent more rapid development), the bend in the 7 minute curve would have been greater than observed.

At 9 or 10 minutes the resistance reaches a maximum phase, and the curve has now become "multiple-target" in character. In figure 6 data are given which were obtained at 10 minutes. The points fit very well a theoretical curve for a double target. However, the fit may be fortuitous, since slight inhomogeneities in the stage of development are to be expected. At the time of maximum resistance, those complexes which are either slightly ahead or behind in stage of development have lower resistances, causing a distortion of the true curve at the moment of maximum resistance. Thereafter, the curve retains a multiple-target shape, but the resistance of the individual targets, as judged by the final slope, decreases progressively as the end of the latent period is approached.

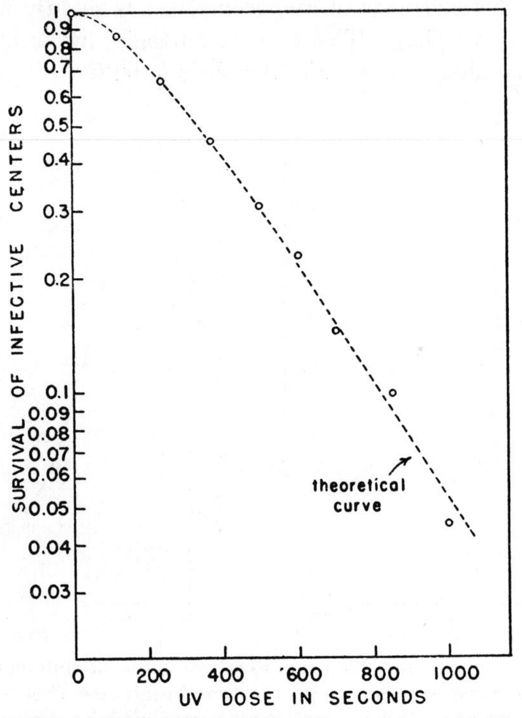

Figure 6. Circles: Survival data obtained for T2r complexes irradiated at the phase of highest resistance to ultraviolet (t = 10 minutes).

Dashed curve: Theoretical survival curve for a double-target complex.

The late curves have slight "tails" which may be due to a small fraction of cells in which the development is retarded.

In some experiments, peculiar composite survival curves were obtained as though the development in about half the cells was arrested at a stage corresponding to around 8 minutes, while the remaining cells continued normally. It has not been found possible to clarify the conditions leading to this result.

According to Doermann's findings, there may be a few infective phage particles per cell at the latest time here studied (15 minutes). These would presumably have the resistance of free phages. If survival as an infective center depends upon survival of either the complex or at least one completed phage, the effect of the phages upon the observed survival curve will be negligible, since at 15 minutes the complex has a much higher survival than have several free phages. By reference to figure 1 it can be seen that even a cluster of 100 phages would be inactivated more rapidly than the 15 minute complexes.

Experiments with T7. A complete set of survival curves for monocomplexes of T7 and strain B irradiated at intervals during the latent period (12 minutes) is given in figure 7. It will be observed that the resistance remains unchanged (at the same value as for free phage) for 3 minutes in the presence of nutrient.

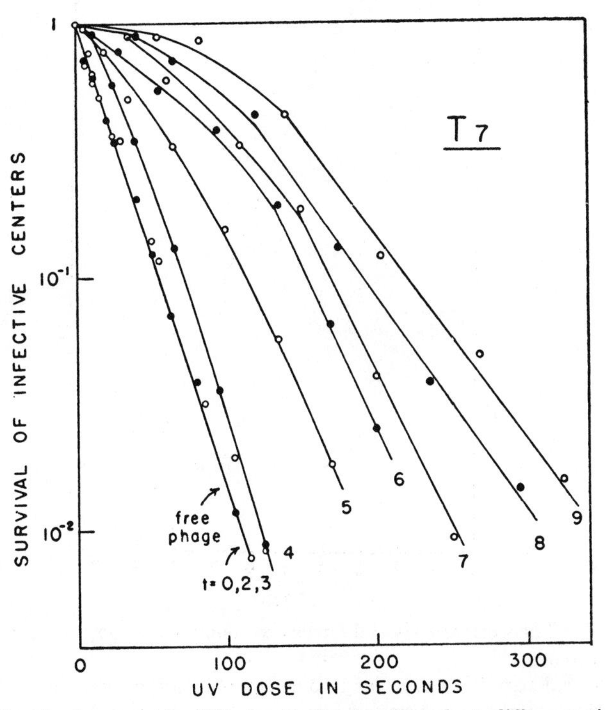

Figure 7. Survival curves for T7 complexes irradiated at different times during the latent period. Each curve is marked with the time in minutes after adding broth to the complexes formed in buffer. All data are from the same growth experiment at 37 C (latent period = 12 minutes). Average multiplicity of infection = 2×10^{-3}.

As time goes on, the curves become multiple-target in character, the average multiplicity continually increasing, while the final slope changes only slightly.

This result stands in marked contrast to T2r and resembles that predicted by target theory. The exact shapes of these curves are not consistent with an assumption of equal multiplicities for all complexes at a particular time. However, the shape may be explained by a distribution of the number of targets, which may be expected as a consequence of different rates of phage multiplication in different cells. It is well known (Delbrück, 1945) that the number of phage particles released by lysis of individual cells has an extremely wide distribution.

To illustrate the effect of such a wide distribution upon our survival curves, a composite curve is plotted in figure 8, assuming a population consisting of equal numbers of cells having the various multiplicities in figure 1. By extrapolation to zero dose of the asymptotic slope of such a curve, it is possible, in principle, to determine the *average* multiplicity. However, this requires precise data at low survival values and cannot be done accurately with the points in figure 7.

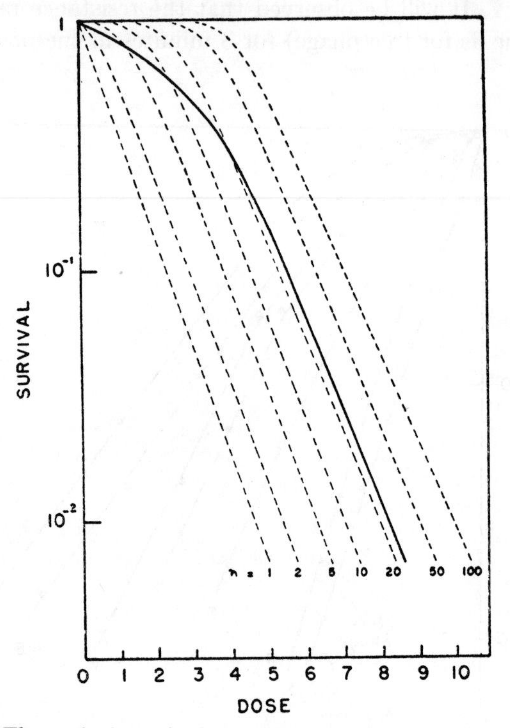

Figure 8. – – – – Theoretical survival curves for complexes containing various numbers of targets (as in figure 1).

——— Theoretical survival curve for a mixed population of complexes. The mixture is assumed to contain equal proportions of complexes having multiplicities 1, 2, 5, 10, 20, 50, and 100.

Note: It is possible, by assumption of a suitable population containing a very wide distribution of multiplicities, to obtain a composite theoretical survival curve which is exponential, simulating a "one-hit" curve (Dulbecco, personal communication).

DISCUSSION

The original intent of Luria and Latarjet's experiment, namely to observe the increase in the number of intracellular phage particles during the latent period, has been achieved with T7. The pattern of growth, so far as radiation resistance is concerned, does not exhibit the anomalies of (T2 and) T2r. There appears to be simply an increase with time of the average number of targets per cell, each target being similar radiologically to a T7 particle.

This result shows that irradiation of intracellular phage, in the case of T7, enables us to discern the existence of multiple intracellular entities at a time when fully infective phages are not yet detectable with the Doermann technique.

The anomalous results with T2r may be of far greater interest, however. During the critical phase between the entrance of one infecting particle and the appearance of intracellular progeny, enormous changes are reflected by the survival curves. It seems likely that these resistance changes may bear a close relation to the phenomenon of multiplicity reactivation. While the resistance changes do not tell us what is actually happening, they at least give us something easy to measure which serves as an empirical *index* to development. The value of this index has already been demonstrated previously in the justification of the techniques used in these experiments (adsorption in buffer, chilling to stop growth).

In the case of T2r, the maximum change in slope is by a factor of over 20 (free phage compared with $t = 10$ minutes). As pointed out by Luria and Latarjet, intracellular accumulation of ultraviolet-absorbing materials (nucleic acid components) must be considered as a possible contributing factor.

By microspectrography of uninfected cells (at 2570 A) Hedén (1951) finds an average extinction through the thickness of a cell of around 0.1, corresponding to 80 per cent transmission. A phage particle which is adsorbed on the surface of a bacterium is therefore shielded from ultraviolet to the extent of 20 per cent in one direction. This should lead to an average increase by only 10 per cent in the resistance (at $t = 0$) compared with free phage (since the cell rotates in all directions during exposure). Penetration of the phage into the cell should have little effect on the magnitude of this average shielding. In order to account for a subsequent change by a factor of 20 in the intensity of ultraviolet reaching the phage, a coating of nucleic acid, 1 μ in diameter, would have to be produced. The measurements of Luria and Human (1950) and Cohen and Arbogast (1950) on optical density and nucleic acid content in suspensions of cells multiple infected with T2 reveal increases during growth, but these are far too small to account for the observed resistance changes during the first 10 minutes.

In the case of T7, however, the small change in slope may well be due to a screening effect.

A plausible interpretation of the increase in resistance of T2r complexes during the first half of the latent period may be the following: A T2r particle, after adsorption to a sensitive bacterium, must undergo a series of successive steps A $\rightarrow$ B $\rightarrow$ C $\rightarrow$ D $\rightarrow$, etc. in the course of reproduction. Each of these steps has a certain cross section for being blocked by ultraviolet (e.g., by inactivation of an enzyme which is concerned with the step). Blockade of any one of these steps prevents normal development and causes inactivation of the phage. At time zero, the total cross section of the phage is therefore the sum of these individual cross sections, and the survival curve is exponential. As development proceeds, the steps which have already been passed are no longer needed, and the effective cross section decreases progressively while inactivation of the remaining steps retains the characteristics of a one-hit phenomenon.

The absence of this behavior in the case of T7 suggests that there may be great differences in the mode of reproduction of T7 and T2r. These two phages are also dissimilar in other respects. T2r is a relatively large particle with a head and a tail and appears to have a kind of membrane (Anderson, 1949); it shows multiplicity reactivation with other particles of T2r, and also undergoes genetic recombination with mutants of T2 and other closely related phages. T7, on the other hand, is much smaller in size, spherical in shape, does not appear to have a membrane, and does not show multiplicity reactivation. Whether it undergoes genetic recombination is not known.

Therefore, the sequence of events in the intracellular development of T2r, which is reflected in the resistance changes, may be characteristic for the multiplication of only certain types of phage.

We stand to learn a great deal about the growth of T2r by making use of the *radiation resistance index*. If conditions are suitable for phage development, the index (i.e., the survival of infective centers after a given standard dose of ultraviolet) goes up (or down, in the latter half of the latent period). If, for any reason, phage development is blocked, the index remains constant; its value marks the stage at which the block occurs. This makes it possible to study the effect, at any chosen part of the latent period (except near the end), of many factors, for example temperature, growth requirements, and specific chemical inhibitors. The results of these investigations will be reported separately.

This tool offers promise not only for studying phage growth but for certain problems in bacterial physiology as well. The growth of phage in a bacterium is dependent upon the metabolic well-being of the cell and on its ability to make use of the substrates supplied to it. By infecting the bacterium with a T2r particle and using the radiation resistance index, the metabolic capabilities of the bacterium under particular conditions can be measured. A unique feature of this technique is that one can determine not only the average rate of metabolism but the *distribution of rates* (from analysis of the survival curves) among the individual cells in the population. This idea is currently being applied to the problem of the kinetics of enzymatic adaptation in bacteria.

SUMMARY

Techniques are described for simultaneous starting and stopping of the growth of bacteriophage in all the host cells of a culture. Using these techniques, a comparison is made of the changes in resistance to ultraviolet of phages T2r and T7 during intracellular growth, following the method of Luria and Latarjet.

Phage T7 gives results similar to expectations from target theory, while the results with T2r confirm the (anomalous) behavior observed by Luria and Latarjet, indicating that there may be large differences in the modes of reproduction of different phages.

The utility of the change in resistance as a tool in studying bacteriophage reproduction and certain problems in bacterial physiology is pointed out.

REFERENCES

ANDERSON, T. F. 1948 The growth of T2 virus on UV killed host cells. J. Bact., **56**, 403–410.

ANDERSON, T. F. 1949 The reactions of bacterial viruses with their host cells. Botan. Revs., **15**, 464–505.

COHEN, S. S., AND ARBOGAST, R. 1950 The mutual reactivation of $T2r^+$ virus inactivated by ultraviolet light and the synthesis of desoxyribose nucleic acid. J. Exptl. Med., **91,** 637–650.

DELBRÜCK, M. 1945 The burst size distribution in the growth of bacterial viruses. J. Bact., **50,** 131–135.

DOERMANN, A. H. 1948 Intracellular growth of bacteriophage. Carnegie Inst. of Wash. Year Book, **47,** 176–182.

DULBECCO, R. 1950 Experiments on photoreactivation of UV-inactivated bacteriophage. J. Bact., **59,** 329–347.

HEDÉN, C. 1951 Studies of the infection of *E. Coli* B with the bacteriophage T2. Acta Path. Microbiol. Scand., Supplementum LXXXVIII.

LATARJET, R. 1948 Intracellular growth of bacteriophage studied by Roentgen irradiation. J. Gen. Physiol., **31,** 529–546.

LURIA, S. E. 1947 Reactivation of irradiated bacteriophage by transfer of self-reproducing units. Proc. Natl. Acad. Sci., **33,** 253–264.

LURIA, S. E., AND DULBECCO, R. 1949 Genetic recombinations leading to production of active bacteriophage from ultraviolet inactivated bacteriophage particles. Genetics, **34,** 93–125.

LURIA, S. E., AND HUMAN, M. L. 1950 Chromatin staining of bacteria during bacteriophage infection. J. Bact., **59,** 551–560.

LURIA, S. E., AND LATARJET, R. 1947 Ultraviolet irradiation of bacteriophage during intracellular growth. J. Bact., **53,** 149–163.

INVESTIGATIONS ON A LYSOGENIC BACILLUS MEGATERIUM

by

André Lwoff and Antoinette Gutmann

Department of Microbial Physiology of the Institut Pasteur

I. Introduction

We call lysogenic bacteria those bacteria which perpetuate the capacity to form bacteriophages without intervention of exogenous bacteriophages. This definition will be discussed and justified in the course of this work. Thanks to the investigations of J. Bordet, of F. Burnet and M. McKie, of Den Dooren de Jong, of E. and E. Wollman, and of J. Gratia, it is known: 1. that in a lysogenic strain lysogeny is an attribute of every bacterium and, in the case of sporogenic species, of every spore; 2. that lysogeny persists after repeated passages in the presence of a specific anti-bacteriophage serum; 3. that lysogenic bacteria adsorb the bacteriophages which they produce; 4. that lysozyme lysis does not liberate bacteriophages from potentially lysogenic bacteria; 5. that, starting from certain sensitive strains infected by a given bacteriophage, one can isolate lysogenic bacteria which produce a bacteriophage identical to the original bacteriophage.

It thus seems strange that the very existence of lysogenic bacteria could have been put in doubt by A. D. Hershey and J. Bronfenbrenner (1948), who wrote: "How virus is transmitted from cell to cell in lysogenic cultures seemingly refractive to lysis remains to be clarified. It must be concluded, however, that the phenomenon of lysogenesis, frequently cited as evidence for the spontaneous intracellular origin of virus, can equally well be explained as some type of association between exogenous virus and incompletely susceptible bacterium." It seems that one must look for the origin of the skepticism in a possibly too narrow definition of "true" lysogeny due to M. Delbrück (1946), which restricts lysogeny to the case where the bacteriophage is liberated by bacteria in the absence of lysis. Since no example of this phenomenon is known, lysogeny vanishes. This "true" lysogeny was contrasted by M. Delbrück with "pseudo-lysogeny," in which bacteriophages are liberated following the lysis of sensitive bacteria, the latter being produced by mutation in the course of the growth of a

Translated from the French and reprinted by permission of the authors and the Institut Pasteur from the Annales de l'Institut Pasteur, **78**, 711-739 (1950). (N.B. A part of the section "Materials and Techniques" has been omitted from the translation of this paper.)

resistant culture contaminated by bacteriophages. But these arbitrary definitions do not exclude lysogeny in the sense in which we have defined it; lysogeny in which the property to produce bacteriophage is hereditary. In 1925 J. Bordet wrote: "The faculty to reproduce bacteriophages is inscribed into the very hereditary weft of the microbe," and Burnet and McKie (1929b) expressed exactly the same idea: "The permanence of the lysogenic character makes it necessary to assume the presence of bacteriophage, or its *anlage*, in every cell of the culture, i.e., it is a part of the hereditary constitution of the strain."

No doubt the experiments on which this conclusion was based — which shall be discussed in the course of this work — however suggestive they were, did not bring the element of certainty. It is true that as late as 1949, in spite of numerous works published on lysogenic bacteria, one still did not know the manner in which lysogenic bacteria liberate the bacteriophage that they produce. Is the bacteriophage secreted by the bacteria in a continuous manner? Is it secreted at the moment of division? Is it liberated by the lysis of certain bacteria? In the absence of any facts, the majority of microbiologists envisaged, along with Bordet and Renaux (1928), and with Burnet and McKie (1929b), that the bacteriophage is "secreted" by the bacterium. But it is really of little importance for the definition of lysogeny whether the bacteriophage is liberated in this or any other manner. The important fact is the reproduction of a bacterium potentially capable of producing a bacteriophage, that is to say the hereditary capacity to produce a bacteriophage. Naturally this does not exclude the mode of liberation of the bacteriophage from being worthy of our attention.

J. Northrop (1939) established a parallelism between enzymes and bacteriophages, based on the observation that the concentration of bacteriophages in a culture of lysogenic bacteria increases, like that of the enzyme gelatinase, in an essentially parallel manner to the multiplication of the bacteria. But it is quite evident that the interpretation which one can draw from such facts will be very different according to whether, for example, in the interval of two divisions every one of 100 individuals of a bacterial population liberates a bacteriophage, or whether a single bacterium liberates 100 bacteriophages.

The principal problems posed by the existence of lysogenic strains are the following: 1. Can the faculty of producing bacteriophages really be perpetuated without intervention of exogenous bacteriophages? 2. How do lysogenic bacteria liberate the bacteriophages which they produce? 3. If the production of bacteriophages appertains to only a certain proportion of the bacteria, then what factors induce the production of bacteriophages in a population of potentially lysogenic bacteria? The experiments presented here in detail were summarized in four preliminary notes (Lwoff and Gutmann, 1949-1950); they furnish a reply to the first two questions. The third question was studied in collaboration with L. Siminovitch and N. Kjeldgaard, and the relevant results shall be the subject of a separate paper.

II. Materials and Techniques

It was evident *a priori* that the study of "mass cultures," as it is usually practiced, can only furnish partial solutions to the problems of lysogenic bacteria. Only observations carried out on individual bacteria, or on microcultures containing a small number of individuals, are capable of leading to definite conclusions.

Strain. Our experiments were carried out on a lysogenic strain of *Bacillus megaterium.* We have used the classic strain "899" of den Dooren and de Jong and an asporogenic sensitive mutilat strain. Lysogenic and mutilat strains were subcultured by passages on peptone broth agar.

Technique of Micromanipulation. One utilizes an incubator box made from transparent plastic material. An electric heater is placed under the bottom of this box, into which 20 or so holes have been drilled. The temperature is thus the same in all parts of the incubator box and a thermoregulator in one corner insures a constant temperature of 37°. The microscope and the receptor for the de Fonbrune micromanipulator are fixed on the base of the Zeiss-Peterfi micromanipulator. We have utilized the oil chamber of de Fonbrune. It is unnecessary to go into details concerning this device, of which one can find a description in the monograph of de Fonbrune (1949). A knowledge of these technical details, however, can prevent considerable loss of time.

Two pieces of glass of 1.5 × 12 × 7 mm. are glued to either side of the depression slide. Their separation is so calculated that it exceeds the length of the coverslips by about .8 mm. The latter, made from neutral glass, are washed in nitric acid, rinsed in double distilled water, wiped with fine cloth and sterilized (as well as the slide) at 150°.

For the preparation of the experiment: 1. one sets a cover slip on the slide and places several drops of paraffin oil on the cover slip, so that it is covered by a layer of oil. 2. One draws out the fine end of a Pyrex glass Pasteur pipette so that the diameter of the terminal capillary allows passage of culture medium and that when the tip of the pipette filled with liquid comes in contact with the cover slip under the oil, one drop of liquid comes out and spreads out on the glass. This drop must have a diameter of about 500 to 800 μ. Nine rows of 9 drops can thus be regularly placed. The second and third rows are interrupted at the point of the fourth, fifth, and sixth drop. It is of course possible to place several different media on the cover slip. The cover slip is then turned upside down and oil is poured between it and the slide. On the bottom of the oil chamber one places drops of distilled water in a manner so as not to disturb the observations; this will prevent any significant evaporation of drops of less than 100 μ diameter. The oil chamber is then placed on the stage of the microscope.

Technique of Sampling. It is necessary that one can transfer one bacterium, or a minimum quantity of liquid of the order of 10^{-5} mm.^{3}, into a tube or onto a petri dish. The dimensions of the liquid column sampled can be measured with the micrometer objective. In order to transfer the content of a pipette into the tube, one can proceed in the following manner: 1. The field of the microscope is disengaged by placing the oil chamber towards the rear. 2. The needle and the needle carrier are turned by 90°, in such a manner that the point of the needle points towards the right. The angle formed by the micropipette is then in a plane parallel to that of the stage of the microscope. The pipette is then displaced towards the left, out of the microscope field. 3. A Pasteur pipette whose tip has been bent at a right angle about two to three mm. from the end is introduced into the right needle carrier of the Peterfi micromanipulator. The pipette contains dilution medium for a length of about 2 cm. It is so oriented that the angle formed by the terminal bend is in a plane parallel to the plane of the stage. 4. The tip of this pipette is brought into the center of the microscope field. The micropipette is then moved towards the right and its level regulated in such a manner that its point is opposite the liquid meniscus of the Pasteur pipette. One introduces the micropipette into the liquid. One inoculates the content of the micropipette into the liquid column of the Pasteur pipette. If one manipulates the bacterium, it is possible to see that bacterium pass from micropipette to Pasteur pipette. In any case, one knows that the operation is finished when a drop of oil appears at the point of the micropipette. All these manipulations are carried out in the incubator box. 5. The Pasteur pipette is then detached from its support, removed from the box and its contents transferred either into a tube or onto a petri plate. After a little practice, these operations can be performed very quickly and with great assurance. All of these manipulations are naturally carried out aseptically. According to our experience, which includes almost 1000 samplings, the chances of contamination are practically nil, since one manipulates liquid quantities of the order of 10^{-5} to 10^{-3} mm^3.

III. Bacterial Multiplication without Liberation of Bacteriophage

a. A diplo-bacillus, after five washings, is inoculated into a drop of peptone water. After each division, one of the daughter cells is removed with a minimum of the liquid. Twenty-two daughter cells are thus successively removed. The entire drop is then removed: no bacteriophages.

b. In another experiment of the same type, one removes successively 42 daughter cells: the result is identical. Furthermore, assays of four samplings in the course of the experiment and of the total sample at the end show no bacteriophages.

c. The washed filament of three bacteria is observed. One removes successively 14 daughter cells and makes 5 samplings. After the last division, the entire fluid is assayed: no bacteriophages.

d. Three diplo-bacilli are washed and inoculated separately into drops of peptone water. When the number of bacteria has attained respectively 24, 47, and 54, the entire fluid is sampled. There are no bacteriophages in the fluid nor in any of the samples previously taken.

e. Three diplo-bacilli are washed and transferred into drops of peptone water of 72 to 100 mμ diameter. Multiplication stops spontaneously when the number of bacteria reaches respectively 8, 12 and 16. All of the fluid is removed and sampled: no bacteriophages.

f. A filament of 7 bacteria is washed and inoculated into a synthetic medium.

After two hours, there are 82 bacteria: all of the liquid is sampled, no bacteriophages.

Discussion. These experiments, as well as those which shall be described in the two following paragraphs, lead to the thought that a lysogenic bacterium multiplies without producing bacteriophages. They demonstrate that *B. megaterium* 899 can grow and multiply without liberating bacteriophages. Thus, liberation of bacteriophages is not a phenomenon which necessarily accompanies growth of a population of a lysogenic bacteria; it appears, rather, to be a contingent phenomenon.

IV. Maintenance of Lysogenic Power in the Absence of Free Bacteriophage

A motile diplo-bacillus is sampled from a culture in peptone water (proteose peptone at 1%). This bacillus is successively transferred in six drops of the same medium. It is left in the sixth. During the entire length of this experiment the diplo-bacillus has remained motile. With *B. megaterium* the separation of the daughter members generally takes place when the daughter bacteria are already partitioned off. Once this separation releases two daughter diplo-bacilli, one injects into the drop approximately $\frac{1}{5}$ of its volume of new medium. One assures a mixing of the fluids by repeated aspiration back and forth of approximately half of the fluid and then removes one of the bacteria in a volume essentially equal to the volume of fluid which has been added. This sample is transferred into a suspension of sensitive mutilat in soft agar and this suspension is then spread on an agar surface. This operation was repeated until the 10th division. At this point, the two daughter bacteria were sampled separately, the latter with the total of the residual fluid. The 11 plates that had been inoculated all showed a single plaque centered by a bacterial colony, with the exception of the first and the eighth, which showed no plaque whatsoever. The absence of the lysogenic colony on the two negative "plates" in this experiment, as in the following, probably results from an accidental loss of the bacterium. This experiment was repeated in peptone water to which glucose and a liver extract had been added. The original diplo-bacillus was followed until the 19th division, after which the two final bacteria were plated. The 20 plates, with the exception of the 4th and the 16th which showed no plaque whatsoever, each had, as in the previous series, one plaque centered by a lysogenic colony. One of these centered colonies, after being picked and isolated, proved itself to be lysogenic: the filtrate of its culture contained bacteriophages.

The absence of any plaque, except for the single plaque centered by a bacterial colony, shows that no free bacteriophages ever appeared in these microcultures. During the experiments, there was never any noticeable decrease in the size of the diplo-bacillus, as would have occurred if one of its members had lysed, nor was lysis ever observed. Incidentally any lysis would have brought some disturbance in the rhythm of the divisions; but the 19 divisions took place in 486 minutes at regular intervals of 25 ± 3 minutes.

Discussion. It was established by Bordet and Renaux (1928) that lysogenic strains of *E. coli* conserve their lysogenic nature after numerous passages in the presence of an antibacteriophage serum. Analogous results had been obtained by F. Burnet and M. McKie for various bacteria (1929a,b) and by E. and E. Wollman (1936) for *B. megaterium.* Since the antibacteriophage serum neutralizes free bacteriophages, these experiments demonstrate that lysogeny can maintain itself in the absence of free bacteriophages, provided that the concentration of antibacteriophage serum during the entire length of the experiment is sufficient to immediately inactivate all bacteriophages. In other words, one must be sure that, under the conditions of these experiments, there is no possibility of a free bacteriophage infecting a bacterium before being neutralized by the serum. This condition was probably met in some of these experiments, but this is not *a priori* certain. And nothing enables us to state categorically that bacteriophages which adsorb to bacteria are actually inactivated by serum.

It is also known that lysogeny maintains itself equally well in cultures growing in media supposedly deprived of calcium; in fact, in media containing oxylate or citrate (E. and E. Wollman, A. Gratia). But numerous organic substances possess the power to form complexes with calcium; these complexes could then dissociate, and, in organic media, it is difficult to ascertain the absence of free Ca^{++} ions. The fact that lysogeny of a culture maintains itself in a citrate medium, whereas the adsorption of bacteriophage does not take place except in the presence of calcium, is but an argument in favor of its endomicrobial perpetuation.

Finally, it was shown by Den Dooren de Jong that the lysogenic function of *B. megaterium* is transmitted in cultures which have been derived from a spore, and even from a heated spore. This is true for all sporogenic lysogenic strains. This is, thus, an additional argument in favor of the endomicrobial transmission of the bacteriophage. But, unfortunately, the form of the bacteriophage within the interior of the spore is not known. If one adds to all of these considerations the fact that in a lysogenic culture every colony — supposedly obtained from a single cell — is lysogenic, one sees that a considerable accumulation of facts favors the conception that the faculty to form bacteriophages is hereditary, that is to say, independent of any exogenous reinfection. In our experiments, lysogeny is maintained in the course of 19 divisions in the absence of free bacteriophage. If the bacteriophage does not multiply within the bacterium and if the maintenance of lysogeny proceeds from particles adsorbed on the original diplo-bacillus and distributed equally over the daughter bacteria, then that diplo-bacillus must have carried a minimum of 2^{19} or 524,288 bacteriophages at the onset. The chance of an unequal repartition over the daughter cells in combination with our selection of that bacterium which happened to have inherited the smallest number of bacteriophages after each such division is so small that it need not be taken into consideration.

S. Bayne-Jones and L. A. Sandholzer (1933) estimated the average volume of a single *B. megaterium* as 2.5 μ^3. Let us assume the value of 6 μ^3 for the average diplo-bacillus. According to McLauchlan, E. M. Clark, and F. W. Boswell (1947), the dimensions of the head of the bacteriophage of *Bacillus megaterium* are 40 by 100 mμ, that is to say, a volume of approximately $.9 \times 10^{-4}\ \mu^3$. Let us suppose that the polyhedral bacteriophages completely fill the entire diplo-bacillus, which could then contain no more than 66,000 bacteriophages. But, in any case, the maximum number of bacteriophages produced by any single bacterium never seems to surpass 1000.

One can consider, without much chance of error, that in a viable lysogenic bacterium the space occupied by the bacteriophages must not surpass 50% of the total bacterial volume. An average viable lysogenic *B. megaterium* diplo-bacillus could thus contain maximally 33,000 bacteriophages. This figure is significantly lower than the value of 524,288 which represents the minimum number of particles which must have been present in the original diplo-bacillus in order to sustain the hypothesis of the perpetuation of the lysogenic function by a simple distribution of pre-existing exogenous particles. This hypothesis thus can be rejected.

The hypothesis, according to which lysogeny perpetuates itself by an endo-microbial route without the necessary intervention of exogenous bacteriophages, seems to us, for the moment, the only one capable of accounting satisfactorily for the experimental facts. The problem of the form in which the lysogeny perpetuates itself shall be discussed in the course of this work. Another conclusion can be drawn from our experiments. One knows (J. Bordet and J. Renaux, 1928; F. Burnet and M. McKie, 1929a,b) that all colonies issuing from a lysogenic culture are lysogenic. Our experiments confirm and validate these data: every diplo-bacillus from a population of *B. megaterium* 899 isolated by means of the macromanipulator gives rise to a lysogenic colony.

V. Lysozyme Lysis Does Not Liberate Bacteriophage

F. Burnet and M. McKie (1929a), F. Burnet and D. Lush (1936) observed that lysis by a bacteriophage X of a lysogenic bacterium sensitive to this bacteriophage X and normally producing a bacteriophage Y does not liberate the bacteriophage Y. F. Burnet and M. McKie understood the whole significance of this phenomenon as early as 1929 and concluded that all bacteria of a permanently lysogenic strain possess in their hereditary constitution some unit which is potentially capable of liberating phage. Burnet and McKie found, nevertheless, that a small proportion (about 1%) of the bacteria, of a 24-hour-old agar culture harbors bacteriophages which can be liberated by treatment with distilled water. E. and E. Wollman and A. Gratia (1936), independently and within a few weeks of each other, made a similar observation: lysozyme lysis of lysogenic *B. megaterium* 899 does not liberate bacteriophages. E. and E. Wollman found one bacteriophage for several thousand bacterial colonies and concluded that the bacteriophage exists in two different forms, phases, or states: the "mature" bacteriophage which one could call corpuscular, or, more simply, bacteriophage-virus as it appears in the free state in the culture medium, and the non-virulent, latent "intracellular bacteriophage" as it exists inside lysogenic bacteria and which we call probacteriophage. Furthermore, it is known that it is impossible to liberate by lysozyme lysis bacteriophages adsorbed to living *B. megaterium* cells.

In contrast, lysozyme lysis does liberate bacteriophages adsorbed to killed bacteria (A. Pirie, 1940). The bacteriophage virus does not transform itself into probacteriophage except in living bacteria.

The importance of these facts stimulated us to verify the action of lysozyme lysis. Washed bacteria are placed into microdrops. In the course of exponential multiplication, one injects into the microcultures a solution of lysozyme of such concentration that its final dilution is 1 to 50,000. The bacteria are lysed in several minutes. In different experiments 12, 34, 80, and 208 bacteria were thus lysed. All of the liquid was sampled: no bacteriophages. The presence of lysozyme at the concentration of 1 to 50,000 in a microdrop does not interfere with the assay because the medium is considerably diluted. These observations thus extend to exponentially growing bacteria the results of E. and E. Wollman and of A. Gratia on *B. megaterium* and they confirm the fundamental observation of F. Burnet and M. McKie (1929b).

VI. How Do Lysogenic Bacteria Liberate Bacteriophages?

We are thus in possession of the following facts: 1. In the lysogenic strain of *B. megaterium* 899, every bacterium isolated in the micromanipulator and washed gives rise to a lysogenic colony. 2. The faculty of producing bacteriophages perpetuates itself in the absence of exogenous bacteriophages, that is to say by an endomicrobial route. 3. Bacteria can multiply without liberating bacteriophages. 4. Lysozyme lysis does not liberate bacteriophages.

Nevertheless, a filtrate of a culture of lysogenic *B. megaterium*, indeed the filtrate of every lysogenic culture, always contains some bacteriophages. We have verified the fact that this is also true for dense cultures in microdrops: one always finds bacteriophages in the liquid of a small drop of peptone water which contains several thousand bacteria. One can thus entertain the hypothesis that only a small percentage of the bacteria produce bacteriophages. We were encouraged to persevere in the investigation of the mode of liberation of bacteriophages by the observation of bacterial "ghosts." The formation of the ghosts was observed in the microdrops. It is the result of a relatively slow degeneration of the bacterium which can take several minutes or several seconds. The ghosts persist for several hours. We thought that we had observed bacteriophage lysis. But assay of the medium after the slow lysis did not reveal any bacteriophages. Nevertheless, we continued to follow the development of the microclones, assaying the medium from time to time. We give here the results of a first series of experiments published previously in a preliminary note (A. Lwoff and A. Gutmann, 1949b).

A. A filament of free bacteria is washed and brought into one drop of medium S. The following table gives the time in minutes (*m*), and the number of bacteria (*b*):

m	*b*	*m*	*b*
0	3	65	7
30	4	105	25
55	6	123	45

After the 123rd minute one removes $28 \times 10^6 \mu^3$ of medium, representing approximately 90% of the volume of the drop: 480 bacteriophages. The bacteria remained united in the long filament. No lysis had been observed. No ghost was visible. We thus concluded that it might be possible that the production of bacteriophages proceeds in the absence of bacterial lysis. At this time we knew only one type of lysis: the slow lysis in which a well recognizable ghost persists and we thought that the absence of such a ghost implies the absence of lysis. Since then, we have recognized another rapid type of lysis, in the course of which the bacteria disappear in less than one second without leaving a recognizable residue. This is the type of lysis which liberates bacteriophages. Several terminal bacteria could well have lysed in the course of this experiment, and this lysis could have gone unnoticed. This experiment can thus not be retained to support the thesis of a liberation of bacteriophage without bacterial lysis.

B. A diplo-bacillus is washed and placed in peptone water. One notices, according to the table below, that one bacteria disappeared between the 50th and the 55th minute, two disappeared between the 61st and the 62nd minute:

m	*b*
0	2
4	4
14	4
31	6
35	7
50	11
55	10
61	13
62	11
83	17
109	43

Samples were taken from the microdrops after 14, 43, and 55 minutes respectively 2.5×10^3, 4×10^3, and $2.4 \times 10^3 \mu^3$: no bacteriophages. At the 63rd minute, one samples $2.4 \times 10^3 \mu^3$: 18 bacteriophages. At the 83rd minute, $3.2 \times 10^3 \mu^3$: 17 bacteriophages. At the 115th minute $5.15 \times 10^3 \mu^3$: 68 bacteriophages. The residual volume was $92 \times 10^3 \mu^3$. The initial volume was thus $149 \times 10^3 \mu^3$. One can thus calculate that the number of bacteriophages at the time of the three samplings was 1130, 725, and 190. It is to be noted that the sampling made at the 55th minute, after the disappearance of one bacterium, did not reveal any bacteriophages. In this experiment the bacteria were motile. It is possible that the first lysis was a slow lysis which did not produce bacteriophages and in which the bacterial ghost remained unnoticed. One also notices that the calculated number of bacteriophages was 1,130, a number which seems to us too high to correspond to the lysis of only two bacteria. It is possible that, in this experiment, the mixing before the first sampling was insufficient.

C. A filament of three bacteria is washed and transferred into peptone water. The history of these three bacteria, *a*, *b*, and *c*, which remained in a single filament, is indicated in the table below. One notices that bacterium *a* divided twice, and that the four bacteria which issued from its division lysed between the 88th and the 114th minute.

m	*a*	*b*	*c*
0	1	1	1
25	1	1	2
55	2	1	2
77	2	1	2
82	4	1	3
88	4	1	4
107	2	1	4
114	0	2	4
120		2	6
134		2	9
142		2	9
155		2	11

A sampling of $1 \times 10^5\ \mu^3$ undertaken at the 114th minute did not reveal bacteriophages. A sampling of 1.4×10^5 at the 142nd minute revealed the presence of 71 bacteriophages. Sampling the total fluid at the 155th minute ($116.3 \times 10^5\ \mu^3$) revealed 400 bacteriophages. If one takes into account the ratio of these volumes, one concludes that the total number of bacteriophages must have been approximately 900 at the instant of the 2nd sampling. It is to be noted that the first sampling at the 114th minute was negative while at the 142nd minute there was the appearance of numerous bacteriophages without there having been any lysis of other bacteria. It is possible that also here, as in the preceding experiment, the mixing of the culture medium was insufficient. It is also possible that after lysis the bacteriophages remained engulfed in the viscous cellular debris for some minutes and thus escaped the action of mixing currents.

Another experiment should allow us to recognize the character of the lysis by the bacteriophage. A diplo-bacillus is washed and inoculated in one drop of proteose peptone. At the 26th minute, there are two diplo-bacilli, of which one is removed. At the 72nd minute, two other diplo-bacilli are removed. There a filament containing 4 bacteria remains in the drop. A sampling of $6.5 \times 10^3\ \mu^3$ made at this moment is negative; at the 143rd minute there is a filament of 8 and a filament of 10 bacteria. One sees one of the bacteria — perhaps one diplo-bacillus? — disappear in about 1 second without leaving any trace. One samples

$8.5 \times 10^4 \mu^3$ of fluid, corresponding to about half the volume of the drop: 110 bacteriophages. The total number of bacteriophages produced is thus about 220. It is this observation which convinced us of the existence of a rapid lysis followed by the appearance of bacteriophages. Subsequently, we have often observed lysis followed by the appearance of bacteriophages. We have noticed that this lysis does not leave any visible ghost and that it often occurs in less than one second. It could thus very well pass unobserved in a drop which contained several diplo-bacilli in the process of multiplication.

We had thought (1949b) that we observed the liberation of bacteriophages without lysis, but after having recognized the two types of lysis — slow and rapid — and having analyzed the possible causes of error which can arise in the course of experiments in microdrops, we have attempted experiments in which a very small number of bacteria shall be present at the same time in a single microdrop. Each time that this was possible, we have worked in such a manner that only a single diplo-bacillus was present in a drop. It is only under these conditions that one can be assured that bacterial lysis is not overlooked.

We have also tried to achieve conditions under which a single diplo-bacillus, or a single bacterium, lyses in one drop. In this way, one can sample the totality of the microdrop, thus avoiding having to measure the dimensions of the micropipette and calculating its volume and reducing the causes of error in the quantitative determinations to a minimum. We took care to stir the drop repeatedly if only a part of the drop was to be sampled. One will see in the following that no liberation of bacteriophage was observed in the absence of bacterial lysis.

Second Series of Experiments. a. A filament of 14 bacteria is washed and transferred into a microdrop of peptone water at time h; at $h + 20$ minutes, there are 18 bacteria. A diplo-bacillus detaches itself and is transferred into a microdrop. Its two members lyse at $h + 40$ minutes, at 40-second intervals. At $h + 68$ minutes, 8 bacteria of the original drop are transferred into microdrops, where they lyse without leaving a trace in less than 10 minutes. There remained 8 bacteria in the original drop. Seven of them lysed under our eyes between $h + 67$ and $h + 71$. The residual bacterium is eliminated. All of the liquid is then sampled. The plaques on the petri dish are almost confluent, impossible to count. It looked as if there were about 2000 plaques on the plate.

b. A filament of three bacteria is washed and brought into a drop A. At time $h + 45$, there are about 4 bacteria. A sampling made then is negative: no bacteriophages. At $h + 60$ minutes, there are 6 bacteria, only 4 at $h + 72$. These four residual bacteria are transferred with a minimum of fluid into one drop B. All of drop A is sampled: 138 phages, corresponding to the lysis of two bacteria. In drop B two out of four bacteria lysed between $h + 72$ and $h + 79$. The two residual bacteria are transferred with a minimum of fluid into a drop C. All of drop B is sampled, where two bacteria have lysed: 38 bacteriophages. The two bacteria remain for 28 minutes in drop C. They are then transferred into D. The total sampling of C does not reveal any bacteriophages. In drop D the two bacteria disappear 4 minutes after their transfer: total sampling indicates 162 bacteriophages. One will notice that in drop C, where two bacteria remained until the fourth minute preceding lysis, there was no liberation of bacteriophages.

c. A diplo-bacillus was washed and brought into a drop A. Samplings made at $h + 35$ and $h + 70$ minutes are negative. At $h + 120$ minutes there are four bacteria. At the 140th minute, lysis of two members of a diplo-bacillus is observed within a 10-second interval. The other two bacteria are transferred into drops B and C. Total sampling of A: 27 bacteriophages. The bacterium in drop B disappears after the 12th minute: 9 bacteriophages. After 17 minutes in drop C, the remaining bacterium is transferred to D, from where, after an additional 17 minutes, it is transferred into drop E. All of drops C and D are sampled: no bacteriophages. In drop E, the bacterium has disappeared after the third minute: 15 bacteriophages. During the 34 minutes that had preceded lysis there was thus no liberation of bacteriophages by the bacterium which had liberated bacteriophages in drop E.

d. A diplo-bacillus is washed and put under observation in a microdrop. At $h + 3$ minutes there are three bacteria, at $h + 48$ minutes: 7 bacteria. At the 65th minute, each of the bacteria has divded in two. There are eight bacteria which have remained together in one filament. At $h + 83$, one of the bacteria is lysed. Within 6 minutes, three other bacteria have lysed. The four bacteria which have disappeared belong to the same mother bacterium. All of the fluid is sampled: 579 bacteriophages. The four remaining bacteria were transferred into another drop: after 22 minutes there were 10 bacteria whose fate was not followed further.

Lyses were observed in numerous other experiments, whose details are unnecessary to give here. The number of phages liberated by the lysis of a single bacterium can be inferred from the following data, where the italicized numbers represent the number of bacteria lysed and the romanized numbers the number of bacteriophages liberated: *2*: 138, *2*: 38, *2*: 162, *2*: 27, *1*: 9, *1*: 15, *4*: 89, *4*: 452, *5*: 235, *1*: 158, *2*: 108, *1*: 178, *4*: 579, *6*: 600. *4*: 166; this corresponds to an average of 72 phages per bacterium lysed. The lowest number was 9, the highest 178. It should be noted that under our observational conditions of utilizing an objective ocular lens of magnification 40 and 12.5 respectively, the septum which separates the two daughter bacteria is not visible at the time when it is already functional.

We often happened to observe the lysis of a bacterium of unique appearance. Half of that bacterium, in fact a diplo-bacillus, disappeared under our eyes, leaving for a short time a mutilated bacterium bounded by a circular surface. Bacteriophage lysis thus reveals the existence of the septum although the latter is not yet visible under the conditions of our observations. It is quite exceptional to see single independent bacteria in the case of *B. megaterium*. Nevertheless, the separation of the two members of a diplo-bacillus was frequently observed before the lysis by the bacteriophage. We thus believe that certain of the numbers which we have given really correspond to the production of phage by a single bacterium. It remains possible, however, that other values which we have reported for one bacterium really correspond to a diplo-bacillus.

An important statement must be made at this time. We have seen under our eyes some hundreds of bacteriophage lyses. We have thus observed the lysis of 16, 8, 4, or 2 contiguous bacteria. But we have never observed the lysis of a single member of the diplo-bacillus. This question shall be discussed in paragraph VII.

Discussion. J. Bordet and Renaux (1928), F. Burnet and M. McKie (1929b), and E. Wollman (1936) envisaged that the bacteriophage is secreted by lysogenic bacteria without the latter being destroyed. The problem of the mode of liberation of bacteriophage by lysogenic bacteria was also discussed by J. Northrop (1939) who, having noticed the appearance of bacteriophages during the growth of lysogenic cultures, concluded that the bacteriophage "is produced during the growth of bacteria and not during the lysis." M. Delbrück and S. E. Luria (1942), on the basis of the observations of E. Cordts, which, to our knowledge, have never been published, thought that lysogenic bacteria can produce bacteriophages without lysis.

It should be noted that in the experiments of J. Northrop the value of the ratio of bacteriophages to bacteria was approximately 2. If, in the interval between two divisions, three bacteria out of every hundred lyse, each liberating 72 bacteriophages, then the value of the ratio of bacteriophages to bacteria will be 216 to 97; that is to say, approximately 2. Lysis of 3% of the bacteria during an interval of two divisions does suffice to account for the relative number of bacteriophages and bacteria observed by Northrop. This lysis would entail only a 3% reduction in the theoretical "growth rate." But it is difficult to measure growth rate with greater accuracy than 5%. Unless a very high proportion of the bacteria lyses, no study of growth curves can thus furnish valid data relevant to the mode of liberation of the bacteriophages. All that can be said is that, in the experiments of Northrop, the bacteriophages are liberated during the growth of a bacterial *population.* But it is impossible to rule out the lysis of a certain percentage of the bacteria.

Our experiments thus bring proof that the bacteriophage produced by the lysogenic *B. megaterium* is liberated by bacterial lysis. Until the third minute prior to lysis no bacteriophage is liberated. For a long time bacteriologists have observed the partial lysis of colonies of lysogenic bacteria. The majority of these workers thought that this lysis was due to the bacteriophage. But we know that lysogenic bacteria can lyse without necessarily producing bacteriophage. Cultures of *B. megaterium* 899 lyse completely in peptone medium if they are deprived of oxygen. This lysis begins as soon as anaerobiosis is established. The lysis does not liberate bacteriophages. The fact that the colonies of a lysogenic bacteria lyse partially or totally does not imply that this lysis corresponds to the production of bacteriophages. *A fortiori,* it is not possible to conclude that under these conditions the bacteriophage is liberated by the lysis of bacteria.

Is it possible to exclude the hypothesis of a secretion of bacteriophages by viable bacteria from the fact that in our experiments liberation of bacteriophages took place only by bacterial lysis? In the case of sensitive *Escherichia coli* infected by bacteriophage T2, the nucleus disappears between the fifth and tenth minute after infection (Luria and Palmer, 1945-1946). If the disintegration of the nucleus obligatorily accompanies the production of bacteriophages, then it is evident that no bacterium could survive phage production. But it is possible to conceive of production of bacteriophages without destruction of an essential bacterial organelle. It is necessary, however, to think of a way for the bacteriophages to come out. One knows that lysogenic bacteria adsorb the bacteriophages. One is thus obliged to envisage a variation of bacterial properties which allows certain bacteria to adsorb bacteriophages at certain stages and to let them out at other stages. It is also possible to conceive that the bacteriophage is liberated when all the elements capable of fixing the bacteriophage are "saturated." Thus liberation of bacteriophages in the absence of bacterial lysis is theoretically possible, but at the present time we do not know of any such case.[1] And in the only case in which the mode of liberation of bacteriophages by a lysogenic strain was studied with techniques offering sufficient guarantees, the mode of liberation of bacteriophages was bacterial lysis.

VII. Factors of Bacteriophage Production

The reader has no doubt noticed that in certain of our experiments all of the bacteria put into a little drop grew and multiplied, whereas in others all the descendants of one bacteria lysed. We thought at the outset that the sudden change of medium was responsible for the onset of bacteriophage production. In order to explain the fact that only a certain percentage of the bacteria was lysed, the hypothesis was envisaged according to which this change only induced the lysis if it took place at certain stages of the life cycle of the bacterium; for instance, during nuclear division. But, we subsequently observed considerable differences between different series of the experiments. On a certain day, for example, we had put 18 bacteria in three drops; all of them divided. The 153 bacteria from these divisions were lysed by lysozyme: no bacteriophages. There had been no production of bacteriophage. On another day, we started with 38 bacteria divided among 5 drops. The descendants of three groups did not show any lysis. The descendants of two groups did lyse partially, and all of the descendants of two other groups lysed. The following results correspond to the study of 104 groups of bacteria:

Initial number	6	4	8	4	8	4	4
Maximum number	17	41	29	13	34	8	10
Number of lysed bacteria	0	0	0	12	14	8	10
Proportion of lysed bacteria	0/17	0/41	0/29	12/13	14/34	8/8	10/10

[1] W. H. Price noticed a massive liberation of bacteriophages by cultures of Staphylococcus muscae of constant optical density. The ratio of bacteriophages to bacteria rises from 0.2 to 26 in about 30 minutes. A similar phenomenon was observed in cultures of *Bacillus megaterium* by A. Lwoff, L. Siminovitch, and N. Kjeldgaard (unpublished observations), who interpret the phenomenon in the following manner: The optical density of the culture remains fairly constant, or increases slightly, but the bacteria lyse in the course of the dilutions which precede spreading for assay on the petri dishes. This phenomenon shall be described and discussed in detail in a communication which shall appear soon in this periodical. We thus consider that the experiments of Price do not bring any proof of liberation of bacteriophages in the absence of bacterial lysis.

The results presented below correspond to a study of 104 groups of bacteria:

Number of drops	104
Initial number of bacteria	295
Final number	947
Number of drops where lysis was observed	3
Number of lysed bacteria	4 + 2 + 8
Total of bacteria lysed	14

The number of bacteria used was relatively restricted, but one can nevertheless infer that, in certain experiments, the proportion of bacteria producing phage was less than 5%, while in others, this proportion represented a quarter, or even a third, of all the bacteria used.

Discussion. The Mutation Hypothesis. The fact that only a certain proportion of bacteria produced bacteriophages poses the problem of the nature of the factors which induced a lysogenic bacterium to produce bacteriophages. If a sensitive mutilat is mixed with bacteriophages, one observes the lysis of some of the cells and the growth of resistant lysogenic colonies. The statistical analysis of the phenomenon, such as has been carried out by M. Dulbrück and S. E. Luria (1942), for *E. coli*, has not been carried out, and it is impossible to state that the resistant bacteria represent spontaneous mutants. This is possible, or even probable. One could envisage the hypothesis that this mutation from sensitivity to resistance is reversible. In the case of a lysogenic bacterium the mutation from resistance to sensitivity would create conditions which permit "inactivation" of the potential bacteriophage and of the lysis of the bacterium. One, thus, conceives the idea that the mutation could intervene in determining the production of bacteriophages by certain lysogenic bacteria.

The mutation rate is generally independent of the conditions of the medium, and we have seen that the percentage of bacteria which lyse varies from .5 to 30%. But this does not necessarily exclude the mutation hypothesis. It is, in fact, conceivable that this variability is the result of the simultaneous coming into play of a high mutation rate and of selection. We would invoke the clonal character of the lysis in support of this hypothesis. Let us recall that we never observed the lysis of a single member of a diplo-bacillus, and that we have sometimes seen the lysis of all of the bacteria in the same filament. This could be interpreted in the following manner: Only the descendants of certain mutants lysed, while there occur from 1 to 4 divisions between mutation and lysis. This hypothesis is not incompatible with the hypothesis of induction. One could see, in effect, that the mutation affects only a genotypic factor, and that the latter does not express itself by the production of bacteriophages except under specific conditions of the medium. It is, however, the study of the kinetics of the production of bacteriophages, which shall now be presented, which allows one to exclude the hypothesis of the intervention of a mutation.

The Induction Hypothesis. The behavior the *B. megaterium* in microdrops has given us the impression that the production of bacteriophages must depend, in part, on the previous history of the bacteria, and the hypothesis was envisaged that the inducing factor intervenes in the course of the development of the mother culture. The drop technique, in spite of long and laborious experiments, did not bring the solution to this problem, which was then taken up with ordinary cultures. Since that time, experiments (A. Lwoff, L. Siminovitch, and N. Kjeldgaard) have shown that it is possible to achieve conditions which induce the lysis of 20 to 30% of a bacterial culture and that this lysis is accompanied by the liberation of bacteriophages. These experiments shall be described in a separate communication. We shall content ourselves here with a discussion of the conclusions to which these experiments led, that is to say, that the production of bacteriophages is induced by external factors.

The Hypothesis of Burnet and McKie. F. Burnet and M. McKie (1929b) realized that all bacteria of the lysogenic strain contain in their hereditary constitution a unit which is potentially capable of liberating bacteriophages; that these bacteriophages can be liberated during the process of normal growth; that activation of the hereditary structure must take place spontaneously for there to be any liberation of bacteriophages; that the data do not allow one to infer whether or not there is an intracellular activation; that the conditions are probably analogous to those which intervene in monomolecular reactions or in radioactive disintegrations. Undoubtedly, some of these concepts did not stand up to the test of time. But the problem was remarkably well stated. And the hypothesis of "activation" should have merited better than a complete indifference.

Everything seems to indicate that the bacteriophage possesses a remarkable attractive power. It inhibits, in effect, bacterial growth, detours to its own end the metabolites necessary for enzymatic adaptation (J. Monod and E. Wollman, 1947) and growth of a different bacteriophage (M. Delbrück and S. E. Luria, 1942; A. D. Hershey and R. Rotman, 1948). H. J. Muller (1947), while discussing the problem of the reproduction of the gene, concluded that only the phenomena of long range forces could account for the duplication. Perhaps the attractive power of bacteriophages is of this same type.

Let us suppose that in a lysogenic bacterium the probacteriophage, under whatever form it might exist, is in competition with a certain number of other particles. In potentially lysogenic bacteria that equilibrium is stable. But if, for one reason or another, the equilibrium is perturbed possibly because the attractive power of the bacterial particles is diminished or because the attractive power of the probacteriophage is increased, the latter will develop and give rise to bacterial virus particles. More concretely and simply, one might envisage that the "key enzyme" necessary for bacteriophage synthesis, which M. Delbrück and S. E. Luria (1942) have postulated in order to explain the phenomenon of interference, becomes available; perhaps, because the normal substrate of this enzyme ceases to be synthesized. Let us note in passing that this defect of substrate synthesis could as well be the consequence of a mutation as a change of the conditions of the medium. In any case, the association or combination of this key enzyme with the probacteriophage would then set off the process of multiplication.

We can now discuss the "activation" theory of Burnet and McKie. The activation could be the consequence of a mutation. But since, as in the case of *B. megaterium*, this activation is induced by conditions of the medium, it is simplest to envisage, at least in the case of the bacterium which we have studied, that the activation is the result of the suppression of a competition between the probacteriophage and a specific substance or particle. This is obviously but a working hypothesis.

According to unpublished observations of A. Lwoff, Louis Siminovitch, and N. Kjeldgaard, the length of the latent period of the bacteriophage of *B. megaterium* in the sensitive strain under the conditions of these experiments is 45 minutes. Thus, in the experiments of these authors, 45 minutes elapsed between the moment of the inflection of the bacterial growth curves and the start of the production of the bacteriophage, which lasted for 20 to 30 minutes. "It seems," they write, "as if a factor, or an ensemble of factors, among which we know that the aeration of the medium plays an important role, determines the condition which sets off the production of the bacteriophages. This sudden drop in the rate of growth is evidently related to the development of the bacteriophage, but one does not know whether it is the effect or the cause or both cause and effect." A. Lwoff, L. Siminovitch, and N. Kjeldgaard envisage that the factors of induction act by modifying the relative speed of multiplication of the bacterium and of the probacteriophage. The equilibrium is modified in an irreversible manner once the number of probacteriophages surpasses a critical value. In order to explain its clonal characteristics, it suffices to suppose that lysis does not take place until several divisions have occurred. The problem of the nature of the factors of induction and of the mechanism of their action shall be discussed in a future communication which shall appear in these *Annales*.

VIII. Definition of Lysogenic Bacteria

Since the liberation of bacteriophages by the lysogenic strain 899 of *B. megaterium* occurs by bacterial lysis, there exists an incompatibility between the production of bacteriophages on the one hand and the survival and, *a fortiori*, perpetuation of the bacterial individual on the other hand. In a "lysogenic" strain, there are bacteria which multiply and other bacteria which produce and liberate bacteriophages.

A lysogenic culture producing bacteriophages can be transferred indefinitely, but only under the condition that it includes bacteria which do not produce bacteriophages. On the contrary, a bacterium producing bacteriophages is a bacterium condemned to death. It is thus appropriate to distinguish between a lysogenic culture and a lysogenic bacterium; in case of the latter the production of bacteriophages is but a potential faculty. For that reason we have proposed the following definition: "A lysogenic bacterium is a bacterium which perpetuates the capacity to form bacteriophages without intervention of exogenous bacteriophages."

In the case of lysogenic bacteria, the bacteriophage perpetuates itself in the form of the probacteriophages and not in the form of bacteriophage virus particles. One can thus compare a lysogenic bacterium to a healthy carrier of germs.

What constitutes the particularity of lysogenic bacterium is that they perpetuate a potentially lethal character. The expression of this character, which can be induced by exogenous factors, involves the death of the bacterium.

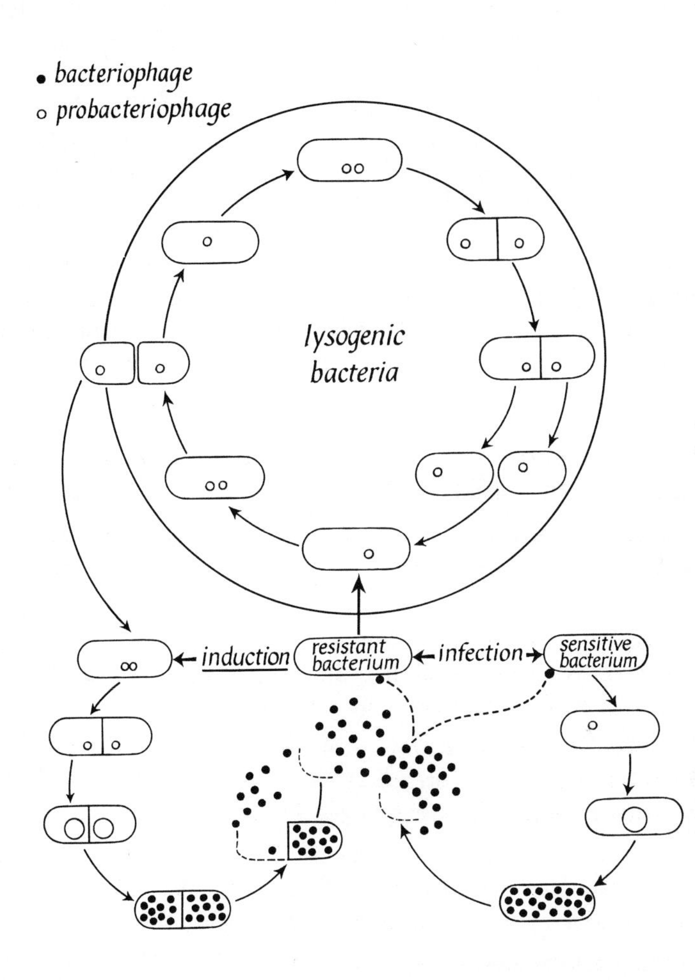

Diagram showing the evolution of bacteriophage and probacteriophage (prophage) in sensitive and lysogenic megaterium bacilli.

Both in the case of the sensitive bacterium, as well as in the case of a resistant bacterium, the penetration of the bacteriophage is followed by a disappearance of the infectious character. In both cases, the infectious corpuscle is not regenerated until a short time prior to the bacterial lysis. In both cases, finally, the multiplication of the bacteriophage involves the lysis of the bacterium. But in the case of a sensitive bacterium the penetration of the bacteriophage and its transformation into a non-infectious form is followed immediately by an important process of multiplication involving the death of the bacterium. In contrast, after the penetration of the bacteriophage into a resistant bacterium destined to become lysogenic the probacteriophage behaves as a nonpathogenic, normal cellular unit, which does not assume a pathological development except as a consequence of an "activation." This development in a bacterium of a particle which ultimately becomes "malignant" recalls in some respect the multiplication of neoplastic cells in a cancerous organism.

One could be tempted to write, as perhaps we ourselves have done, that potentially lysogenic bacteria live "in equilibrium" with their bacteriophage. But, in fact, they live in equilibrium with a probacteriophage. There exists an incompatibility between the structure "bacteriophage-virus" and the survival of the bacterium.

It is true that lysogenic bacteria are resistant to the bacteriophages which their sisters produce. But no more than a sensitive bacterium does a lysogenic bacterium resist the multiplication of bacteriophages. It is thus the multiplication of bacteriophages which constitute the pathologic fact.

IX. Resumé and Conclusions

1. *Bacillus megaterium* cells washed and isolated in microdrops were utilized in an attempt to resolve some of the problems posed by lysogenic bacteria.

2. *B. megaterium* can multiply without liberating bacteriophage: production of bacteriophages thus does not obligatorily accompany the growth and the division of the bacteria.

3. The capacity to produce bacteriophages was maintained in the course of 19 divisions in the absence of all free bacteriophages: the faculty to produce bacteriophages is thus perpetuated intrabacterially.

4. Rapid lysis of lysogenic bacteria was observed under the microscope. This lysis is followed, and never preceded, by liberation of bacteriophages. *B. megaterium* thus liberates bacteriophages by lysis.

5. The proportion of bacteria which liberate bacteriophages varies within considerable proportions: from less than 5% to 30%. All indications are that the production of bacteriophages is induced by external factors.

6. Lysogenic bacteria are defined as bacteria in which the capacity to produce bacteriophages is perpetuated without intervention of exogenous bacteriophages.

7. The theory of the activation of an intracellular *anlage* of the bacteriophage (F. Burnet and M. McKie) has been discussed, developed, and amended.

BIBLIOGRAPHY

Adams (M. H.). *J. Immunol.*, 1949, *62*, 505-516.
Bayne-Jones (S.) et Sandholzer (L. A.). *J. exp. Med.*, 1933, *57*, 279-304.
Bordet (J.). *Ces Annales*, 1925*a*, *39*, 717; C. R. *Soc. Biol. Belge*, 1925*b*, *93*, 1054.

BORDET (J.) et RENAUX (E.). *Ces Annales*, 1928, *42*, 1283.
BURNET (F. M.) et LUSH (D.). *Austr. J. exp. Biol.*, 1936, *14*, 27-38.
BURNET (F. M.) et McKIE (M.). *Austr. J. exp. Biol.*, 1929*a*, *6*, 21-31 et 1929*b*, *6*, 277-284.
FONBRUNE (P. DE). *Technique de micromanipulation.* Masson, edit., Paris, 1949.
DELBRÜCK (M.). *Biol. Rev.*, 1946, *21*, 30-40.
DELBRÜCK (M.) et LURIA (S. E.). *Arch. Biochem.*, 1942, *1*, 111-141.
DEN DOOREN DE JONG (L. E.). *Zentralbl. Bakt.*, 1931*a*, *120*, 1-23; *Ibid.*, 1931*b*, *122*, 277-286; *Ibid.*, 1934, *131*, 401-410.
DUGGAR (B. M.) et ARMSTRONG (J. K.). *Ann. Missouri Bot. Garden*, 1923, *10*, 191.
FOSTER (R.). *J. Bact.*, 1948, *56*, 795-809.
GORINI (L.) et FROMAGENOT (C.). C. R. *Acad. Sci.*, 1949, *229*, 559-561.
GRATIA (A.). *Ces Annales*, 1936*a*, *56*, 307; C. R. *Soc. Biol. Belge*, 1936*b*, *122*, 812; *Ibid.*, 1936*c*, *123*, 506; *ces Annales*, 1936*d*, *57*, 652.
GRATIA (A.) et WELCH (M.) C. R. *Soc. Biol. Belge*, 1939; *132*, 330.
HERSHEY (A. D.). *Genetics*, 1946*a*, *31*, 620-640; *Cold Spring Harbor Symp. Quant. Biol.*, 1946*b*, *11*, 67-77.
HERSHEY (A. D.) et BRONFENBRENNER (J.). *In* "Viral and rickettsial infections of man." Lippincott, édit., 1948.
HERSHEY (A. D.) et ROTMAN (R.). *Proceed. Natl. Acad. Sci.*, 1948, *34*, 89-96; *Genetics*, 1949, *34*, 44-71.
LATARJET (R.). *J. gen. Physiol.*, 1948, *31*, 529-546.
LURIA (S. E.). *Proceed. Nat. Acad. Sci.*, 1948, *33*, 253-264.
LURIA (S. E.) et DELBRÜCK (M.). *Genetics*, 1943, *28*, 491-511.
LURIA (S. E.) et DULBECCO (R.). *Genetics*, 1949, *34*, 92-125.
LURIA (S. E.) et LATARJET (R.). *J. Bact.*, 1947, *53*, 149-163.
LURIA (S. E.) et PALMER (J. L.). *Carnegie Inst. Washington Yearbook*, 1945-1946, 154.
LWOFF (A.). *In* "Unités biologiques douées de continuité génétique," C.N.R.S., édit., Paris, 1949, 7-24.
LWOFF (A.) et GUTMANN (A.). C. R. *Acad. Sci.*, 1949*a*, *229*, 605-607; *Ibid.*, 1949*b*, *229*, 679-682: *Ibid.*, 1949*c*, *229*, 789-791; *Ibid.*, 1950, *230*, 154-156.
LWOFF (A.), SIMINOVITCH (L.) et KJELGAARD (N.). C. R. *Acad. Sci.*, 1950, *230*, 1219; *Ces Annales* (sous presse).
McLAUGHLAN (T. A.), CLARK (E. M.) et BOSWELL (F. W.). *Nature*, 1947, *160*, 755-756.
MONOD (J.) et AUDUREAU (A.). *Ces Annales*, 1946, *72*, 868.
MONOD (J.) et WOLLMAN (Elie). *Ces Annales*, 1947, *73*, 937.
MULLER (H. J.). *Am. Naturalist*, 1922, *56*, 32; *Proceed. Roy. Soc. B.*, 1947, *134*, 1-37.
NORTHROP (J. H.). *J. gen. Physiol.*, 1939, *23*, 59-79.
PIRIE (A.). *Brit. J. exp. Path.*, 1940, *21*, 125-132.
PRICE (W. H.). *J. gen. Physio.*, 1949, *32*, 481-488.
RHOADES (M. M.). *In* "Unités biologiques douées de continuité génétique," C.N.R.S., édit., Paris, 1949, 37-44.
WOLLMAN (E.) et (E.). C. R. *Soc. Biol.*, 1936*a*, *121*, 126; *Ibid.*, 1936*b*, *122*, 190; *Ibid.*, 1936*c*, *122*, 871; *Ces Annales*, 1936*d*, *56*, 137; *Ibid.*, 1936*e*, *56*, 316; C. R. *Soc. Biol.*, 1937, *124*, 931; *Ces Annales*, 1938, *60*, 13.

MICROBIOLOGY

INDUCTION OF BACTERIOPHAGE LYSIS OF AN ENTIRE POPULATION OF LYSOGENIC BACTERIA[1]

by

André Lwoff, Louis Siminovitch, and Niels Kjeldgaard

Presented by Robert Courrier

In a culture of lysogenic *Bacillus megaterium*, some bacteria multiply without liberating bacteriophages and perpetuate the lysogenic strain, while others produce bacteriophages which are liberated by lysis.[2] Under normal conditions of exponential growth, only a very small percentage of bacteria produce bacteriophages.[2,3]

We have succeeded in inducing bacteriophage lysis of an entire population of lysogenic bacteria by means of irradiation by ultraviolet light.

B. megaterium is grown in a yeast extract medium.[2] During the exponential growth phase, when the number of bacteria has attained 34×10^6 per ml., a 2 mm layer of the culture is irradiated with ultraviolet light from a high pressure mercury vapor lamp, which delivers to the surface of the liquid an energy of 2000 ergs per mm^2 per minute of radiation of wave length 2537 A. The culture is then shaken at 37° and its optical density (O.D.) increases for about 80 minutes. The normal growth rate, that is to say the number of doublings per hour, is 3. Immediately after irradiation the growth rate is in the neighborhood of 1.5. At about the 80th minute, when the O.D. has increased by a factor of 3 to 4, bacterial lysis takes place: the culture clears in 40 to 80 minutes. The fraction of bacteria surviving is usually less than 10^{-4}. Lysis is accompanied by the liberation of about 70 to 150 bacteriophages per bacterium. Analogous results have been obtained with irradiation for 20, 30, 90, or 120 seconds.

A culture growing in synthetic medium and similarly irradiated from 1 to 60 seconds does not lyse. On the other hand, if a culture growing in yeast medium is centrifuged, resuspended in synthetic medium, and then irradiated for 5, 10, 20, or 30 seconds, bacteriophage lysis does take place.

Translated from the French and reprinted by permission of the authors and the Imprimérie Gauthier-Villars from the COMPTES RENDUS DES SÉANCES DE L'ACADÉMIE DES SCIENCES, **231**, 190-191 (1950).

Finally if yeast extract is added to a culture growing in synthetic medium and the culture irradiated immediately for 10, 20, 30, or 60 seconds, no lysis takes place. But irradiation carried out 20 to 40 minutes after addition of the yeast extract (by which time the O.D. has increased by about 50%) induces bacteriophage lysis. UV irradiation thus induces production of bacteriophages only with bacteria which have grown for 20 to 40 minutes in a complex organic medium such as yeast extract.

Irradiation for 30 to 60 seconds of a non-lysogenic culture of *B. megaterium* growing in yeast extract does not appear to affect bacterial growth. The lysis of the lysogenic strain is thus probably not a direct effect of the UV irradiation.

It has been demonstrated previously that all bacteria of a lysogenic strain are capable of perpetuating the lysogenic character.[2] The experiments described here, which have been complemented by studies of bacteria irradiated and then isolated in microdrops, now demonstrate that under certain conditions, *all* the bacteria of a lysogenic population are capable of undergoing lysis with liberation of bacteriophages.

---

[1]Supported by a grant of the National Institutes of Health of the United States of America.

[2]A. Lwoff and A. Gutmann, *Ann. Inst. Pasteur*, *78*, 711-739, (1950).

[3]A. Lwoff, A. Siminovitch, and N. Kjeldgaard, *Comptes rendus*, 230, 1219-1221, (1950); *Ann. Inst. Pasteur*, *79*, 815 (1950).

GENETICS

LYSOGENY AND GENETIC RECOMBINATION IN ESCHERICHIA COLI K12

by

Élie L. Wollman and François Jacob

Presented by Jacques Tréfouel

Crosses between *E. coli* K12 Hfr and F^-, both lysogenic, show that the λ prophage and Gal_4 are situated on the segment TL Lac_1. Spontaneous induction of the prophage suppresses those of the zygotes which received a λ prophage whenever the Hfr parent is lysogenic and the F^- parent non-lysogenic. This modifies the distribution among the recombinants of characters linked to the λ prophage.

It had been supposed until now that the presence of the λ prophage does not alter the results of genetic analysis of *E. coli* K12. The phenomenon of spontaneous induction observed in the course of crosses between lysogenic Hfr (ly^+) bacteria and non-lysogenic F^- (ly^-) bacteria established the fact that in the course of certain crosses an important fraction of the zygotes can be eliminated.[1] One might ask whether this elimination does not affect preferentially some segments of genetic material, thus exercising a counterselection with respect to certain classes of recombinants. In particular, it might be possible to explain in this way the anomalies found in crosses of the type $F^+ ly^+ \times F^- ly^-$.[2]

In crosses of Hfr $T^+ L^+ S^s \times F^- T^- L^- S^r$ in which the bacteria are mixed in the proportion of 1 Hfr bacterium for 20 F^- bacteria the frequency of recombination (the number of $T^+ L^+ S^r$ recombinants divided by the initial number of Hfr) varies considerably according to the actual cross carried out. This frequency, which is of the order of 5 to 10% for crosses Hfr $ly^+ \times F^- ly^-$, surpasses 50% in crosses of Hfr $ly^+ \times F^- ly^+$ and of Hfr $ly^- \times F^- ly^-$.

Translated from the French and reprinted by permission of the authors and the Imprimérie Gauthier-Villars from the Comptes Rendus des Séances de l'Académie des Sciences, **239,** 455-456 (1954).

The distribution of non-selected markers among the recombinants is also affected by the nature of the crosses. In a cross of Hfr ly^- Lac_1^+ Gal_4^+ × F^- ly^- Lac_1^- Gal_4^- 55% of the recombinants are Lac^+, 45% are Gal^+. The simultaneous passage of lac^+ and Gal^+ occurs in 40% of the cases, which indicates linkage between Lac_1 and Gal_4. In a cross of Hfr ly^+ Lac_1^+ Gal_4^+ × F^- ly^- Lac_1^- Gal_4^-, in contrast, 25% of the recombinants are Lac,$^+$ but only 3% are Gal^+, of which about half are also Lac^+. Among these recombinants, only 0.2% are lysogenic.

It is known that there exists a direct linkage between lysogeny and the character Gal_4.[3,2] The extreme rarity of lysogenic recombinants, as well as the considerable diminution of the proportion of Gal^+ recombinants, is the consequence of the spontaneous induction of the prophage in a large fraction of the zygotes. The relatively smaller diminution of the proportion of Lac^+ recombinants similarly reflects this phenomenon, but shows at the same time that the character Lac_1 is much less linked to the characters Gal_4 and ly than the latter are linked to each other. Lac_1 is apparently located between TL and Gal_4. The localization of the prophage in this region of the bacterial chromosome is demonstrated by crosses of the type Hfr ly^+ Lac_1^+ $T1^s$ × F^- ly^+ Lac_1^- $T1^r$, in which the two lysogenic strains perpetuate different λ prophages. The prophage of the Hfr parent is transmitted to 30% of the recombinants while the Lac and the $T1^s$ characters are each transmitted in 50 and 75% of the cases.

It should be noted that the establishment of the prophage of the Hfr parent in the recombinants is one third as frequent as the development of this prophage in the zygote in the course of crosses Hfr ly^+ × F^- ly^-.

It is known that in a cross of Hfr × F^- the high frequency of recombination observed concerns only the segment TL Lac_1. We have verified this fact in all of our crosses. The relatively high frequency of recombination of the character λ lysogeny thus localizes the λ prophage in this segment.

The elimination of a chromosomal segment by spontaneous induction of the λ prophage could also occur, though to an extent difficult to evaluate, in crosses of the type ly^+ × ly^+ or F^+ ly^- × F^- ly^+. It offers a model which might conceivably explain the segmental eliminations described by J. Lederberg in heterozygote diploids[5] and by W. Hayes[4] in recombinants of Hfr strains.

---

[1] F. Jacob and E. L. Wollman, *Comptes rendus, 239*, 317, (1954).

[2] E. L. Wollman, *Ann. Inst. Pasteur, 84*, 281, (1953); R. K. Appleyard, *Cold Spring Harbor Symp., 18*, 95, (1953).

[3] E. M. and J. Lederberg, *Genetics, 38*, 51, (1953).

[4] W. Hayes, *Cold Spring Harbor Symp., 18*, 75, (1953).

[5] J. Lederberg, *Proc. Natl. Acad. Sci., 35*, 178, (1949).

GENETICS

SPONTANEOUS INDUCTION OF THE DEVELOPMENT OF BACTERIOPHAGE λ IN GENETIC RECOMBINATION OF ESCHERICHIA COLI K12

by

François Jacob and Élie Wollman

Transmitted by Jacques Tréfouel

In the course of crosses between lysogenic Hfr and non-lysogenic F^- bacteria of *E. coli* K12, the prophage passes from the lysogenic to the non-lysogenic parent becomes induced, and develops in the latter. This process leads to the destruction of the zygote formed.

In crosses between lysogenic (ly^+) and non-lysogenic (ly^-) *Escherichia coli* K12 we have not been able to demonstrate the transfer of the lysogeny of the F^+ parent to a recombinant possessing essentially F^- genome.[1] Nevertheless, the lysogenic character segregated and appeared to be linked to another genetic factor.[2,1] Since the λ prophage is inducible, it appeared possible that recombination between F^+ly^+ and F^-ly^- involves the development of the phage and the destruction of the zygotes formed. The discovery of strains giving a high frequency of recombination (Hfr)[3] makes it possible to verify this hypothesis.

Hfr ly^+ S^s bacteria (lysogenic and sensitive to streptomycin) and F^- ly^-/λ S^r bacteria (non-lysogenic and resistant to λ and to streptomycin) are mixed in broth in the proportion of 1 Hfr to 20 F^-. This mixture is shaken at 37° and at various times samples are removed and spread on streptomycin containing agar seeded with indicator bacteria resistant to streptomycin but sensitive to phage λ. A control culture of Hfr is treated in the same manner.

One observes that the number of infective centers in the mixture increases linearly as a function of time until about the 40th minute, when a plateau is reached which corresponds to approximately half of the initial

---

[1]E. L. Wollman, *Ann. Inst. Pasteur, 84,* 281, (1953).
[2]E. M. and J. Lederberg, *Genetics, 38,* 51, (1953).
[3]L. L. Cavalli and H. Heslot, *Nature, 164,* 1057, (1949); W. Hayes, *Cold Spring Harb. Symp. 18,* 75, (1953); W. Hayes has sent us his strains of Hfr.

Translated from the French and reprinted by permission of the authors and the Imprimérie Gauthier-Villars from the COMPTES RENDUS DES SÉANCES DE L'ACADÉMIE DES SCIENCES, **239,** 317-319 (1954).

number of Hfr. This number is 100 times greater than the number of infective centers found in the control. After the 60th minute, the number of infective centers suddenly increases and at about the 150th minute reaches a value 50 to 100 times greater than that of the first plateau.

The difference between the mixture and the control Hfr is further accentuated if anti-phage serum and streptomycin are added to the two cultures at the beginning of the experiment. For, the number of infective centers in the control falls rapidly to zero while the number of infective centers in the mixture is only reduced by one-half.

The development of phage λ has thus been induced by putting Hfr ly^+ in contact with F^- ly^-. This development can only take place in F^- bacteria (or in the zygotes), since the Hfr bacteria were sterilized by streptomycin. If the same cross is repeated with an F^- S^s strain, addition of streptomycin during the latent period arrests the development of the phage.

An even more direct demonstration of the passage of the prophage from Hfr to F^- bacteria (or to the zygote) and of its development in the latter is furnished by the following experiment. It is known that certain bacterial strains confer a phenotypic modification to the bacteriophages which they produce.[4] Thus bacteriophage λ(K12) produced by *E. coli* K12(λ), whose efficiency of plating is identical on *E. coli* K12 S and on *E. coli* C, has a greatly reduced efficiency of plating (10^{-2} to 10^{-3}) on K12 S after passage on *E. coli* C. If development of the prophage actually takes place in the non-lysogenic F^- bacteria, then in a cross of K12 Hfr(λ) S^s with C/λ F^- S^r the bacteriophages produced should be λ(C) and not λ(K12). Experiments show this to be the case.

When F^- bacteria perpetuate a prophage, normal or defective, the immunity which the prophage confers on them[5] protects them equally against the development of a prophage coming from the Hfr parent.

If one crosses Hfr bacteria superinfected with virulent mutants of the type λ_v,[5] one observes little or no passage of the superinfecting phages into the F^- bacteria. This result indicates that the transfer of phage material from Hfr to F^- takes place in the prophage state and not in the vegetative state. It also indicates that the induction of phage development in the course of recombination takes place in the F^- bacterium (or in the zygote) and not in the Hfr bacterium.

It is evident that the effect described here must introduce important distortions in the genetic analysis of *E. coli* K12: in effect, only those zygotes give rise to recombinants in which no multiplication of the phage has taken place. The proportion of these survivors will vary considerably depending on the nature of the cross. Thus in the cross of Hfr ly^+ B_1^- S^s by W678 T^- L^- B_1^- $ly^-/\lambda S^r$ the number of recombinants of the type

[4] G. Bertani and J. J. Weigle, *J. Bact.*, *65*, 113, (1953).
[5] F. Jacob and E. L. Wollman, *Cold Spring Harb. Symp.*, *18*, 101, (1953).

T^+ L^+ S^r does not exceed 5% of the initial number of Hfr bacteria, although more than 50% of these bacteria give rise to infective centers. Among 200 recombinants examined not one was lysogenic. In a comparable cross in which the F^- strain perpetuates a defective prophage, the number of T^+ L^+ S^r recombinants reaches 50% of the initial number of Hfr, although the number of infective centers does not surpass 5%. Among the recombinants about 30% are normal lysogenics.

The phenomenon of spontaneous induction of the prophage is also found in crosses of F^+ ly^+ by F^- ly^- and thus explains the observed absence of the transmission of lysogeny in these crosses. It could also be the origin of other anomalies found in the study of the genetics of *E. coli* K12.

Transduction of Lysogeny in *Escherichia coli*

FRANÇOIS JACOB

Service de Physiologie microbienne, Institut Pasteur, Paris

Received, March 2, 1955

SUMMARY

Transduction provides a new tool for a genetic analysis of lysogeny. Recently, transduction has been shown by Lennox to occur, through phage P1, in various strains of *Escherichia coli*. Another strain of temperate phage has been isolated, which is also able to transfer genetic characters from a donor to an acceptor strain of *E. coli* K12. Linked characters can be transduced simultaneously. Lysogeny or nonlysogeny, with respect to each of three different prophages is transduced together with a galactose marker, to which these three prophages are linked as shown by bacterial recombination evidence. When two genetically different and complementary prophages—one in the donor and one in the acceptor cells—are used in transduction experiments, recombination of prophages has been shown to occur.

INTRODUCTION

A new mechanism allowing the transfer of genetic characters from one bacterial strain to another was found in *Salmonella* by Zinder and Lederberg (1952). This mechanism, for which the term "transduction" was coined, appears to involve phage particles as vectors of the genetic material of the bacteria (Zinder, 1953; Stocker *et al.*, 1953). Transduction can be observed when phage-sensitive bacteria, acting as acceptor cells, are infected with phage particles grown on donor bacteria which differ from the acceptor by one or several genetic characters. Some of the infected bacteria that survive phage infection acquire and transmit to their progeny one or several characters of the donor strain. The transducing ability seems to be restricted to some strains of temperate phages.

It has recently been shown by Lennox (1955) that phage P1 is able to transduce various markers from one strain of *E. coli* to another and that linked characters can be transduced together. This finding makes it possible to compare linkage data provided by transduction and by bacterial recombination which was demonstrated by Tatum and Lederberg (1947) to occur in strain K12 of *E. coli*.

Reprinted by permission of the author and Academic Press, Inc.
from VIROLOGY, 1 (2), 207-220 (1955).

This paper is mainly concerned with preliminary results on transduction of lysogeny in *E. coli* K12 by the use of a strain of temperate phage isolated in our laboratory. Previously, information on the genetics of λ lysogeny was gained through bacterial recombination experiments with *E. coli* K12 (Lederberg and Lederberg, 1953; Wollman, 1953; Appleyard, 1954*a*; Wollman and Jacob, 1954). The results indicated that the λ-lysogenic character segregates in crosses between lysogenic and nonlysogenic bacteria and, moreover, that this character is linked to a marker that plays a role in galactose utilization. Nevertheless, whereas the presence of a nuclear unit controlling lysogeny was thus demonstrated, it had not yet been proved fully that this bacterial unit was identical to the prophage, i.e., to the genetic material of the phage in the lysogenic condition (Lwoff, 1953). Transduction of lysogeny offers a new way of analyzing the relations between prophage and bacterium, as well as the size and orientation of the prophage.

MATERIAL AND METHODS

Transducing phage. Various kinds of temperate phages have been tested for their transducing ability in *E. coli* K12. Of twenty-three phages released by different lysogenic strains of *E. coli* isolated from patients, only one was active: phage 363. It forms tiny turbid plaques on *E. coli* K12 (Fig. 1A). Its latent period in broth is about 50 minutes, and its burst size is 200 to 300. Its frequency of lysogenization is higher at 20° than at 37°. Phage 363 appears to belong to the same group as phage P1, previously described by Bertani and Nice (1954) and used by Lennox (1955) in his transduction experiments. Bacteria lysogenic for 363 are immune against P1, and vice versa. Phage 363 is inactivated, although at a lower rate than P1, by an anti-P1 serum.[1]

Transduced prophage. The properties of phage λ and its relationship with the bacterial host have been described (Lederberg and Lederberg, 1953; Weigle and Delbrück, 1951). Two other temperate and ultraviolet-inducible phages, released by lysogenic *E. coli* isolated from patients, have also been used in these experiments: phages 82 and 434 (Fig. 1B, D). The properties of these two phages will be described elsewhere. Phages 82, λ, and 434 can easily be distinguished by their host range, as shown in Table 1.

Bacterial strains. The bacterial strain used as a donor was a prototroph, K12, sensitive to 363, 82, λ, and 434.

[1] A sample of anti P1 serum (anti H^-) was kindly supplied by Dr. J. Beumer.

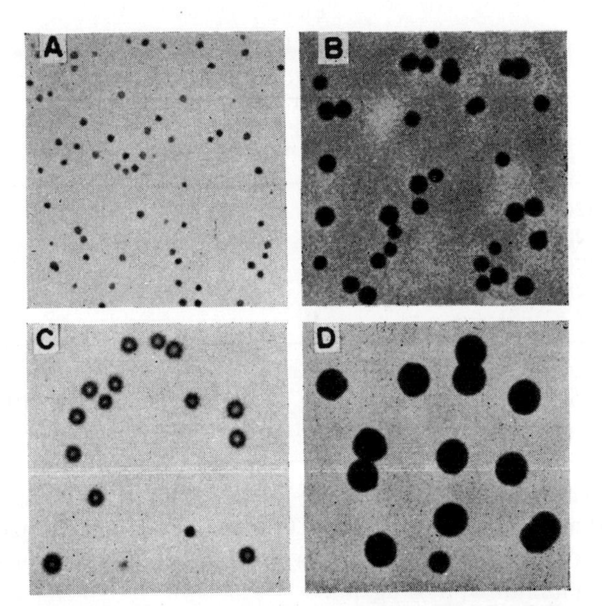

FIG. 1. Plaques formed on *E. coli* K12 by (A) phage 363, (B) phage 82, (C) phage λm_5, and (D) phage 434.

The acceptor strain was a derivative of W677 (Lederberg, 1947) prepared by Dr. E. L. Wollman. This strain, called P678, is unable to synthesize threonine (T^-), leucine (L^-), or vitamin B_1 (B_1^-) or to ferment lactose (Lac_1^-), xylose (Xyl^-), mannitol (Man^-), maltose (Mal^-), or galactose (Gal_5^+, Gal_b^-). It is not lysogenic for λ $(\lambda)^-$ and is resistant to streptomycin (S^r). The Gal_b marker of this strain is closely linked to the λ locus. Its relationship to other galactose loci in the same region is unknown.

Substrains of K12 and P678, lysogenic for one or more of the four prophages (363, 82, λ, and 434), have been isolated. In the description of the following experiments, P678$(\lambda)^+$ will refer to a substrain of P678 lysogenic for λ. Variants resistant to one or more of the three phages have also been used: P678/λ will refer to a variant of P678 resistant to λ.

Preliminary crosses between $Gal_b^+S^s$Hfr, nonlysogenic, and $Gal_b^-S^r$F$^-$, lysogenic for one of the prophages, indicate that both prophages 82 and 434, as well as λ, are located in the Gal_b region. When S^r and Gal_b^+ are used as selective markers, the proportion of nonlysogenic recombinants is about 90% with phage 82, 80% with phage λ, and 70% with phage 434. Prophage 363 is located in a different region.

TABLE 1
HOST RANGE OF PHAGES 82, λ, AND 434

Bacterial strain	Phages		
	82	λ	434
K12(82)+	0	+	+
K12(λ)+	+	0	+
K12(434)+	+	+	0
K12/λ	+	0	+
K12/82, 434	0	+	0

Media. For infection experiments, broth supplemented with 10^{-3} *M* $CaCl_2$ was used.

The selective medium was the following: KH_2PO_4—13.6 g; $(NH_4)_2SO_4$—2 g; Ca $(NO_3)_2$—0.001 g; $MgSO_4 \cdot 7\ H_2O$—0.02 g; Difco agar—20 g; H_2O—1000 ml; KOH added to pH 7.0. Sugars were added separately at a concentration of 1%. Amino acids were added at a concentration of 100 μg/ml; vitamin B_1 at 5 μg/ml.

Transduction experiments. Phage 363 was grown on the prototroph strain K12, either lysogenic or not. The preparations were sterilized with chloroform. Their titer usually reached between 2 and 8 × 10^9 particles per milliliter.

For transduction experiments, about 5 × 10^8 particles of phage 363 were added to 4 ml of a broth culture containing about 2 × 10^8 bacteria per milliliter of the acceptor strain, P678 S^r. This mixture was shaken for 2 hours at room temperature and then centrifuged and washed. The bacterial pellet was resuspended in buffer, and aliquots were plated on selective minimal medium supplemented with streptomycin to avoid contamination. In each experiment, the phage preparation was tested for sterility as well as for plaque count, and a noninfected culture was assayed as a control for spontaneous mutants.

EXPERIMENTAL RESULTS

Evidence for transfer of bacterial genetic material through phage 363. Phage 363 can transfer various kinds of characters from donor to acceptor cells. As previously found by Lennox (1955), unlinked characters are transduced independently, whereas characters which are known to be linked can be transduced simultaneously. In Table 2 are reported the results of an experiment in which several characters have been trans-

TABLE 2

TRANSDUCTION OF VARIOUS MARKERS WITH PHAGE 363

Selection for	Colonies per 5.6×10^8 uninfected bacteria	Colonies per 5.6×10^8 bacteria infected with 1.2×10^8 phage 363
Threonine$^+$	4	730
Leucine$^+$	1	1280
Threonine$^+$ + leucine$^+$	0	23
Lactose$^+$	0	63
Galactose$_b^+$	0	129

Acceptor P678 bacteria infected with phage 363 grown on prototrophic K12 (multiplicity of infection, 0.3), and uninfected control bacteria were shaken for 2 hours at room temperature. After centrifugation, the bacteria were resuspended in buffer and plated on various selective media.

duced. Aliquots of noninfected P678 bacteria and of bacteria infected with phage 363 grown on a prototrophic strain were plated on various selective media. It is seen in Table 2 that the nutritional characters threonine$^+$ or leucine$^+$ are transferred separately with a frequency of about 10^{-5} per adsorbed particle. These two markers, which are known to be linked from bacterial recombination experiments (Lederberg, 1947), can be transferred simultaneously with a frequency of about 10^{-7} per phage particle.

The two fermentative markers, Lac^+ and Gal_b^+, are transmitted with a lower efficiency than T^+ or L^+. Gal_b^+, with which the experiments reported in this paper will be mainly concerned, is transferred with a frequency of about 0.7 to 1.5×10^{-6} per phage particle. Four hundred colonies selected for transduction of Gal_b^+ were assayed for threonine, leucine, lactose, mannitol, and xylose. None of them had acquired any of these characters other than galactose utilization.

The efficiency of transduction varied widely from one experiment to another and from one preparation of phage 363 to another. In various experiments, the frequency of lysogenization with phage 363 in the transduced clones was found to vary from 30 to 70%. Nevertheless, in a given experiment, this proportion was about the same for each class of transduced cells, independently of the selective marker.

Transfer of nonlysogeny. In order to demonstrate transfer of nonlysogeny, bacteria lysogenic for one of the three prophages—82, λ, or 434—and resistant (nonabsorber) to the homologous phage were infected

TABLE 3

TRANSFER OF NONLYSOGENY

Experiment No.	Acceptor strain	Selection for						
		Threonine⁺		Lactose⁺		Galactose⁺		
		Number of colonies tested	Number of non-lysogenic	Number of colonies tested	Number of non-lysogenic	Number of colonies tested	Number of nonlyso-genic	%
1	P678(82)⁺/82	200	0	200	0	200	19	9.5
2	P678(82)⁺/82			200	0	400	53	13
1	P678(λ)⁺/λ	200	0	200	0	200	12	6
2	P678(λ)⁺/λ	200	0	200	0	400	32	8
1	P678(434)⁺/434	160	0	160	0	160	3	1.8
2	P678(434)⁺/434					400	2	0.5

Acceptor bacteria P678 lysogenic for one of the three prophages—82, λ, or 434—and resistant to the homologous phage were infected with a preparation of phage 363 grown on nonlysogenic K12. After plating on various selective media, colonies were tested for their ability to release the original phage, 82, λ, or 434.

with a preparation of 363 grown on prototrophic nonlysogenic bacteria. Infected bacteria were plated on various selective media, and colonies were tested for their ability to release the phage of the parent strain (82, λ, or 434). The results of such experiments are reported in Table 3. It is seen, on the one hand, that among the T^+, L^+, or Lac^+ colonies none was found to be nonlysogenic. On the other hand, a small fraction of the Gal^+ clones was found to be nonlysogenic, the proportion of nonlysogenic clones depending on the nature of the prophage involved This result is in agreement with bacterial recombination experiments which show that each of these prophages exhibits a different linkage to the Gal_b locus.

A question raised by the transduction of nonlysogeny is whether only a piece of the prophage can be replaced by an homologous region of nonlysogenic bacteria. Such a partial substitution could eventually result in an immune defective clone, i.e. a clone in which bacteria possess a fragment of the prophage which does not allow the synthesis of infective particles, but prevents phage multiplication after infection with homologous particles. In order to detect such clones, transduction of nonlysogeny was also performed on lysogenic bacteria able to adsorb homologous phage particles. With prophage λ, no defective immune clone was found. With phage 82, it was found that 2 out of 21 *Gal*+ clones which did not produce infective phage were immune against phage 82 and its virulent mutant, 82*c*. After ultraviolet induction, these two strains exhibited a small degree of lysis, but no infective phage was released. After several generations, both strains had become sensitive to phage 82. These results suggest that recombination might have occurred between the prophage and an homologous genetic fragment issued from nonlysogenic bacteria. Unfortunately, because of the lack of markers on phage 82, no genetic analysis was undertaken.

Transfer of lysogeny. In order to demonstrate transfer of lysogeny, nonlysogenic bacteria 678/λ/82, 434 were infected with preparations of 363 grown on prototrophic bacteria lysogenic for one of the three phages (82, λ, or 434), and the bacteria were plated on various selective media. The results of such experiments are listed in Table 4. As in the case of nonlysogeny, lysogenic colonies were found only among those selected for galactose utilization. For each prophage, the frequency of transfer of lysogeny appears to be of the same order of magnitude as that found for the transfer of non-lysogeny.

TABLE 4

TRANSFER OF LYSOGENY

Experiment No.	Phage 363 grown on strain	Selection for						
		Threonine+		Lactose+		$Galactose^+_b$		
		Number of colonies tested	Number of lysogenic	Number of colonies tested	Number of lysogenic	Number of colonies tested	Number of lysogenic	%
1	K12(82)+	200	0	200	0	200	21	10.5
2	K12(82)+					400	49	12.25
1	K12(λ)+	200	0	200	0	200	11	5.5
2	K12(λ)+					400	24	6
1	K12(434)+	200	0	200	0	200	2	1
2	K12(434)+					400	1	0.5

Acceptor nonlysogenic P678/λ/82, 434 bacteria were infected with one of three preparations of phage 363 grown on prototrophic lysogenic strain, K12(82)+, K12(λ)+, and K12(434)+, respectively. After plating of each mixture on various selective media, colonies were tested for their ability to release the corresponding phage, 82, λ, or 434.

In another experiment, a preparation of phage 363 was grown on a double lysogenic prototroph, K12(82)$^+$(λ)$^+$, and used for infecting nonlysogenic P678/82/λ. The colonies having acquired the Gal_b^+ character were tested for their ability to release phages 82 or λ, and some were found to release both.

As has already been mentioned, in a given experiment, the proportion of transduced clones which are found to be lysogenic for 363 is independent of the selective marker. This is also true in transduction experiments involving the transfer of lysogeny for one or more of the three prophages—82, λ, and 434. The proportion of clones found to be lysogenic for 363 is the same, whether or not the transduced clones have become lysogenic for 82, λ, or 434. Since such transduction experiments were performed with a multiplicity of infection lower than one, it is clear that the transfer of lysogeny for 82, λ, or 434 is performed through phage 363 and is not the result of some kind of "phenotypic mixing."

Reconstruction experiments show that no appreciable reinfections and lysogenizations with phage 363 occur on the selective plates. It appears therefore that the genetic material of several viruses can be included in a single phage coat.

In transduction experiments, the transfer of lysogeny has been found to be about as frequent as that of nonlysogeny. This finding is not in agreement with the results found in bacterial recombination. In crosses between lysogenic Hfr(λ)$^+$ and nonlysogenic F$^-$, λ prophage develops in most of the zygotes (Jacob and Wollman, 1954*a*). This development brings out the destruction of such zygotes which lyse and release phage particles. Lysogenic recombinants are therefore very rare. On the contrary, little or no development of the prophage is observed in the reverse cross between nonlysogenic Hfr and lysogenic F$^-$(λ)$^+$, and the frequency of nonlysogenic recombinants found agrees with expectations. The discrepancy between the results obtained by transduction and those obtained by bacterial recombination can be due to the fact that transduction experiments were performed at 20°, a temperature at which phages 82, λ, and 434 do not multiply, whereas bacterial crosses were performed at 37°. It is therefore possible that, at 37°, a fraction of the transduced prophages is able to develop during transduction experiments. A temperature effect on the frequency of λ-lysogeny transfer was observed by Appleyard (1954*a*).

In order to test this possibility, the following experiment was designed (see Table 5). Phage λ (as well as 82 or 434) forms plaques with the same

TABLE 5

DEVELOPMENT OF TRANSDUCED λ PROPHAGE

Preparation of 363 grown on K12(λ)$^+$	Number of particles per milliliter forming a 363 plaque when plated on K12/λ	Number of particles per milliliter forming a λ plaque when plated on	
		K12(363)$^+$	K12/363
Untreated	1.8×10^8	2.3×10^3	1.15×10^3
10 minutes after addition of anti-λ serum	1.7×10^8	1.2×10^3	1.3×10^2
30 minutes after addition of anti-λ serum	1.9×10^8	1.4×10^3	7.9×10^1
Same preparation, previously treated with anti-λ serum, 30 minutes after addition of anti-363 serum	3.7×10^6	4.1×10^1	4.9×10^1

To a preparation of phage 363 grown on K12(λ)$^+$, anti-λ serum was added at time 0 and the mixture was incubated at 37°. After 30 minutes, anti-363 serum was added. Before addition of any serum, and at various times during the experiment, samples were removed and diluted. Aliquots were plated as follows (after 30 minutes preadsorption at 37°): (*1*) on K12/λ (for plaques of 363); (*2*) on K12(363)$^+$, which adsorbs both λ and 363 without multiplication of the latter (for total λ plaques); (*3*) on K12/363, which adsorbs λ but not 363 (for free λ phage). Figures indicate the number of plaques found without treatment, after treatment with anti-λ serum alone, or after successive treatments with both sera.

efficiency of plating on K12, K12(363)$^+$, or K12/363. In the preparations of 363 grown on lysogenic K12(λ)$^+$, there are always some free λ particles which have been released during the growth of the bacteria. Such preparations give the same number of λ plaques on K12, K12(363)$^+$, and K12/363. When most of the free λ particles are neutralized by anti-λ serum, a higher number of λ plaques is found by plating on K12(363)$^+$, which adsorbs 363 without allowing its multiplication, than on K12/363 phage, which does not adsorb phage 363. If, now, the preparation previously treated with anti-λ serum is exposed to anti-363 serum, the number of λ plaques on K12(363)$^+$ is reduced at a rate similar to the one found for inactivation of total plaques of 363. After about 30 minutes of exposure to anti-363 serum, the same number of λ plaques is found by plating on K12(363)$^+$ or on K12/363.

The results of this experiment show, therefore, that at 37° the λ material carried in particles of phage 363 is able to multiply vegetatively if injected in λ nonlysogenic bacteria. If it is assumed that, as in the case of bacterial recombination, most of the transduced λ prophages develop when transduction is performed at high temperature, such an experiment enables one to estimate the fraction of particles of 363 carrying λ material as between 10^{-6} and 10^{-5}. This proportion is of the same order of magnitude as the fraction of particles of 363 found to be able to transduce threonine or leucine characters.

Prophage recombination. Prophage recombination between two genetically different and complementary prophages has been shown to occur in transduction. In such experiments, phage λ was used because its genetic system had been investigated extensively (Jacob and Wollman, 1954*b*; Kaiser, 1954). All the known markers of λ are located on a single linkage group, which has been represented in Fig. 2. When sensitive bacteria are infected with genetically marked phages, some become lysogenic. The phage particles released by such bacteria and their progeny remain genetically identical to the original particles used for infection. The markers available for the study of λ genetics during the vegetative phase can therefore be used for studying the prophage.

In the experiments described below, three markers have been used: m_5 (medium-sized plaques), c_o (cocarde) and m_i (minute plaques). These markers cover most of the known length of the λ linkage group; in crosses involving these three markers the two parental and the six recombinant types can be distinguished easily and all are temperate. During the vegetative phase, the recombination frequency is about 7 to 9% between m_5 and c_o and 4 to 5% between c_o and m_i.

In the experiment reported in Table 6, lysogenic bacteria P678 ($\lambda m_5 c_o m_i^+$)/λ were infected with particles of 363 grown on K12($\lambda m_5^+ c_o^+ m_i$). The mixture was plated on galactose medium. After reisolation on galactose agar individual colonies were grown in broth and analyzed for the type of phage spontaneously released. It is seen in Table 6 that, of 240 colonies, 213 released only the original type $\lambda m_5 c_o m_i^+$. The other 27 can be classified in two groups. In the first group, corresponding to 18 colonies (7.5%), one or several of the original prophage markers have

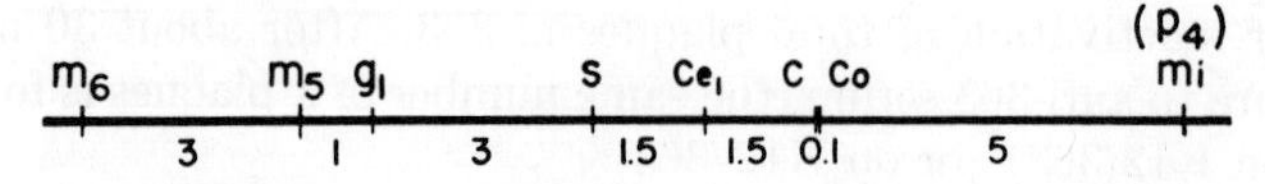

FIG. 2. The linkage group of bacteriophage λ. Figures indicate percentage of recombinants found in two factor crosses.

TABLE 6

λ-PROPHAGE RECOMBINATION THROUGH TRANSDUCTION

Number of clones	Types of phage released	Phage alleles present	Phage alleles transduced
213	$m_5c_om_i^+$	$m_5c_om_i^+$	
2	$m_5c_om_i$	$m_5c_om_i$	m_i
6	$m_5c_o^+m_i$	$m_5c_o^+m_i$	$c_o^+m_i$
9	$m_5^+c_o^+m_i$	$m_5^+c_o^+m_i$	$m_5^+c_o^+m_i$
1	$m_5c_o^+m_i^+$	$m_5c_o^+m_i$	c_o^+
1	$m_5c_om_i^+$ $m_5c_om_i$	$m_5c_om_i^+$ m_i	m_i
3	$m_5c_om_i^+$ $m_5c_o^+m_i$ $m_5c_o^+m_i^+$ $m_5c_om_i$	$m_5c_om_i^+$ $c_o^+m_i$	$c_o^+m_i$
4	$m_5c_om_i^+$ $m_5c_om_i$ $m_5^+c_o^+m_i$ $m_5^+c_o^+m_i^+$ $m_5c_o^+m_i$ $m_5c_o^+m_i^+$ $m_5^+c_om_i^+$ $m_5^+c_om_i$	$m_5c_om_i^+$ $m_5^+c_o^+m_i$	$m_5^+c_o^+m_i$
1	$m_5c_om_i^+$ $m_5^+c_om_i^+$	$m_5c_om_i^+$ m_5^+	m_5^+

Lysogenic acceptor bacteria P678($\lambda m_5c_om_i^+$)$^+$/λ were infected with phage 363 grown on prototrophic lysogenic K12($\lambda m_5^+c_o^+m_i$)$^+$. After plating on galactose medium, colonies were reisolated and tested for the type of phage released.

been *replaced* by markers of the transduced prophage. In spite of the small numbers involved, it is clear that the markers of the prophage λ are not independently substituted, the frequency of substitution decreasing progressively from the m_i to the m_5 end of the λ linkage group.

In the second group, corresponding to 9 cases (3.8%), the bacteria were found to release, besides the original $m_5c_om_i^+$ type, one or more other types of λ particles, even in single-burst experiments. This finding shows that alleles issued from the transduced prophages have been *added* to the original prophage. Here, again, the m_i region is the most frequently added.

These clones, in which bacteria carry two phage alleles at one or several loci, appear to be rather stable, since they were tested for phage production after two successive isolations on agar and growth in broth, corresponding to at least 50 generations. Nevertheless, single-burst experiments show that phage markers are very heterogeneously distributed in the population. During the multiplication of such strains, bacterial clones segregate which have lost one or more prophage alleles. Very often, clones are found in which only the original $m_5c_om_i^+$ prophage remains. Other clones exhibit various types of phage allele combinations. Attempts to demonstrate some kind of diploidy for the Gal_b marker in these strains were unsuccessful. After two successive isolations on galactose-selective medium, colonies were grown in broth and streaked on EMB galactose agar. All contained only Gal^+ bacteria. These results seem analogous to those found after mixed infection with two genetically labeled λ phages (Appleyard, 1954*b*; Jacob, unpublished results).

The results of this experiment show conclusively that the transduced prophage can either recombine with, or be added to, the prophage of the acceptor bacteria. Since the probability of being incorporated decreases from the m_i to the m_5 end of the λ linkage group and since, in addition, m_i has no selective advantage over m_5 in establishing lysogeny after infection, it seems likely (although the data are statistically not very significant) that the m_i end of the λ prophage is the closest to the Gal_b locus. Although no definite conclusion can be drawn from the small numbers of cases, the ratio of the probabilities of bringing either m_i alone or m_i and c_o together (3:9) is not in disagreement with the ratio of the frequencies of recombination m_ic_o/c_om_5 found in crosses between vegetative phages (4:9).

DISCUSSION

The experiments reported in this paper show that the phage material present as a prophage in the donor bacterium can be transferred to an acceptor bacterium by means of a transducing phage. The transduced phage material can develop in the nonlysogenic acceptor bacterium when experiments are performed at 37°. It seems likely, however, that this phage material is transferred as a constituent of the donor bacterial chromosome, i.e., as a prophage, since in transduction, as well as in bacterial recombination, the same linkages between lysogeny and nutritional markers are found. Moreover, at 20°, the transfer of lysogeny occurs with about the same frequency as the transfer of nonlysogeny.

In *E. coli* K12, two relative measures of linkage between two given characters, such as threonine and leucine, can be obtained, one by transduction and one by recombination. The relationship between these two scales of measure is about the same when lysogeny is one of the characters involved. In transduction experiments, lysogeny behaves therefore exactly like any other genetic character. These results confirm previous findings of Lederberg and Lederberg (1953) and of Wollman (1953), gained by means of bacterial recombination and showing that lysogeny is controlled by a genetic determinant of the bacterium. In transduction experiments the same efficiency is found in the transfer of lysogeny to nonlysogenic bacteria and of prophage markers to already lysogenic bacteria, proof that the genetic determinant of the bacterium which controls lysogeny is the prophage itself. The three prophages which have been used in this study are likely to be located at closely linked loci. Their relationship is now the subject of more detailed investigation.

Although we know little about the orientation of the prophage with respect to the bacterial chromosome, data concerning prophage recombination during transduction seem to indicate that the m_i end of the λ prophage is the closest to the Gal_b locus. If the size of the transducing piece is not too widely distributed and if recombination inside the prophage region behaves in the same way as in other regions, such an experiment may allow us to estimate the genetic size of the prophage as compared to that of the adjacent bacterial region. In the case of the experiment previously described and in spite of the small numbers involved, the m_i–m_5 distance may be estimated at about 4 to 6% of the Gal_b–m_i distance. Such an estimation is probably premature, because we still lack a definite picture of the relationship between the prophage and the bacterial chromosome.

The case of bacteria found after transduction or mixed infection, which carry several pairs of prophage alleles that segregate during bacterial multiplication, is unclear. In such bacteria, the two prophages are likely to be located on the same region of the bacterial chromosome, since both additions and substitutions of prophage alleles are found in a single transduction experiment.

One of the most striking facts derived from transduction of lysogeny is that a phage coat can contain, besides homologous genetic material, the genetic material of one or more other viruses.

ACKNOWLEDGMENT

The author wishes to thank Mlle Y. Nicolas for valuable technical assistance and Dr. C. Levinthal for criticisms and help in the preparation of the manuscript.

REFERENCES

APPLEYARD, R. K. (1954*a*). Segregation of lambda lysogenicity during bacterial recombination in *Escherichia coli* K12. *Genetics* **39**, 429–439.

Appleyard, R. K. (1954*b*). Segregation of new lysogenic types during growth of a doubly lysogenic strain derived from *Escherichia coli* K12. *Genetics* **39,** 440–452.

Bertani, G., and Nice, S. J. (1954). Studies on lysogenesis. II. The effect of temperature on the lysogenization of *Shigella dysenteriae* with phage P1. *J. Bacteriol.* **67,** 202–209.

Jacob, F., and Wollman, E. L. (1954*a*). Induction spontanée du développement du bactériophage λ au cours de la recombinaison génétique chez *Escherichia coli* K12. *Compt. rend.* **239,** 317–319.

Jacob, F., and Wollman, E. L. (1954*b*). Etude génétique d'un bactériophage tempéré d'*Escherichia coli*. I. Le système génétique du bactériophage. *Ann. inst. Pasteur* **87,** 653–673.

Kaiser, A. D. (1954). A genetic analysis of bacteriophage lambda. Ph. D. Thesis, California Institute of Technology, Pasadena.

Lederberg, E. H., and Lederberg, J. (1953). Genetic studies of lysogenicity in *Escherichia coli*. *Genetics* **38,** 51–64.

Lederberg, J. (1947). Gene recombination and linked segregation in *Escherichia coli*. *Genetics* **32,** 505–525.

Lennox, E. (1955). Transduction of linked characters of the host by bacteriophage P1. *Virology* **1,** 190–206.

Lwoff, A. (1953). Lysogeny. *Bacteriol. Revs.* **17,** 269–337.

Stocker, B. A. D., Zinder, N. D., and Lederberg, J. (1953). Transduction of flagellar characters in *Salmonella*. *J. Gen. Microbiol.* **9,** 410–433.

Tatum, E. L., and Lederberg, J. (1947). Gene recombination in the bacterium *Escherichia coli*. *J. Bacteriol.* **53,** 673–684.

Weigle, J. J., and Delbrück, M. (1951). Mutual exclusion between an infecting phage and a carried phage. *J. Bacteriol.* **62,** 301–318.

Wollman, E. L. (1953). Sur le déterminisme génétique de la lysogénie. *Ann. inst. Pasteur* **84,** 281–293.

Wollman, E. L., and Jacob, F. (1954). Lysogénie et recombinaison génétique chez *Escherichia coli* K12. *Compt. rend.* **239,** 455–456.

Zinder, N. D. (1953). Infective heredity in bacteria. *Cold Spring Harbor Symposia Quant. Biol.* **18,** 261–269.

Zinder, N. D., and Lederberg, J. (1952). Genetic exchange in *Salmonella*. *J. Bacteriol.* **64,** 679–699.

Recombination between Related Temperate Bacteriophages and the Genetic Control of Immunity and Prophage Localization[1]

A. D. KAISER AND F. JACOB

Department of Microbiology, Washington University School of Medicine, St. Louis, Missouri, and Service de Physiologie Microbienne, Institut Pasteur, Paris, France

Accepted August 31, 1957

Lysogenic bacteria are immune to infection with phage homologous to the prophage. By means of crosses between phages showing different immunity specificities it is shown that immunity specificity is determined by the same segment of the phage genetic material that controls the ability of the phage to lysogenize. Furthermore, this same segment, called the "c_I region", also determines which locus is occupied by the prophage on the chromosome of *Escherichia coli* K12.

INTRODUCTION

Lysogenic bacteria possess and transmit to their offspring the power to produce bacteriophage. The phage that lysogenic bacteria produce is capable of making new lysogenic strains by infection of sensitive bacteria. By morphological, serological, and genetic criteria, the phage produced by such a lysogenized strain is identical with the phage used for the lysogenizing infection. Thus each lysogenic bacterium carries all the genetic information present in an infective phage particle. Nevertheless, disruption of lysogenic bacteria fails to reveal infective particles. The structure bearing the genetic information of the phage in a lysogenic bacterium is called a "prophage" (Lwoff, 1953). There is strong evidence that the prophage is the genetic material of the phage bound to a specific site of the bacterial chromosome (Lederberg and Lederberg, 1953; Wollman, 1953; Appleyard, 1953; Jacob, 1955).

The presence of the prophage confers upon the host bacterium a resistance to infection with the homologous phage and its mutants. This

[1] Part of this work was supported by grant E-1275 from the National Institutes of Allergy and Infectious Diseases, National Institutes of Health, Bethesda, Maryland.

Reprinted by permission of the authors and Academic Press, Inc. from VIROLOGY, 4 (3), 509-521 (1957).

property, called *immunity*, is phage specific since lysogenic bacteria remain, with some exceptions, sensitive to all other phages that can infect their nonlysogenic counterparts. Immunity is reciprocal, in the sense that a bacterium lysogenic for any temperate mutant of a phage is immune against the wild type and its mutants. Several experiments (Jacob, 1954; Bertani, 1954; Goodgal, 1956) support the idea that the deoxyribonucleic acid (DNA) of homologous phage can penetrate into a lysogenic bacterium, suggesting that immunity is due to a block, which prevents phage multiplication inside the bacterium.

Little is known about the mechanism of immunity or the origin of its high degree of specificity. It has been suggested that there is a relation between immunity and the specific location occupied by a prophage on the chromosome of its host (Lwoff, 1953).

A new experimental approach to the problem of immunity was opened when a series of temperate phages, all active on *E. coli* K12, was isolated. Each of these phages has a different specificity of immunity: bacteria lysogenic for any one of them are still sensitive to the others. Yet, genetic recombination occurs between pairs of these phages when they multiply together in the same bacterium. Thus, the genetic control of immunity could be studied by phage crosses. Not only do these phages differ in their specificity of immunity, but they differ also in their location as prophages in the host. Each of them appears to occupy a specific location on the bacterial chromosome (Jacob and Wollman, 1957). Phage crosses offer, therefore, the possibility of determining which part of the phage genetic material determines the specificity of immunity and which part determines the specificity of the prophage location on the bacterial chromosome. The results of such crosses are the substance of this report.

MATERIALS AND METHODS

Only those materials and methods which were not described in a previous publication (Kaiser, 1957) will be given here.

Media. EMB galactose agar contains 10 gm of Bacto-tryptone, 5 gm of yeast extract, 2 gm of K_2HPO_4, 0.4 gm of eosin Y, 0.065 gm of methylene blue, 5 gm of D-galactose, and 15 of gm Bacto-agar per liter of distilled water.

Bacteria. A galactose negative mutant of *E. coli* K12 strain C600 was selected by the penicillin method (Davis, 1948; Lederberg and Zinder, 1948) following an irradiation with ultraviolet light. This mutant is

TABLE 1

IMMUNITY AND HOST RANGE OF PHAGES λ, 434, 82, AND 21

Phage	Host bacterium						
	K12	K12(λ)	K12(434)	K12(82)	K12(21)	K12/λ	K12/434
λ	+	−	+	+	+	−	+
434	+	+	−	+	+	+	−
82	+	+	+	−	+	+	−
21	+	+	+	+	−	−	+

KEY: + indicates ability of phage to grow on the host; − indicates inability to grow.

NOTE: Loopfuls containing 2×10^8 or more phage particles were inoculated onto the surface of an agar plate seeded with bacteria. Lysis of the bacteria within the inoculated area was taken as the sign of phage multiplication.

related to the gal_1^- of Morse *et al.* (1956), since it can be transduced to gal^+ by λHFT gal_2^- but not by λHFT gal_1^-.

Phages. Coli phages 434, 82, and 21 (Jacob and Wollman, 1956) are capable of lysogenizing *E. coli* K12. All three are serologically related to phage λ. Phage λ is the wild type described previously (Kaiser, 1957). The ability of phages λ, 434, 82, and 21 to grow on various lysogenic and resistant strains of *E. coli* K12 is shown in Table 1. It may be seen that each phage is distinguished from the others by its ability to grow on all of the lysogenic strains except the homologous one: each of the four phages has a different immunity specificity.

Crosses. The technique of crossing these phages is the same as the one already described for λ × λ crosses (Kaiser, 1957).

Because many stocks of λ mutants are available, crosses were made between λ and each of the other phages.

RESULTS

1. Genetic recombination between λ, *434, 82, and 21*. The first series of crosses involved phages 434, 82, or 21 as one parent, and λ marked either with m_5, co_2, c_1, co_1, or *mi* as the other parent. A map giving the position of the markers on the λ linkage group is given in Fig. 1. The purpose of these crosses is to see if 434, 82, and 21 carry and are able to transfer to λ the wild type alleles m_5^+, co_2^+, c_1^+, co_1^+, and mi^+. Thus, for example, λm_5, which forms medium-sized plaques, was crossed to 434 and the offspring of the cross plated on K12(434), to examine only the phages with the immunity specificity of λ. The presence of some large plaques,

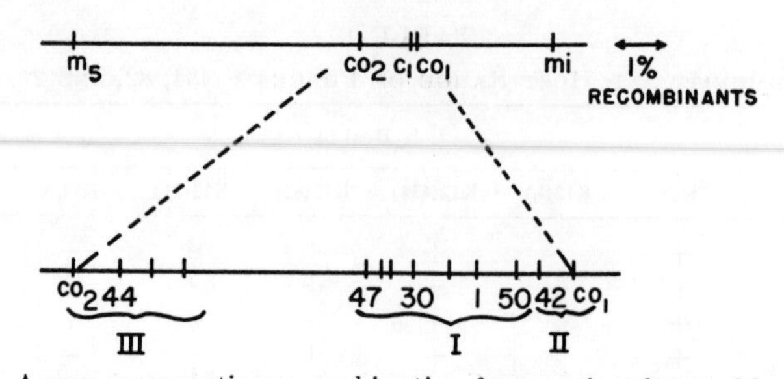

FIG. 1. A map representing recombination frequencies observed between pairs of λ mutants (Kaiser, 1957). The *c* segment is shown on an expanded scale.

m_5^+, indicated that m_5^+ was present in 434 and that recombination can occur between the m_5 locus and the locus controlling immunity specificity. Similar experiments were carried out with co_2, c_1, co_1, and *mi*. The markers co_2, c_1, and co_1 cause the production of clear plaques, their corresponding wild alleles controlling the production of turbid plaques. The marker *mi* causes minute plaques with a halo. The results of these crosses, summarized in Table 2, are that in the cross λ × 434 recombination can occur between m_5, co_2, co_1, and *mi* on the one hand, and the loci controlling the specificity of immunity on the other hand. In crosses λ × 21, recombination of m_5, co_2, and *mi* with immunity specificity can occur and in crosses λ × 82 the loci m_5, co_1, and *mi* can recombine with the loci controlling the specificity of immunity. The pattern of recombination is similar in the three types of crosses of λ with 434, 82, and 21 in that recombination can occur at the ends, m_5 and *mi*, but not in the middle, c_1, of the λ linkage map. The three types of crosses differ, however, in the length of the middle region which fails to recombine with the loci controlling immunity specificity. In the cross λ × 21 this region includes both c_1 and co_1, in the cross λ × 82 both co_2 and c_1, while in the cross λ × 434 only c_1 fails to recombine. Because the region within which recombination fails to occur is the shortest for the cross λ × 434, a more detailed study of recombination between λ and 434 was undertaken. Crosses were made between 434 and a selected series of clear mutants of λ. The clear mutants were selected to mark different regions of the *c* segment.

The *c* segment of λ consists of at least three regions. Each region is probably responsible for the performance of a specific function in lysogenization (Kaiser, 1957). One mutant, number c_{44}, was selected from region III; 4 mutants, c_{47}, c_{30}, c_1, and c_{50}, from region I; and two mutants,

TABLE 2

OCCURRENCE OF WILD TYPE RECOMBINANTS WITH THE IMMUNE SPECIFICITY OF λ IN CROSSES BETWEEN A SERIES OF λ MUTANTS AND THREE RELATED PHAGES

Cross	λ Mutant employed				
	m_5	co_2	c_1	co_1	mi
434 × λ	+	+	−	+	+
21 × λ	+	+	−	−	+
82 × λ	+	−	−	+[a]	+

[a] Recombinants arose which were more turbid than λco_1, but less turbid than λco_1^+.

KEY: + signifies the occurrence of wild type recombinants with the immune specificity of λ; − indicates failure to detect wild type recombinants among 1000 offspring with the immune specificity of λ.

NOTE: Several mutants of λ ($\lambda\, m_5$, $\lambda\, co_2$, $\lambda\, c_1$, $\lambda\, co_1$, and $\lambda\, mi$) were crossed to 434 and the phage progeny was plated on K12(434), where plaques with the wild type morphology and the immunity specificity of λ could be detected. Analogous crosses were carried out with phages 21 and 82.

c_{42}, and co_1, from region II. A map showing the positions of the clear mutants employed is given in Fig. 1.

The crosses made were 434 × λc_x, where c_x represents individual members of the selected series of clear mutants. The progeny of each cross were plated on K12(434) and on K12(λ). The presence of turbid plaques on K12(434) demonstrates the presence in 434 of a c_x^+ allele, which can recombine with the locus controlling immunity specificity of λ. Clear plaques on K12(λ) reveal phages with the immunity of 434 which have picked up a c_x allele from λ. A comparison of the proportion of turbid plaques on K12(434) with the proportion of clear plaques on K12(λ) serves as an internal control, because they are reciprocal recombinants and should therefore have the same frequency. When 434 alone is plated on K12(λ), there are 0.07 % clear plaques due to mutants in the 434 stock. This proportion is, naturally, present as a background in the yield of all of the crosses. The proportion of turbid mutants in a stock of clear λ is less than 1 in 10^4 and is therefore too low to be detected in the crosses.

The results of this series of crosses, given in Table 3, show that recombinants arise from the crosses with mutants c_{44}, c_{42}, and co_1, but for none of the others. There is, therefore, recombination between 434 and λ in regions II and III of the c segment but not in region I. The

TABLE 3

CROSSES λ CLEAR × 434 TURBID

Cross	Plated on C600(434)			Plated on C600(λ)			Plated on C600		
	Number turbid	Number clear	% Turbid	Number turbid	Number clear	% clear	Number turbid	Number clear	% Clear
λc_{44} × 434	81	2232	3.5	2977	119	3.8			
λc_{47} × 434	0	12528	<0.01	8166	4	0.05			
λc_{30} × 434	0	3080	<0.03	3632	2	0.06			
λc_{1} × 434	0	9132	<0.01	5518	4	0.07			
λc_{50} × 434	0	5212	<0.02	3615	1	0.03			
λc_{42} × 434	41	7612	0.54	6542	32	0.49			
λco_{1} × 434	65	5182	1.2	4249	170	3.8			
λc^{+} × 434							1550	0	<0.1
434 alone				3000	1	0.03	2500	3	0.1
λc_{44} alone	2	3744	0.05						
λc_{42} alone	0	4296	<0.03						
λco_{1} alone	0	2502	<0.04						

NOTE: Progeny of crosses of the type λ clear by 434 turbid, plated on C600, C600(λ), or C600(434) were scored for the number of clear and turbid plaques. The clear mutants of λ employed in these crosses were selected to mark different regions of the *c* segment: c_{47}, c_{30}, c_1, and c_{50} to mark region I, c_{42} and co_1 to mark region II, and c_{44} to mark region III.

limits of recombination between λ and 434 lie, on one side, between c_{44} and c_{47} and, on the other side, between c_{50} and c_{42}. The precise location of the limits between these pairs of markers is suggested by the frequencies of recombination with c_{44} and c_{42}, i.e., 3.5% recombination to the right of 44 and 0.54% recombination to the left of c_{42}.

The recombination pattern in λ × 434 crosses can be understood if it is postulated that the c_{I} region controls immunity specificity, that there is a c_{I} region specific for the immunity of λ and a c_{I} region specific for the immunity of 434.

2. 434-λ Hybrid. Hybrid phages which have only the immunity determining region of 434 and the rest of their chromosome from λ were isolated from 5 successive backcrosses of 434 to λ. The first step was to cross 434, which forms tiny turbid plaques, with λc_1, which forms large clear plaques. A few large turbid plaques were found among the progeny. They were tested and all found to have the immunity of 434. The second step was to cross one of the large turbid 434 to λc_{44} and to isolate a 434 c_{44}

by plating on K12(λ). Step three consisted in replacing c_{44} by c_{44}^+ by crossing to λc_1 and picking the turbid recombinants on K12. In step four, 434 c_{44}^+ was crossed to λc_{42}. A 434 $c_{44}^+c_{42}$ was selected by picking a clear plaque on K12(λ). The final step consisted in replacing c_{42} by c_{42}^+ by crossing 434 $c_{44}^+c_{42}$ to λc_1 and plating on K12. At each stage in the backcrosses the immunity pattern was checked. This sequence of 5 successive backcrosses would be expected to replace all of the parts of the 434 chromosome capable of recombination with the homologous parts from λ. We have, therefore, a phage which should possess the c_I region of 434 embedded in an otherwise λ genome. This phage will now be designated 434hy.

The hybrid character of 434hy is evidenced by the following properties. Apart from its immunity pattern, which is that of 434, phage 434hy behaves like λ. On K12 it forms large turbid plaques identical to those of λ and it has the host range of λ. Whereas phage 434 is inactivated by anti-λ serum at a slower rate than is λ, the hybrid is inactivated at the rate characteristic of λ, as is shown in Fig. 2. Further evidence for the homology of 434hy with λ is shown by a comparison of λ × 434hy with λ × λ crosses. In a cross $\lambda m_5 c_1$ × 434hy *mi*, 12% recombination was observed between m_5 and c_1 and 4% between c_1 and *mi*. A corresponding cross between $\lambda m_5 c$ and λmi gave 8% and 5% recombination, respec-

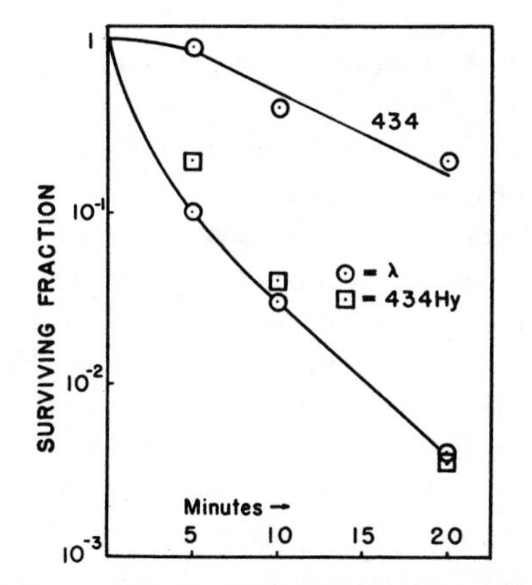

FIG. 2. Neutralization was measured by incubating a mixture of phage and a 1/100 dilution of rabbit anti-λ serum at 37°. At the times indicated aliquots were withdrawn, diluted at least $1/10^4$ and plated on C600. The surviving fraction is the ratio of the number of plaques at time *t* to the number at time zero.

tively, in the two regions. The absence of a significant difference in recombination frequencies suggests that 434hy is homologous to λ. Since the c_I region is only about 1% long, absence of homology there would not be expected to depress recombination frequencies significantly in this cross.

Bacteria lysogenic for 434hy behave exactly like K12(434) in response to infection by λ, 434, λ*c*, 434 *c*, and434hy. Thus the 434hy prophage determines the immunity pattern characteristic of the wild type 434.

The existence of hybrids with a c_I region from 434 and the rest of their chromosome from λ, which have the specific immunity pattern of 434 but not that of λ, demonstrates that the c_I region (or a portion of it) controls the specificity of immunity.

Wild type T4 is capable of multiplication on K12(λ), but the r_{II} mutants of T4 are not (Benzer, 1955). T4r_{II} was tested on K12(434) and on K12(434hy); it was found to multiply on both strains. T4r^+ was able to multiply on both also. This suggests that the block in T4r_{II} multiplication is caused by the c_I region of λ since replacement of the c_I region of λ by the c_I region of 434 eliminates the block.

3. Chromosomal localization of 434hy prophage in E. coli *K12*. Prophage λ and prophage 434 occupy distinct but closely linked loci on the linkage map of *E. coli* K12 near certain galactose loci (Jacob and Wollman, 1957). It must, therefore, be determined whether prophage 434hy occupies the λ locus, the 434 locus, or neither.

In K12(λ) prophage λ occupies the λ locus and in K12(434) prophage 434 occupies the 434 locus, by definition. Allelism tests between K12(434hy) and K12(λ), and between K12(434hy) and K12(434), should localize the 434hy prophage.

Allelism tests were performed by means of transduction with phage P1 (Lennox, 1955). The occurrence of transductants nonlysogenic for the prophage of the donor and the prophage of the recipient would indicate that the two prophages are nonallelic. The absence of nonlysogenic transductants indicates allelism, subject of course to the limitation in the number of transductants examined.

In the experiments to be reported, a stock of Plkc (Lennox, 1955) was prepared on a gal$^+$ donor strain. The gal$^-$ recipient was infected with this Plkc stock and gal$^+$ transductants isolated, purified, and tested for prophage by replica plating on C600, C600(λ), and C600(434). The recipient strains had all been rendered /λ/434 to prevent infection by free phage λ or 434.

TABLE 4

PROPHAGE SEGREGATION IN TRANSDUCTION

Donor gal⁺		Recipient gal⁻	Transductants gal⁺				
			Non-lysogenic	Lysogenic: Produce phage with the immunity specificity of			Total
				λ	434	λ and 434	
(434hy)	A	(λ)	75	267	39	16	397
(434hy)	B	(λ)	103	122	114	59	398
(434hy)		(434)	0	0	789	0	789
(434)		(434hy)	0	0	785	0	785
(λ)		(434hy)	36	38	320	21	415
(434)	A	(λ)	39	228	25	6	298
(434)	B	(λ)	23	370	7	0	400
(λ)		(434)	18	29	71	2	120
(λ)		(λ)	0	943	0	0	943
(434)		(434)	0	0	200	0	200
(434hy)		(434hy)	0	0	400	0	400

NOTE: The transductions were performed by infecting the recipient with phage P1 that had been grown on the donor. The infected mixture was incubated 1 hour at 25°, then spread on EMB galactose agar. Galactose positive transductants were isolated, purified by two serial single-colony isolations and then scored for the type of phage production by replica plating onto K12, K12(λ), and K12(434). A and B indicate strains isolated independently using the same stock of phage and sensitive bacterial strain. The donor strains were all prepared from C600 and the recipient strains from C600 gal⁻.

The results of these tests, presented in Table 4, are that nonlysogenic transductants did arise when the pair K12(λ), K12(434hy) was tested, independently of which was the donor and which the recipient. However, *no* nonlysogenic transductants arose when the pair K12(434), K12(434hy) was tested. Therefore, prophage 434 hybrid occupies the 434 locus. Incidentally, the absence of nonlysogenic transductants when the pairs K12(λ), K12(λ) or K12(434), K12(434) were tested is a strong argument in favor of the uniqueness of the λ and the 434 loci.

If prophage 434hy occupied the same locus as prophage 434 in K12, then the same frequencies of recombination would be expected between the locus of prophage 434hy and the locus of prophage λ as between the locus of prophage 434 and the locus of prophage λ. Referring to Table 4, it may be seen that when the donor was lysogenic for 434hy and the recipient lysogenic for λ an average of 22% (75 + 103/397 + 398) of the gal^+ transductants were nonlysogenic. But when the donor was lysogenic for 434 and the recipient lysogenic for λ, 9% (39 + 23/298 + 400) of the gal^+ were nonlysogenic. In the reciprocal transductions where the donor was lysogenic for λ and the recipient lysogenic for 434hy or for 434, the frequencies of nonlysogenic strains among the gal^+ were 9% (36/415) and 15% (18/120), respectively. The significance of the differences in each case is questionable for two reasons. First, differences of the same order were observed when the same transduction was repeated with independent isolates of the same donor strain, as may be seen by comparing examples A and B in Table 4. Second, the hypothesis that prophage 434hy and prophage 434 occupy different loci would require that a particular order be assignable to the loci of the three prophages involved. Neither the order λ − 434 − 434hy nor the order λ − 434hy − 434 is consistent with the frequencies of nonlysogenic transductants observed in reciprocal transductions. For, whereas the order λ − 434 − 434hy might have been indicated when the donor was lysogenic for 434 or for 434hy and the recipient lysogenic for λ due to a greater frequency of nonlysogenic strains in the latter transduction than in the former, the reverse order λ − 434hy − 434 would have been indicated by the reciprocal transductions when the donor was lysogenic for λ, due to a greater frequency of nonlysogenic transductants when the recipient was lysogenic for 434 than when the recipient was lysogenic for 434hy. These data, therefore, are not incompatible with the idea that prophage 434hy occupies the same locus as prophage 434.

Allelism of prophage 434hy to prophage 434 was independently confirmed by the bacterial cross Hfr $T^+L^+S^s$ gal^+(434) × $F^+T^-L^-S^r$(434hy) gal^-/λ/434. Among 400 gal^+S^r prototrophs no nonlysogenic strains were found.

Bacteria lysogenic for both λ and 434 or for λ and 434hy were found in some of the transduction experiments reported in Table 4. Ten strains of each type were examined in detail; all of them had the following properties. They produced two types of phage, one type which plated on K12(λ) and another type which plated on K12(434). When induced with ultraviolet light and plated, before lysis, on C600, they produced mottled plaques like those of C600 mixedly infected with λ and 434. These strains were immune both to λ and to 434 and did not support the growth of $T4r_{II}$.

DISCUSSION

In crosses between λ and any one of the other phages studied, 434, 82, and 21, genetic recombination observed in the m_5 and *mi* regions indicates clearly that genetic homology exists between the linkage maps of these phages, at least in their outer parts. That the degree of homology may vary according to the pair of phages is shown by the fact that in crosses with λ, the regions of the map within which recombination can occur is different for 434, 82, and 21.

The most interesting of these three phages is 434, which appears to exhibit complete homology with λ except for a small region of its linkage map, the c_I region. The c_I region of the genetic material of phage λ has been defined as that segment of the linkage map within which are located all mutations (22 out of 22 studied) that suppress the ability of the phage to lysogenize or, at least, reduce the lysogenization frequency to less than 10^{-5} (Kaiser, 1957). Mixed infection with different pairs of c_I mutants have indicated that the c_I region is probably a single cistron or functional unit as defined by Benzer (1957).

The failure to find intra-c_I recombinants in a λ × 434 cross may be explained by two kinds of hypotheses. Either the c_I regions of λ and 434 fail to pair, or recombination occurs but the recombinants are inviable because of the hybrid character of their c_I region. In both models, structural dissimilarity of the c_I regions of λ and 434 would seem to be implied by the absence of recombination there.

The main result obtained by comparing the properties of λ and 434hy is that these two phages, which have in common the whole linkage map except the c_I region, differ both by their immunity pattern and by their specific location as prophages on the bacterial chromosome. The conclusion, therefore, seems inescapable that the c_I region controls not only a reaction involved in the lysogenization process, but also the immunity pattern and the specificity of prophage location. The question arises, therefore, whether these properties are but different expressions of the same function.

To understand what this function might be it is necessary to consider the nature of prophage. Prophage is defined as that element in a lysogenic bacterium which is responsible for the production of a particular bacteriophage (Lwoff, 1953). Bacterial crosses between K12 strains lysogenic for different mutants of λ (Appleyard, 1953) as well as transduction of prophage (Lennox, 1955; Jacob, 1955) demonstrate that prophage is the genetic material of a phage associated with a particular locus of the bacterial chromosome. If then the c_I region of the phage were responsible for the association, the three functions—lysogenization, localization, and immunity—would all depend on the c_I region. In the following discussion this idea will be explored in more detail.

The simplest way to explain how the c_I controls the specificity of prophage localization would seem to be that the prophage is attached to the bacterial chromosome by its c_I region. The c_I region of λ would attach to the λ locus in K12, the c_I region of 434 to the 434 locus. A slight structural change in a c_I region might prevent attachment. Thus it would be easy to see how a mutation in the c_I region could prevent lysogenization.

The role of the c_I region in immunity may be summarized in the following way. The fact that λ but not 434hy can reproduce in K12(434) shows that immunity is directed against the c_I region of a superinfecting phage. The fact that λ but not 434 can reproduce in K12(434hy) shows that immunity is governed by the c_I region of the prophage. Thus the prophage controls the inhibition of vegetative multiplication of superinfecting particles possessing an homologous c_I region. This may be explained by two types of hypothesis. Either immunity operates in the bacterium at the chromosomal level and is due to some steric hindrance, or immunity is a cytoplasmic expression of a genetic function of the prophage. This could be either the production of an "immunity substance" (Bertani, 1955) by the prophage-bacterial chromosome system or the inhibition by the prophage of the production by the bacterium of a substance necessary for the multiplication of homologous particles. No decision between these hypotheses can be reached until further attempts have been made to dissociate the genetic control of lysogenization, specificity of prophage location, and specificity of immunity.

The c_I region of the prophage also controls the ability of $T4r_{II}$ to multiply on lysogenic K12. The mechanism of this effect remains unknown but the same hypothesis as those proposed for immunity may be considered (Lederberg, 1957).

ACKNOWLEDGMENTS

We want to thank Dr. André Lwoff in whose laboratory at the Institut Pasteur much of this work was carried out. During this time the senior author was a fellow in cancer research of the American Cancer Society.

REFERENCES

APPLEYARD, R. K. (1953). Segregation of lambda lysogenicity during bacterial recombination in *E. coli* K12. *Cold Spring Harbor Symposia Quant. Biol.* **18,** 95–97.

BENZER, S. (1955). Fine structure of a genetic region in bacteriophage. *Proc. Natl. Acad. Sci. U.S.* **41,** 344–354.

BENZER, S. (1957). The elementary units of heredity. In *The Chemical Basis of Heredity* (W. D. McElroy and B. Glass, eds.), p. 70, The Johns Hopkins Press, Baltimore.

BERTANI, G. (1954). Studies on lysogenesis. III. Superinfection of lysogenic *Shigella dysenteriae* with temperate mutants of the carried phage. *J. Bacteriol.* **67,** 696–707.

BERTANI, G. (1955). The role of phage in bacterial genetics. *Brookhaven Symposia in Biol. No.* **8,** 50–56.

DAVIS, B. D. (1948). Isolation of biochemically deficient mutants of bacteria by penicillin. *J. Am. Chem. Soc.* **70,** 4267.

GOODGAL, S. H. (1956). Incorporation of phage DNA on lysogenization of *Shigella dysenteriae*. *Biochim. et Biophys. Acta* **19,** 333–340.

JACOB, F. (1954). *Les Bactéries Lysogènes et la Notion de Provirus.* Monographies de l'Institut Pasteur, Paris.

JACOB, F. (1955). Transduction of lysogeny in *Escherichia coli*. *Virology* **1,** 207–220.

JACOB, F., and WOLLMAN, E. (1956). Sur le processus de conjugaison et de recombinaison chez *Escherichia coli*. I. L'induction par conjugaison ou induction zygotique. *Ann. inst. Pasteur* **91,** 486–510.

JACOB, F., and WOLLMAN, E. (1957). Genetic aspects of lysogeny. In *The Chemical Basis of Heredity* (W. D. McElroy and B. Glass, eds.), p. 468, The Johns Hopkins Press, Baltimore.

KAISER, A. D. (1957). Mutations in a temperate bacteriophage affecting its ability to lysogenize *Escherichia coli*. *Virology* **3,** 42–61.

LEDERBERG, E., and LEDERBERG, J. (1953). Genetic studies of lysogenicity in *Escherichia coli*. *Genetics* **38,** 51–64.

LEDERBERG, J., and ZINDER, N. (1948). Concentration of biochemical mutants of bacteria with penicillin. *J. Am. Chem. Soc.* **70,** 4267.

LEDERBERG, S. (1957). Suppression of the multiplication of heterologous bacteriophages in lysogenic bacteria. *Virology* **3,** 496–513.

LENNOX, E. (1955). Transduction of linked genetic characters of the host by bacteriophage P1. *Virology* **1,** 190–206.

LWOFF, A. (1953). Lysogeny. *Bacteriol. Rev.* **17,** 269–337.

MORSE, M., LEDERBERG, E., and LEDERBERG, J. (1956). Transductional heterogenotes in *Escherichia coli*. *Genetics* **41,** 758–779.

WOLLMAN, E. L. (1953). Sur le déterminisme génétique de la lysogénie. *Ann. inst. Pasteur* **84,** 281–293.